KT-229-508

MATHEMATICAL THEORY OF CONTROL

MATHEMATICAL THEORY OF CONTROL

EDITED BY

A. V. Balakrishnan

UNIVERSITY OF CALIFORNIA
LOS ANGELES

Lucien W. Neustadt

UNIVERSITY OF SOUTHERN CALIFORNIA
LOS ANGELES

Proceedings of a conference held at the University of Southern California Los Angeles, January 30-February 1, 1967

1967

ACADEMIC PRESS New York and London

COPYRIGHT © 1967, BY ACADEMIC PRESS INC.
ALL RIGHTS RESERVED.
NO PART OF THIS BOOK MAY BE REPRODUCED IN ANY FORM,
BY PHOTOSTAT, MICROFILM, OR ANY OTHER MEANS, WITHOUT
WRITTEN PERMISSION FROM THE PUBLISHERS.

ACADEMIC PRESS INC.
111 Fifth Avenue, New York, New York 10003

United Kingdom Edition published by
ACADEMIC PRESS INC. (LONDON) LTD.
Berkeley Square House, London W.1

LIBRARY OF CONGRESS CATALOG CARD NUMBER: 67-23152

PRINTED IN THE UNITED STATES OF AMERICA

PREFACE

This book is based on papers presented at the Conference on the Mathematical Theory of Control held at the University of Southern California from January 30 to February 1, 1967. Among the topics highlighted were

1) Optimal Control Theory.
2) Control Theory and Partial Differential Equations.
3) Differential Games.
4) Stochastic Control.
5) Stability Theory.

The articles in this volume have been grouped roughly in these categories.

Of the total of forty-two papers included herein, eight were invited: those by L. D. Berkovitz, L. Cesari, R. Conti, H. Halkin, J. L. Lions, E. J. McShane, L. S. Pontryagin, and B. N. Pshenichniy.

The ussian language papers were translated into English by J. R. LaFrieda.

The Conference was international in character and almost every country active in the mathematical theory of control was represented. A feature of the Conference was the large number of Soviet and Eastern European participants. We are grateful to the USSR Academy of Sciences for their help in arranging the visits of six Soviet delegates. Four other Soviet mathematicians (V. F. Dem'yanov, A. I. Egorov, F. M. Kirillova, and B. N. Pshenichniy), as well as one from Czechoslovakia (P. V. Brunovský) were unable to attend, but we are happy that their papers were made available to us for inclusion in this volume. Participation of other delegates from abroad was facilitated by travel grants from AFOSR, U. S. Air Force, and we are grateful to Colonel B. R. Agins for his help in making MAC travel arrangements.

We owe special thanks to the members of the Organizing Committee (B. R. Agins, H. A. Antosiewicz, E. K. Blum, and M. R. Hestenes) for their generous help throughout. Further, this conference would not have been possible without the support and active cooperation of the Departments of Mathematics at USC and UCLA, the Department of Engineering at UCLA, and Dean Chauncy Starr in particular, and especially the Department of Electrical Engineering at USC.

Finally, we are grateful to Academic Press for making it possible to publish the Proceedings with a minimum time delay.

A. V. Balakrishnan
L. W. Neustadt

Los Angeles, California, May 1967

FOREWORD

Control theory is gaining world-wide importance as our social and technological systems and sub-systems become more complex and more highly interconnected. Practical engineering solutions to such complexity require mathematical insight to the fundamental relationships among many parameters.

As a result of brilliant work not only in the USA and the USSR, but other countries as well, significant understanding has been gained in the basic optimization problems of control theory. One can now hopefully look forward to eventual engineering approaches to the control of complex systems involving stochastic parameters, inaccurate or noisy inputs, and even systems with an apparently intractable number of variables. This should lead to increasing success in the control of complicated industrial processes, and perhaps eventually to the analysis and control of our socio-economic systems.

This Conference reflects the truly international nature of the contributions in this important dual area of sophisticated mathematics and practical control engineering. I am delighted that the Proceedings will now be available to a larger audience.

Chauncey Starr
Dean, College of Engineering
University of California,
Los Angeles, California

May 1967

LIST OF CONTRIBUTORS

CONTENTS

OPTIMAL CONTROLS, RELAXED AND ORDINARY

E. J. McShane*
Department of Mathematics
University of Virginia
Charlottesville, Virginia

In optimal control problems that have no solution in the ordinary sense, it may be possible to come arbitrarily close to an optimal result by using what Gamkrelidze calls chattering controls, this being a vivid expression for an idea that L. C. Young introduced thirty years ago. I would like to start by explaining a purely mathematical reason for considering such relaxed or chattering controls.

To be specific, let us consider a problem in the Lagrange form. We are given closed sets A and U, in $(n + 1)$-space and m-space respectively, and $n + 1$ functions $f^o(x,t,u),\cdots,f^n(x,t,u)$ defined and continuous for (x,t) in A and u in U. We are also given end-conditions of the form "$(x(t_o),t_o,x(t_1),t_1)$ is in a closed set E in $(2n + 2)$-space". The problem is to find a control-function $u(t), t_o \leqq t \leqq t_1$ and a corresponding trajectory $x(t)$ which satisfy the end-conditions and the equations

$$(1)\quad x^i(t) = x^i(t_o) + \int_{t_o}^{t} f^i(x(t),t,u(t))\, dt$$

$$(i = 1,\cdots,n,\ t_o \leqq t \leqq t_1)$$

and give the minimum value to

$$(2)\quad \int_{t_o}^{t_1} f^o(x(t),t,u(t))\, dt.$$

Guided by the familiar pattern, we naturally try first to find a "minimizing sequence" of admissible control functions which converges in some sense or other to a limit, and then show that this limit furnishes the optimum. But the obvious concepts of convergence for sequences $u_n(t)$ are quickly found to be unsuitable in general. We need a kind

*Sponsored by Army Research Office Grant G-662

of convergence such that if the u_n converge to u_o, the x_n satisfying (1) will converge at least pointwise to the x_o corresponding to u_o. Otherwise stated, for a family of functions f^i large enough to give us control of the situation we want the integral in (1) to be a continuous functional of the function u. The smallest such family of f^i that we could hope to get by with consists of those that are continuous, independent of x, and vanish outside some bounded set of u's; and in fact these turn out to be enough, less restricted f^i being manageable by limit processes. So for each continuous $\phi(t,u)$ vanishing outside a bounded u-set we define for each control-function u(t) $(t_o \leqq t \leqq t_1)$ a corresponding

(3) $\Phi(t|u) = \int_{-\infty}^{t} \chi_{[t_o,t_1]}(t)\phi(t,u(t))\,dt,$

and we define $u_n \to u_o$ to mean that for every such ϕ, $\Phi(t|u_n)$ converges uniformly to $\Phi(t|u_o)$. It is in fact easy to introduce a distance-function ρ in the space of (measurable) control functions in such a way that $\rho(u_n,u_o) \to 0$ if and only if $u_n \to u_o$ in the sense just described.

However, it is almost trivially evident that the space of control-functions, thus metrized, is not complete. We can of course complete it in the standard manner; there is (up to isomorphism) just one complete space in which the space of control-functions is dense. But it is decidedly preferable to have a concrete representation of this completion in terms of some familiar objects, about which we already know a large number of useful theorems. Fortunately such a concrete representation is constructible. The members of the complete space in which the (ordinary) control functions are embedded are the "relaxed controls", which are the functions $\mu_t (t_o \leqq t \leqq t_1)$ such that for each t, μ_t is a probability measure on $\bar{U}$, and whenever $\phi(t,u)$ is bounded and continuous for $t_o \leqq t \leqq t_1$ and u in U, the expected value

(4) $\int_U \phi(t,u)\mu_t\,(du)$

is a Lebesgue-measurable function of t. The integral (4) may of course exist for a much larger class of integrands than those described.

The optimal relaxed-control problem is now that of finding a relaxed control μ_t, $t_o \leqq t \leqq t_1$ and a trajectory x(t) satisfying the end-conditions and the equations

(5) $x^i(t) = x_o^i(t_o) + \int_{t_o}^{t} \int_U f^i(x(s),s,u)\mu_s\,(du)\,ds$

and minimizing the integral (analogous to (2))

(6) $\int_{t_o}^{t_1} \int_U f^o(x(t),t,u)\mu_t\,(du)\,dt.$

It is easy and not very interesting to state conditions that guarantee the existence of a minimizing sequence whose trajectories all lie in a bounded set. If U is compact, it now becomes no more than a routine exercise in using the Ascoli theorem and the diagonal process to show that an optimal relaxed control exists. If U is unbounded, we need some sort of order-of-growth condition to keep the μ_t in bounds. It is enough to assume that

(7) $\lim_{||u|| \to \infty} f^o(x,t,u)/[1 + \sum_{j=1}^{n} |f^j(x,t,u)|] = \infty$

uniformly on every bounded set of (x,t).

In fact, we can use this result to deduce an apparently more general theorem. We shall allow the control set to vary with time and place; for each (x,t) in (n + 1)-space, U(x,t) is a closed set in m-space. We assume that U(x,t) is such that the set M of all points (x,t,u) in (n + 1 + m)-space with u in U(x,t) is a closed set. If the U(x,t) are unbounded we assume (7); there is no loss of generality in supposing that $f^o,\cdots,f^n$ are continuous and satisfy (7) on all of (n + 1 + m)-space. To reduce this to the form already considered we take U to be R^m, and we define $f^{n+1}(x,t,u)$ to be a continuous function that vanishes on M and satisfies $0 < f^{n+1}(x,t,u) \leqq 1$ on the rest of (n + 1 + m)-space. Then (7) still holds with n replaced by n + 1. We add a new space-coordinate x^{n+1} (the f^i are unchanged, and are independent of x^{n+1}); a new equation (5), with i = n + 1; and new end-conditions $x^{n+1}(t_o) = 0$, $x^{n+1}(t_1) \leqq 0$. Now, by the theorem for fixed U, there is a relaxed control function μ_t ($t_o \leqq t \leqq t_1$) and a corresponding solution x(t) of (5) that satisfy the end-conditions and give to the integral (6) the lower bound of its possible values. The last of equations (5) and the last end-condition now guarantee that for almost all t in $[t_o,t_1]$ we have

$$\int_{R^m} f^{n+1}(x(t),t,u)\mu_t\,(du) = 0.$$

Therefore, for all such t the support of the measure μ_t is in $U(x(t),t)$. We thus see that under the conditions on the f^i and the sets $U(x,t)$, there is a probability-measure valued function μ_t ($t_o \leqq t \leqq t_1$) and a corresponding solution $(x^1(t),\cdots,x^n(t))$ of equations (5) such that for almost all t, the support of μ_t is contained in $U(x(t),t)$, and the end-conditions are satisfied, and (6) takes the lower bound of its possible values.

But this existence theorem is by no means a place to rest. For one thing, we have not solved the original problem of finding an optimal ordinary control. Instead, we have replaced this problem by another and shown that the substitute has a solution, without saying much about detecting this solution. Even if we are tolerant enough to accept the substitute as an adequate facsimile of the original problem, we still have the duty of trying to find the criteria by which we can distinguish the optimal relaxed control, and to find conditions under which we can be sure than an optimal relaxed control exists which possesses additional virtues of behavior that will make it easier to study and compute; and the most obvious of such virtues is the property of being an ordinary control. (Others will be continuous differentiability between corners and still stronger smoothness conditions.)

The easiest way to guarantee the existence of an ordinary optimal control is to assume (in addition to the previous hypotheses) that for each (x,t) in R^{n+1} the set $K(x,t)$ consisting of those points $(z^o,\ldots,z^n)$ such that for some u in $U(x,t)$

$$z^o \geqq f^o(x,t,u) \text{ and } z^i = f^i(x,t,u) \quad (i = 1,\cdots,n),$$

is a convex set. For if μ_t is the optimal relaxed control, for each t the points $(f^o(x(t),t,u),\cdots,f^n(x(t),t,u))$ with u in $U(x(t),t)$ all belong to $K(x(t),t)$, hence so does their centroid

$$\left(\int_U f^o(x(t),t,u)\mu_t\,(du),\ldots,\int_U f^n(x(t),t,u)\mu_t\,(du)\right).$$

This assures us that there is a $u_o(t)$ in $U(x(t),t)$ for which $x^{i\prime}(t) = f^i(u_o(t))$ $(i = 1,\cdots,n)$, and for which

$$f^o(x(t),t,u_o(t)) \leqq \int_U f^o(x(t),t,u)\mu_t\,(du).$$

By Filippov's lemma it is possible, if u_o is not already measurable, to replace it by a measurable function which also satisfies these conditions. Thus $u_o(t)$ is an ordinary control which yields the same trajectory as the optimal relaxed control μ_t (so that the end conditions and the condition that the trajectory lie in A are satisfied), and by integrating the preceding inequality we see that

$$\int_{t_o}^{t_1} f^o(x(t),t,u_o(t))\, dt$$

is not above the minimum. So u_o is an optimal ordinary control.

We are left with the problem of finding necessary conditions satisfied by this minimizing $u_o(t)$ and its corresponding trajectory $x(t)$. But if we reverse the order of operations and find the conditions satisfied by the optimizing relaxed control μ_t, we obtain information about optimal relaxed controls even when there is no optimal ordinary control, including the standard information about ordinary controls, and we can deduce more delicate conditions than mere convexity that will produce optimal ordinary controls.

To do this we adapt the idea of a variation to the context of relaxed controls, restricting ourselves to the case of fixed control-set U. The obvious way to vary a measure continuously is to add z times another measure to it (z real). We wish to use only non-negative measures, which can be written as $c(t)\mu_t$ with $c(t) \geqq 0$ and μ_t a probability measure. It is in fact enough to consider variations of the form

$$\sum_{j=1}^{k} z_j c_j \mu_{j,t}$$

in which the c_j are non-negative constants and the $\mu_{j,t}$ are probability measures for which (4) is measurable in t. Then for all real $z_1,\cdots,z_s$ the set-function

$$\mu_{t,z} = (1 - c_1 z_1 - \cdots - c_k z_k)\mu_t + \sum_{j=1}^{k} c_j z_j \mu_{j,t}$$

is a (signed) measure, and if the z are small and non-negative it is a probability measure. Now we suppose that A is all of R^n, and for simplicity we consider only the case in which the end-points are fixed. If U is bounded, or if a fairly straightforward growth condition on the

f^i and their derivatives holds, whenever the $\mu_{j,t}$ have bounded supports the equations

$$x_z^i(t) = x^i(t_o) + \int_{t_o}^{t} \int_U f^i(x_z(s),s,u)\mu_{s,z}(du)ds$$

have solutions $x_z(t)$ on $[t_o,t_1]$ for all fixed z near 0. To this solution corresponds a point Y with coordinates

$$Y^o(z) = \int_{t_o}^{t_1}\int_U f^o(x_z(t),t,u)\mu_{t,z}(du)dt - \int_{t_o}^{t_1}\int_U f^o(x(t),t,u)\mu_t(du)dt,$$

$$Y^i(z) = x_z^i(t_1) - x^i(t_1) \quad (i = 1,\ldots,n).$$

If the z are non-negative and small, this point cannot lie on the negative Y^o-axis. For then the vanishing of the last n coordinates would imply that the end conditions are satisfied, and the negativeness of $Y^o(z)$ would imply that $\mu_{t,z}$ provided a better-than-optimal control.

It follows that the tangent vectors $\partial Y/\partial z_1,\ldots,\partial Y/\partial z_k$ cannot point along the edges of a cone (pyramid) with the negative Y^o-axis in its interior, for then by the implicit functions theorem we could vary the z_i simultaneously in such a way that Y(z) would slide down the negative Y^o-axis. This in turn implies that the whole cone generated by all vectors of the type $\partial Y/\partial z$ will not contain any point of the negative Y^o-axis, so that there is a non-trivial set of constants $\ell_o \geq 0, \ell_1,\ldots,\ell_n$ such that $\sum \ell_j \partial Y^j/\partial z \geq 0$ for all such vectors.

This statement is the source of generalizations to relaxed control problems of all the customary first-order conditions of the calculations, whether expressed in the formalism of Euler-Lagrange and Weierstrass conditions or in the formalism of the "Pontryagin maximal theorem". All that is left to do is to concoct properly chosen variations and transform the inequality by rather elementary devices. These can be expressed in (approximately) the Pontryagin form if we use Lagrange multipliers $\lambda_o,\ldots,\lambda_n$ and introduce the symbols

$$F(x,t,u,\lambda) = \sum_{j=0}^{n} \lambda_j f^j(x,t,u),$$

$$M(x,t,\lambda) = \inf_{u\in U} F(x,t,u,\lambda).$$

We can then deduce:

If μ_t minimizes the integral (6) in the class of relaxed controls and trajectories satisfying equations (5) and having given ends, there exist functions $\lambda_o(t),\ldots,\lambda_n(t)$ $(t_o \leq t \leq t_1)$ such that

(i) $\lambda_o(t)$ is constantly 0 or constantly 1,

(ii) $\sum|\lambda_i(t)| > 0$ for all t,

(iii) the functions $\lambda_1,\ldots,\lambda_n$ satisfy

$$\lambda_i(t) = \lambda_i(t_o) - \int_{t_o}^{t} \int_U F_{x^i}(x(s),s,u,\lambda(s))\mu_s(du)ds$$

for $t_o \leq t \leq t_1$;

(iv) there is a constant c such that

$$\int_{t_o}^{t} \int_U F_t(x(s),s,u,\lambda(s))\mu_s(du)ds \leq M(x(t),t,\lambda(t)) - c$$

for all t in $[t_o,t_1]$, equality holding for all t if U is bounded and for almost all t if U is unbounded;

(v) for almost all t in $[t_o,t_1]$ the equation

$$F(x(t),t,u_o,\lambda(t)) = M(x(t),t,\lambda(t))$$

holds for all u_o in the support of the measure μ_t.

If the end-points are variable, a corresponding transversality condition is satisfied.

With the help of this theorem we can find strong restrictions on the possible measures μ_t that correspond to a given x(t), t and $\lambda(t)$ belonging to the optimal trajectory. If for each x, t,λ we define $S(x,t,\lambda)$ to be the set of all u in U at which $F(x,t,u,\lambda)$ attains its minimum value $M(x,t,\lambda)$, then by (v) for almost all t the support of μ_t lies in $S(x(t),t,\lambda(t))$; that is $\mu_t[U - S(x(t),t,\lambda(t))] = 0$. But we can easily sharpen this a great deal. There is a set T in $[t_o,t_1]$, with measure $t_1 - t_o$, on which equality holds in (iv) and all the integrals from t_o to t named in (iii) and (iv) have derivatives equal to their integrands. Suppose now that t is a point of T and u' a point of $S(x(t),t,\lambda(t))$. Then by (v) and the definition of M, the function

$$F(x(s),s,u',\lambda(s)) - M(x(s),s,\lambda(s)) \qquad (t_o \leq s \leq t_1)$$

is never negative and is 0 at s = t. Hence its derivative must vanish at s = t, so by (5),(iii) and (iv)

$$\text{(vi)} \quad \int_U \Big\{ \sum_{i=1}^{n} \big[F_{x^i}(x(t),t,u',\lambda(t)) f^i(x(t),t,u) - f^i(x(t),t,u') F_{x^i}(x(t),t,u,\lambda(t)) \big] + F_t(x(t),t,u',\lambda(t)) - F_t(x(t),t,u,\lambda(t)) \Big\} \mu_t\,(du) = 0.$$

This must hold for all u' in $S(x(t),t,\lambda(t))$, which in many examples restricts the possibilities for μ_t so much as to force the control to be ordinary. To give a concrete example, interesting only because the theorem can be applied to it with very little calculation, suppose we want to minimize

$$\int_0^1 \{[(x')^2 - 1]^2 + e^x\} dt$$

in the class of absolutely continuous functions with $x(0) = x(1) = 0$. The corresponding relaxed control problem is to minimize the integral

$$\int_0^1 \int_U \{[u^2 - 1]^2 + e^{x(t)}\} \mu_t\,(du)dt$$

in the class of controls and trajectories such that

$$x(t) = \int_0^t \int_U u\, \mu_s(du)ds$$

and $x(1) = 0$. Now

$$F(x,t,u,\lambda) = \lambda_o\{[u^2 - 1]^2 + e^x\} + \lambda_1 u,$$

which is a fourth degree polynomial in u and assumes its minimum at one or two points. In the latter case, $\lambda_1 = 0$, and the minimizing set $S(x,t,\lambda)$ consists of two points 1 and -1. The equation (vi) becomes

$$\int_U \{e^{x(t)} u - u' e^{x(t)} - 0\} \mu_t\,(du) = 0,$$

which must hold at $u' = 1$ and at $u' = -1$. Substituting these two values and subtracting yields

$$2e^{x(t)} = 0,$$

which is impossible. Therefore for almost all t the set $S(x(t),t,\lambda(t))$ contains only one point, so μ_t is concentrated at one point and the optimal control is ordinary.

For this problem, as for many similar ones, we can in fact deduce even better information about the optimal control. The necessary conditions can be used to show that λ_1 can have at most one zero, so that the minimizing x(t) is either a single continuously differentiable function, or else its graph has a single corner and is elsewhere smooth.

NONLINEAR NONCONVEX PROGRAMMING IN AN INFINITE DIMENSIONAL SPACE*

by Hubert Halkin

University of California
Department of Mathematics
San Diego, California

Introduction

The aim of the present paper is to give some results concerning programming in an infinite dimensional space which are useful in control theory.

By a mathematical programming problem we mean a problem of the following type: given a set L and real valued functions φ_i, $i=-\mu,\cdots,0,\cdots,m$ defined on L (where m and μ are given nonnegative integers), find an element $\hat{x} \in L$ which minimizes φ_0 on the set of all $x \in L$ that satisfy the constraints $\varphi_i(x) \leq 0$ for $i=-\mu,\cdots,-1$ and $\varphi_i(x) = 0$ for $i=1,\cdots,m$.

When the set L is a finite dimensional space and the functions $\varphi_{-\mu},\cdots,\varphi_m$ are linear the preceding problem becomes the well known linear programming problem. When the set L is a finite dimensional space but the functions $\varphi_{-\mu},\cdots,\varphi_m$ are not linear we have what is called a nonlinear programming problem which can be further characterized by the

*This research was supported by the U.S. Air Force Office of Scientific Research, Office of Aerospace Research, under AFOSR grant 1039-66.

words convex, quadratic, etc., according to the corresponding properties of the functions $\varphi_{-\mu},\cdots,\varphi_m$. Calculus of variations and optimal control theory can also be viewed as mathematical programming where the set L is an infinite dimensional set of functions. This is the reason why the set L considered in the present paper will not be assumed to be finite dimensional. The theory of mathematical programming over an infinite dimensional space was initiated by L. Hurwicz (8). In the present paper we develop different aspects of the theory of programming over an infinite dimensional space because for the applications to control theory which we have in mind we need results which were not considered by L. Hurwicz and his followers.

We use the term "nonconvex" to mean "not necessarily convex" in keeping with a tradition for which "nonlinear" means "not necessarily linear."

1. Linear-convex Programming over a Convex Set

We shall first consider a linear-convex programming problem over a convex set, i.e. we shall assume that the set L is a convex subset of some linear space X, that $\varphi_{-\mu},\cdots,\varphi_0$ are convex functions defined on X and that $\varphi_1,\cdots,\varphi_m$ are linear-plus-a-constant functions defined on X. We shall assume that an optimal solution $\hat{x}$ exists. In the derivation of our results we shall also assume, without loss of generality and with a substantial simplification of the notation, that $\hat{x} = 0$ and $\varphi_0(0) = 0$. In the statement of our results however, we shall not make those simplifying assumptions. Since $\varphi_i(\hat{x}) = 0$ for $i=1,\cdots,m$ it follows that the functions $\varphi_1,\cdots,\varphi_m$ are linear.

We shall denote by φ the mapping $(\varphi_{-\mu},\cdots,\varphi_m)$ from X into $E^{\mu+m+1}$ and by K the set $\{(\alpha_{-\mu},\cdots,\alpha_m): \alpha_i < 0$ for $i=-\mu,\cdots,0$, and $\alpha_i = 0$ for $i=1,\cdots,m\}$. From the optimality of $\hat{x} = 0$ we know that the sets K and $\varphi(L) = \{\varphi(x): x \in L\}$ are disjoint. From the convexity of $\varphi_{-\mu},\cdots,\varphi_0$ and the linearity of $\varphi_1,\cdots,\varphi_m$ it follows that the sets K and $\varphi(L) - K = \{\varphi(x) - \alpha: x \in L, \alpha \in K\}$ are also disjoint. Moreover the sets K and $\varphi(L) - K$ are convex and $\varphi(\hat{x})$ belongs to $\overline{K}$ and $\overline{\varphi(L) - K}$, hence the sets $\overline{K}$ and $\varphi(L) \subset \overline{\varphi(L) - K}$ are separated by some hyperplane passing through the point $\varphi(\hat{x})$, i.e. there exists a nonzero vector $\lambda = (\lambda_{-\mu}, \cdots, \lambda_m)$ such that

$$\lambda \cdot (y - \varphi(\hat{x})) \quad \leq 0 \quad \text{for all } y \in \varphi(L) \qquad (1.1)$$

$$\geq 0 \quad \text{for all } y \in \overline{K} \qquad (1.2)$$

From Relation (1.1) we obtain

$$\lambda \cdot \varphi(x) \leq \lambda \cdot \varphi(\hat{x}) \quad \text{for all } x \in L$$

and from Relation (1.2) we obtain*

$$\lambda_i \leq 0 \text{ and } \varphi_i(\hat{x})\,\lambda_i = 0 \quad \text{for all } i = -\mu, \cdots, 0 \qquad (1.3)$$

We have thus proved the following result

Theorem I. If $\hat{x}$ is an optimal solution of a linear-convex programming problem over a convex set L then there exists a nonzero vector $\lambda = (\lambda_{-\mu}, \cdots, \lambda_m)$ such that

$$\text{(i)} \quad \varphi(\hat{x}) \cdot \lambda \geq \varphi(x) \cdot \lambda \quad \text{for all } x \in L$$

$$\text{(ii)} \quad \lambda_i \leq 0 \quad \text{for all } i = -\mu, \cdots, 0$$

$$\text{(iii)} \quad \lambda_i \varphi_i(\hat{x}) = 0 \quad \text{for all } i = -\mu, \cdots, -1$$

2. Nonconvex Nonlinear Programming over a Nonconvex Set

The assumptions of Theorem I are too restrictive for most applications in control theory. In this section we show that if the set L can be "approximated" by some convex

---

*If $e_{-\mu}, \cdots, e_m$ are the unit vectors in $E^{\mu+m+1}$ we have $\varphi(\hat{x}) - e_i$ and $\varphi(\hat{x}) - \varphi_i(\hat{x})\, e_i \in \overline{K}$ for all $i = -\mu, \cdots, 0$. Relation (1.3) is obtained by substituting each of these expressions in Relation (1.2).

set M, if the functions $\varphi_{-\mu},\cdots,\varphi_0$ can be "approximated" by some convex functions $h_{-\mu},\cdots,h_0$, and if the functions $\varphi_1,\cdots,\varphi_m$ can be "approximated" by some linear functions $h_1,\cdots,h_m$, then the conclusions of Theorem I "approximatively" hold. The main consideration in our choice of the particular type of "approximation" defined and used in the present paper was to obtain results containing all the standard necessary conditions as particular cases.*

Any concept of approximation presupposes some topology: in this section we assume that X is a normed linear space.

As in Section I we assume that an optimal solution $\hat{x}$ exists and, without loss of generality, that $\hat{x} = 0$ and $\varphi_0(0) = 0$.

Assumption H_1.

(1) The functions $\varphi = (\varphi_{-\mu},\cdots,\varphi_m)$ and $h = (h_{-\mu},\cdots,h_m)$ are continuous.

(2) $$\lim_{|x|\to 0} \frac{|\varphi(x) - h(x)|}{|x|} = 0 \qquad (2.1)$$

(3) h_i is convex for $i=-\mu,\cdots,0$ and linear for $i=1,\cdots,m$

*Many classical applications of functional analysis to calculus of variations and many recent papers on mathematical programming in infinite dimensional spaces (e.g. Russell (12)) could be formulated in the framework of the present paper. In all those cases the corresponding approximations are much more "natural" than the approximation proposed in the present paper, but, unfortunately, those "natural" approximations lead to much weaker results than those given here, e.g. they lead to the Euler-Lagrange equations but not to the Weierstrass E-test or Pontryagin Maximum Principle.

Assumption H_2.

(1) M is a convex subset of X and $0 \in M$.
(2) for any set $S = \{x_1, \cdots, x_{m+1}\}$ of linearly independent elements of M there exists a function ζ from $co\{0, x_1, \cdots, x_{m+1}\}$ into L such that
  (i) for all $\delta \in [0,1]$, $\zeta(\delta x)$ is continuous in x over co S

  (ii) $\lim_{\delta \to 0+} \frac{\zeta(\delta x)}{\delta} = x$ uniformly in x over co S
(2.2)

Theorem II. If Assumptions H_1 and H_2 hold then there a nonzero vector $\lambda = (\lambda_{-\mu}, \cdots, \lambda_m) \in E^{m+\mu+1}$ such that
  (i) $\lambda \cdot h(\hat{x}) \geq \lambda \cdot h(x)$ for all $x \in M$
  (ii) $\lambda_i \geq 0$ for $i=-\mu, \cdots, 0$
  (iii) $\lambda_i h_i(\hat{x}) = 0$ for $i=-\mu, \cdots, -1$.

Before going into the proof of Theorem II we establish the following results:

Lemma 2.1. If a convex function f on a normed linear space X is continuous at the origin then it is Lipschitz continuous in some neighborhood of the origin

Lemma 2.2. If Assumptions H_1 and H_2 hold and if ζ is the mapping given in Assumption H_2 for a set S then
(1) for all $\delta \in [0,1]$, $h(\zeta(\delta x))$ is continuous in x over co S

(2) $\lim_{\delta \to 0+} \frac{\varphi(\zeta(\delta x)) - h(\delta x)}{\delta} = 0$, uniformly in x over co S.
(2.3)

Definitions: $\widetilde{M} = \{x: x \in M, h_i(x) < 0 \text{ for } i=-\mu, \cdots, 0\}$
$N = \{(h_1(x), \cdots, h_m(x)): x \in \widetilde{M}\}$ if $m > 0$

Lemma 2.3. If $m = 0$ and if Assumptions H_1 and H_2 hold then the set $\widetilde{M}$ is empty.

Lemma 2.4. If $m > 0$ and if Assumptions H_1 and H_2 hold $0 \notin \text{int } N$.

Proof of Lemma 2.1. Since f is continuous at the origin there exists a $\delta > 0$ such that $|f(x) - f(0)| \leq 1$ for all $|x| \leq \delta$. We conclude by proving that

$$f(y) - f(x) < \frac{8}{\delta} |x - y| \text{ if } |x| \text{ and } |y| \leq \frac{\delta}{2}.$$

Indeed if

$$f(y) - f(x) > \frac{8}{\delta} |x - y| \tag{2.4}$$

for some $|x|$ and $|y| \leq \frac{\delta}{2}$ let

$$z = x + (y - x) \frac{\delta}{2|y - x|}$$

We have $|z - x| = \frac{\delta}{2}$ and $|z| \leq \delta$. From the convexity of f and Relation (2.4) we obtain

$$f(z) - f(x) > \frac{8}{\delta} |x - z| = 4$$

which cannot be since

$$|f(z) - f(x)| \leq | f(z) - f(0)| + |f(x) - f(0)| \leq 2.$$

This concludes the proof of Lemma 2.1.

Proof of Lemma 2.2. Statement (1) is obvious since $h(x)$ is continuous in x and $\zeta(\delta x)$ is continuous in x for every $\delta \in [0,1]$. Statement (2) follows from Relations (2.1) and (2.2) and the inequalities

$$\frac{|\varphi(\zeta(\delta x)) - h(\delta x)|}{\delta}$$

$$\frac{|\varphi(\zeta(\delta x)) - h(\zeta(\delta x))|}{\delta} + \frac{|h(\zeta(\delta x)) - h(\delta x)|}{\delta}$$

and

$$|h(\zeta(\delta x)) - h(\delta x)| \leq Q|\zeta(\delta x) - \delta x|$$

where Q is the Lipschitz constant for h in some neighborhood of the origin given by Lemma 2.1. This concludes the proof of Lemma 2.2.

Proof of Lemma 2.3. If $x_1 \in M$ then there exists an $\eta > 0$ such that $h_i(x_1) < -\eta$ for all $i=-\mu,\cdots,0$. Since $h_{-\mu}(0),\cdots,h_0(0) \leq 0$ and since the functions $h_{-\mu},\cdots,h_0$ are convex we have then

$$h_i(\delta x_1) \leq -\delta\eta$$

for all $i=-\mu,\cdots,0$ and all $\delta \in [0,1]$. Let ζ be the mapping from $co\{0,x_1\}$ into L satisfying the Assumption H_2. From Relation (2.3) there exists a $\delta^* \in (0,1]$ such that

$$\varphi_i(\zeta(\delta^* x_1)) < -\frac{\delta^*\eta}{2} \text{ for } i=-\mu,\cdots,0$$

Since $\zeta(\delta^* x_1) \in L$ we have obtained a contradiction to the optimality of $\hat{x} = 0$. This concludes the proof of Lemma 2.3.

Proof of Lemma 2.4. Let $h_+ = (h_1,\cdots,h_m)$. If $0 \in \text{int } N$ then there exists an $\varepsilon > 0$ and a set $S = \{x_1,\cdots,x_{m+1}\} \subset \tilde{M}$ such that $N(0,\varepsilon) \subset co\, h_+(S)$. The vectors $x_1,\cdots,x_{m+1}$ are linearly independent since h_+ is linear and $0 \notin \tilde{M}$. Let $\eta > 0$ such that $h_i(x_j) < -\eta$ for all $i=-\mu,\cdots,0$ and all $j=1,\cdots,m+1$. Since $h_{-\mu}(0),\cdots,h_0(0) \leq 0$ and since the functions $h_{-\mu},\cdots,h_0$

are convex it follows that

$$h_i(\delta x) \leq -\delta\eta$$

for all $i=-\mu,\cdots,0$, all $\delta \in [0,1]$ and all $x \in \text{co } S$. Let ζ be the mapping from $\text{co}\{0,x_1,\cdots,x_{m+1}\}$ into L satisfying Assumption H_2. From Relation (2.3) there exists a $\delta^* \in (0,1]$ such that for all $x \in S$ we have

$$\varphi_i(\zeta(\delta^* x)) < -\frac{\delta^*\eta}{2} \quad \text{for } i=-\mu,\cdots,0 \tag{2.5}$$

and

$$|\varphi_+(\zeta(\delta^* x)) - h_+(\delta^* x)| < \frac{\delta^*\varepsilon}{2} \tag{2.6}$$

where $\varphi_+ = (\varphi_1,\cdots,\varphi_m)$.

By h_+^{-1} we shall denote the unique linear-plus-a-constant mapping from E^{m+1} into X such that

$$h_+^{-1}(h_+(x)) = x \quad \text{for all } x \in S$$

We shall now define a mapping Ψ from $\delta^*\text{co } h_+(S)$ into E^{m+1} by the relation

$$\Psi(y) = y - \varphi_+(\zeta(\delta^* h_+^{-1}(y/\delta^*)))$$

The mapping Ψ is continuous in y over $\delta^*\text{co } h_+(S)$, and Ψ maps $\delta^*\text{co } h_+(S)$ into $N(0,\frac{\delta^*\varepsilon}{2}) \subset \delta^*\text{co } h_+(S)$, see Relation 2.6. Hence from the Brouwer Fixed Point Theorem there exists a point $y^* \in \delta^*\text{co } h_+(S)$ such that $\Psi(y^*) = y^*$. Let $x = h_+^{-1}(y^*/\delta^*) \in \text{co } S$ we have then

$$\varphi_i(\zeta(\delta^* x^*)) < -\frac{\delta^*\eta}{2} \quad \text{for } i=-\mu,\cdots,0$$

$$\varphi_i(\zeta(\delta^* x^*)) = 0 \quad \text{for } i=1,\cdots,m$$

Since $\zeta(\delta^* x^*) \in L$ we have obtained a contradiction to the optimality of $\hat{x} = 0$. This concludes the proof of Lemma 2.4.

Proof of Theorem II in the case $m = 0$. We define two sets D and K_* in $E^{\mu+1}$ by the relations

$$D = \{(h_{-\mu}(x),\cdots,h_0(x)) : x \in M\}$$

$$K_* = \{(\xi_{-\mu},\cdots,\xi_0) : \xi_{-\mu},\cdots,\xi_0 < 0\}$$

The sets K_* and $D - K_*$ are convex by definition and disjoint by Lemma 2.3. Moreover the point $(h_{-\mu}(\hat{x}),\cdots,h_0(\hat{x}))$ belongs to $\overline{K_*}$ and $\overline{D - K_*}$. Hence there exists a nonzero vector $\lambda = (\lambda_{-\mu},\cdots,\lambda_0)$ such that

$$\lambda\cdot(y - (h_{-\mu}(\hat{x}),\cdots,h_0(\hat{x}))) \begin{array}{ll} \leq 0 & \text{for all } y \in D \\ \geq 0 & \text{for all } y \in \overline{K_*} \end{array}$$

From these two relations we obtain immediately Statements (i), (ii) and (iii) of Theorem II. This concludes the proof of Theorem II in the case $m = 0$.

Proof of Theorem II in the case $m > 0$. In Lemma 2.4 we have proved that the origin is not an interior point of the set $N \subset E^m$. Hence there exists a nonzero vector $(\overline{\lambda_1},\cdots,\overline{\lambda_m})$ such that

$$\sum_{i=1}^{m} \overline{\lambda_i} h_i(x) \geq 0 \quad \text{for all } x \in \widetilde{M}$$

We now define two sets B and K_+ in $E^{\mu+2}$ by the relations

$$B = \{(h_{-\mu}(x), \cdots, h_0(x), \sum_{i=1}^{m} \overline{\lambda_i}\, h_i(x)) : x \in M\}$$

$$K_{\dagger} = \{(\xi_{-\mu}, \cdots, \xi_0, \xi_1) : \xi_{-\mu}, \cdots, \xi_1 < 0\}$$

The sets $K_{\dagger}$ and $B - K_{\dagger}$ are convex and disjoint, and the point $(h_{-\mu}(\hat{x}), \cdots, h_0(\hat{x}), 0)$ belongs to $\overline{B - K_{\dagger}}$ and $\overline{K_{\dagger}}$. Hence there exists a nonzero vector $\lambda^* = (\lambda^*_{-\mu}, \cdots, \lambda^*_1)$ such that

$$\lambda^* \cdot (y - (h_{-\mu}(\hat{x}), \cdots, h_0(\hat{x}), 0)) \leq 0 \quad \text{for all } y \in B$$

$$\geq 0 \quad \text{for all } y \in \overline{K_{\dagger}}$$

From these relations we obtain

$$\sum_{i=-\mu}^{0} \lambda^*_i h_i(x) + \lambda^*_1 \sum_{i=1}^{m} \overline{\lambda_i}\, h_i(x)$$

$$\leq \sum_{i=-\mu}^{0} \lambda^*_i h_i(\hat{x}) + \lambda^*_1 \sum_{i=1}^{m} \overline{\lambda_i}\, h_i(\hat{x}) \text{ for all } x \in M$$

and

$$\lambda^*_i \leq 0 \quad \text{and} \quad \lambda^*_i h_i(\hat{x}) = 0 \quad \text{for} \quad i = -\mu, \cdots, 0.$$

The statements (i), (ii) and (iii) of Theorem II follow then by defining $\lambda = (\lambda_{-\mu}, \cdots, \lambda_m)$ by the relations

$$\lambda_i = \lambda^*_i \quad \text{if} \quad i = -\mu, \cdots, 0$$

$$\lambda_i = \lambda^*_1 \overline{\lambda_i} \quad \text{if} \quad i = 1, \cdots, m$$

This concludes the proof of Theorem II.

Section 3. Some Applications of Separation Theorems in Infinite Dimensional Spaces

The fundamental inequality of Theorem II

$$\sum_{i=-\mu}^{m} \lambda_i h_i(x) \le \sum_{i=-\mu}^{m} \lambda_i h_i(\hat{x}) \quad \text{for all } x \in M$$

can be transformed into

$$\sum_{i=-\mu}^{m} \lambda_i \overline{h_i}(x) \le 0 \quad \text{for all } x \in M \tag{3.1}$$

if we define functions $\overline{h}_{-\mu},\cdots,\overline{h}_m$ by the relation $\overline{h}_i(x) = h_i(x) - h_i(\hat{x})$. The left side of inequality (3.1) is concave in x over X since $\lambda_i \le 0$ and $\overline{h_i}$ is convex for $i = -\mu,\cdots,0$ and since $\overline{h_i}$ is linear for $i=1,\cdots,m$. For many applications we would like to replace the concave function $\sum_{i=-\mu}^{m} \lambda_i \overline{h_i}$ by a linear function of the form $\sum_{i=-\mu}^{m} \lambda_i \ell_i$ where each ℓ_i is a linear function such that

$$\ell_i(x) \le \overline{h_i}(x) \quad \text{for all } x \in X \text{ and all } i=-\mu,\cdots,m \tag{3.2}$$

and

$$\sum_{i=-\mu}^{m} \lambda_i \ell_i(x) \le 0 \quad \text{for all } x \in M \tag{3.3}$$

In the present section we prove that we can define continuous linear functions $\ell_{-\mu},\cdots,\ell_m$ over X which satisfy Conditions (3.2) and (3.3).

For $i=1,\cdots,m$ we set $\ell_i = \overline{h_i}$. In order to define $\ell_{-\mu},\cdots,\ell_0$ we need the following result:

> Lemma 3.1. Let M be a convex subset of a normed linear space X such that $0 \in M$, let f and g be continuous convex functions on X such that $f(0) = g(0)$ and let $\sigma \leq 0$. We assume that $\sigma f(x) \leq g(x)$ for all $x \in M$. Then there exists a continuous linear function ℓ on X such that $\ell(x) \leq f(x)$ for all $x \in X$ and $\sigma\ell(x) \leq g(x)$ for all $x \in M$.

The proof of Lemma 3.1 will be given at the end of the present section.

We shall now define step by step continuous linear functions $\ell_{-\mu},\cdots,\ell_0$ satisfying Relations 3.2 and 3.3.

We first apply Lemma 3.1 to the case $f = \overline{h_{-\mu}}$, $g = -(\sum_{i=-\mu+1}^{0} \lambda_i \overline{h_i} + \sum_{i=1}^{m} \lambda_i \ell_i)$ and $\sigma = \lambda_{-\mu}$, and we obtain a continuous linear function $\ell_{-\mu}$ such that

$$\ell_{-\mu}(x) \leq \overline{h_{-\mu}}(x) \quad \text{for all} \quad x \in X$$

and

$$\lambda_{-\mu}\ell_{-\mu}(x) + \sum_{i=\mu+1}^{0} \lambda_i \overline{h_i}(x) + \sum_{i=1}^{m} \lambda_i \ell_i(x) \leq 0 \quad \text{for all } x \in M.$$

We now apply Lemma 3.1 to the case $f = \overline{h}_{-\mu+1}$, $g = -(\lambda_{-\mu}\ell_{-\mu} + \sum_{i=-\mu+2}^{0} \lambda_i \overline{h_i} + \sum_{i=1}^{m} \lambda_i \ell_i)$ and $\sigma = \lambda_{-\mu+1}$, and we obtain a continuous linear function $\ell_{-\mu+1}$ such that

$$\ell_{-\mu+1}(x) \leq \overline{h}_{-\mu+1}(x) \quad \text{for all } x \in X$$

and

$$\lambda_{-\mu}\ell_{-\mu}(x) + \lambda_{-\mu+1}\ \ell_{-\mu+1}(x) + \sum_{i=-\mu+2}^{0} \lambda_i \overline{h_i}(x) + \sum_{i=1}^{m} \lambda_i \ell_i(x) \le 0$$

for all $x \in M$

By repeating again the same process for $i=-\mu + 2,\cdots,0$ we obtain the desired result.

The preceeding results allow us to enlarge Theorem II into

<u>Theorem III.</u> If Assumptions H_1 and H_2 hold then there exists a nonzero vector $\lambda = (\lambda_{-\mu},\cdots,\lambda_m) \in E^{m+\mu+1}$ and a continuous linear-plus-a-constant function $\ell = (\ell_{-\mu},\cdots,\ell_m)$ from X into $E^{\mu+m+1}$ such that

(i) $\lambda\cdot h(x) \le \lambda\cdot\ell(x) \le \lambda\cdot\ell(\hat{x}) = \lambda\cdot h(\hat{x})$ for all $x \in M$

(ii) $\lambda_i \ge 0$ for $i=-\mu,\cdots,0$

(iii) $\lambda_i h_i(\hat{x}) = \lambda_i\ell_i(\hat{x}) = 0$ for $i=-\mu,\cdots,-1$

(iv) for $i=-\mu,\cdots,0$ we have
$\ell_i(x) \le h_i(x)$ for all $x \in X$ and $\ell_i(\hat{x}) = h_i(\hat{x})$

(v) for $i=1,\cdots,m$ we have $\ell_i = h_i$.

<u>Proof of Lemma 3.1.</u> The sets

$$S_1 = \{(x,t): x \in X,\ t < - f(x)\}$$

and

$$S_2 = \begin{cases} \{(x,t): x \in M,\ t > -\frac{1}{\sigma}\, g(x)\} & \text{if } \sigma < 0 \\ \{(0,t): t > 0\} & \text{if } \sigma = 0 \end{cases}$$

are disjoint convex subsets of the normed linear space $X \times E^1$ and S_1 has an interior point since we have assumed that f is continuous on X. Hence, Dunford-Schwartz (3) Theorem 8 page 417, there exists a nonzero continuous linear function $L(x,t)$ and some real number α such that

$$L(x,t) \leq \alpha \quad \text{if} \quad (x,t) \in S_1$$
$$\geq \alpha \quad \text{if} \quad (x,t) \in S_2$$

We have $\alpha = 0$ since $(x,t) \in S_1$ (respectively S_2) implies that $(\varepsilon x, \varepsilon t) \in S_1$ (respectively S_2) for all $\varepsilon \in (0,1]$. We have $L(x,t) = L(0,t) + L(x,0)$ and $L(0,t) = ct$ for some constant c. We cannot have $c = 0$ because this would imply $L(x,0) \leq 0$ for all $x \in X$, i.e. $L(x,0) = 0$ for all $x \in X$, and hence $L(x,t) = 0$ for all $(x,t) \in X \times E^1$, which cannot be since $L(x,t)$ is a nonzero continuous linear function on $X \times E^1$. We cannot have $c < 0$ because it would then be possible to find a $t > 0$ such that $L(0,0) + ct < 0$ which cannot be since $(0,t) \in S_2$ if $t > 0$. We have then $c > 0$. Let $\ell(x) = \frac{1}{c} L(x,0)$. The functional ℓ is linear and continuous. Moreover for each $x \in X$ we have

$$\ell(x) + t \leq 0 \quad \text{for all} \quad t < - f(x)$$

and for each $x \in M$ we have

$$\ell(x) + t \geq 0 \quad \text{for all} \quad t > - \frac{1}{\sigma} g(x) \text{ if } \sigma < 0 .$$

The required conditions follow then immediately. This concludes the proof of Lemma 3.1.

Final Remarks

The proof of Theorem II would be much simpler if we would have assumed that the functions $h_{-\mu}, \cdots, h_0$ were not only convex but linear. It is worth noting however, that such a simplified form of Theorem II is indeed sufficient to derive most necessary conditions in Calculus of Variations and Optimal Control Theory (see Halkin (4) and (7)). In Section II we have assumed that the functions $h_{-\mu},\cdots,h_0$ are convex but not necessarily linear because this extends the application of Theorem II to the optimal control problem with bounded phase coordinates.

A result essentially equivalent to Theorem II was introduced early in 1966, (Halkin (5). Our main motivation at that time was to provide a simpler frame of reference and a simple proof for some important results announced by Neustadt in 1965, (Neustadt (9)) and proved later in 1966 (Neustadt (10), (11)). Those results were further extended in a joint paper with L. W. Neustadt (Halkin-Neustadt (6)). A novel feature of the present paper is the separation of the assumptions concerning the set M and the functions $h_{-\mu},\cdots,h_m$, (see Assumptions H_1 and H_2 of Section II).

The results stated in the present paper can be applied to the study of optimal control problems for systems described by nonlinear difference equations. However the reader whose interest is limited to those problems should realize that results much weaker than those stated here are sufficient for that purpose, (Canon-Cullum-Polak (1), Da Cunha-Polak (2)) since in that case one is justified in assuming that the space X is of finite dimension and that the functions $h_{-\mu},\cdots,h_0$ are linear.

REFERENCES

(1) M. Canon, C. Cullum and E. Polak, Constrained Minimization Problems in Finite Dimensional Spaces, SIAM J. on Control, 4, 1966, pp. 528-547.

(2) N. O. Da Cunha and E. Polak, Constrained Minimization under Vector-Valued Criteria in Finite Dimensional Spaces, Memorandum ERL-M188, Electronics Research Laboratory, University of California, Berkeley, October 1966.

(3) Dunford, N., and J. T. Schwartz, Linear Operators, Part I: General Theory (New York: Interscience, 1958).

(4) H. Halkin, Finite Convexity in Infinite Dimensional spaces, in Proceedings of the Colloquium on Convexity, ed. W. Fenchel (Copenhagen, 1965), pp. 126-131.

(5) H. Halkin, An abstract framework for the theory of process optimization, Bull. Am. Math. Soc., 72, 1966, pp. 677-678.

(6) H. Halkin, Optimal Control as Programming in Infinite Dimensional Spaces, Centro Internazionale Mathematico Estivo (C.I.M.E.), Bressanone, Italy, June 1966. Available as report of the Mathematics Department, University of California, San Diego, California.

(7) H. Halkin and L. W. Neustadt, General necessary conditions for optimization problems, Proc. Nat. Acad. Sciences, 56, 1966, pp. 1066-1071.

(8) Hurwicz, L., "Programming in linear spaces," in Studies in Linear and Nonlinear Programming, ed. K. J. Arrow, L. Hurwicz, and H. Uzawa (Stanford University Press 1958), pp. 38-102.

(9) L. W. Neustadt, Optimal control problems as extremal problems in a Banach space, Proceedings of Poly. Inst. of Brooklyn Symposium on System Theory, April 1965.

(10) L. W. Neustadt, An abstract variational theory with applications to a broad class of optimization problems I: General Theory, to appear in SIAM J. on Control 4 (1966). Available as report on the Electronic Sciences Laboratory, University of Southern California, Los Angeles, California, February 1966.

(11) L. W. Neustadt, An abstract variational theory with applications to a broad class of optimization problems II: Applications, to appear. Available as report of the Electronic Sciences Laboratory, University of Southern California, Los Angeles, California, May 1966.

(12) D. L. Russell, The Kuhn-Tucker Conditions in Banach Space with an Application to Control Theory, J. Math. An. Appl., 15, (1966), pp 200-212.

A MAXIMUM PRINCIPLE IN EXTREMAL PROBLEMS WITH DELAYS

G. L. Kharatishvili
Tbilisi State University
Tbilisi, USSR

In this paper, we formulate an extremal problem with delays of a quite general type, and, on the basis of results set forth in (1, 2), we derive a necessary condition for extremality which generalizes the maximum principle to an optimal control problem in which the delays are contained both in the controls and in the phase coordinates, and the initial function is to be found in the class of piecewise-continuous functions. The author previously derived a maximum principle in the case where the delays occurred only in the phase coordinates [see (3)].

We shall denote column vectors by Latin letters, and row vectors by Greek letters. Further, f_x denotes the partial derivative of the function f with respect to x.

Let G be a region in an n-dimensional vector space R, and I the interval $a<t<b$ on the time axis.

Furthermore, let

$$F = \{ f(x_1, \dots, x_m, t) \}$$

be a family of n-dimensional vector functions $f(x_1,\dots,x_m,t)$ defined on the direct product $G^m \times I$, measurable with respect to t for fixed $x_1, \dots, x_m$, of class C^1 with respect to $x_1, \dots, x_m$ for fixed t, and, satisfying on $X \times I$ the conditions:

$$|f(x_1, \dots, x_m, t)| \leq M(t)$$

$$|f_{x_j}(x_1, \dots, x_m, t)| \leq M(t), \quad j = 1, \dots, m,$$

where X is an arbitrary compact set in G^m, and M(t) is a

function integrable on I, which may depend on f and X.

Let us consider the differential equation with delays

$$\frac{dx(t)}{dt} = f(x(t-\eta_1), \ldots, x(t-\eta_m), t), \tag{1}$$

where $f \in F$, and in place of the arguments $x_1, \ldots, x_m$, we substitute, respectively, $x(t-\eta_1), \ldots, x(t-\eta_m)$ where $\eta_1 > \eta_2 > \ldots > \eta_m \geq 0$ are given numbers. In order to uniquely determine a trajectory $x(t)$ on some closed interval $[t_1, t_2] \subset I$, it is necessary to fix the function $f \in F$, the initial value $x(t_1) = x_1 \in G$, and the initial function h: $x(t) = h(t)$, $t_1 - \eta_1 \leq t \leq t_1$. We shall choose the initial function from the family of piecewise-continuous functions (with a finite number of discontinuities of the first kind), taking on their values in G.

We shall call a trajectory $x(t)$ of Eq. (1), which is uniquely determined on the interval $[t_1, t_2] \subset I$ by the data t_1, t_2, $x_1 \in G$, h, $f \in F$, an admissible trajectory.

Let there be given a scalar-valued function $J(t_1, t_2, x_1, x_2)$, and a k-dimensional vector-valued function $\ell(t_1, t_2, x_1, x_2)$, where both functions are defined on $I^2 \times G^2$ and are continuously differentiable.

We shall call an admissable trajectory $y(t)$ of Equation (1), defined on an interval $[\tau_1, \tau_2] \subset I$, an extremal if τ_1, τ_2, $y_1 = y(\tau_1)$, $y_2 = y(\tau_2)$ satisfy the condition $\ell(\tau_1, \tau_2, y_1, y_2) = 0$ and in so doing minimize the functional $J(\tau_1, \tau_2, y_1, y_2)$.

In what follows, we shall assume that the family F is quasiconvex (see (2)).

Let $y(t)$ be an extremal corresponding to data τ_1, τ_2, $y_1 \in G$, h^*, $f^* \in F$. By the definition of quasiconvexity, for any $f \in F$ and any $\varepsilon \in (0, 1)$, there exists an n-dimensional vector-valued function $g(x_1, \ldots, x_m, t)$ such that $f^* + \varepsilon(f - f^*) + g \in F$, and such that, for any point $(x_1, \ldots, x_m) \in G$ in some fixed neighborhood of the curve $(y(t-\eta_1), \ldots, y(t-\eta_m))$, $\tau_1 \leq t \leq \tau_2$ and any t_1, t_2 in I,

$$\left| \int_{t_1}^{t_2} g(x_1, \ldots, x_m, t)\, dt \right| \leq \varepsilon^2.$$

Let us consider the sets

$$V_{f^*} = \{f^* + \varepsilon(f - f^*) + g \in F : f \in F\},$$
$$V_{h^*} = \{h^* + \varepsilon(h - h^*)\},$$
$$V_{y_1} = \{x \in R : |x - y_1| < \varepsilon\},$$
$$V_{\tau_i} = \{t \in I : |t - \tau_i| < \varepsilon\}, \; i = 1, 2,$$
$$S = [0, +\infty).$$

Obviously, V_{f^*} is quasiconvex, and V_{h^*}, V_{y_1}, V_{τ_i}, S are convex. Therefore $D = S \times V_{\tau_1} \times V_{\tau_2} \times V_{y_1} \times V_{h^*} \times V_{f^*}$ is quasiconvex.

Let us consider the (k+1)-dimensional vector-valued function

$$q(s, t_1, t_2, x_1, x_2) =$$
$$(J(t_1, t_2, x_1, x_2) - J(\tau_1, \tau_2, y_1, y_2) + s, \ell(t_1, t_2, x_1, x_2))$$

For $\varepsilon > 0$ sufficiently small, the following mapping P from D into (k+1)-space is defined:

$$P(s, t_1, t_2, x_1, h, f) = q(s, t_1, t_2, x(t_1), x(t_2)).$$

The point $w^* = (0, \tau_1, \tau_2, y_1, h^*, f^*) \in D$ is a critical point of the mapping P (see (1)).

Suppose that the mapping P has, at the point w^*, a differential $\delta P(\delta w)$ for $\delta w \in D - w^*$. Then there exists a non-zero (k+1)-dimensional vector $\chi = (\chi_o, \chi_1, \ldots, \chi_k)$, and a neighborhood $Q \subset D$ of the critical point w^* such that

$$\chi \cdot \delta P(\delta w) \leq 0, \quad \delta w \in K_{w^*} - w^*,$$

where K_{w^*} is a closed cone with vertex w^*, spanned over the convex hull of Q (see (1)).

By direct calculations, we conclude that

$$\chi \cdot \delta P(\delta w) = \chi(q_{t_1} + q_{x_1} f_1^*)\,\delta t_1 + \chi(q_{t_2} + q_{x_2} f_2^*)\,\delta t_2 + \chi q_{x_1} \delta x_1 +$$
$$+ \chi q_{x_2} \delta x_2 + \chi_o \delta s \leq 0. \tag{2}$$

Here,

$$q_{t_i} = q_{t_i}(0, \tau_i, \tau_2, y(\tau_1), y(\tau_2)),$$
$$q_{x_i} = q_{x_i}(0, \tau_1, \tau_2, y(\tau_1), y(\tau_2)),$$
$$f_i^* = f^*(y(\tau_i - \eta_1), \ldots, y(\tau_i - \eta_m), \tau_i), \quad i = 1, 2;$$

where δt_1, δt_2, δx_1 are arbitrary, $\delta s \geq 0$, and $\delta x_2 = \delta x(\tau_2)$, where $\delta x(t)$, $\tau_1 \leq t \leq \tau_2$, is the solution of the variational equation corresponding to the initial value δx_1 and the arbitrary initial function $\delta h = h - h^*$. The variational equation has the form

$$\frac{d\delta x(t)}{dt} = \sum_{j=1}^{m} f_{x_j}^*(t)\,\delta x(t-\eta_j) + f(t) - f^*(t), \quad \tau_1 \leq t \leq \tau_2,$$

where

$$f_{x_j}^*(t) = f_{x_j}^*(y(t-\eta_1), \ldots, y(t-\eta_m), t), \quad j = 1, \ldots, m,$$

$$f(t) = f(y(t-\eta_1), \ldots, y(t-\eta_m), t).$$

Let us introduce the function

$$\Delta_j(t) = \begin{cases} 1, & t \in [\tau_1, \tau_2 - \eta_j] \\ 0, & t \notin \tau_1, \tau_2 - \eta_j], \quad j = 1, \ldots, m \end{cases}$$

and let us consider the equation

$$\frac{d\psi(t)}{dt} = -\sum_{j=1}^{m} \Delta_j(t)\,\psi(t+\eta_j)\, f_{x_j}(t+\eta_j) \tag{3}$$

for the auxiliary n-dimensional vector-valued function $\psi(t)$. Let $\psi(t)$, $\tau_1 \leq t \leq \tau_2$, be the solution of Eq. (3) satisfying the condition $\psi(\tau_2) = \chi q_{x_2}$. Let us evaluate $\psi(\tau_2)\,\delta\chi_2$. We have

$$\psi(\tau_2)\delta x_2 - \psi(\tau_1)\delta x_1 = \int_{\tau_1}^{\tau_2} (\psi(t)\cdot\delta x(t))'\,dt = \int_{\tau_1}^{\tau_2} \psi(t)\,[f(t) - f^*(t)]\,dt +$$

$$\sum_{j=1}^{m} \int_{\tau_1}^{\tau_2} \psi(t) f_{x_j}^*(t)\,\delta x(t-\eta_j)\,dt - \sum_{j=1}^{m} \int_{\tau_1}^{\tau_2} \Delta_j(t)\,\psi(t+\eta_j)\, f_{x_j}^*(t+\eta_j)\,\delta x(t)\,dt =$$

$$= \int_{\tau_1}^{\tau_2} \psi(t)\,[f(t)-f^*(t)\,]\,dt + \sum_{j=1}^{m} \int_{\tau_1}^{\tau_2} \psi(t) f^*_{x_j}(t)\,\delta x(t-\eta_j)\,dt -$$

$$- \sum_{j=1}^{m} \int_{\tau_1+\eta_j}^{\tau_2} \psi(t)\, f^*_{x_j}(t)\,\delta x(t-\eta_j)\,dt.$$

Thus,

$$\psi(t_2)\delta x_2 = \chi q_{x_2}\delta x_2 = \psi(\tau_1)\delta x_1 + \int_{\tau_1}^{\tau_2} \psi(t)\,[f(t)-f^*(t)\,]\,dt +$$

$$\int_{\tau_1-\eta_1}^{\tau_1} \sum_{j=1}^{m} \sigma_j(t)\,\psi(t+\eta_j)\, f^*_{x_j}(t+\eta_j)\,\delta h(t)\,dt,$$

where

$$\sigma_j(t) = \begin{cases} 1, & t \in [\tau_1-\eta_j,\ \tau_1], \\ 0, & t \notin [\tau_1-\eta_j,\ \tau_1],\ j = 1, \ldots, m. \end{cases}$$

Eliminating $\chi q_{x_2}\delta x_2$ from inequality (2), and taking into account that the variables δt_1, δt_2, δx_1, and $\delta h = h - h^*$ are arbitrary, $f \in F$, and $\delta s \geq 0$ we obtain the following relations:

$$(\chi q_{t_1},\ \chi q_{t_2},\ \chi q_{x_1},\ \chi q_{x_2}) = (\psi_1 f^*_1,\ -\psi_2 f^*_2,\ -\psi_1,\ \psi_2), \quad (4)$$

$$\int_{\tau_1-\eta_j}^{\tau_1} \sum_{j=1}^{m} \sigma_j(t)\,\psi(t+\eta_j)\, f^*_{x_j}(t+\eta_j)\, h^*(t)\,dt \geq$$

$$\geq \int_{\tau_1-\eta_1}^{\tau_1} \sum_{j=1}^{m} \sigma_j(t)\,\psi(t+\eta_j)\, f^*_{x_j}(t+\eta_j)\, h(t)\,dt, \quad (5)$$

$$\int_{\tau_1}^{\tau_2} \psi(t) f^*(y(t-\eta_1), \ldots, y(t-\eta_m), t)\, dt \geq$$

$$\geq \int_{\tau_1}^{\tau_2} \psi(t) f(y(t-\eta_1), \ldots, y(t-\eta_m), t)\, dt, \qquad (6)$$

for any $f(x_1, \ldots, x_m, t) \in F$,

$$\chi_o \leq 0. \qquad (7)$$

Thus, the following theorem holds.

Theorem 1. Let the admissible trajectory $y(t)$, $\tau_1 \leq t \leq \tau_2$, of Equation (1), corresponding to the data τ_1, τ_2, y_1, h^*, f^* be an extremal. Then there exists a non-zero $(k+1)$-dimensional vector $\chi = (\chi_o, \chi_1, \ldots, \chi_k)$, and a non-trivial solution $\psi(t)$, $\tau_1 \leq t \leq \tau_2$, of Equation (3) such that conditions (4), (5), (6), (7) are satisfied.

Let us now consider applying Theorem 1 to optimal processes with delays.

Let Ω be an arbitrary subset of an r-dimensional vector space E, let $X \subset G^m$ and $U \subset E^p$ be arbitrary compact sets, and let $\theta_1 > \theta_2 > \ldots > \theta_p \geq 0$ be given numbers.

Let $\mathcal{J}(x_1, \ldots, x_m, u_1, \ldots u_p, t)$ be an n-dimensional vector function defined on $G^m \times E^p \times I$, of class C^1 with respect to $x_1, \ldots, x_m$ for fixed $u_1, \ldots, u_p$, t, measurable with respect to $u_1, \ldots, u_p$, t for fixed $x_1, \ldots, x_m$ and satisfying on $X \times U \times I$ the conditions

$$|\mathcal{J}(x_1, \ldots, x_m, u_1, \ldots, u_p, t)| \leq M(t)$$

$$|\mathcal{J}_{xj}(x_1, \ldots, x_m, u_1, \ldots, u_p, t)| \leq M(t), \quad j = 1, \ldots, m,$$

where $M(t)$ is a function integrable on I, which may depend on $\mathcal{J}$, $\tilde{X}$ and U.

Let $\tilde{F}$ be the following family of functions:

$$\tilde{F} = \{ \mathcal{J}(x_1, \ldots, x_m, v(t-\theta_1), \ldots, v(t-\theta_p), t) \}.$$

Here, $v(t)$ is an arbitrary measurable function which is

essentially bounded on the interval $a - \theta_1 < t < b$, and satisfies the condition $v(t) \in \Omega$ almost everywhere on this interval.

The quasiconvexity of $\tilde{F}$ follows from the approximation lemma (see (2)). Therefore, Theorem 1 remains valid if, in place of F, we insert $\tilde{F}$. In this case, Equation (1) assumes the form

$$\frac{dx(t)}{dt} = \mathcal{F}(x(t-\eta_1), \ldots, x(t-\eta_m), v(t-\theta_1), \ldots, v(t-\theta_p), t). \quad (8)$$

We shall show that if the functions in $\tilde{F}$ are continuous in all of the arguments $u_1, \ldots, u_p$, t, then Theorem 1, in the present case, can be formulated in the form of a maximum principle.

Let z(t) be an extremal corresponding to the data τ_1, τ_2, z_1, h^*, $\mathcal{F}(x_1, \ldots, x_m, u(t-\theta_1), \ldots, u(t-\theta_p), t) \in \tilde{F}$. Then, condition (6) assumes the form

$$\int_{\tau_1}^{\tau_2} \psi(t)\, \mathcal{F}(z(t-\eta_1), \ldots, z(t-\eta_m), u(t-\theta_1), \ldots, u(t-\theta_p), t)dt \geq$$

$$\int_{\tau_1}^{\tau_2} \psi(t)\, \mathcal{F}(z(t-\eta_1), \ldots, z(t-\eta_m), v(t-\theta_1), \ldots v(t-\theta_p), t)dt, \quad (9)$$

where $\psi(t)$ is a non-trivial solution of the equation

$$\frac{d\psi(t)}{dt} = -\sum_{j=1}^{m} \Delta_j(t)\psi(t+\eta_j)\, \mathcal{F}_{x_j}(z(t+\eta_j-\eta_1), \ldots, z(t+\eta_j-\eta_m),$$

$$u(t+\eta_j-\theta_1), \ldots, u(t+\eta_j-\theta_p), t+\eta_j). \quad (10)$$

Let $\tau \in (\tau_1, \tau_2)$ be a regular point for the function u(t) and let

$$v(t) = \begin{cases} v \in \Omega, & t \in [\tau - \varepsilon, \tau], \\ u(t), & t \notin [\tau - \varepsilon, \tau]. \end{cases}$$

Then, on the basis of inequality (9) we conclude that,

$$\sum_{j=1}^{p} \mu_j(\tau)\, \psi(\tau+\theta_j)\, \mathcal{J}(\tau+\theta_j) \geq$$

$$\geq \sum_{j=1}^{p} \mu_j(\tau)\, \psi(\tau+\theta_j)\, \mathcal{J}_j(\tau+\theta_j)\ ,$$

where

$$\mathcal{J}(t) = \mathcal{J}(z(t-\eta_1), \ldots, z(t-\eta_m), u(t-\theta_1), \ldots, u(t-\theta_p), t),$$

$$\mathcal{J}_j(t) = \mathcal{J}(z(t-\eta_1), \ldots, z(t-\eta_m), u(t-\theta_1), \ldots, u(t-\theta_{j-1}), v,$$

$$u(t-\theta_{j+1}), \ldots, u(t-\theta_p), t)$$

$$\mu_j(t) = \begin{cases} 1, & t \in [\tau_1,\ \tau_2-\theta_j]\ , \\ 0, & t \notin [\tau_1,\ \tau_2-\theta_j],\quad j=1, \ldots, p. \end{cases}$$

Since the set of regular points of u(t) has full measure on the interval $\tau_1 \leq t \leq \tau_2$, then

$$\sum_{j=1}^{p} \mu_j(t)\, \psi(t+\theta_j)\, \mathcal{J}(t+\theta_j) \geq \sum_{j=1}^{p} \mu_j(t)\, \psi(t+\theta_j)\, \mathcal{J}_j(t+\theta_j), \tag{11}$$

for almost all $t \in [\tau_1,\ \tau_2]$.

Similarly, on the basis of inequality (5), it is possible to obtain the inequality

$$\sum_{j=1}^{m} \sigma_j(t)\, \psi(t+\eta_j)\, \mathcal{J}_{x_j}(t+\eta_j)\, h^*(t) \geq$$

$$\geq \sum_{j=1}^{m} \sigma_j(t)\, \psi(t+\eta_j)\, \mathcal{J}_{x_j}(t+\eta_j)\, h(t), \tag{12}$$

$$\tau_1 - \eta_1 \leq \tau \leq \tau_1 .$$

Finally, condition (4) yields

$$(\chi q_{t_1}, \chi q_{t_2}, \chi q_{x_1}, \chi q_{x_2}) = (\psi_1 \mathcal{F}_1, -\psi_2 \mathcal{F}_2, -\psi_1, \psi_2) \qquad (13)$$

Thus, we have the following theorem.

Theorem 2 (The Maximum Principle). Let the admissible trajectory $z(t)$ of Equation (8), corresponding to the data τ_1, τ_2, z_1, h^*, and $\mathcal{F}(x_1, \ldots, x_m, u(t-\theta_1), \ldots, u(t-\theta_p), t) \epsilon \tilde{F}$ be an extremal. Then there exist a non-zero $(k+1)$-dimensional vector $\chi = (\chi_o, \chi_1, \ldots, \chi_k)$, and a non-trivial solution $\psi(t)$, $\tau_1 \leq t \leq \tau_2$, of Eq. (10) such that conditions (11), (12), (13), (7) are satisfied.

References

1. R. V. Gamkrelidze, G. L. Kharatishvili, "The Theory of the First Variation in Extremal Problems", Soobšč. Akad. Nauk GSSR (1967).

2. R. V. Gamkrelidze, "On Some Extremal Problems in the Theory of Differential Equations with Applications to the Theory of Optimal Control", J. SIAM on Control, Vol. 3, No. 1 (1965), pp. 106-128.

3. G. L. Kharatishvili, "Optimal Processes with Delays", METSNIEREBA , Tbilisi, 1966.

LEXICOGRAPHICAL ORDER, RANGE OF INTEGRALS AND "BANG-BANG" PRINCIPLE

Czeslaw Olech

Brown University, Division of Applied Mathematics,
Providence, Rhode Island
and
Institute of Mathematics, Polish Academy of Sciences,
Krakow, Poland

INTRODUCTION. Let J denote a compact interval, say $[0,1]$, E -- an Euclidean n-space, M -- the space of Lebesgue measurable functions of I into E. For any $u, v \in M$ the equality $u = v$ will mean $u(t) = v(t)$ almost everywhere (a.e.) in J. The topology in M will be that given by the convergence in measure.

The purpose of this paper is to study in detail the range of integrals of a subset $K \subset M$ which satisfies the following three conditions

(i) K is closed in M with respect to convergence in measure

(ii) $|\int_J u(\tau)d\tau| \leqq m$ for each $u \in K$

(iii) If $u, v \in K$, $0 < t_1 < 1$, and $w(t) = u(t)$ if $0 \leqq t < t_1$ and $v(t)$ if $t_1 \leqq t \leqq 1$, then $w \in K$.

The motivation to study the range of integrals of such a class K comes from linear control theory. Indeed let us consider the system of the form

$$\dot{x}(t) = A(t)x(t) + f(t,u(t)), \tag{S}$$

where the function f satisfies the well know Caratheodory

*This research was supported in part by the National Aeronautics and Space Administration under Grant No.NGR-40-002-015, and in part by the United States Army Research Office, Durham, under Contract No. DA-31-124-ARO-D-270.

conditions. Take as admissible control functions the class of Lebesgue measurable $u: I \to U$, where U is a compact subset of an m-dimensional space. Any solution of (S) can be represented in the form $x(t) = X(t)(x_0 + \int_0^t v(\tau)d\tau)$, where $X(t)$ is the fundamental matrix solution of the corresponding homogeneous system, x_0 is the initial value for $t = 0$ and $v(t) = X^{-1}(t)f(t,u(t))$. It is easy to verify that the class

$$L = \{v: v(t) = X^{-1}(t)f(t,u(t)), u \text{ -- admissible}\}$$

satisfies conditions (i), (ii), and (iii). A basic result for the existence of a time-optimal solution for (S) is that the so-called attainable set

$$\Omega(t) = \{x: X(t)(x_0 + \int_0^t v(\tau)d\tau),\ v \in L\}$$

is convex, compact and continuous in t. Up to a linear transformation and a translation this set is seen to be the range of integrals over L. This result among others will be proved here but probably more interesting is an extension of LaSalle's "bang-bang" principle. Roughly speaking the "bang-bang" principle as stated by LaSalle (2) says that in general one can restrict the range U of admissible controls to a subset U_0 without restricting the attainable set. In LaSalle's case f was linear in u, U was a compact cube and he proved U_0 to be the set of vertices of U. Later this result has been extended by several authors, cf. for example (1),(3),(4). Our extension of the "bang-bang" principle is Theorem 1 and states that there is a smallest subclass K_0 of K satisfying (iii) but not necessarily (i) such that the range of integrals over K_0 is the same as over K. In LaSalle's case the restricted class of "bang-bang" controls satisfies (i), too.

The results presented here generalize those recently published by the author in (5). In (5) the class K was given by $\{v \in M: v(t) \in G(t)\}$ where G is a measurable map [cf. (6)] of T into the space of compact subsets of E. In the situation concerning system (S) discussed above the set-valued map is given by $\{X^{-1}(t)f(t,u): u \in U\}$.

There is a close connection between our results and the Liapunov theorem on the range of non-atomic vector valued measures. For details we refer the reader to (5).

The following notations will be used. By (x,y), $x, y \in E$, we denote the scalar product of x and y, by $|x|$ the Euclidean norm of $x \in E$. Thus $|u|$ and (u,v) if $u, v \in M$ will stand for the function taking $t \to |u(t)|$ and

and $t \to (u(t), v(t))$, respectively. By I and I_t we denote the integral operator $\int_J$ and $\int_0^t$ respectively. Thus $I(u) = \int_J u(\tau)d\tau$ and $I(K) = \{I(u): u \in K\}$.

LEXICOGRAPHICAL ORDER IN E AND IN M. Let $x, y \in E$ and let $\{x_i\}$, $\{y_i\}$ denote the coordinates of x and y respectively with respect to a fixed coordinate system in E. We will write

$$x \leqq y \text{ iff } x_i = y_i \text{ for } i = 1, \ldots, k \text{ and if } k < n \text{ then } x_{k+1} < y_{k+1}. \tag{1}$$

In particular, k may be equal 0. The relation (1) is the so-called lexicographical order in E and it is easy to see that it is a linear order. If $n = 1$, then (1) is the natural order for reals. If, in (1), $k < n$ then we will use "$<$" instead of "$\leqq$". Since the order is linear, any finite subsets of E admits a unique maximum with respect to (1). Thus we have

$$\underset{1 \leqq i \leqq s}{\text{lex.max}} \{x^i\} = x^j \text{ iff } x^i \leqq x^j \text{ for } i = 1, \ldots, s \tag{2}$$

If, $u, v \in M$ then we will write

$$u \leqq v \text{ iff } u(t) \leqq v(t) \text{ a.e. in } J \tag{3}$$

and refer to (3) as the lexicographical order in M. The order "$\leqq$" in M is no longer linear but is a lattice, since for any finite set $\{u^i\}$, $1 \leqq i \leqq s$ of M the lex. sup exists and we have

$$v = \underset{1 \leqq i \leqq s}{\text{lex sup}} \{u^i\} \text{ iff } v(t) = \underset{1 \leqq i \leqq s}{\text{lex.max}} \{u^i(t)\}. \tag{4}$$

We note the following obvious propositions.

<u>Proposition 1. If $u, v \in M$ are integrable and $u \leqq v$ then $I(u) \leqq I(v)$.</u>

<u>Proposition 2.</u> If $u \leqq v$ and $I(u) = I(v)$ then $u = v$.

<u>Proposition 3.</u> If $u, v \in M$ are integrable, $w = \text{lex.sup}\{u, v\}$, $I(u) = p = (p_i)$, $I(v) = q = (q_i)$, $I(w) = r = (r_i)$, $i = 1, \ldots, n$, and if $r_i = q_i = p_i$ for $i = 1, \ldots, k \leqq n$, then $u_i = v_i$ for $i = 1, \ldots, k$, where $u_i(t)$, $v_i(t)$ are coordinates of $u(t)$ and $v(t)$ respectively.

Notice that the lexicographical order in E or M depends on the coordinate system in E. Thus if $\xi = (x^1, \ldots, x^n)$,

$x^i \in E$, is a basis in E then by "$\leqq_\xi$" we will denote the lexicographical order corresponding to ξ. In the sequel we restrict ourselves to the orthonormal bases in E. Thus we will be interested in the set

$$\Xi = \{\xi : \xi = (x^1, \ldots, x^n), (x^i, x^j) = \delta_{ij}, i,j=1,\ldots,n\};$$

where $\delta_{ij} = 1$ if $i=j$ and 0 otherwise.

Let $A \subset E$ be compact, then to each $\xi \in \Xi$ there is a unique point denoted by $e(A, \xi)$ of A, which is the lexicographical maximum of A with respect to "$\leqq_\xi$", and is determined by the conditions: $e(A,\xi) \in A$ and $x \leqq_\xi e(A,\xi)$ for each $x \in A$. The next proposition can be found in (7) in a slightly different form but for completeness we include here a detailed proof.

Proposition 4. Let $A \subset E$ be compact, then the set

$$B = \bigcap_{\xi \in \Xi} \{x : x \leqq_\xi e(A,\xi)\} \tag{5}$$

is the convex hull of A. Moreover, the set

$$D = \{e(A,\xi) : \xi \in \Xi\} \tag{6}$$

is the profile of $\ddot{B}$ of B; that is, the set of extreme points of B.

Proof. Let $C \subset E$ be convex and let $p \notin C$. Then there is a $\xi \in \Xi$ such that

$$x <_\xi p \quad \text{for each} \quad x \in C. \tag{7}$$

If $n = 1$ then (7) is obvious. For n arbitrary there is an $a \in E$, $|a| = 1$ such that $(p,a) \geqq (x,a)$ for each $x \in C$. If $(p,a) > (x,a)$ for each $x \in C$, then (7) holds for any $\xi = (x^1, \ldots, x^n) \in \Xi$ if $x^1 = a$. If $(p,a) = (x,a)$ for some $x \in C$ then the set $C_1 = C \cap \{x : (x,a) = (p,a)\}$ is non-empty, convex and of dimension n-1 at the most, and p does not belong to C_1 but does belong to the hyperplane containing C_1. Thus we have the same situation but in a smaller dimension. Therefore an easy induction argument completes the proof of (7). Let C be now the convex hull of D given by (6). It follows from (7) that if $p \notin C$ then $p \notin B$ given by (5). Hence $B \subset C$. But B is convex and $D \subset A \subset B$. Therefore C as the convex hull of D is contained in B. Hence $C = B$ and B given by (5) is the convex hull of E and since $D \subset A \subset B$, B is the convex hull of A as well. In particular B is compact. To end the proof, let us recall that a point $b \in B$ is an extreme point of B if and only if $B\setminus\{b\}$ is convex. Let $b = e(A,\xi)\in D$. By (5), $B\setminus\{b\} = B \cap \{x : x <_\xi e(A,\xi)\}$. Manifestly the latter set is convex for each $\xi \in \Xi$ and we conclude that $D \subset \ddot{B}$. Suppose now that $b \in \ddot{B}$. Then $B\setminus\{b\}$ is convex and by (7) there is a $\xi \in \Xi$ such that $x <_\xi b$ for each $x \in B\setminus\{b\}$. Hence $b = e(B,\xi)$. It is easy to see by (5) that $e(A,\xi) = e(B,\xi)$ for each $\xi \in \Xi$. Therefore $b \in D$ and in consequence $\ddot{B} \subset D$ which completes the proof.

PRELIMINARY LEMMAS. In this section we will always assume that the class K satisfies conditions (i), (ii) and (iii). A coordinate system in E is fixed.

LEMMA 1. Let $\{A_i\}$, $1 \leq i \leq k$ be a decomposition of J into k disjoint measurable subsets. Let $\{u^i\}_{1\leq i\leq k} \subset K$. Put $u(t) = u^i(t)$ if $t \in A_i$. Then $u \in K$.

<u>Proof</u>. Since A_i can be approximated arbitrarly closely by disjoint unions of intervals, therefore by (iii) u can be approximated by a sequence $\{u^i\} \subset K$ converging to u in measure. Thus (i) completes the proof.

LEMMA 2. The lexicographical order on K is a lattice; that is if $u^i \in K$ for $i=1,\dots,k$ then so does $v = \text{lex.}\sup_{1\leq i\leq k}\{u^i\}$.

<u>Proof</u>. By (4), $v(t) = u^i(t)$ if $t \in A_i\{t : u^i(t) = \text{lex.}\max_{1\leq i\leq k}\{u^i(t)\}$, $u^j(t) < u^i(t)$ if $j < i\}$. It is easy to see that these A_i satisfy the assumptions of Lemma 1. Hence the latter finishes the proof.

LEMMA 3. Let $u^i = (u_1^i,\dots,u_n^i)\in K$ for $i=1,2,\dots$. Assume that $u_j^i \to u_j^o$ a.e. in J if $j=1,\dots,k-1$, $1\leq k\leq n$ and put $u_k^o = \lim_i \sup u_k^i$. Then there is a $v = (v_1,\dots,v_n)\in K$ such that $v_j = u_j^o$ if $j=1,\dots,k$.

<u>Proof</u>. Take an $\varepsilon > 0$. There exist i_o, sets $F, G \subset J$, $\mu(F) < \varepsilon$, $\mu(G) < \varepsilon$ and an integer p such that

$$|u_j^i(t) - u_j^o(t)| < \varepsilon \quad \text{if} \quad 1\leq j\leq k-1,\ i \geq i_o \ \text{and} \ t \in J\setminus F \tag{8}$$

and

$$\min_{i_o\leq i\leq i_o+p} |u_k^i(t) - u_k^o(t)| < \varepsilon \quad \text{if} \quad t \in J\setminus G. \tag{9}$$

Put $A_s = \{t : |u^{i_o+s}(t) - u_k^o(t)| < \varepsilon$ and $|u_k^{i_o+r}(t) - u_k^o(t)| \geq \varepsilon$ for $r < s\}$, $s = 0,1,\dots,p$. Clearly the A_s are measurable and disjoint and, by (9), $\cup_{s=0}^{T} A_s \supset J \setminus G$. Define $v(t) = u^{i_o+s}(t)$ if $t \in A_s$, $s = 0,1,\ldots,p$ and $v(t) = u(t)$ if $t \in J \setminus \cup_{=0}^{T} A_s$, where $u \in K$. By Lemma 1, $v \in K$ and by (8) and (9) we get

$$|v_j(t) - u_j^o(t)| < \varepsilon \quad \text{if} \quad t \in J \setminus (F \cup G),\ 1 \leq j \leq k. \tag{10}$$

Ineq. (10) shows that a sequence $v^i \in K$ can be defined such that $v_j^i \to u_j^o$ a.e. in J for $j=1,\ldots,k$. If $k=n$ then the last statement and (i) proves Lemma 3. If $k < n$, then it proves that $\{v^i\}$ satisfies assumptions of Lemma 3 for k increased by 1. Hence the proof can be completed by induction.

COROLLARY 1. Let S be a linear subspace of E and denote by K_S the class of functions of J into S obtained by the orthogonal projection of elements of K into S. Then K_S satisfies (i), (ii) and (iii).

Proof. Conditions (ii) and (iii) obviously hold for K_S, while condition (i) follows from Lemma 3.

COROLLARY 2. There is an integrable $m: J \to R$ such that $|u(t)| \leq m(t)$ a.e. in J for each $u \in K$.

Proof. By Corollary 1 $K_i = \{u_i : (u_1,\ldots,u_i,v,\ldots,u_n) \in K\}$ satisfies (i) (ii) and (iii) for each $i=1,\ldots,n$. By (ii) $\alpha_i = \sup_{v \in K_i} I(v) < +\infty$. Let $\{v^i\} \subset K_i$ be such that $I(v^i) \to \alpha_i$ as $j \to \infty$. By Lemma 2 without any loss of generality we may assume that $\{v^j\}$ is non-decreasing. Thus there exists $\lim_j v^j = \psi_i$ and by (i) $\psi_i \in K_i$. Therefore $I(v^j) \leq I(\psi_i) \leq \alpha$ and as a consequence $I(\psi_i) = \alpha$. Now for any $v \in K_i$, $I(\sup\{v,\psi_i\}) = \alpha$ and Proposition 2 implies that $u \leq \psi_i$ for each $v \in K_i$. Similarly one can prove that there is $\varphi_i \in K_i$ such that $\varphi_i \leq v$ for each $v \in K$. Since i is arbitrary we get Corollary 2 by putting $m(t) = \max(|\psi(t)|, |\varphi(t)|)$, where $\psi = (\psi_1,\ldots,\psi_n)$ and $\varphi = (\varphi_1,\ldots,\varphi_n)$.

Now we will prove the main lemma.

LEMMA 4. Suppose $\{u^i\} \subset K$ and assume that $I(u^i) \to p$ as $i \to \infty$. Then there is $v \in K$ such that

$$p \leq I(v). \tag{11}$$

Proof. Suppose that u_j^i converges in the L_1 norm for $j=1,\ldots,k-1$ to u_j^o but does not converge if $j=k$. Such a k exists, since k may be equal 1. It follows that

$$I(u_j^i) \to I(u_j^o) = p_j \quad \text{if} \quad j = 1,\ldots,k-1 \tag{12}$$

If $k-1 = n$ then (12) completes the proof of (11). If $k \leqq n$ then for $j=k$ there is an $\varepsilon_o > 0$ such that for each i_o there are $s \geqq i_o$ and $r \geqq i_o$ with $I(|u_k^s - u_k^r|) \geqq \varepsilon_o$. Without any loss of generality we may assume that $u_j^i \to u_j^o$ a.e. in J as $i \to \infty$. Let us choose i_o such that $|I(u_k^i) - p_k| < \varepsilon_o/4$ if $i \geqq i_o$, where p_k is k-th coordinate of p. By these inequalities $I(\sup(u_k^s, u_n^r)) - p_k > \varepsilon_o/4$. Put $u_k^o(t) = \limsup_i u_k^i(t)$ and $u^i = \sup_{m \geqq i}\{u_k^m\}$. Then we see that v^i is non-increasing, $v^i \to u_k^o$ as $i \to \infty$ and by the last inequality $I(v^i) \geqq p_k + \varepsilon_o/4$ if $i \geqq i_o$. Since by Corollary 2 the v^i are bounded by an integrable function, Lebesgue theorem implies that

$$I(v^i) \to I(u_n^o) \geqq p_k + \varepsilon_o/4 > 0 \tag{13}$$

It follows from Lemma 3 that there is $v \in (v_1, \ldots, v_n) \in K$ such that $v_j = u_j^o$ if $j=1,\ldots,k$ and for this v (12) and (13) imply (11) which was to be proved.

PRINCIPAL RESULTS. Again we assume throughout this section that K satisfies conditions (i),(ii) and (iii). By $e(K,\xi)$ we denote the maximal element of K with respect to "$\leqq_\xi$", $\xi \in \Xi$. By Lemma 2 if $e(K,\xi)$ exists then it is uniquely defined up to a set of measure zero. We will call $e(K,\xi)$ an extremal element of K. The set of extremal elements of K will be denoted by $E(K)$, then $E(K) = \{e(K,\xi) : \xi \in \Xi\}$.

THEOREM 1. For each $\xi \in \Xi$ there exists an extremal element $e(K,\xi)$ of K corresponding to ξ and

$$I(e(K,\xi)) = e(\overline{I(K)},\xi) = e(I(K),\xi) \text{ for each } \xi \in \Xi. \tag{14}$$

Proof. By (ii) the set $I(K)$ is bounded; thus, the closure $\overline{I(K)}$ of $I(K)$ is a compact subset of E^n. Let us fix $\xi \in \Xi$ and let $p = e(\overline{I(K)},\xi)$. By Lemma 4 there is $v \in K$ such that $p \leqq_\xi I(v)$. But $I(v) \in I(K)$ implies by the definition of p that $I(v) \leqq_\xi p$. Hence $I(v) = p$ and $p \in I(K)$. Let now $u \in K$ be arbitrary and $w = \text{lex}_\xi \sup\{u,v\}$. We have $u \leqq_\xi w$, $v \leqq_\xi w$ and $p = I(v) \leqq_\xi I(w) \leqq_\xi p$. Therefore by Proposition 2, $v = w$. Hence $u \leqq_\xi v$ for each $u \in K$. This means $v = e(K,\xi)$ and (14) is manifestly satisfied.

THEOREM 2. The set $D = \{x = I(e(K,\xi)) : \xi \in \Xi\} = I(E(K))$ is the profile $\ddot{B}$ of the convex hull B of $\overline{I(K)}$.

Proof. By (14), $D = \{x : x = e(\overline{I(K)},\xi), \xi \in \Xi\}$, and Proposition

4 implies Theorem 2.

Notice that both Theorems 1 and 2 hold if J is replaced by $[0,t]$, $0 < t \leq 1$ and I by I_t. Thus if we denote by $B(t)$ the convex hull of $\overline{I_t(K)}$, then by Theorem 2 we have the equality $\ddot{B}(t) = I_t(E(K))$.

THEOREM 3. The set valued function on J taking $t \to B(t)$, the convex hull of $I_t(K)$, is continuous in the Hausdorff sense; that is

$$\max_{a \in B(t), b \in B(s)} (r(a,B(s)), r(b,B(t))) \to 0 \quad \text{as} \quad |s-t| \to 0 \qquad (15)$$

where $r(\ ,\ )$ stands for the distance of a point from a set in E.

Proof. Let B, C be two compact convex subsets of E^n. There are $b \in B$ and $c \in C$ such that $|b-c| = r(c,B) = \max_{x \in C} r(x,B)$. Note that if C were an interval, then c can be assumed to be one of the ends of C. This remark shows that in the general case c can be assumed to be an extreme point of C and that there is a $\xi \in \Xi$ such that $c = e(C,\xi)$. But obviously, $r(c,B) \leq |x-c|$ for each $x \in B$. In particular, we have the inequality $|b-c| \leq |e(B,\xi)-e(C,\xi)|$ for a $\xi \in \Xi$. Therefore the distance in (18) can be estimated by $|e(B(t),\xi)-e(B(s),\xi)| \leq \int_t^s |e(K,\xi)(t)|dt$ for the same $\xi \in \Xi$ and Corollary 2 completes the proof.

THEOREM 4 For each $b \in B$, the convex hull of $\overline{I(K)}$, there are two sequences $\xi^1, \ldots, \xi^k \in \Xi$ and $0 = t_o < t_1 < \ldots < t_k = 1$ such that if we put

$$u(t) = e(K,\xi^i)(t) \quad \text{for} \quad t_{i-1} \leq t < t_i, i=1,\ldots,k, \qquad (16)$$

then $k \leq n+1$ and

$$b = I(u). \qquad (17)$$

Proof. The proof will be by induction with respect to n. Thus suppose first that $n=1$. In this case Ξ consists of two elements and by Theorem 1 so does $E(K)$. That is, there are $\varphi, \psi \in K$ such that $\varphi \leq u \leq \psi$ for each $u \in K$. The set B is the interval $[I(\varphi), I(\psi)]$. Consider the function

$$\lambda(t) = \int_o^t \psi(t)dt + \int_t^1 \varphi(t)dt . \qquad (18)$$

Manifestly λ is continuous and maps J onto $[I(\varphi), I(\psi)]$

Thus for each $b \in B$, there is a $t_1 \in J$ such that $\lambda(t_1)=b$. Setting $u(t) = \psi(t)$ if $0 \leqq t < t_1$ and $u(t) = \varphi(t)$ if $t_1 \leqq t \leqq 1$ we see that u is of the form (16) and (17) holds.

Suppose now that n is arbitrary and assume that Theorem 4 holds for $n-1$. Let $b \in B$ and take an arbitrary $\bar{\xi} \in \Xi$. Consider the function

$$x(t) = b - \int_t^1 e(K,\bar{\xi})(\tau)d\tau \tag{19}$$

Since both $x(t)$ and $B(t)$ are continuous, there is a $T \in J$ such that $x(T)$ belongs to the boundary of $B(T)$ and if $T < 1$ then $x(t) \in \inf B(t)$ for $T < t \leqq 1$. Since $B(T)$ is convex and compact there is an $a \in E^n$, $|a| = 1$ such that

$$\alpha = (x(T),a) = \max (x,a) \quad \text{for} \quad x \in B(T). \tag{20}$$

Let $\Xi_a = \{\xi \in \Xi: \xi = (x^1,\ldots,x^n), x^1 = a\}$. Put $B_a = B(T) \cap \{x: (x,a) = \alpha\}$ and $A = I_T(K) \cap \{x: (x,a) = \alpha\}$. It is easy to see that B_a is compact and convex, the profile $\ddot{B}_a$ of B_a is equal to $\{I(e(K,\xi)): \xi \in \Xi_a\} \subset A$. Thus A is not empty and B_a is equal to the convex hull of $\bar{A}$ as well as of A.

It follows from Proposition 3 that $I_T(u) \in A$, where $u \in K$, if and only if $(u(t),a) = \psi(t)$ a.e. in $[0,T]$, where ψ has the property that for each $u \in K$ $(u(t),a) \leqq \psi(t)$ a.e. in J. Therefore A can be considered as $I_T(K_a)$ where $K_a = \{u \in K: (u(t),a) = \psi(t)$ a.e. in $J\}$ and ψ is uniquely defined by K and a. Since each $u \in K_a$ can be uniquely decomposed into the sum $v + a\psi$, where v is a function of J into E_1 and E_1 is the $n-1$ dimensional subspace perpendicular to a, the set K_a can be considered as a class of functions of J into $n-1$ dimensional Euclidean space. Obviously, K_a satisfies conditions (i), (ii) and (iii) and by our assumption we can apply Theorem 4 to K_a. Hence there is a $u \in K_a$ such that $u(t) = e(K_a,\xi^i) = e(K,\xi^i)(t)$ if $t_{i-1} \leqq t < t_i$, $\xi^i \in \Xi_a$, $i = 1,\ldots,k-1$, $t_o = 0 < t_1 < \ldots < t_{k-1} = T_v$ and such that

$$I_T(u) = x(T) \tag{21}$$

Setting $u(t) = e(K,\bar{\xi})(t)$ if $t_{k-1} = T \leqq t \leqq 1 = t_k$ (thus putting $\xi^k = \bar{\xi}$) we see that u is of the form (16) and (19) and (21) implies (17). Manifestly $k \leqq n+1$ since

$k-1 \leqq n$.

CONCLUDING RESULTS. In this section we state three immediate consequences of the preceding theorems.

THEOREM 5. If K satisfies (i),(ii) and (iii) then $I(K)$ is convex and compact.

Proof. By (iii) any function of the form (16) belongs to K; thus Theorem 5 follows from Theorems 2 and 4.

If $u \in K$ is an extremal element of I (or $I(u)$ is an extreme point of $I(K)$) then the following implication holds (compare Proposition 1 and Theorem 2):

$$\text{if } v \in K \text{ and } I(v) = I(u) \text{ then } v = u \tag{22}$$

On the other hand one can see from the proof of Theorem 4 that if $b \in I(K)$ is not an extreme point of $I(K)$ then there are at least two different $u, v \in K$ such that $I(u) = I(v) = b$. Therefore we have

THEOREM 6. If K satisfies (i),(ii) and (iii) and $u \in K$ then u is an extremal element of K if and only if the implication (22) holds for u.

Let K_o denote the class we obtained by closing $E(K)$ with respect to property (iii). Elements of K_o may be referred to as piecewise extremal elements of K.

THEOREM 7. If $K_1 \subset K$ satisfies (iii) and $I(K_1) = I(K)$, then $K_o \subset K_1$

Proof. By Theorem 6, K_1 must contain $E(K)$. The definition of K_o and K_1 satisfing (iii) imply $K_1 \supset K_o$.

Theorem 7 says that K_o is the smallest subclass of K satisfying (iii) and having the same range of integrals as K.

Let us observe that if $K = \{u \in M : u(t) \in G(t) \text{ a.e. in } J\}$ and G is a measurable set-valued function with values being compact subsets of E then $e(K,\xi)(t) = e(G(t),\xi)$ (cf. (6)). So in that case the extremal elements of K can be computed if one knows G.

Under some more restrictive assumptions LaSalle (2), Halkin (1) and Levinson (3) proved that the "bang-bang" controls (elements of K_o in our case) can be chosen to be piecewise constant or piecewise continuous. From Theorem 7 it follows that this can be the case if and only if each extremal element of K is piecewise continuous (or differs from such on a set of measure zero). Also if we knew that the number of discontinuities of $e(K,\xi)$ is finite and bounded for $\xi \in \Xi$, then by Theorem 4 there is a subset K_* of K composed of piecewise continuous and piecewise extremal functions such that $I(K_*) = I(K)$ and the number of discontinuities of u is finite and bounded if $u \in K_*$. This is the case if A in (S) is constant and $f(t,u) = B(t)u$, where the entries of B are piecewise analytical and U is a compact polyhedron (cf. (1),(3)). This is also the case when G is a continuous set-valued function in the sense of Hausdorff with values being strictly convex and compact subsets of E, since in this case $e(G(t),\xi)$ is continuous in t for each $\xi \in \Xi$. Note that because of strict convexity of $G(t)$, $e(G(t),\xi)$ is uniquely determined by the first vector of ξ.

Theorem 5, under essentially the same assumptions has been obtained by Neustadt (4). Note that as in (4) we did not make any convexity assumption concerning K.

Theorem 6 has some implications concerning the uniqueness of time optimal solutions of the system (S). For details, we refer the reader to (5).

REFERENCES

(1) H. Halkin, A generalization of LaSalle's bang-bang principle, J. SIAM Control, 2(1965), 199-202.

(2) J.P. LaSalle, The time optimal control problem., Contribution to the Theory of Nonlinear Oscillations, Vol.5, Princeton Univ. Press, 1960, 1-24.

(3) N. Levinson, Minimax, Liapunov, and "Bang-Bang", J. Diff. Eqns., 2(1966), 218-241.

(4) L.W. Neustadt, The existence of optimal control in the absence of convexity, J. Math. Anal. Appl., 7(1963), 110-117.

(5) C. Olech, Extremal solutions of a control system, J. Diff. Eqns., 2(1966), 74-101.

(6) C. Olech, A note concerning set-valued measurable functions, Bull. Acad. Pol. Sci. Math. Astron. Phys., 13 (1965), 317-321.

(7) C. Olech, A note concerning extremal points of a convex set, Bull. Acad. Pol. Sci. Math. Astron. Phys., 13 (1965), 347-351.

ATTAINABLE SETS IN LINEAR SYSTEMS WITH UNBOUNDED CONTROLS

Marc Q. Jacobs
Brown University, Division of Applied Mathematics
Providence, R. I.

INTRODUCTION

The control system is given by the real ordinary differential equation

$$\dot{x}(t) = A(t)x(t) + \varphi(u,t), \qquad (1)$$

where $x = (x^1,\dots,x^p)\in R^p$, $u = (u^1,\dots,u^q)\in R^q$, A is a continuous $p\times p$ matrix-valued function, and φ is a function, $\varphi: R^q\times R \to R^p$ (φ will be identified more specifically later). Let T be a positive constant, and let Ω and Γ be nonempty closed subsets of R^q and $[0,T]$ respectively. Define a set $\mathcal{F}$ to be the collection of all ordered pairs (u,t_1) such that $t_1\in\Gamma$ and u is a measurable function, $u: [0,t_1] \to R^q$, for which the conditions: (a) $u(t)\in\Omega$, $0 \leq t \leq t_1$, (b) the mapping, $h: t\in[0,t_1] \to \varphi(u(t),t)$ is integrable on $[0,t_1]$, are both satisfied. The fixed-time cross sections of $\mathcal{F}$ are denoted by $\mathcal{F}(t_1)$, where $\mathcal{F}(t_1)$ is defined by the relation $\mathcal{F}(t_1) = \{u \mid (u,t_1)\in \mathcal{F}\}$ for $t_1\in\Gamma$. Thus if $(u,t_1)\in \mathcal{F}$, then there is a unique absolutely continuous function (response) $x(\cdot,u):[0,t_1] \to R^p$ satisfying Eq.(1) a.e. on $[0,t_1]$ and the initial condition

$$x(0,u) = x_0. \qquad (2)$$

By the method of variation of parameters this response is

$$x(t,u) = X(t)[x_0 + \int_0^t X^{-1}(\xi)\varphi(u(\xi),\xi)d\xi],\ 0 \leq t \leq t_1, (3)$$

where X is the fundamental matrix defined by $\dot{X} = AX$, $X(0) = I (I = p \times p$ identity matrix). A point x in R^p is said to be <u>attainable</u> if there exists a (u,t_1) in $\mathcal{F}$

such that $x(t_1,u) = x$. The <u>attainable set</u> is defined to be the set $\mathscr{R} = \{x \in R^p | x$ <u>is attainable</u>$\}$. The fixed-time cross sections of $\mathscr{R}$ are denoted by $\mathscr{R}(t_1)$, $t_1 \in \Gamma$. These sets $\mathscr{R}(t_1)$, $t_1 \in \Gamma$ are the points in R^p which are attainable using the elements of $\mathscr{F}(t_1)$.

Neustadt (9) showed that if Ω is compact, and if the function φ in Eq. (1) is continuous, then $\mathscr{R}$ is compact. If we add to Neustadt's hypotheses the hypothesis that $\varphi(\Omega,t)$ is convex for each t in $[0,T]$, then Roxin's results (12) specialize to yield the same conclusion. If the mapping φ is continuous in $u \in \Omega$ for each fixed t, if φ is Lebesgue measurable in t for each fixed $u \in \Omega$, if Ω is compact, and if there is a function $m: R \to R$ which is Lebesgue integrable on each finite interval of R such that $|\varphi(u,t)| \leq m(t)$ for each $(t,u) \in R \times \Omega$, then Olech (10, Corollary 3.1, pg. 79) has proved that $\mathscr{R}$ is compact. The purpose of this paper is to extend the results in (9, 10, and 12) to allow closed sets Ω which need not be bounded. A "natural extension" of Neustadt's theorem would seem to be: If Ω is closed, if φ is continuous, and if $\varphi(\Omega,t)$ is closed for each t in $[0,T]$, then $\mathscr{R}$ is closed. This "natural extension" is false, however, even in relatively simple examples (cf. Example 1). A more reasonable conjecture is: If Ω is closed, if φ is continuous, if $\varphi(\Omega,t)$ is closed for each t in $[0,T]$, and if the convex hull of $\varphi(\Omega,t)$ is closed for each t in $[0,T]$, then $\mathscr{R}$ is closed. The author has so far been unable to give a definite answer to this conjecture. But by adding further assumptions we are able to extend Neustadt's and Olech's results (9, 10, resp.) to permit unbounded controls and still infer that $\mathscr{R}$ is compact (cf. Theorem 1). For linear systems, Theorem 2 is an extension of Roxin's results (12). In case φ is continuous, a very general closure theorem proved by Cesari (3) can be used to prove Theorem 2.

1. COMPACTNESS OF ATTAINABLE SETS

All statements concerning the measurability of sets or of functions are to be understood in terms of ordinary Lebesgue measure μ. We denote the measurable subsets of an interval $[a,b]$ by $M[a,b]$. A set function

$F:M[a,b] \to R^p$ is absolutely continuous if for each $\epsilon > 0$ there is a $\delta > 0$ such that $E \in M[a,b]$ and $\mu(E) < \delta$ imply $|F(E)| < \epsilon$. For any set E the characteristic function of E is denoted by K_E.

LEMMA 1. *Let* S *denote a family of functions in* $L_1[a,b]$ *with range in* R^p. *Let the family* S *satisfy the condition:* $f,g \in S$ *imply* $f \cdot K_E + g \cdot K_{[a,b]\setminus E} \in S$ *for each* E *in* $M[a,b]$. *Then the set* $\{\int_a^b f(t)dt \mid f \in S\}$ *is convex.*

This lemma is a slight extension of a result obtained by Halkin (6, pp. 69-70). In Halkin's statement the functions in S must be bounded. This assumption is obviated by making appropriate use of the fact that the set functions, $E \in [a,b] \to \int_E f(t)dt$, are absolutely continuous for $f \in S$ (cf. 8, pg. 156).

LEMMA 2. *Let* Ω *be a nonempty closed subset of* R^q. *Let* φ *be a mapping,* $\varphi:\Omega \times [0,T] \to R^p$, *which is measurable in* t *for each fixed* u *in* Ω, *and which satisfies the condition: For every* $\epsilon > 0$ *there is an open set* E_ϵ *contained in* $[0,T]$ *such that* $\mu(E_\epsilon) < \epsilon$ *and* φ *is continuous on* $\Omega \times ([0,T]\setminus E_\epsilon)$. *Let* g *be a measurable function* $g:[0,t_1] \to R^p (t_1 \leqq T)$ *such that* $g(t) \in \varphi(\Omega,t)$ *for* t *in* $[0,t_1]$. *Then there is a measurable function* $u:[0,t_1] \to \Omega$, *such that* $g(t) = \varphi(u(t),t)$ *for* t *in* $[0,t_1]$.

Castaing's Theorem 3(2) can be applied to the situation in Lemma 2. The proof of a similar result obtained by the author (7) will also work here. The proof is omitted because of space limitations.

THEOREM 1. *Let the following hypotheses be satisfied:*

(i) *The sets* Γ,Ω, *and* $\varphi(\Omega,t)$, $0 \leqq t \leqq T$ *are closed subsets of* $[0,T]$, R^q *and* R^p *respectively;*

(ii) *The mapping* φ *is integrable in* t *for each fixed* $u \in \Omega$, *and* φ *has the property: For every* $\epsilon > 0$ *there exists an open set* E_ϵ *contained in* $[0,T]$ *such that* $\mu(E_\epsilon) < \epsilon$ *and*

φ is continuous on $\Omega \times [0,T]\setminus E_\epsilon$);

(iii) The set functions, $E \in M[0,t_1] \to \int_E \varphi(u(\xi),\xi)d\xi$, $(u,t_1) \in \mathcal{F}$, are uniformly absolutely continuous.

Then $\mathcal{R}$ is compact.

The proof is a modification of Neustadt's arguments (8), and consequently it depends on Blackwell's Theorem 4 (1, pg. 393). The proof also draws heavily on material in Chapter 4 of (8) dealing with uniformly absolutely continuous set functions. We note also that in view of Nagumo's theorem (8, pg. 176), hypothesis (iii) of Theorem 1 is implied by

(iiia) Φ is a mapping, $\Phi:[0,\infty) \to [0,\infty)$ such that $\Phi(r)/r \to \infty$ as $r \to \infty$, and there is a constant $D > 0$ such that

$$\int_0^{t_1} \Phi(|\varphi(u(\xi),\xi)|)d\xi \leq D \text{ for } (u,t_1) \in \mathcal{F}.$$

Let C be a convex subset of R (i.e., C is an interval). A function $\Phi:C \to R$ is quasi-convex if $\Phi(\frac{s+t}{2}) \leq \max\{\Phi(s),\Phi(t)\}$ for each $s, t \in C$.

THEOREM 2. Let the following hypotheses be satisfied:

(i) Γ and Ω are nonempty closed subsets of $[0,T]$ and R^q respectively; $\varphi(\Omega,t)$ is a closed, convex subset of R^p for each t in $[0,T]$.

(ii) p_o is a given real number $p_o \geq 1$. The function $\varphi(\cdot,u)$ is an element of $L_{p_o}[0,T]$ for each fixed $u \in \Omega$. The mapping φ has the property: For every $\epsilon > 0$ there exists an open set E_ϵ contained in $[0,T]$ such that $\mu(E_\epsilon) < \epsilon$ and φ is continuous on $\Omega \times ([0,T]\setminus E_\epsilon)$;

(iii) Φ is a quasi-convex mapping, $\Phi:[0,\infty) \to [0,\infty)$ such that $\Phi(r)/r \to \infty$ as $r \to \infty$. The functional, $I:r \in L_{p_o}[0,t_1] \to \int_0^{t_1} \Phi(|r(\xi)|)d\xi$ is

<u>defined and lower semicontinuous for</u> $t_1 \epsilon \Gamma$;

(iv) $N_1, N_2, \ldots, N_p$ <u>are positive constants</u>. $\mathcal{F}^*(t_1)$, $t_1 \epsilon \Gamma$ <u>is defined by the relation that</u>

$$\mathcal{F}^*(t_1) = \{u \epsilon \mathcal{F}(t_1) | \varphi(u(\cdot), \cdot) \epsilon L_{p_o}[0, t_1] \text{ and } \int_o^{t_1} \Phi(|\varphi^i(u(\xi), \xi)|) d\xi \le N_i,\ i = 1, 2, \ldots, p\},$$

<u>and</u> $\mathcal{F}^*$ <u>is defined by</u> $\mathcal{F}^* = \bigcup_{t_1 \epsilon \Gamma} \mathcal{F}^*(t_1) \times \{t_1\}$.

<u>Then the attainable set</u> $\mathcal{R}^*$ <u>relative to</u> $\mathcal{F}^*$ <u>is compact</u>.

The proof of Theorem 2 is based on a recent result of Poljak (<u>11</u>) concerning weakly lower semicontinuous functionals, and a combinatorial lemma dealing with weakly convergent sequences (<u>4</u>, Corollary <u>14</u>, pg. 422).

EXAMPLE 1. This example shows that the first conjecture stated in the introduction is false. Assume that in Eq.(1) we have that $p = q = 2$, $A \equiv 0$, and $\varphi(u,t) = (\varphi^1((u^1,u^2),t), \varphi^2((u^1,u^2),t)) = (u^1,u^2) \epsilon R^2$. Define Ω to be $E_1 \cup E_2$, where $E_1 = \{(u^1,u^2) | u^2 = 1/u^1, u^1 > 0\}$ and $E_2 = \{(u^1,u^2) | u^2 = -1/u^1, u^1 < 0\}$. We also assume $T = 1$, and $\Gamma = \{1\}$. Then φ is continuous, Ω is closed, and $\varphi(\Omega,t)$ is closed for each t in $[0,1]$. The initial point $x_o = (x_o^1, x_o^2)$ is any point in R^2. The attainable set, however, is the set $x_o + \{(x^1,x^2) | x^2 > 0\}$ which is not closed.

The next two examples give simple applications of Theorems 1 and 2.

EXAMPLE 2. In Eq. 1 we assume $p = q = 1$. Let the data in Theorem 1 be as follows: Ω is the set of non-negative integers; $T = 1$, $\Gamma = \{1\}$; A is any continuous real valued function;

$$\varphi(u,t) = \begin{cases} \frac{u}{\sqrt{t}} \sin \frac{1}{u}, & \text{if } ut \neq 0; \\ 0, & \text{if } t = 0,\ u \neq 0; \\ 1/\sqrt{t}, & \text{if } u = 0,\ t \neq 0. \end{cases}$$

The initial point x_o is any real number. Then Theorem 1 applies to show that $\mathcal{R}$ is compact.

EXAMPLE 3. Again we assume that $p = q = 1$. Let the data for Theorem 2 be as follows: $p_o = 5/2$; $\Phi(t) = t^2 + t$, $t \geqq 0$; $\Omega = \{u | u \geqq 0\}$; $T = 1$, $\Gamma = \{1\}$; $\varphi(u,t) = u^2$; $N_1 = 1$. A is any continuous real valued function. The functional $I{:}r \in L_{5/2}[0,1] \to \int_o^1 [r(\xi)]^2 + |r(\xi)| d\xi$ is actually continuous. For suppose $\{r_n\}$ is a sequence in $L_{5/2}[0,1]$ which converges to r with respect to the norm of $L_{5/2}[0,1]$. Then one can use the Hölder inequality to show that r_n converges to r_o in the norm of $L_a[0,1]$ for $1 \leqq a < 5/2$. Thus $I(r_n) \to I(r_o)$ as $n \to \infty$. Therefore the hypotheses of Theorem 2 are satisfied by this example, and we infer that $\mathcal{R}^*$ is compact.

ADDENDUM. Dr. G. S. Goodman pointed out in his paper, "An Application of Quasi-continuity in the Sense of Scorza Dragoni to an Existence Question in the Theory of Optimal Control", (this Conference) that a result of G. Scorza Dragoni (Rend. Sem. Mat. Univ. Padova, 17 (1948) pp. 102-106) can be used to show that when Ω is compact, then the assumption that φ is integrable in t for each fixed u, and continuous in u for each fixed t implies that hypothesis (ii) of Theorem 1 is fulfilled. From this fact one can deduce that the same result holds when Ω is any closed set.

REFERENCES

1. D. Blackwell, "The Range of Certain Vector Integrals", Proc. Amer. Math. Soc., 2 (1951), pp. 390-395.

2. C. Castaing, "Quelques Problemes de Mesurabilité Lies à la Théorie de la Commande", C. R. Acad. Sc. Paris, 262 (1966), pp. 409-411.

3. L. Cesari, "Existence Theorems for Weak and Usual Optimal Solutions in Lagrange Problems with Unilateral Constraints", I and II. Trans. Amer. Math. Soc., 124 (1966), pp. 369-412 and pp. 413-429.

4. N. Dunford and J. Schwartz, Linear Operators, Part I. Interscience Publishers, Inc., New York, 1958.

5. A. F. Filippov, "On Certain Questions in the Theory of Optimal Control", SIAM J. Control, Ser. A, 1 (1962), pp. 76-84.

6. H. Halkin, "On the Necessary Condition for Optimal Control of Nonlinear Systems", Journal D'Analyse Mathématique, 12(1964), pp. 1-82.

7. M. Jacobs, "A Filippov-Type Implicit Functions Theorem and an Application to an Existence Theorem for an Optimal Control Problem with Unbounded Controls." To appear.

8. E. J. McShane, Integration. Princeton University Press, Princeton, N. J., 1944.

9. L. W. Neustadt, "The Existence of Optimal Controls in the Absence of Convexity Conditions", J. Math. Anal. and Appls., 7 (1963), pp. 110-117.

10. C. Olech, "Extremal Solutions of a Control System", J. of Diff. Eqs., 2 (1966), pp. 74-101.

11. B. T. Poljak, "Existence Theorems and Convergence of Minimizing Sequences in Extremum Problems with Restrictions", Dokl. Akad. Nauk. SSSR, 166 (1966), pp. 72-75 (Translation).

12. E. Roxin, "The Existence of Optimal Controls", Mich. Math. J., 9 (1962), pp. 109-119.

This Research was supported in part by the Air Force Office of Scientific Research, Office of Aerospace Research, U. S. Air Force under Grant No. 693-66, in part by the U. S. Army Research Office, Durham, under Contract No. DA-31-124-ARO-D-270, and in part by the National Science Foundation, under Grant No. GP-5970.

ON THE SOLUTION OF SOME NONLINEAR OPTIMAL CONTROL PROBLEMS

V. F. Dem'yanov
Computing Center, Leningrad State University
Leningrad, U.S.S.R.

1. Let the motion of an object be described by the non-linear system of ordinary differential equations:

$$\frac{dX(t)}{dt} \equiv \dot{X}(t) = f(X(t), u(t), t) \quad (1.1)$$

$$X(0) = X_o \quad (1.2)$$

Here, $X(t) = (x^1(t), \ldots, x^n(t)); f(X, u, t) = (f^1(X, u, t), \ldots, f^n(X, u, t))$ is an n-dimensional real vector-valued function, $u(t) = (u^1(t), \ldots, u^r(t))$, the control, is an r-dimensional real vector-valued function. The control must be chosen from a certain class U of functions which is described below.

The functions in the right-hand side of Eq. (1.1) are assumed to be continuously differentiable with respect to x^i $(i = 1, \ldots, n)$, and continuous in the u^j $(j=1, \ldots, r)$ and t in the domain of admissable values for x, u and t. The domain of admissable values for t is $[0, T]$, where $T \in (0, \infty)$ is fixed. The domain of admissable values for u is Q, a set in E_r, and the domain of admissable values for x is defined by the class of controls U, the system (1.1) and the initial conditions (1.2).

We shall consider the class U of admissable controls to be the set of real, r-dimensional vector-valued functions, square-integrable over $[0, T]$ such that, for each t:

$$u(t) \in Q \subset E_r ,$$

where Q is some closed, bounded set in r-dimensional Euclidean space.

For example, we may take U to be the set of all real, r-dimensional functions square integrable on $[0, T]$ which satisfy on $[0, T]$ one of the following constraints:

$$1. \quad |u^i(t)| \leq 1; \ i=1,\ldots, r; \ t\in[0,T]; \tag{1.3}$$

$$2. \quad u^*(t)\, N\, u(t) \leq 1; \quad t\in[0,T]; \tag{1.4}$$

where N is a real, positive-definite rxr matrix;

$$3. \quad |u^i(t)| = 1; \ i=1,\ldots, r; \ t\in[0,T]; \tag{1.5}$$

$$4. \quad |u^i(t)| \in \{a_{i1}, a_{i2}, \ldots, a_{ip_i}\} \tag{1.6}$$

$$p_i \leq p < \infty; \ i = 1,\ldots, r; \ t\in[0,T],$$

where the a_{ij} are given, finite, non-negative numbers.

For any $u\in U$, we shall denote by $X(t, u)$ the solution of system (1.1) satisfying the initial condition (1.2).

Let us consider the functional

$$J(t,u) = \int_0^t F(X(\tau,u), u(\tau), \tau)d\tau, \tag{1.7}$$

where the scalar-valued function $F(X, u, t)$ is assumed to be uniformly continuous in all of its arguments in the domain of their admissable values.

Let

$$\Phi(t) = \inf_{u\in U} J(t,u) \tag{1.8}$$

It is clear that the function $\Phi(t)$ is continuous on $[0,T]$.

Let us fix $t\in[0,T]$, and let us consider, for each $\varepsilon>0$, the sets $M_\varepsilon(t)\subset E_n$ defined as follows: $X\in M_\varepsilon(t)$ if there exists a $u\in U$ such that $X(t,u) = X$ and

$$J(t,u) \leq \inf_{v\in U} J(t,v) + \varepsilon .$$

It is clear that $M_{\varepsilon_1}(t)\subset M_{\varepsilon_2}(t)$, when $\varepsilon_1 < \varepsilon_2$.

We now form the set $M^*(t)\subset E_n$ as follows: $X\in M^*(t)$, if there exists a sequence

$$u_1, u_2, \ldots; \ u_s\in U \quad \text{for each } s,$$

such that $X_s = X(t, u_s)\in M_{\varepsilon_s}(t)$ for each s where $\varepsilon_s \to 0$ as $s\to\infty$, and $X_s \to X$ as $s\to\infty$. Such a sequence of controls will be called a $\mu(t)$-sequence. The set $M^*(t)$ is closed and bounded (in particular, it may consist of a finite or a countably infinite number of points). Also,

$$M_\varepsilon(t) \xrightarrow[\varepsilon\to 0]{} M^*(t),$$

that is,

$$\rho(\varepsilon) = \max_{Z \in M^*(t)} \min_{y \in M_\varepsilon(t)} (Y-Z)^2 \xrightarrow[\varepsilon \to 0]{} 0$$

We note that

$$M^*(t+\Delta) \xrightarrow[\Delta \to 0^+]{} \bar{M}(t+0) \subset M^*(t)$$

$$M^*(t-\Delta) \xrightarrow[\Delta \to 0^+]{} \bar{M}(t-0) \subset M^*(t)$$

In this connection, it may turn out that

$$\bar{M}(t+0) \neq \bar{M}(t-0)$$

$$[M^*(t) \setminus \bar{M}(t+0)] \cup \bar{M}(t-0) \neq \Lambda$$

In many applications, it is useful to know whether the function $\Phi(t)$, given by relation (1.8), is differentiable.

Let

$$\frac{d\Phi(t+0)}{dt} = \lim_{\Delta \to 0^+} \frac{1}{\Delta} [\Phi(t+\Delta) - \Phi(t)]. \tag{1.9}$$

Carrying out the required calculations, we obtain that

$$\frac{d\Phi(t+0)}{dt} = \min_{X \in M^*(t)} \min_{u \in Q} F(X, u, t) \tag{1.10}$$

Similarly it is possible to obtain that

$$\frac{d\Phi(t-0)}{dt} = \lim_{\Delta \to 0^+} \frac{1}{\Delta} [\Phi(t) - \Phi(t-\Delta)] =$$

$$= \max_{X \in M^*(t)} \min_{u \in Q} F(X, u, t) \tag{1.11}$$

Remarks:

1. The formulas for $\frac{d\Phi(t \pm 0)}{dt}$ can be obtained also in the case when $u \in Q(t) \subset E_r$, where $Q(t)$ is a piecewise continuously varying set.

For example, then

$$\frac{d\Phi(t+0)}{dt} = \min_{X \in M^*(t)} \min_{u \in Q(t+0)} F(X, u, t), \tag{1.12}$$

where $Q(t+0) = \lim_{\tau \to 0^+} Q(t+\tau)$.

2. It is possible to consider for U the set of continuous functions satisfying the constraint

$$\int_0^t u^{i2}(\tau) d\tau \leq C_i(t); \; t \in [0, T]; \; i=1,2,\ldots, r, \tag{1.13}$$

or
$$\int_0^t \sum_{i=1}^{r} u^{i2}(\tau)d\tau \leq C(t); \quad t \in [0, T] \tag{1.14}$$

where $C_i(t) \geq 0$ and $C(t) \geq 0$ are piecewise-continuous functions bounded on $[0, T]$. Let us cite, for example, the formula for $\frac{d\Phi(t)}{dt}$ for constraints of the type (1.14).

$$\frac{d\Phi(t)}{dt} = \min_{u \in E_r} F(X(t, u_t), u, t) \tag{1.15}$$

$$\text{if } \int_0^t \sum_{i=1}^{r} u_t^{i2}(\tau)d\tau < C(t);$$

$$\frac{d\Phi(t)}{dt} = F(X(t, u_t), u_t(t), t) - \frac{1}{2}\left(\frac{\partial F(X(t, u_t), u_t(t), t)}{\partial u}\right)^* u_t(t)$$

$$\text{if } \int_0^t \sum_{i=1}^{r} u_t^{i2}(\tau)d\tau = C(t), \tag{1.16}$$

where $u_t(\tau) \in U$ is such that
$$\Phi(t) = J(t, u_t) = \inf_{u \in U} J(t, u).$$

2. An Application to the Solution of Time-Optimal Problems. Let us consider once again system (1.1) with initial conditions (1.2). In a given class of controls U (U is the set of integrable functions satisfying one of the relations (1.3)-(1.6), (1.13), or (1.14)), one is required to find a control $u \in U$ such that

1. for some $T > 0$, $X(T, u) = 0$,
2. such T is the smallest possible.

This is the time-optimal problem. In case the system (1.1) is linear, effective methods of successive approximations, similar to one another in concept, have been developed (1-5).

To solve the nonlinear time-optimal problem, we shall make use of the following:

We shall denote by $R(t)$ the region of attainability for the system (1.1)-(1.2) at the time t, i.e., $Z \in R(t)$, if there exists an admissable control $u \in U$ such that $X(t, u) = Z$. We shall say that the system (1.1) is linear if it is of the form
$$\dot{X}(t) = A(t)X(t) + B(t)u(t) + F(t),$$

where $A(t)$ is an nxn matrix, $B(t)$ is an nxr matrix, and $F(t)$ is an n-dimensional vector, and the elements of A, B, and F are piecewise-continuous, bounded functions of time. In this case, $R(t)$ is convex, closed, and bounded for any t $(0 < t < \infty)$.

Let us consider the function

$$\varphi(t) = \min_{Z \in R(t)} (1/2) Z^2 = \min_{u \in U} (1/2) X^2(t, u). \qquad (2.1)$$

It is clear that $\varphi(t)$ is a continuous non-negative function. The minimum time T is the smallest non-negative root of the equation $\varphi(t) = 0$, i.e., T is the first time for which $\varphi(T) = 0$. (See (6)).

In (7), for the case of linear systems, a method for finding the values of the function $\varphi(t)$ for any t $(0 < t < \infty)$ was proposed. In (8) there were suggested methods of successive approximations for finding the values of $\varphi(t)$ for the case of nonlinear systems, which, however, can lead to a local minimum of the function $(1/2) Z^2$ on the set $R(t)$.

Since $\varphi(t)$, to within an arbitrary constant, is the function $\Phi(t)$ for $F(X(\tau, u), u(\tau), \tau) = X^*(\tau, u) f(X(\tau, u), u(\tau), \tau)$, it is sufficient to find the smallest root of the equation $\varphi(t) = 0$.

Let the constraints on the controls be of the form (1.3)-(1.6). Let us fix some $t_1 > 0$. Let the set $M^*(t_1)$ consist of a single point.

On $[0, t](t > t_1)$ we define the control $u(\tau)$ as follows:

$$u(\tau) = \begin{cases} u(\tau) & \tau \in [0, t_1] \\ u_1 & \tau \in (t_1, t] , \end{cases} \qquad (2.2)$$

where $u(\tau)$ and u_1 are such that $X_1 = X(t_1, u) = M^*(t_1)$,

$$F(X_1, u_1, t_1) = \min_{u \in Q} F(X_1, u, t_1) . \qquad (2.3)$$

Further, let us consider the function

$$h(t) \equiv J(t, u). \qquad (2.4)$$

For $t > t_1$, we have that

$$h(t) \equiv J(t, u) = J(t_1, u) + \int_{t_1}^{t} F(X(\tau), u_1, \tau) d\tau , \qquad (2.5)$$

where

$$\dot{X}(\tau) = f(X(\tau), u_1, \tau) \tag{2.6}$$
$$X(t_1) = X_1 . \tag{2.7}$$

Then,

$$\frac{d\, h(t+0)}{dt} = F(X(t), u_1, t)$$

$$\frac{d\, h(t_1+0)}{dt} = F(X_1, u_1, t_1) = \frac{d\Phi(t_1+0)}{dt} . \tag{2.8}$$

It is clear that

$$\frac{d^2 h(t_1+0)}{dt^2} = \left(\frac{\partial F(X_1, u_1, t_1)}{\partial X}\right)^* f(X_1, u_1, t_1) + $$
$$+ \frac{\partial F(X_1, u_1, t_1)}{\partial t} \equiv H(u_1) . \tag{2.9}$$

We note that, for $t > t_1$,

$$\frac{d\, h(t+0)}{dt} = \frac{d\, h(t-0)}{dt} .$$

If the $u_1 \in Q$ that satisfies Eq. (2.3) is not unique, then in Eq. (2.9) one must choose a u_1 such that

$$\frac{d^2 h(t_1)}{dt^2} = \min_{u_1} H(u_1) . \tag{2.10}$$

To find the smallest root of the equation $\varphi(t) = 0$, it is possible to apply well-known methods (Newton's method, methods of chords, secants, etc.), since we can calculate the right-hand and left-hand derivatives of the function $\varphi(t)$ at any point.

Suppose that t_k has been found, and let $u^k(t) \in U$ be such that

$$\frac{1}{2} X^2(t_k, u^k) = \varphi(t_k) . \tag{2.11}$$

Let us consider, at the point t_k, the function $h(t)$ in place of the function $\varphi(t)$. The derivatives of φ and h at t_k are equal. Then it is possible to use the values of the second derivatives of $h(t)$ in order to more precisely obtain the next approximation t_{k+1}.

Suppose now that t_{k+1} has been found. In order to find $\varphi(t_{k+1})$, it is possible to use the method presented in (8).

If $\varphi(t_{k+1}) = 0$, then it is still necessary to verify whether or not t_{k+1} is the smallest root of the equation $\varphi(t) = 0$.

If, however, $\varphi(t_{k+1}) > 0$, then we go on to the next step.

Let us dwell on further details for the calculation of $\varphi(t_{k+1})$.

First suppose that $t_{k+1} > t_k$.

To speed up the convergence, it is possible to make a more reasonable choice for the first approximation $u_1^{k+1}(t)$. For example, we may set

$$u_1^{k+1}(t) = \begin{cases} u^k(t) & t \in [0, t_k] \\ w(t) & t \in (t_k, t_{k+1}] \end{cases}$$

where $u^k(t)$ satisfies (2.11), and the control $w(t)$ is chosen by one of the following methods:

1. $$X_k^* f(X_k, w(t), t) = \min_{u \in Q} X_k^* f(X_k, u, t) \equiv \Psi_1(t), \tag{2.12}$$

where

$$X_k = X(t_k, u^k);$$

2. $$X_k^* f(X(t), w(t), t) = \min_{u \in Q} X_k^* f(X(t), u, t) \equiv \Psi_2(t), \tag{2.13}$$

where

$$\dot{X}(t) = f(X(t), w(t), t), \tag{2.14}$$

$$X(t_1) = X_k; \tag{2.15}$$

3. $$X^*(t) f(X(t), w(t), t) = \min_{u \in Q} X^*(t) f(X(t), u, t) \equiv \Psi_3(t), \tag{2.16}$$

where $X(t)$ satisfies system (2.14) with initial conditions (2.15).

If, however, $t_{k+1} < t_k$, then we shall set

$$u_1^{k+1}(t) = u^k(t) \quad (t \in [0, t_{k+1}]).$$

We note that it is not necessary to find the exact value

of $\varphi(t_{k+1})$, and that one can confine onself to some approximations thereto. In this case, it is sufficient to make several iterations towards finding $\varphi(t_{k+1})$.

Having found t_k and $u^k(t)$ (where $u^k(t)$ may also not satisfy condition (2.11) exactly), it is also possible to do the following in order to find t_{k+1} and u^{k+1}:

Let $\dot{\varphi}(t_k+0) < 0$ and $\dot{\varphi}(t_k-0) < 0$. Then we set

$$u_1^{k+1}(t) = \begin{cases} u^k(t) & t \in [0, t_k] \\ w(t) & t > t_k \end{cases},$$

where w(t) satisfies Eqs. (2.12), (2.13) or (2.16), and $u^k(t)$ satisfies Eq. (2.11). We also set

$$t_{k+1} = \min \{ T, t_k' \},$$

where T is the time for which it is known that

$$\min_{t \in [0, T]} \varphi(t) = 0,$$

and $t_k' > t_k$ is such that

$$\Psi(t) < 0 \quad \text{for} \quad t \in [t_k, t_k')$$
$$\Psi(t_k') = 0,$$

where $\Psi(t)$ is either $\Psi_1(t)$, $\Psi_2(t)$, or $\Psi_3(t)$.

If however

$$\dot{\varphi}(t_k - 0) > 0,$$

then we can find t_{k+1} from the condition

$$X^2(t_{k+1}, u^k) = \min_{t \in [0, t_k]} X^2(t, u^k). \tag{2.17}$$

If there exists several t_{k+1} satisfying (2.17), then we find the smallest such t_{k+1}.

If we apply the above-indicated algorithms to linear systems as particular cases, it is possible to obtain methods similar to those in (1-5).

References

1. Neustadt, L. W. "Synthesizing Time Optimal Control Systems", J. Math. Anal. Appl., 1960, Vol. 1, No. 3, pp. 484-493.
2. Eaton, J. H. "An Iterative Solution to Time Optimal Control", J. Math. Anal. Appl., 1962, Vol. 5, No. 2, pp. 329-344.

3. Kirin, N. E. "On a Numerical Method for the Linear Time Optimal Problem", Metody Vychisl., 1963.
4. Pshenichniy, B.N. "A Numerical Method of Computing Time Optimal Controls in Linear Systems", Zh. Vychisl. Mat. i Mat. Fiz., No. 1, vol. 4, (1964), pp. 52-60. English Translation in U.S.S.R. Comput. Math. and Math. Phys., 1964, vol. 4, No. 1, pp. 71-82.
5. Babunashvili, T. G. "Synthesis of Linear Optimal Systems", Dokl. Akad. Nauk SSSR, 1964, vol. 155, No. 2. English Translation in J. SIAM on Control, 1964, Vol. 2, No. 2, pp. 261-265.
6. Ho, Y.C. "A Successive Approximation Technique for Optimal Control Systems Subject to Input Saturation", J. Basic Engr. Trans. A.S.M.E., 1962, vol. 84, pp. 33-40.
7. Dem'yanov, V.F. "Determination of the Optimum Program in a Linear System", Automation and Remote Control, July 1964, Vol. 25, No. 1, pp. 1-10.
8. Dem'yanov, V.F. "Solution of Certain Extremal Problems", Automation and Remote Control, July 1965, Vol. 26, No. 7, pp. 1144-1151.

COMPUTATION OF OPTIMAL CONTROLS ON CONVEX REACHABLE SETS

Robert O. Barr
Michigan State University, Systems Science Program
East Lansing, Michigan

1. Introduction

This paper presents iterative procedures applicable to a wide variety of optimal control problems. The essence of the procedures is a new method for solving quadratic programs on a compact, convex set K in E^n. The method is quite different from the quadratic programming algorithms usually given in the literature since it does not require the constraint set K to be described by some set of functional inequalities. The only requirement is that K have a known contact function (see Section 2). This requirement is particularly appropriate for the solution of problems in optimal control.

The basic method, called Iterative Procedure 1 (IP1), is described in Section 2. The method extends the procedure given by E. G. Gilbert (1) so that on each iteration a quadratic minimization problem is solved on a convex polyhedron instead of on a line segment. As with Gilbert's procedure, convergence is guaranteed and computable error bounds are available. Results which indicate that the extended procedure has more rapid convergence are presented.

Section 3 contains another iterative procedure which on each iteration involves IP1 and which allows solution of a broader class of optimal control problems. Then in Section 4 the connection between the iterative procedures and optimal control problems is described.

2. The Basic Problem and Iterative Procedure 1

Let K be a compact, convex set in E^n and let $\eta(\cdot)$ denote the support function of K. A <u>contact function</u> of K is a function $s(\cdot)$ from E^n to K such that $y \cdot s(y) = \max_{z \in K} y \cdot z$. Thus $y \cdot s(y) = \eta(y)$ and for $y \neq 0$, $s(y)$ lies on the intersection of K and the support hyperplane of K having outward normal y. As is illustrated in Fig. 1, $s(y)$, $y \neq 0$, need not be uniquely determined. For all sets K in the sequel it is assumed that a method for evaluating a contact function is available.

The basic problem is:

BP <u>Given</u>: <u>K a compact, convex set in</u> E^n. <u>Find</u>: <u>a point</u> $z^* \in K$ <u>such that</u> $|z^*|^2 = \min_{z \in K} |z|^2$.

Since $|z|$ (Euclidean norm of z) is continuous and K is compact, a solution z^* exists. Furthermore, z^* is unique; $z^* = 0$ if and only if $0 \in K$; for $0 \notin K$, $z^* \in \partial K$.

Consider now the iterative procedure for solving BP:

ITERATIVE PROCEDURE 1 (IP1) Let $s(\cdot)$ be an arbitrary contact function of the set K. Take $z_0 \in K$ and choose a positive integer p. Then a sequence of vectors $\{z_k\}$, $k = 0,1,\ldots$, is generated as follows:

<u>Step 1</u> Select any p vectors $y_1(k), y_2(k), \ldots, y_p(k)$ in K and let
$H_k = \Delta\{y_1(k), y_2(k), \ldots, y_p(k), s(-z_k), z_k\}$
(Δ denotes convex hull).

<u>Step 2</u> Find $z_{k+1} \in H_k$ such that
$$|z_{k+1}|^2 = \min_{z \in H_k} |z|^2.$$

Gilbert's procedure (<u>1</u>) differs from IP1 in that z_{k+1} is obtained by minimizing over the line segment $\Delta\{s(-z_k), z_k\}$ instead of over H_k.

It is important to note the distinction between BP and Step 2, both of which are quadratic programming problems on a compact, convex constraint set. The set K in BP is described only by a contact function $s(\cdot)$ of K whereas the convex polyhedron H_k in Step 2 is the convex hull of p+2 known points. Thus Step 2 is simpler than BP and can be shown to be solvable by standard quadratic programming techniques (<u>2</u>).

Before stating a convergence theorem for IP1, it is convenient to introduce:

$$\gamma(z) = |z|^{-2} z \cdot s(-z), \quad |z| > 0,\ z \cdot s(-z) > 0$$
$$= 0, \quad z = 0 \text{ or } |z| > 0,\ z \cdot s(-z) \leq 0 \tag{1}$$

$$\mu(z) = |z|^{-1} z \cdot s(-z), \quad z \neq 0$$
$$= 0, \quad z = 0. \tag{2}$$

Thus $\gamma(\cdot)$ and $\mu(\cdot)$ are functions which are defined on K. Fig. 2 indicates their geometric significance for the case $|z| > 0$, $z \cdot s(-z) > 0$: $\gamma(z)z$ is the intersection of the line through 0 and z with the support hyperplane of K having outward normal $-z$; $|\mu(z)|$ is the Euclidean distance from the origin to this support hyperplane. It is not difficult to show that for $z \varepsilon K$: $0 \leq \gamma(z) \leq 1$; $\mu(z) \leq |z|\gamma(z) \leq |z^*|$; $\mu(z^*) = |z^*|$.

THEOREM 1 <u>Consider the sequence</u> $\{z_k\}$ <u>generated by</u> IP1. <u>For</u> $k \geq 0$ <u>and</u> $k \to \infty$: i) $z_k \varepsilon K$; ii) $|z_k| \geq |z_{k+1}|$, $|z_k| \to |z^*|$, <u>and</u> $|z_k| = |z_{k+1}|$ <u>implies</u> $z_k = z^*$; iii) $z_k \to z^*$; iv) $|z_k|\gamma(z_k) \leq |z^*|$ <u>and</u> $|z_k|\gamma(z_k) \to |z^*|$; v) $|z_k - z^*| \leq \sqrt{1 - \gamma(z_k)}|z_k|$ <u>and</u> $\sqrt{1 - \gamma(z_k)}|z_k| \to 0$; vi) $|s(-z_k) - z^*| \leq |s(-z_k) - \gamma(z_k)z_k|$.

The proof of this convergence theorem is given in reference (<u>2</u>). Since the bounds in parts iv), v), vi) are computable as the iterative process proceeds, they may be used to generate stopping criteria for the termination of the iterative process.

There are a great variety of selection rules for choosing the vectors $y_1(k)$, ..., $y_p(k)$ in Step 1 of IP1 and each selection rule gives a different version of IP1. One selection rule which leads to a significant improvement in rate of convergence for IP1 compared with Gilbert's procedure is the following:

<u>Selection Rule</u> Take $p = n$ and

for $k = 0$: Set $y_i(0) = s(-z_0)$, $i=1,2,\ldots,n$, and define scalars $\mu_1, \mu_2, \ldots, \mu_n$ equal to $\mu(z_0)$.

for $0 < k \leq n$: Set $y_i(k) = y_i(k-1)$, $i=1,2,\ldots,n$. Then set $y_k(k) = s(-z_{k-1})$ and $\mu_k = \mu(z_{k-1})$.

for $k > n$: Set $y_i(k) = y_i(k-1)$, $i=1,2,\ldots,n$. Then let $\underline{\mu} = \min\{\mu_1, \mu_2, \ldots, \mu_n\}$ and let j be the smallest integer in $[1,n]$ for which $\mu_j = \underline{\mu}$. Whenever $\mu_j \leq \mu(z_{k-1})$, replace $y_j(k)$ by $s(-z_{k-1})$ and μ_j by $\mu(z_{k-1})$.

Hence for $k > n$, $y_1(k)$, ..., $y_n(k)$ are the boundary points of K corresponding to the n largest values of $\mu(\cdot)$ on previous iterations. For the case $z^* \in \partial K$, which is most important in applications, this enables the surface ∂H_k in the vicinity of z_{k+1} to approximate ∂K in the vicinity of z^*. Therefore, it is likely that improved convergence can be obtained. Extensive computations indicate that this is indeed the case.

Some computational results for the set $K = \{z : z^1 \geq \nu + \frac{1}{2}\sum_{i=2}^{n}(z^i)^2\lambda_i^{-1},\ z^1 \leq 10\}$, where $\nu,\lambda_2,\lambda_3,\ldots,\lambda_n > 0$ and $z = (z^1,z^2,\ldots,z^n)$, are shown in Table 1. The optimum is $z^* = (\nu,0,0,\ldots,0)$ and the λ_i are the principal radii of curvature of ∂K at z^*. Since many other convex sets K have a boundary surface which is closely approximated by a similar representation in the neighborhood of z^*, this example is of general interest.

Table 1. Number of Iterations to Satisfy $|z_k| - |z^*| \leq \varepsilon$

$n = 3$, $z_0 = (6,2,2)$, $\nu = 1$

		Gilbert's Procedure			IP1 (with above Selection Rule)		
λ_2	λ_3 \ ε	1	10^{-3}	10^{-6}	1	10^{-3}	10^{-6}
10	10	4	28	41	3	7	12
100	100	10	59	111	4	9	13
1000	1000	82	216	340	4	10	12
100	10	11	27	81	6	17	32
1000	1	14	218	321	6	11	17
1000	10	83	229	359	7	20	29
1000	100	81	197	358	8	23	32

The results for criteria other than $|z_k| - |z^*| \leq \varepsilon$ and for different n, z_0, and λ_i are similar. The improvement of IP1 over Gilbert's procedure has three facets: (1) much more rapid convergence, (2) very little dependence on the parameter $\bar{\lambda}\nu^{-1}$ where $\bar{\lambda} = \max\{\lambda_i\}$, (3) small influence of the initial point z_0 (when $|z_0|$ remains fixed). For IP1, the rate of decrease of $|z_k| - |z^*|$ is, roughly speaking, dependent on n alone. The number of iterations per decade after a few iterations is approximately 2 for n = 2, 4 for n = 3, 6 for n = 4, 9 for n = 5, and 13 for n = 6.

3. The General Problem and Iterative Procedure 2

Certain optimal control problems are related directly to BP. However, an abstract problem which has application to a much broader class of optimal control problems is the following general problem:

GP <u>Let</u> $\Omega = [0,\hat{\omega}]$, $\hat{\omega} > 0$, <u>be a compact interval in</u> E^1 <u>and for</u> $\omega \in \Omega$ <u>let sets</u> $K(\omega) \subset E^n$ <u>be compact, convex, and continuous in</u> ω. <u>Assume that there exists</u> $\omega^* \in \Omega$ <u>such that</u> $0 \notin K(\omega)$, $0 \leq \omega < \omega^*$, <u>and</u> $0 \in K(\omega^*)$. <u>Find</u>: ω^*.

Note that the continuity of $K(\omega)$ implies $0 \in \partial K(\omega^*)$. An iterative procedure for solving GP is:

ITERATIVE PROCEDURE 2 (IP2) Let $s(\omega,\cdot)$ be an arbitrary contact function of $K(\omega)$ and let $\eta(\omega,\cdot)$ be the support function of $K(\omega)$. Define:

$$\begin{aligned} \gamma(\omega,z) &= |z|^{-2} z\cdot s(\omega,-z), && |z| > 0,\ z\cdot s(\omega,-z) > 0 \\ &= 0, && z=0 \text{ or } |z| > 0,\ z\cdot s(\omega,-z) \leq 0 \end{aligned} \tag{3}$$

Choose θ, $0 < \theta < 1$, and begin by setting $\omega_0 = 0$.

<u>Step 1</u> With ω_i fixed, $0 \leq \omega_i \leq \omega^*$, apply IP1 to the minimization of $|z|^2$, $z \in K(\omega_i)$. If $\omega_i = \omega^*$, get sequence of points which converges to 0. If $\omega_i < \omega^*$, continue until a point $z_i \in K(\omega_i)$ is obtained such that $\gamma(\omega_i,z_i) \geq \theta$; then proceed to Step 2.

<u>Step 2</u> With z_i fixed, let ω increase from ω_i until $\eta(\omega,-z_i) = 0$. Take ω_{i+1} as this value of ω.

There is little difficulty in showing that IP2 exists. Moreover, the following convergence theorem holds (for a proof, see (<u>2</u>)).

THEOREM 2 <u>Consider</u> IP2 <u>and assume the condition</u> $\omega_i = \omega^*$ <u>in Step 1 does not occur for</u> $i < \infty$. <u>Furthermore, assume that</u> $\dfrac{\eta(\omega_a,y) - \eta(\omega_b,y)}{\omega_a - \omega_b}$ <u>is bounded from above for all</u> ω_a, ω_b $\in \Omega$, $\omega_a \neq \omega_b$, <u>bounded</u> $y \in E^n$. <u>Then</u> IP2 <u>generates sequences</u>

$\{\omega_i\}$ _and_ $\{z_i\}$ _which for_ $i \geq 0$ _and_ $i \to \infty$ _satisfy_: i) $\omega_i \in [0,\omega^*)$ _and_ $z_i \in K(\omega_i)$; ii) $\{\omega_i\}$ _is strictly increasing_ $(\omega_i < \omega_{i+1})$ _and_ $\omega_i \to \omega^*$; iii) $z_i \to 0$.

4. Application to Optimal Control Problems

The iterative procedures can be applied to many optimal control problems in which there are: i) a system differential equation of the form

$$\dot{x}(t) = A(t)x(t) + f(u(t),t), \quad x(0) \text{ specified}, \tag{4}$$

where x is the m-dimensional state vector, x(0) is the initial state, u(·) is an r-dimensional control vector, admissible if measurable with range in a compact set U, the matrix function A(t) and vector function f(u,t) are continuous in their arguments; ii) compact, convex target sets W(t) in E^m which are continuous in t; iii) a cost functional

$$J_t(u) = \int_0^t [a(\sigma)\cdot x_u(\sigma) + f^0(u(\sigma),\sigma)]d\sigma + h^0(x_u(t)), \tag{5}$$

where $x_u(t)$ is the solution of the system equation corresponding to the control u(·), $h^0(\cdot)$ is a convex function from E^m to E^1, the vector function a(t) and scalar function $f^0(u,t)$ are continuous in their arguments; iv) an optimization objective corresponding to fixed or free terminal time. For a fixed terminal time T > 0 the objective is: find an admissible control u*(·) such that $x_{u^*}(T) \in W(T)$ and the cost for u*(·) at T ≤ the cost for u(·) at T where u(·) is any admissible control for which $x_u(T) \in W(T)$; if the terminal time is free: find an admissible control u*(·) and an optimal time t* such that $x_{u^*}(t^*) \in W(t^*)$ and the cost for u*(·) at t* ≤ the cost for $\tilde{u}(\cdot)$ at $\tilde{t}$ where $\tilde{u}(\cdot)$ is any admissible control for which $x_{\tilde{u}}(\tilde{t}) \in W(\tilde{t})$, any $\tilde{t}$.

The set of all solutions of the system equation at a particular time t which are generated by admissible controls is the reachable set R(t). This set is (1) compact, (2) convex, (3) continuous in t, and (4) has a contact function which can be evaluated. These four properties are the essential features which permit application of the iterative procedures to optimal control problems.

The compactness and convexity of R(t) were shown by Neustadt (3) and the continuity property follows from the continuity of f(·,·) and A(·). Since

$$R(t)=\{\Phi(t)[x(0) + \int_0^t \Phi^{-1}(\sigma)f(u(\sigma),\sigma)d\sigma] \; : \; u(\cdot) \text{ admissible}\} \quad (6)$$

where $\dot{\Phi} = A(t)\Phi$, $\Phi(0) = I$, it can be shown (4) that a contact function of $R(T)$ is $s(y) = x_{u(t,y)}(T)$. Here $u(t,y)$ is any admissible control satisfying

$$\psi(t,y)\cdot f(u(t,y),t) = \max_{v\varepsilon U} \psi(t,y)\cdot f(v,t) \quad (7)$$

and $\psi(t,y)$ solves the adjoint differential equation

$$\dot{\psi} = -A'(t)\psi(t), \qquad \psi(T) = y. \quad (8)$$

For the minimum-error regulator where $J(u) = |x_u(T)|$ and $W(T) = E^m$, IP1 can be applied directly by defining $K = R(T)$. The iterative procedure generates a point $\tilde{z}$ arbitrarily close to z^*. The details of constructing an admissible control which drives the system to $\tilde{z}$ are given in references (2) and (4).

For the minimum time problem where $J_t(u) = t$, IP2 can be applied by defining $\omega = t$ and $K(\omega) = \{z : z = x - y, x \; \varepsilon \; R(t), y \; \varepsilon \; W(t)\}$. If a contact function of $W(\omega)$ is available then $s(\omega,\cdot)$ for $K(\omega)$ can be easily found: $s(\omega,\beta) = s_R(\omega,\beta) - s_W(\omega,-\beta)$, $\beta \; \varepsilon \; E^m = E^n$.

Other optimal control problems can be treated similarly. Computational results have been obtained for a minimum fuel terminal control problem with double-integrator plant. These results, which will be published elsewhere, illustrate the effectiveness of IP2 in solving optimal control problems (2).

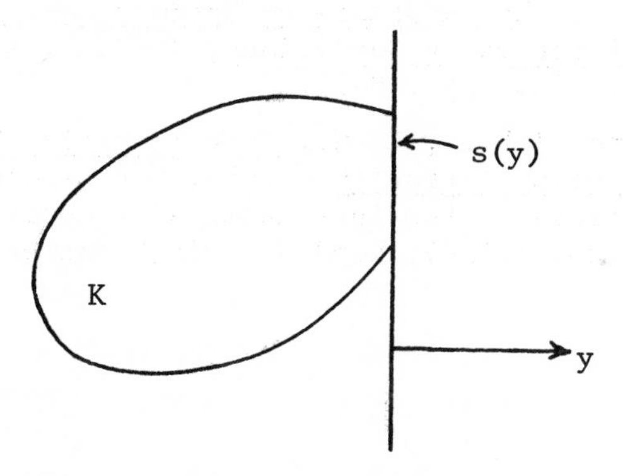

Fig. 1. The Contact Function s(y).

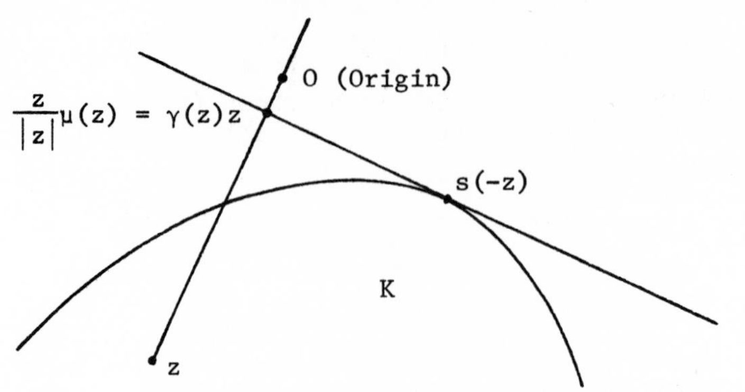

Fig. 2. Geometric Significance of $\gamma(\cdot)$ and $\mu(\cdot)$.

Acknowledgement

This research was supported by the United States Air Force, Office of Scientific Research, under grant numbers AF-AFOSR-814-65 and AF-AFOSR-814-66.

References

(1) Gilbert, E. G., An Iterative Procedure for Computing the Minimum of a Quadratic Form on a Convex Set, SIAM J. on Control, Ser. A, Vol. 4, No. 1, 1966, pp 61-80.

(2) Barr, R. O., "Computation of Optimal Controls by Quadratic Programming on Convex Reachable Sets," Ph.D. thesis, University of Michigan, 1966.

(3) Neustadt, L. W., The Existence of Optimal Controls in the Absence of Convexity Conditions, J. Math. Anal. and Appl., Vol. 7, 1963, pp 110-117.

(4) Barr, R. O. and Gilbert, E. G., Some Iterative Procedures for Computing Optimal Controls, "Proceedings of the Third Congress of the International Federation of Automatic Control (IFAC), London, 1966," Butterworth, London.

SOLUTION OF NONLINEAR TWO-POINT BOUNDARY VALUE PROBLEMS BY LINEAR PROGRAMMING*

J. B. Rosen & Robert Meyer
Computer Sciences Department
University of Wisconsin
Madison, Wisconsin

1. INTRODUCTION

A system of n nonlinear ordinary differential equations is considered on the interval [a, b] with at least one of the n boundary conditions specified at each end of the interval. In addition, any available a priori bounds on the solution vector may be imposed. An iterative method for solution is described which is essentially a Newton-Raphson method with a linear programming solution at each iteration. Every iterate is a minimax solution to a linearized finite difference approximation to the original system subject to the boundary conditions and the a priori bounds. The method will always converge at least as fast as Newton-Raphson, and may converge when Newton-Raphson fails. A number of computational examples are described.

This approach was suggested in a previous paper [1] dealing with discrete optimal control problems. The fundamental recurrence relations to be used here were developed in an earlier report on discrete optimal control [2]. These relations serve to decouple the system and to reduce the dimension of the linear programming problem solved at each iteration.

---

* Sponsored by NSF Research Grant GP 6070.

2. PROBLEM STATEMENT

We will first consider a class of continuous problems of the following kind: determine an n-dimensional function $y(t)$ such that

$$\dot{y}(t) = f(y, t), \quad 0 \leq t \leq 1 \tag{2.1}$$

$$y_i(0) = q_{i0}, \quad i = 1, \dots, \ell < n \tag{2.2}$$

and

$$y_i(1) = q_{im}, \quad i = 1, \dots, n-\ell \tag{2.3}$$

where f is assumed to be a continuous vector function of y and t with continuous first partial derivatives with respect to the components y_i, $i = 1, \dots, n$ of y. The boundary conditions (2.3) are specified for the first $n-\ell$ components for the sake of notational simplicity below; the method can be applied to any properly posed problem.

We approximate (2.1) by the finite difference scheme

$$\frac{x_{j+1} - x_j}{\Delta t} = \tfrac{1}{2}\left[f(x_{j+1}, t_{j+1}) + f(x_j, t_j)\right] \tag{2.4}$$

$$j = 0, \dots, m-1$$

where $\Delta t = \frac{1}{m}$, $t_j = j\Delta t$, and the x_j, $j=0, \dots, m$ are to be determined so that (2.4) and the boundary conditions are satisfied.

3. ITERATIVE SOLUTION

In order to linearize the nonlinear system (2.4) we use the approximation

$$f(x_j, t_j) \cong f(x_j^k, t_j) + F_j^k[x_j - x_j^k] \tag{3.1}$$

where the $n \times n$ matrix F_j^k is the Jacobian with respect to x of $f(x, t)$ evaluated at (x_j^k, t_j) and x_j^k is the k'th approximation to x_j. The initial approximate trajectory ($k = 0$) is usually taken to be a constant or linear function, and need not satisfy the boundary conditions. The approximation (3.1) is used to transform (2.4) into the linear system of mn equations in mn unknowns

$$\frac{x_{j+1} - x_j}{\Delta t} = \tfrac{1}{2} F^k_{j+1} x_{j+1} + \tfrac{1}{2} F^k_j x_j + \tfrac{1}{2} [s^k_{j+1} + s^k_j] \tag{3.2}$$

where $s^k_j = f(x^k_j, t_j) - F^k_j x^k_j$, a constant vector. In order to generalize the Newton-Raphson algorithm, we introduce a control term on the right hand side of (3.2) to obtain

$$\frac{x_{j+1} - x}{\Delta t} = \tfrac{1}{2} F^k_{j+1} x_{j+1} + \tfrac{1}{2} F^k_j x_j + \tfrac{1}{2} [s^k_{j+1} + s^k_j] + \mu_j s \tag{3.3}$$

$$j = 0, \ldots, m-1$$

where the μ_j, $j = 0, \ldots, m-1$, are scalars to be determined and s (the sum vector) $\in E^n$ is a constant vector with every component equal to 1. If at any iteration there is no solution of the system (3.2) satisfying the boundary conditions and the inequality constraints to be specified below, there may be a solution of (3.3) with some $\mu_j \neq 0$. The scalars μ_j play the role of a scalar control (representing an error in the finite difference equation), and are introduced to allow intermediate solutions to be obtained even when the linear system from a Newton-Raphson method might not have a solution. Denoting by X the set $\{x_j | j=0, \ldots, m\}$, by U the set $\{\mu_j | j=0, \ldots, m-1\}$, and by $\| U \|$ the $\max_j |\mu_j|$, we will determine by linear programming the pair (X^*, U^*) which minimizes $\| U \|$ over all pairs (X, U) which satisfy (3.3), the boundary conditions, and the inequality constraints below.

The size of this linear programming problem is reduced by partitioning it into smaller problems. This reduction is accomplished in two stages. The first stage consists of solving (3.3) for x_{j+1} to obtain

$$x_{j+1} = K_j x_j + \mu_j v_j + \bar{s}_j \tag{3.4}$$

where

$$K_j = [I - \tfrac{1}{2m} F^k_{j+1}]^{-1} [I + \tfrac{1}{2m} F^k_j] \tag{3.5}$$

$$v_j = \frac{1}{m} [I - \frac{1}{2m} F^k_{j+1}]^{-1} s \tag{3.6}$$

and

$$\bar{s}_j = \frac{1}{2m} [I - \frac{1}{2m} F^k_{j+1}]^{-1} [s^k_{j+1} + s^k_j] \tag{3.7}$$

In the second stage the recursion relation (3.4) is used to express the terminal vector in terms of x_0 and the μ_j, giving

$$x_m = V_0 x_0 + \sum_{j=0}^{m-1} \mu_j h_j + g \tag{3.8}$$

where

$$g = \sum_{j=0}^{m-1} V_{j+1} \overline{s}_j \tag{3.9}$$

and

$$h_j = V_{j+1} v_j, \quad j=0, \ldots, m-1 \tag{3.10}$$

The matrices V_j, $j = m-1, \ldots, 0$ are determined by the recursion relations

$$V_m = I, \; V_j = V_{j+1} K_j \tag{3.11}$$

We now specify upper and lower bounds on the unknown initial and terminal conditions to obtain the inequality constraints cited above. (It should be noted that all of these bounds are not necessary in order to employ the method. However, whatever information on bounds is available should be used in setting up the problem, because it facilitates the solution. Furthermore, upper or lower bounds on any components of any of the x_j can easily be handled. For notational simplicity we consider below only the case of upper and lower bounds at the boundaries.)

We thus specify bounds $\underline{q}_{i0}$ and $\overline{q}_{i0}$ and require

$$\underline{q}_{i0} \le \xi_i \le \overline{q}_{i0}, \quad i = \ell + 1, \ldots, n \tag{3.12}$$

where the ξ_i denote the components of x_0. If in addition we let

$$\underline{q}_{i0} = \overline{q}_{i0} = q_{i0}, \; i = 1, \ldots, \ell \tag{3.13}$$

then we can write (2.2) and (3.12) in vector notation as

$$\underline{q}_0 \le x_0 \le \overline{q}_0 . \tag{3.14}$$

Similarly, if we have bounds $\underline{q}_{im}$ and $\overline{q}_{im}$ on the unknown terminal values, we require

$$\underline{q}_m \leq x_m \leq \overline{q}_m \tag{3.15}$$

where the first $(n-\ell)$ components of (3.15) express the boundary conditions (2.3).

We want to find x_0 so that the initial and terminal bounds are satisfied, and so that $\mu_j = 0$, $j = 0, \ldots, m-1$. If such a solution exists, it will be found by solving the following linear programming problem

$$\min_{x_0, \mu_j, \gamma} \left\{ \gamma \;\middle|\; \begin{array}{l} \underline{q}_0 \leq x_0 \leq \overline{q}_0 \\ \underline{q}_m \leq V_0 x_0 + \sum_{j=0}^{m-1} \mu_j h_j + g \leq \overline{q}_m \\ -\gamma \leq \mu_j \leq \gamma, \quad j = 0, \ldots, m-1 \end{array} \right\} \tag{3.16}$$

If no solution with $\mu_j = 0$ for all j exists, then (3.16) finds a solution for which $\max |\mu_j|$ = minimum provided there exists any solution at all to the inequalities. The state vectors x_j^{k+1}, $j = 1, \ldots, m$ are then immediately determined by (3.4). These new values are the $(k+1)$st approximation to the solution.

If these new values differ from those obtained in the previous iteration by less than a specified tolerance, we consider the solution to have converged, and terminate the iterations. Otherwise, we use the $(k+1)$st approximation to determine a new V_0, g, and new h_j, and repeat the process. Note that each approximation thus satisfies the boundary conditions and the upper and lower bounds, but does not in general satisfy (2.4) or (3.2). If the original set of equations (2.4) has a solution satisfying (3.14) and (3.15), we can expect, however, that only the first few iterates will not satisfy (3.2).

To put (3.16) into the format of a standard dual linear programming problem, let $u \in E^m$ be the vector with components μ_j, let $V = V_0'$, and let H be the $(m \times n)$ matrix whose j^{th} row is h_j'. Define a vector $c \in E^{2m+4n}$ and a $(m+n+1) \times (2m+4n)$ matrix A as follows

$$c' = (\underline{q}_0' \mid -\bar{q}_0' \mid \underline{q}_m' - g' \mid g' - \bar{q}_m' \mid 0 \ldots 0 \mid 0 \ldots 0)$$

$$A = \begin{bmatrix} I_n & -I_n & V & -V & 0 & 0 \\ 0 & 0 & H & -H & I_m & -I_m \\ 0 & 0 & 0 & 0 & 1 \ldots 1 & 1 \ldots 1 \end{bmatrix}$$

Also let $w, b \in E^{m+n+1}$ be given by

$$w = \begin{pmatrix} x_0 \\ u \\ \gamma \end{pmatrix}, \qquad b = \begin{pmatrix} 0 \\ \vdots \\ 0 \\ 1 \end{pmatrix}.$$

The problem (3.15) is in the form of an (unsymmetric) dual linear programming problem [3], and can now be written as

$$\min_w \{b'w \mid A'w \geq c\}. \tag{3.17}$$

Computationally, it is convenient to actually solve the corresponding primal problem

$$\max_z \{c'z \mid Az = b, \quad z \geq 0\} \tag{3.18}$$

The method can be carried over with obvious modifications to true optimal control problems. Indeed, it was originally devised to handle such problems [1]. When tested on a constrained brachistochrone problem [4], it proved to be at least as accurate and efficient as other techniques used in solving that problem.

4. CONVERGENCE

In order to discuss convergence, it is necessary that there exist solutions to the given problem and the approximating linear problems. For nonlinear boundary value problems, existence theorems have been constructed only for certain special classes of problems. McGill and Kenneth [5, 6] show that if the length of the time interval $[a, b]$ is "sufficiently small," the continuous nonlinear problem has a unique solution, and that the Newton-Raphson method converges quadratically to the solution provided the initial guess lies in a certain region containing the line connecting the boundary values. Lees [7] obtains a convergence theorem for second order systems with positive semidefinite Jacobians. Kalaba [8] gives results on differential inequalities which may be used to prove global, monotone convergence under some additional convexity assumptions in the case of a single second-order equation.

It should be emphasized that all of these results are concerned with sufficient conditions for convergence, and that convergence will often take place even when the conditions are not satisfied. Rather crude initial guesses such as linear or constant functions which do not satisfy the sufficient conditions will often be satisfactory. Problems with multiple solutions are not considered in the theoretical investigations mentioned above.

Finally, as noted above, the method developed in this report will converge whenever the Newton-Raphson method converges (provided the constraints are properly chosen), and it may converge even when Newton-Raphson fails.

5. EXAMPLES

1. Equation: $\ddot{y} = 2y^3$
   Boundary Conditions: $y(0) + \dot{y}(0) = 0, \quad y(1) = 1/2$
   Other Constraints: $0 \le y(0) \le 5, \quad -5 \le \dot{y}(0) \le 0$
   Number of Solutions: 1
   Comments: The initial approximate trajectory (IAT) was chosen to be identically zero. With this IAT, the matrix inversion required by Newton-Raphson could not be performed, but the control method converged.

2. Equation: $\ddot{y} = e^{-3y}$
   Boundary Conditions: $y(0) = y(1) = 0$
   Other Constraints: Case (a) $-5 \le \dot{y}(0) \le 0$
   (b) $-5 \le \dot{y}(0) \le 0$
   (c) $-1 \le \dot{y}(0) \le 0$
   (d) $-2 \le \dot{y}(0) \le 0$
   Number of Solutions: (a) 2; (b) 2; (c) 1; (d) 1

Comments: (a) IAT chosen so that Newton-Raphson converged to upper (in (y, t) plane) of two solutions. See Fig. 1. (b) IAT chosen so that Newton-Raphson converged to lower solution. See Fig. 2. (c) Same IAT as in (b), but constraints (c) chosen to exclude lower solution. Newton-Raphson cannot furnish solution satisfying constraint (c), but control method does. See Fig. 3. (d) Same IAT as in (b) and (c). Constraint (d) chosen so that lower solution (which has $\dot{y}(0) = -2.09$) just barely excluded. This time control method converges to a trajectory satisfying (d) and close to the excluded lower solution. This limiting trajectory does not quite satisfy the differential equation, but is rather a constrained local minimum. See Fig. 4.

3. Equation: $\ddot{y} = e^{-3.6y}$

Boundary Conditions: $y(0) = y(1) = 0$

Other Constraints: $-1.3 \leq \dot{y}(0) \leq 1.0$

Number of Solutions: 0 (Even without the other constraints, the analytic problem has no solution.)

Comments: Newton-Raphson does not converge (Fig. 5). With a slight modification to prevent cycling (similar to a device used by Griffith and Stewart [9]; see [3] for details), the control method converged to a trajectory that almost satisfied the discretized equation (minimax error of 0.0106). See Fig. 6.

4. Equation: $y = A_1 y + \gamma\, b_1(y)$, where A_1 is a 2x2 positive-definite constant matrix, γ is a scalar parameter (values used: $\gamma = 0, 1, 10$), and $b_1(y)$ is a vector of positive definite quadratic forms in y.

Boundary Conditions: $y_1(0) = y_2(0) = y_1(1) = y_2(1) = 1$

Comments: An equation of the indicated form was used so that the results of Lees could be applied, and so that the effect of "increasing the nonlinearity" could be tested. In addition, as shown in the table at the end of the section, error estimates were obtained.

5. Equation: $\ddot{y} = A_2 y + \gamma b_2(y)$, where A_2 is a 4x4 positive-definite constant matrix, γ a scalar ($\gamma = 0, 1, 10$ used), and $b_2(y)$ a vector of positive definite quadratic forms.

Boundary Conditions: $y_i(0) = 1$, $y_i(1) = 0$ $(i = 1, \ldots, 4)$.

Comments: This yielded a system of 8 first-order equations, and was the largest system dealt with. The number of iterations required remained small. See Table.

6. Equation: $\ddot{y} = A_2 y + \gamma b_2(y)$; $\gamma = 0, 1, 2$

Boundary Conditions: $y_i(0) = -1$, $y_i(1) = 1$ $(i = 1, \ldots, 4)$

Comments: The boundary conditions were chosen so that the Jacobian would not necessarily be positive definite for γ sufficiently large. The largest value for which a solution was obtained was $\gamma = 2$. The largest estimated errors (for a given mesh) were obtained in this case. See Table.

In the following table relating to examples 4, 5, and 6, $m = 1/\Delta t$. For $\gamma = 0$, the problem is linear, so only one iteration is needed. For $\gamma \neq 0$, the number of iterations decreases as m increases, since the limiting trajectory for a given grid is used as the IAT for the next finer grid. For each fixed grid the optimal LP basis from each iteration is used as the initial basis for the next iteration. This substantially decreases the number of basis changes needed in the final iterations. The quantity σ_{max} is chosen such that

$$\sigma_{max} \cdot [(\Delta t)^2 - (\Delta t^*)^2] = \| y - y^* \|_\infty$$

where y is the solution obtained using Δt, and y^* the solution obtained using the smallest grid size Δt^*. The estimated maximum error is then given by $\bar{\sigma}_{max} \cdot (\Delta t^*)^2$, where $\bar{\sigma}_{max}$ is the average of the σ_{max} values for different grid sizes.

Comparisons of Results for Quadratic System
of Differential Equations

Ex.	γ	m	Iterations Required	σ_{max} (x 10^3)	Estimated Maximum Error
4	0	10	1	72.1	
4	0	20	1	72.0	
4	0	40	1	71.9	
4	0	80	1		1.1×10^{-5}
4	1	10	3	248.8	
4	1	20	2	248.4	
4	1	40	1	248.3	
4	1	80	1		3.9
4	10	10	4	2364.1	
4	10	20	2	2368.7	
4	10	40	2	2369.9	
4	10	80	1		37
5	0	10	1	458.1	
5	0	20	1	457.4	
5	0	40	1		28.6
5	1	10	3	1043.9	
5	1	20	2	1031.6	
5	1	40	1		65
5	10	10	4	13933	
5	10	20	2	12811	
5	10	40	2		870
6	0	10	1	905.6	
6	0	20	1	903.4	
6	0	40	1		56.5
6	1	10	2	1925.1	
6	1	20	2	1929.2	
6	1	40	1		121
6	2	10	3	3666.7	
6	2	20	2	3678.5	
6	2	40	2		229

BIBLIOGRAPHY

1. Rosen, J. B., "Iterative Solution of Nonlinear Optimal Control Problems," J. SIAM Control, 4, pp. 223-244, (1966).
2. Rosen, J. B., "Optimal Control and Convex Programming," Proceedings of the IBM Scientific Computing Symposium on Control Theory and Applications, IBM, (1966).
3. Hadley, G., Linear Programming, Addison-Wesley, 1963.
4. Rosen, J. B. and Meyer, Robert, "Solution of Nonlinear Two-Point Boundary Value Probelms by Linear Programming," Computer Sciences Technical Report No. 1, Univ. of Wis., Jan. 1967.
5. McGill, R. and Kenneth, P., "A Convergence Theorem on the Iterative Solution of Nonlinear Two-Point Boundary Value Systems," XIVth International Astronautical Federation Congress, Paris, France, 1963.
6. McGill, R. and Kenneth, P., "Two-Point Boundary Value Problem Techniques," Advances in Control Systems, Vol. 3, C. T. Leondes (Ed.), Academic Press, (1966), pp. 69-109.
7. Lees, Milton, "Discrete Methods for Nonlinear Two-Point Boundary Value Problems," Numerical Solution of Partial Differential Equations, James Bramble (Ed.), Academic Press, 1966.
8. Kalaba, R., "On Nonlinear Differential Equations, The Maximum Operation, and Monotone Convergence," J. Math. Mech., 8 (1959), pp. 519-574.
9. Griffith, R. E. and Stewart, R. A., "Nonlinear Programming Technique for the Optimization of Continuous Processing Systems," Management Sciences, 7 (1961), pp. 379-392.

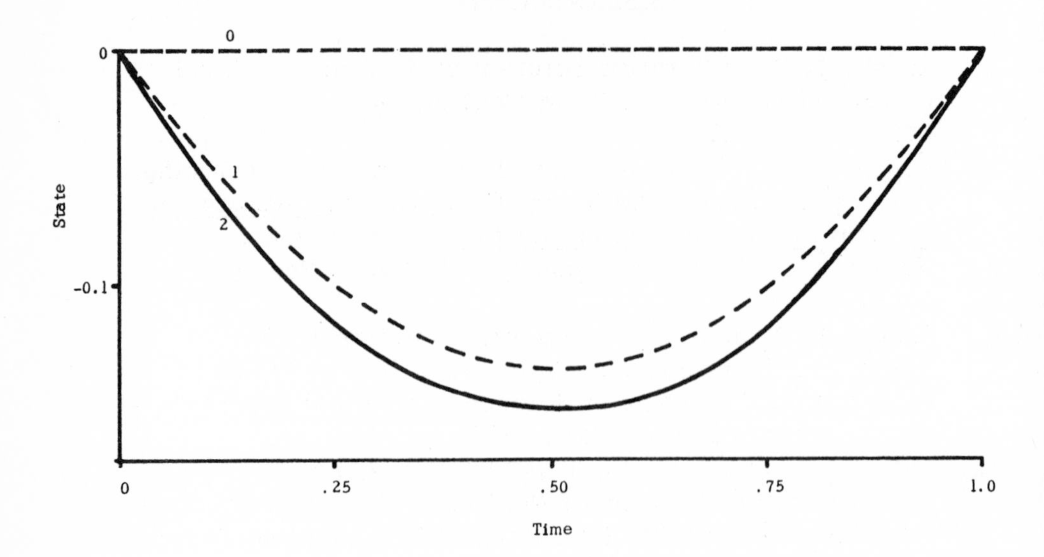

Figure 1. Iterative State Solutions for Example 2, Case (a)

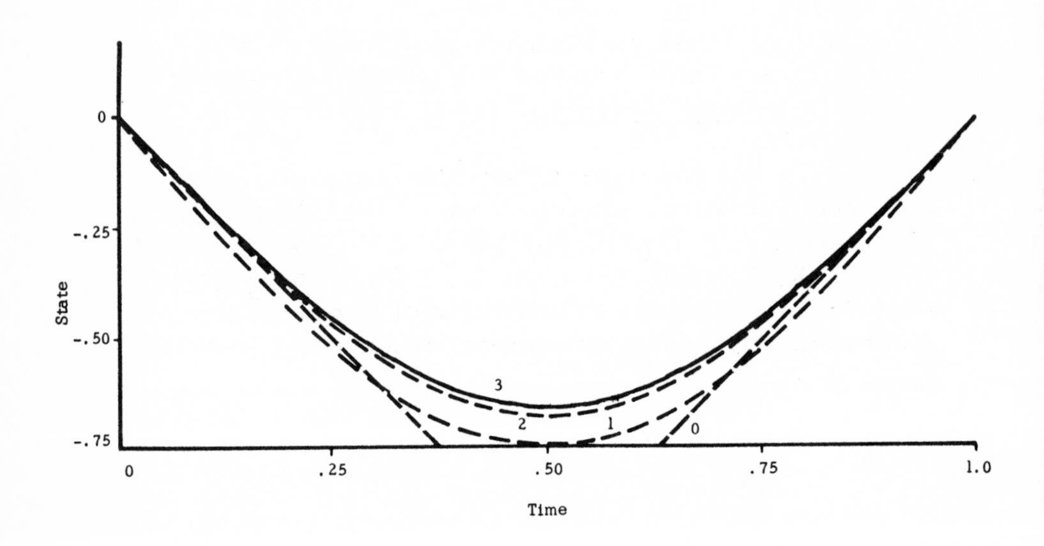

Figure 2. Iterative State Solutions for Example 2, Case (b)

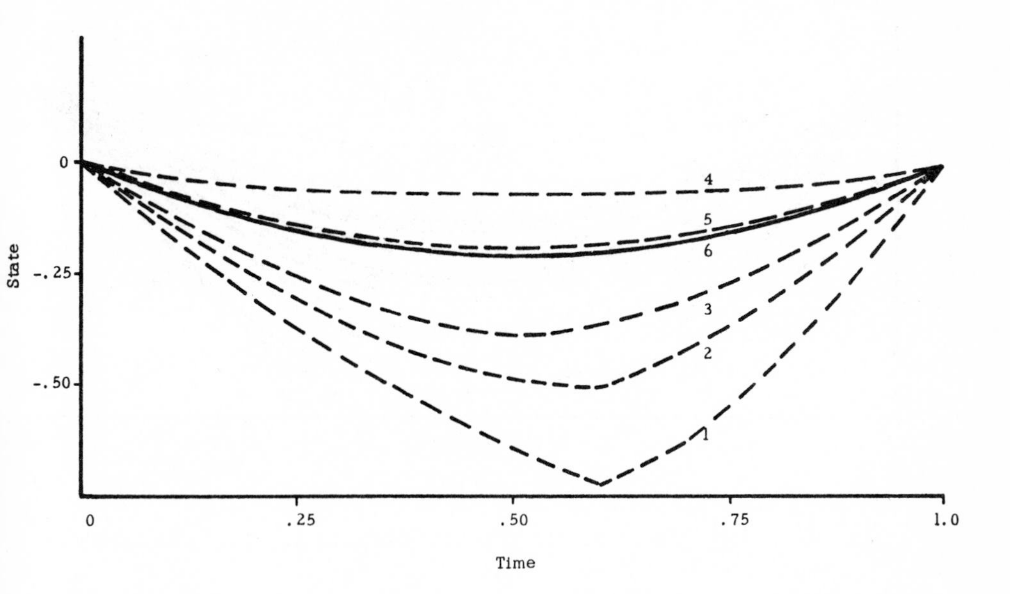

Figure 3. Iterative State Solutions for Example 2, Case (c)

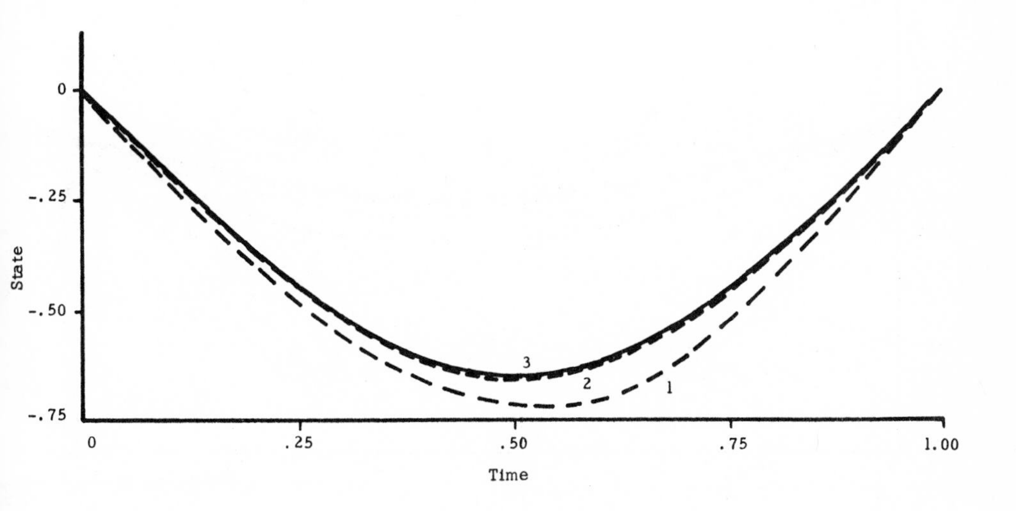

Figure 4. Iterative State Solutions for Example 2, Case (d)

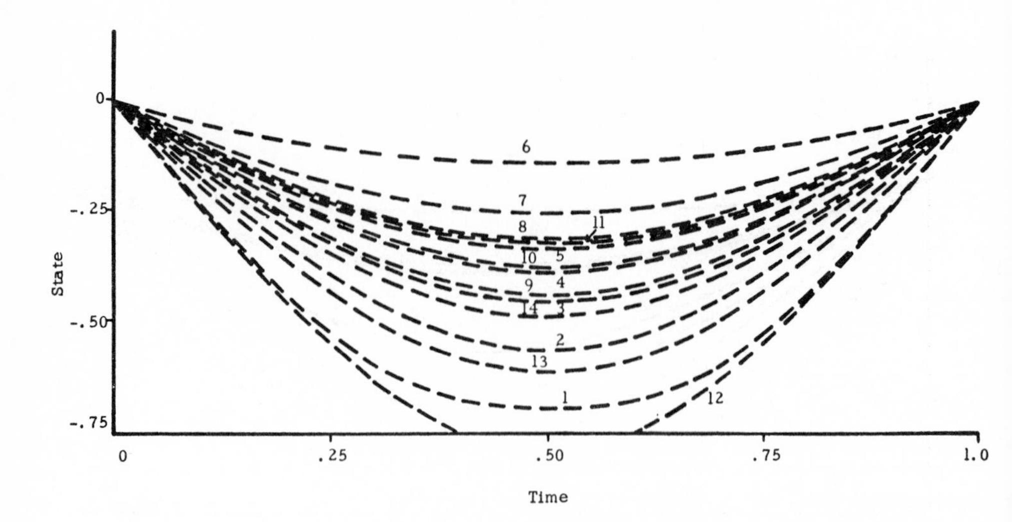

Figure 5. Iterative State Solutions for Example 3. No Convergence.

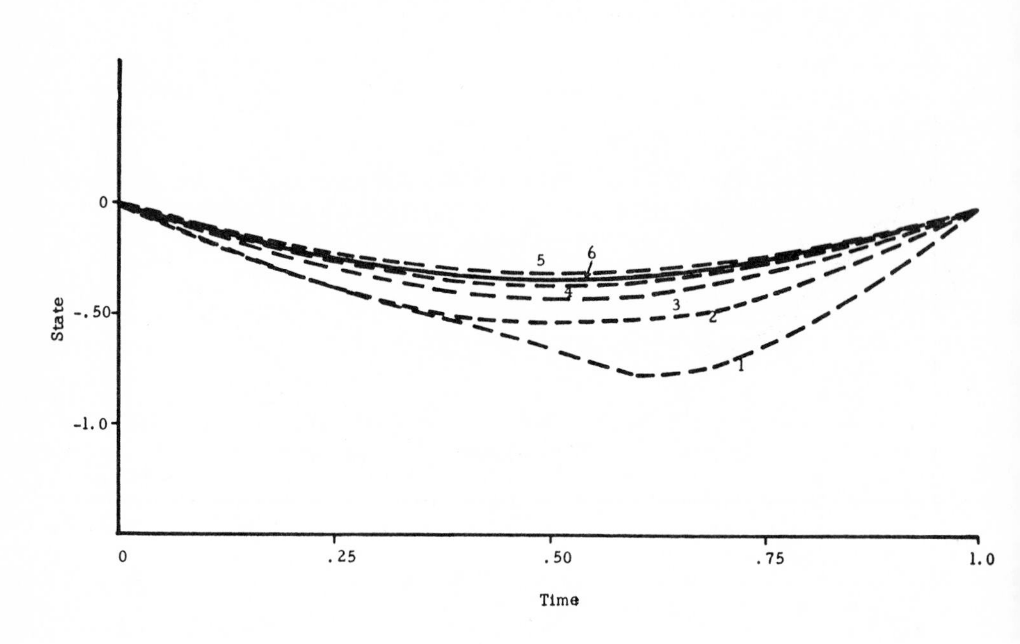

Figure 6. Iterative State Solutions for Example 3. Forced Convergence

A MAXIMUM PRINCIPLE IN MATHEMATICAL PROGRAMMING

O. L. Mangasarian and S. Fromovitz
Shell Development Company
Emeryville, California

Abstract

The aim of this paper is to start from some well known necessary optimality conditions of mathematical programming and from these derive necessary optimality conditions of the "maximum principle" type. Hopefully, this will clarify the relationships between mathematical programming and discrete optimal control. Halkin (1), (2), Halkin and Neustadt (3) and Canon, Cullum and Polak (4) have derived conditions of the maximum principle type by using a separation theorem for convex sets and a fixed point theorem. The present approach is strictly from the mathematical programming side. The generalized Fritz John necessary optimality criteria (5) are the fundamental tools of the present work. By using these criteria a maximum principle is first obtained for a general non-convex mathematical programming problem. This result is then applied to obtain two maximum principles for discrete optimal control problems with constrained control and state variables.

1. Introduction

Let Ω be a subset of the n-dimensional Euclidean space E^n, let $\theta(x)$, $g(x)$ and $h(x)$ be respectively a scalar function, an ℓ-dimensional vector function, and an m-dimensional vector function, all defined on Ω. Consider the following mathematical programming problem

$$\begin{aligned} &\text{Maximize } \theta(x), \text{ subject to} \\ &x \in \Omega \\ &g(x) \geqq 0 \\ &h(x) = 0. \end{aligned} \tag{1}$$

If $\bar{x}$ is a solution of the above problem, what necessary optimality conditions does it satisfy? Without any further assumptions on problem (1), this question, in general, cannot be answered. For the case when Ω is convex, $\theta(x)$ and the components $g_i(x)$ of $g(x)$ are concave functions on Ω, and the components $h_i(x)$ of $h(x)$ are linear, then a saddle-point necessary optimality criterion (6),(7) is satisfied by the solution $\bar{x}$. Part of this saddle-point criterion may be interpreted as a maximum principle (8). However, the linearity of the $h_i(x)$ render this type of maximum principle useless for discrete optimal control problems described by nonlinear difference equations.

For the case when Ω is a closed set in E^n described by a finite number of inequalities, $f_i(x) \geq 0$, and $\theta(x)$, $f_i(x)$, $g_i(x)$ and $h_i(x)$ have continuous first partial derivatives, then the generalized Fritz-John (5) necessary optimality criteria are satisfied by the solution $\bar{x}$ to problem (1). These conditions are not of the maximum-principle type. However, by imposing some conditions on the set Ω, a maximum-principle can be derived from these conditions. This is done in Section 2. This maximum principle is then applied to a discrete optimal control problem. Under two sets of assumptions two different maximum principles are obtained. The first maximum principle, Section 3, is similar to that of Canon, Cullum and Polak (4, Theorem 6) but our assumptions are different from theirs. The second maximum principle, Section 4, is similar to that of Halkin (1), but again our assumptions are different from his.

Vector notation will be used. Vectors will be denoted by single letters. Subscripts may denote components of a vector or different vectors, depending on the context. A vector will be either a column or row vector. Thus we shall write the inner product of two vectors x and y in E^n simply as xy. The partial differential operator

$$\left[\frac{\partial}{\partial x_1}, \ldots, \frac{\partial}{\partial x_n}\right]$$

will be denoted by ∇ when applied to a function of x alone, e.g., $\nabla\theta(x)$, and by ∇_x when applied to a function of x and, say, u, e.g., $\nabla_x\varphi(x,u)$. When applied to a scalar function, ∇ yields an n-dimensional vector function of x, and when applied to an m-dimensional vector function, ∇ yields an m-by-n (Jacobian) matrix function of x. We shall say that a vector function $g(x)$ has a certain property, such as convexity or non-negativity, if and only if each of its components $g_i(x)$ have that property.

2. A Maximum Principle in E^n

We consider the following restricted version of problem (1) here

$$\begin{aligned} &\text{Maximize } \theta(x), \text{ subject to} \\ &x\epsilon\Omega = \{x \mid x\epsilon E^n,\ f(x) \geqq 0\} \\ &g(x) \geqq 0 \\ &h(x) = 0, \end{aligned} \tag{2}$$

where $f(x)$ is a k-dimensional continuous vector function on E^n, and $\theta(x)$, $f(x)$, $g(x)$ and $h(x)$ have continuous first partial derivatives on some open set containing Ω. By using the generalized Fritz John necessary optimality criteria (5) it is possible to derive a maximum principle for problem (2).

Theorem 1: Let $\bar{x}$ be a solution of problem (2) and let

$$J = \{i \mid f_i(\bar{x}) = 0\}. \tag{3}$$

Then there exist $\bar{\alpha}\epsilon E^1$, $\bar{v}\epsilon E^\ell$, $\bar{w}\epsilon E^m$, not all zero, such that

$$(\bar{\alpha}\nabla\theta(\bar{x}) + \bar{v}\nabla g(\bar{x}) + \bar{w}\nabla h(\bar{x}))(x - \bar{x}) \leqq 0 \text{ for all } x\epsilon\Omega \tag{4}$$

$$\bar{\alpha} \geqq 0 \tag{5}$$

$$\bar{v} \geqq 0 \tag{6}$$

$$\bar{v}g(\bar{x}) = 0 \tag{7}$$

provided that for the case when J is not empty any one of the following assumptions holds

(A) $\nabla f_i(\bar{x})$, $i\epsilon J$, form a pointed cone (that is, there exists a $y\epsilon E^n$ such that $\nabla f_i(\bar{x})y > 0$ for all $i\epsilon J$), and $f_i(x)$, $i\epsilon J$, are differentiably quasi-concave at $\bar{x}$ (that is, for $i\epsilon J$ and $x\epsilon\Omega$, $f_i(x) \geqq f_i(\bar{x})$ implies that $\nabla f_i(\bar{x})(x - \bar{x}) \geqq 0$); or

(B) $f_i(x)$, $i\epsilon J$, are concave and have a relative interior (that is, there exists an $\hat{x}$ such that $f_i(\hat{x}) > 0$, $i\epsilon J$); or

(C) $f_i(x)$, $i\epsilon J$, are strictly concave and there is at least another $\tilde{x}\epsilon\Omega$ different from $\bar{x}$.

Remark: None of the assumptions (A), (B) or (C) above necessarily imply that the set Ω is convex. If however $J = \{1,2,\ldots,k\}$, then assumptions (B) and (C) imply that Ω is convex.

Proof: We first show either of assumptions (B) or (C) implies (A). If (B) holds then

$$f_i(x) - f_i(\bar{x}) \leqq \nabla f_i(\bar{x})(x - \bar{x}), \; i\epsilon J,$$

and hence $f_i(x)$, $i\epsilon J$, are differentiably quasi-concave at $\bar{x}$. Since $f_i(\bar{x}) = 0$, and $f_i(\hat{x}) > 0$, for $i\epsilon J$, we have that $0 < \nabla f_i(\bar{x})(\hat{x} - \bar{x})$ and hence $\nabla f_i(\bar{x})$, $i\epsilon J$, form a pointed cone (take $y = \hat{x} - \bar{x}$, then $\nabla f_i(\bar{x})y > 0$, $i\epsilon J$). If (C) holds then

$$f_i(x) - f_i(\bar{x}) < \nabla f_i(\bar{x})(x - \bar{x}), \; x \neq \bar{x}, \; i\epsilon J,$$

and hence $f_i(x)$, $i\epsilon J$, are differentiably quasi-concave at $\bar{x}$. Since $f_i(\bar{x}) = 0$, and $f_i(\tilde{x}) \geqq 0$, for $i\epsilon J$, we have that $0 < \nabla f_i(\bar{x})(\tilde{x} - \bar{x})$ and hence $\nabla f_i(\bar{x})$, $i\epsilon J$, form a pointed cone.

We establish the theorem now under assumption (A). According to the necessary Fritz John optimality criteria (5) there must exist $\bar{\alpha}\epsilon E^1$, $\bar{v}\epsilon E^\ell$, $\bar{w}\epsilon E^m$, $\bar{u}\epsilon E^k$, not all zero, such that

$$\bar{\alpha}\nabla\theta(\bar{x}) + \bar{v}\nabla g(\bar{x}) + \bar{w}\nabla h(\bar{x}) + \bar{u}\nabla f(\bar{x}) = 0 \qquad (8)$$

$$f(\bar{x}) \geqq 0 \qquad (9)$$

$$\bar{\alpha} \geqq 0 \qquad (10)$$

$$\bar{u} \geqq 0 \qquad (11)$$

$$\bar{v} \geqq 0 \qquad (12)$$

$$\bar{u}f(\bar{x}) = 0 \qquad (13)$$

$$\bar{v}g(\bar{x}) = 0 \qquad (14)$$

Relations (10), (12) and (14) are identical to (5), (6) and (7). It remains to show that $\bar{\alpha}$, $\bar{v}$, $\bar{w}$ cannot all vanish and that (4) holds. From (3), (9), (11) and (13) we have that

$$\bar{u}_i = 0, \; i\notin J. \qquad (15)$$

Now if J is empty, then $\bar{u} = 0$, and $\bar{\alpha}$, $\bar{v}$, $\bar{w}$ cannot all vanish. Suppose J is not empty, then if $\bar{\alpha}$, $\bar{v}$, $\bar{w}$ are all zero, it follows from (8), (11) and (15) that

$$\sum_{i\epsilon J} \bar{u}_i \nabla f_i(\bar{x}) = 0, \; \bar{u}_i \geqq 0, \; i\epsilon J, \qquad (16)$$

and not all $\bar{u}_i$, $i\epsilon J$, are zero. But by assumption (A) there exists a $y\epsilon E^n$ such that

$$\nabla f_i(\bar{x})y > 0, \quad i\epsilon J.$$

Hence

$$\sum_{i\epsilon J} \bar{u}_i \nabla f_i(\bar{x})y > 0.$$

This contradicts (16), and $\bar{\alpha}$, $\bar{v}$, $\bar{w}$ cannot all be zero.

Now from (8) and (15) we have that

$$(\bar{\alpha}\nabla\theta(\bar{x}) + \bar{v}\nabla g(\bar{x}) + \bar{w}h(\bar{x}))(x - \bar{x}) = -\sum_{i\epsilon J} \bar{u}_i \nabla f_i(\bar{x})(x - \bar{x}). \quad (17)$$

We also have from the definition of Ω and (3) that

$$f_i(x) \geq f_i(\bar{x}), \quad i\epsilon J, \text{ for all } x\epsilon\Omega.$$

Hence by assumption (A) we have that

$$\nabla f_i(\bar{x})(x - \bar{x}) \geq 0, \quad i\epsilon J, \text{ for all } x\epsilon\Omega,$$

and by (11) we get that

$$\sum_{i\epsilon J} \bar{u}_i \nabla f_i(\bar{x})(x - \bar{x}) \geq 0, \text{ for all } x\epsilon\Omega. \quad (18)$$

Relations (17) and (18) imply (4). Q.E.D.

3. First Maximum Principle for Discrete Optimal Control Problems

We shall consider here an optimization problem for a system described by nonlinear difference equations. We shall employ Halkin's formulation (1). Our assumptions however will be different from his, and also the maximum principle of this section, Theorem 2, will be different from his (1, (3.1)) for the general case. However, for the more specific case where the control variables appear linearly in the difference equations, this maximum principle (Corollary below) becomes similar to his, although our assumptions for this case also are still somewhat different from his. The present maximum principle has also been derived by Canon, Cullum and Polak (4, Theorem 6) under different assumptions and by a completely different approach.

We begin by describing the problem. (The reader is warned here that the letter symbols of this section do not represent the same quantities as in the previous section. Each symbol is defined as it appears.) The state of the system is described by the state vectors $x_o, x_1, \ldots, x_k$, which are elements of E^n, the system is controlled by the control vectors $u_o, u_1, \ldots, u_{k-1}$, which are elements of E^r, and time will assume the discrete values 0, 1, ..., k. (For mnemonic purposes, the subscript i will refer to time steps, while the subscript j will refer to vector components at a specific time step.) The objective of the problem is to

$$\text{Maximize } g_o(x_k) \tag{19}$$

subject to the initial conditions

$$-h(x_o) = 0, \tag{20}$$

the difference equations

$$-x_{i+1} + x_i + f_i(x_i, u_i) = 0, \; i = 0, \ldots, k-1, \tag{21}$$

the terminal conditions

$$g(x_k) = 0, \tag{22}$$

the state variable constraints

$$e_i(x_i) \geq 0, \; i = 0, \ldots, k, \tag{23}$$

and the control variable constraints

$$u_i \epsilon \Omega_i = \{u_i | c_i(u_i) \geq 0\}, \; i = 0, \ldots, k-1, \tag{24}$$

where $g_o(x_k)$, the ℓ_o components of $h(x_o)$, the n components of each $f_i(x_i, u_i)$, the ℓ_k components of $g(x_k)$, the n_i components of each $e_i(x_i)$, and the m_i components of each $c_i(u_i)$ have continuous first partial derivatives over the entire appropriate Euclidean spaces.

We shall assume, for the above problem, that the control $\bar{u}_o, \ldots, \bar{u}_{k-1}$ is optimal and that the corresponding optimal state is given by $\bar{x}_o, \ldots, \bar{x}_k$. Let

$$J_i = \{j | c_{ij}(\bar{u}_i) = 0\}, \tag{25}$$

where $c_{ij}(u_i)$ denotes the j-th component of the m_i-dimensional vector function $c_i(u_i)$. In analogy to assumptions (A), (B) and (C) we shall need one of the following assumptions for each non-empty J_i:

(A1) For i = 0, ..., k-1, $\nabla c_{ij}(\bar{u})$, $j \epsilon J_i$, form a pointed cone (that is, for i = 0, ..., k-1, there exist

$y_i \epsilon E^r$ such that $\nabla c_{ij}(\bar{u}_i)y_i > 0$ for all $j\epsilon J_i$) and $c_{ij}(u_i)$, $j\epsilon J_i$, are differentiably quasi-concave at $\bar{u}_i$ (that is, for $i\epsilon J_i$ and $u_i \epsilon \Omega_i$, $c_{ij}(u_i) \geqq c_{ij}(\bar{u}_i)$ implies that $\nabla c_{ij}(\bar{u}_i)(u_i - \bar{u}_i) \geqq 0$).

(B1) For $i = 0, \ldots, k-1$, $c_{ij}(u_i)$, $j\epsilon J_i$, are concave and have a relative interior (that is, for $i = 0, \ldots, k-1$, there exists a $\hat{u}_i$ such that $c_{ij}(\hat{u}_i) > 0$ for all $j\epsilon J_i$).

(C1) For $i = 0, \ldots, k-1$, $c_{ij}(u_i)$, $j\epsilon J_i$, are strictly concave and there is at least another $\tilde{u}_i \epsilon \Omega_i$ different from $\bar{u}_i$.

With any of the above assumptions it is possible to establish the following maximum principle for the discrete optimal control problem.

Theorem 2: Let $\bar{u}_o, \ldots, \bar{u}_{k-1}, \bar{x}_o, \ldots, \bar{x}_k$, be a solution of (19) to (24), and let assumption (A1), (B1) or (C1) hold. Then there exist $\bar{p}_i \epsilon E^n$, $i = 1, \ldots, k$, $\bar{q}_i \epsilon E^{n_i}$, $i = 0, \ldots, k$, $\bar{a} \epsilon E^{\ell o}$, $\bar{b} \epsilon E^{\ell k}$, and a scalar $\bar{\beta}_o$, not all zero, such that

$$\bar{p}_{i+1} \nabla u_i f_i(\bar{x}_i, \bar{u}_i)(u_i - \bar{u}_i) \leqq 0 \qquad (26)$$

for all $u_i \epsilon \Omega_i$, $i = 0, \ldots, k-1$,

$$-\bar{p}_i + \bar{p}_{i+1} + \bar{p}_{i+1} \nabla x_i f_i(\bar{x}_i, \bar{u}_i) + \bar{q}_i \nabla e_i(\bar{x}_i) = 0, \quad i = 1, \ldots, k-1 \qquad (27)$$

$$\bar{q}_i e_i(\bar{x}_i) = 0, \; i = 0, \ldots, k, \qquad (28)$$

$$\bar{q}_i \geqq 0, \; i = 0, \ldots, k. \qquad (29)$$

$$-\bar{a} \nabla h(\bar{x}_o) + \bar{p}_1 + \bar{p}_1 \nabla x_o f_o(\bar{x}_o, \bar{u}_o) + \bar{q}_o \nabla e_o(\bar{x}_o) = 0 \qquad (30)$$

$$\bar{\beta}_o \nabla g_o(\bar{x}_k) - \bar{p}_k + \bar{b} \nabla g(\bar{x}_k) + \bar{q}_k \nabla e_k(\bar{x}_k) = 0 \qquad (31)$$

$$\bar{\beta}_o \geqq 0 \qquad (32)$$

Proof: Either of assumption (B1) or (C1) implies assumption (A1). This follows in the same manner as in the proof of Theorem 1 above. We apply now Theorem 1. It is easy to see that assumption (A1) is equivalent to assumption (A). For there exist $y_i \epsilon E^r$, $i = 0, \ldots, k-1$, such that

$$\nabla c_{ij}(\bar{u}_i)y_i > 0, \text{ for all } j\epsilon J_i.$$

By picking $y = (y_o, y_1, \ldots, y_{k-1}, 0) \epsilon E^{kr + (k+1)n}$ we have that $\nabla c_{ij}(\bar{u}_i)$, $j\epsilon J_i$, $i = 0, \ldots, k-1$, form a pointed cone in the overall $(kr + (k+1)n)$-dimensional space of $u_o, \ldots, u_{k-1}, x_o, \ldots, x_k$.

Theorem 1 may now be invoked to get the following result. There exist $\bar{p}_i \epsilon E^n$, $i = 1, \ldots, k$, $\bar{q}_i \epsilon E^{n_i}$,

$i = 0, \ldots, k$, $\bar{a}\epsilon E^{\ell_o}$, $\bar{b}\epsilon E^{\ell_k}$, and a scalar $\bar{\beta}_o$, not all zero, such that for all $u_i \epsilon \Omega_i$, $i = 0, \ldots, k-1$, and all $x_i \epsilon E^n$, $i = 0, \ldots, k$ we have that

$$[-\bar{a}\nabla h(\bar{x}_o) + \bar{p}_1 + \bar{p}_1 \nabla_{x_o} f_o(\bar{x}_o, \bar{u}_o) + \bar{q}_o \nabla e_o(\bar{x}_o)](x_o - \bar{x}_o)$$

$$+\sum_{i=1}^{k-1} [-\bar{p}_i + \bar{p}_{i+1} + \bar{p}_{i+1} \nabla_{x_i} f_i(\bar{x}_i, \bar{u}_i) + \bar{q}_i \nabla e_i(\bar{x}_i)](x_i - \bar{x}_i)$$

$$+ [\bar{\beta}_o \nabla g_o(\bar{x}_k) - \bar{p}_k + \bar{b}\nabla g(\bar{x}_k) + \bar{q}_k \nabla e_k(\bar{x}_k)](x_k - \bar{x}_k)$$

$$+\sum_{i=0}^{k-1} [\bar{p}_{i+1} \nabla_{u_i} f_i(\bar{x}_i, \bar{u}_i)](u_i - \bar{u}_i) \leqq 0 \qquad (33)$$

$$\bar{\beta}_o \geqq 0 \qquad (34)$$

$$\bar{q}_i e_i(\bar{x}_i) = 0 \qquad (35)$$

$$\bar{q}_i \geqq 0. \qquad (36)$$

Conditions (28), (29), and (32) are identical to conditions (35), (36) and (34). Condition (26) follows from (33) by setting $x_i = \bar{x}_i$, $i = 0, \ldots, k$, and all u_i, except the one under consideration, equal to $\bar{u}_i$. Condition (27) follows from (33) as follows. Set $x_o = \bar{x}_o$, $x_k = \bar{x}_k$, $u_i = \bar{u}_i$, $i = 0, \ldots, k-1$, and all x_i, except the one under consideration, equal to $\bar{x}_i$. For this x_i, set each of its components equal to the components of $\bar{x}_i$ except one, say $(x_i)_j$. Set this once $(x_i)_j > (\bar{x}_i)_j$ and once $(x_i)_j < (\bar{x}_i)_j$. By repeating this for all $j = 1, \ldots, n$, condition (27) is obtained. Conditions (30) and (31) follow from (33) in a similar manner. Q.E.D.

Corollary: Under the assumptions of Theorem 2, if $f_i(\bar{x}_i, u_i)$, $i = 0, \ldots, k-1$, are linear in u_i, then condition (26) may be replaced by

$$\bar{p}_{i+1} f_i(\bar{x}_i, u_i) \leqq \bar{p}_{i+1} f_i(\bar{x}_i, \bar{u}_i) \text{ for all } u_i \epsilon \Omega_i, \quad i = 0, \ldots, k-1. \qquad (37)$$

This Corollary follows from Theorem 2 by observing that if $f_i(\bar{x}_i, u_i)$ is linear in u_i, then

$$\nabla_{u_i} f_i(\bar{x}_i, \bar{u}_i)(u_i - \bar{u}_i) = f_i(\bar{x}_i, u_i) - f_i(\bar{x}_i, \bar{u}_i).$$

Note that $f_i(x_i, u_i)$ may be nonlinear in x_i here.

4. Second Maximum Principle for Discrete Optimal Control Problems

In this section we derive a maximum principle which is essentially identical to that of Halkin (1) and Canon, Cullum and Polak (4), but under different assumptions from theirs. Our results also include state variable constraints. In order to avoid somewhat complicated arguments and assumptions we restrict our $f_i(x_i, u_i)$ as follows

$$f_i(x_i, u_i) = f_{1i}(x_i) + f_{2i}(u_i), \ i = 0, \ldots, k\text{-}1. \quad (38)$$

The control variables u_i satisfy

$$u_i \epsilon \Gamma_i \subset E^r, \ i = 0, \ldots, k\text{-}1, \quad (39)$$

where Γ_i are arbitrary, non-empty sets in E^r. As in the previous section, we require that $g_o(x_k)$, $h(x_o)$, $f_i(x_i, u_i)$, $g(x_k)$, $e_i(x_i)$ all have continuous first partial derivatives. Define

$$\Lambda_i(\overline{x}_i) = \{z_i | z_i = f_i(\overline{x}_i, u_i), u_i \epsilon \Gamma_i\}.$$

We shall assume that $\Lambda_i(\overline{x})$ can be represented as follows

$$\Lambda_i(\overline{x}_i) = \{z_i | z_i \epsilon E^n, s_i(z_i) \geq 0\}, \ i = 0, \ldots, k\text{-}1, \quad (40)$$

where $s_i(z)$ are vector functions defined on E^n that have continuous first partial derivatives. Call the control problem (19) to (24) with the restriction (38), and with (39) replacing (24), the Modified Control Problem. Let $\overline{u}_o, \ldots, \overline{u}_{k-1}, \overline{x}_o, \ldots, \overline{x}_k$, be a solution. Define

$$z_i = f_i(\overline{x}_i, u_i), \ i = 0, \ldots, k\text{-}1 \quad (41)$$

$$\overline{z}_i = f_i(\overline{x}_i, \overline{u}_i), \ i = 0, \ldots, k\text{-}1 \quad (42)$$

$$I_i = \{j | s_{ij}(\overline{z}_i) = 0\}, \ i = 0, \ldots, k\text{-}1. \quad (43)$$

We need now one of the following assumptions.

(A2) For $i = 0, \ldots, k\text{-}1$, $\nabla s_{ij}(\overline{z}_i)$, $j \epsilon I_i$, form a pointed cone and $s_{ij}(z_i)$, $j \epsilon I_i$, are differentiably quasi-concave at $\overline{z}_i$.

(B2) For $i = 0, \ldots, k\text{-}1$, $s_{ij}(z_i)$, $j \epsilon I_i$, are concave and have a relative interior.

(C2) For $i = 0, \ldots, k\text{-}1$, $s_{ij}(z_i)$, $j \epsilon I_i$, are strictly concave and there is at least another $\tilde{z}_i \epsilon \Lambda_i(\overline{x}_i)$.

Theorem 3: Let $\bar{u}_0, \ldots, \bar{u}_{k-1}, \bar{x}_0, \ldots, \bar{x}_k$, be a solution of the Modified Control Problem (that is, (19) to (24) with the restriction (38), and (39) replacing (24)), let (40) hold and let assumption (A2), (B2) or (C2) hold. Then there exist $\bar{p}_i \epsilon E^n$, $i = 1, \ldots, k$, $\bar{q}_i \epsilon E^{n_i}$, $i = 0, \ldots, k$, $\bar{a} \epsilon E^{\ell_0}$, $\bar{b} \epsilon E^{\ell_k}$, and a scalar $\bar{\beta}_0$, not all zero, such that (37) and (27) to (32) hold.

Proof: We observe first that

$$f_i(x_i, u_i) = f_{1i}(x_i) + f_{2i}(u_i) = f_{1i}(x_i) - f_{1i}(\bar{x}_i) + z_i, \quad (44)$$

and that $u_i \epsilon \Gamma_i$ implies that $z_i \epsilon \Lambda_i(\bar{x}_i)$. Hence the Modified Control Problem can be written as follows

$$g_0(\bar{x}_k) = \underset{x_0,..,x_k,z_0,..,z_{k-1}}{\text{Maximum}} \left\{ g_0(x_k) \;\middle|\; \begin{array}{l} -h(x_0) = 0 \\ -x_{i+1} + x_i + \\ \;f_{1i}(x_i) - f_{1i}(\bar{x}_i) + \\ \;z_i = 0, \\ i = 0, \ldots, k-1 \\ z_i \epsilon \Lambda_i(\bar{x}_i), \; i=0,..,k-1 \\ e_i(x_i) \geq 0, \\ \;i = 0, \ldots, k \\ g(x_k) = 0 \end{array} \right\} \quad (45)$$

Application of Theorem 1 to this problem yields $\bar{p}_i \epsilon E^n$, $\bar{q}_i \epsilon E^{n_i}$, $\bar{a} \epsilon E^{\ell_0}$, $\bar{b} \epsilon E^{\ell_k}$, $\bar{\beta}_0 \epsilon E^1$, not all zero, such that for $z_i \epsilon \Lambda_i(\bar{x}_i)$, $i = 0, \ldots, k-1$, and all $x_i \epsilon E^n$, $i = 0, \ldots, k$, we have that

$$\begin{aligned} &[-\bar{a} \nabla h(\bar{x}_0) + \bar{p}_1 + \bar{p}_1 \nabla_{x_0} f_0(\bar{x}_0, \bar{u}_0) + \bar{q}_0 \nabla e_0(\bar{x}_0)](x_0 - \bar{x}_0) \\ &+ \sum_{i=1}^{k-1} [-\bar{p}_i + \bar{p}_{i+1} + \bar{p}_{i+1} \nabla_{x_i} f_i(\bar{x}_i, \bar{u}_i) + \bar{q}_i \nabla e_i(\bar{x}_i)](x_i - \bar{x}_i) \\ &+ [\bar{\beta}_0 \nabla g_0(\bar{x}_k) - \bar{p}_k + \bar{b} \nabla g(\bar{x}_k) + \bar{q}_k \nabla e_k(\bar{x}_k)](x_k - \bar{x}_k) \\ &+ \sum_{i=0}^{k-1} \bar{p}_{i+1}(z_i - \bar{z}_i) \leq 0, \end{aligned} \quad (46)$$

$$\overline{\beta}_o \geq 0 \qquad (47)$$

$$\overline{q}_i e_i(\overline{x}_i) = 0 \qquad (48)$$

$$\overline{q}_i \geq 0 \qquad (49)$$

The necessary conditions (27) to (32) follow from the above as in Theorem 2. We get (37) from (46) by setting $x_o = \overline{x}_o$, $x_i = \overline{x}_i$, $x_k = \overline{x}_k$ and all z_i except the one under consideration equal to $\overline{z}_i$. This gives

$$\overline{p}_{i+1}(z_i - \overline{z}_i) \leq 0 \text{ for all } z_i \epsilon \Lambda_i(\overline{x}_i),\ i = 0, \ldots, k-1. \qquad (50)$$

By making use of the definition of $\Lambda_i(\overline{x})$, (41) and (42), we get (37). Q.E.D.

Finally, we point out the fact that none of the assumptions (A2), (B2) or (C2) imply necessarily that the set $\Lambda_i(\overline{x}_i)$ is convex as is the case in both (1) and (4).

References

(1) H. Halkin: "A maximum principle of the Pontryagin type for systems described by nonlinear difference equations", SIAM J. Control, 4, 1966, 90-111.

(2) H. Halkin: "An abstract framework for the theory of process optimization", Bull. Amer. Math. Soc., 72, 1966, 677-678.

(3) H. Halkin, L. W. Neustadt: "General necessary conditions for optimization problems", Proc. Nat. Acad. Sci. USA, 56, 1966, 1066-1071.

(4) M. Canon, C. Cullum, E. Polak: "Constrained minimization problems in finite-dimensional spaces", SIAM J. Control, 4, 1966, 528-547.

(5) O. L. Mangasarian, S. Fromovitz: "The Fritz John necessary optimality conditions in the presence of equality and inequality constraints", J. Math. Anal. Appl., 17, 1967, 37-47.

(6) S. Karlin: "Mathematical methods and theory in games, programming, and economics", Vol. 1, Addison-Wesley, Reading, Mass., 1959, 201-203.

(7) H. Uzawa: "The Kuhn-Tucker theorem in concave programming", in "Studies in linear and non-linear programming", editors, K. J. Arrow, L. Hurwicz, H. Uzawa, Stanford Univ. Press, Stanford, Calif., 1958, 32-37.

(8) H. Halkin: Private communication, April 1965.

CONSTRAINED MINIMIZATION UNDER VECTOR-VALUED CRITERIA IN LINEAR TOPOLOGICAL SPACES

N. O. Da Cunha
Technical Institute of Aeronautics
San Jose dos Campos
Sao Paulo, Brazil
and
E. Polak
Electronics Research Laboratory
Department of Electrical Engineering
and Computer Sciences
University of California, Berkeley

Introduction

Vector criterion optimization problems arise when several optimality criteria are relevant to a physical situation and their relative importance is not obvious. The first formulation of such a problem was given by the economist Pareto in 1896 (1), and since then discussions of vector valued optimization have kept reappearing in economics, operations research and, more recently, in control engineering. References (2), (3), (4), (5), (6), (7) form a representative sampling of the related literature in these fields.

In this paper we extend some of the necessary conditions and theorems on "scalarization" (i.e., the conversion of the problem into a family of optimization problems with a scalar criterion), which we gave in (7) for problems defined in R^n, to linear topological spaces. It will be observed that our derivation of necessary conditions follows the well trodden path established in (8), (9), (10).

The problem of scalarization is very important,

since whenever scalarization is possible, standard non-linear programming algorithms become applicable. We concentrate on scalarization by weighting the components of the vector cost with strictly positive coefficients into a real valued function, since this represents the physically most meaningful case. Our major result in this area is theorem (4), for which we give a proof suggested by Prof. H. Halkin of University of California, San Diego, and which is shorter than our original proof in (7) and (11).

I. The Basic Problem and Necessary Conditions

Let E^s, where s is a positive integer, be the s-dimensional Euclidean space with the usual norm topology. Let $\mathcal{X}$ be a real, linear topological space; let $h : \mathcal{X} \to E^p$ and $r : \mathcal{X} \to E^m$ be continuous functions, and let Ω be a subset of $\mathcal{X}$. Furthermore, suppose that we are given a partial ordering in E^p with the property that for every y in E^p there exists an index set $J(y) \subset \{1, 2, \ldots, p\}$ and a ball $B(\varepsilon_0, y)$ with center y and radius $\varepsilon_0 > 0$ such that every $\tilde{y} \in B(\varepsilon_0, y)$ satisfies $\tilde{y}^i < y^i$ for all $i \in J(y)$, if and only if $\tilde{y} \prec y$ and $y \not\prec \tilde{y}$.

Definition 1: We shall call the index set $J(y)$ and the ball $B(\varepsilon_0, y)$, defined above, the critical index set and the critical neighborhood for the point y, respectively.

Examples: Suppose that $y_1 \prec y_2$ if and only if $y_1^i \leq y_2^i$ for $i = 1, 2, \ldots, p$, then we see that $J(y) = \{1, 2, \ldots, p\}$ for all $y \in E^p$. Again, suppose that $p > 1$ and $y_1 \prec y_2$ if and only if $\mathrm{Max}\{y_1^i \mid i = 1, 2, \ldots, p\} \leq \mathrm{Max}\{y_2^i = 1, 2, \ldots, p\}$. Now $J(y) \neq \{1, 2, \ldots, p\}$ and it is seen to change from point to point in E^p.

The problems we wish to consider can always be cast in the following standard form.

Basic Problem: Find a point $\hat{x}$ in $\mathcal{X}$, such that: (i) $\hat{x} \in \Omega$ and $r(\hat{x}) = 0$; (ii) for every x in Ω with $r(x) = 0$, the relation $h(x) \prec h(\hat{x})$ implies that $h(\hat{x}) \prec h(x)$.

As a first step in obtaining necessary conditions for a point $\hat{x}$ to be a solution to the Basic Problem, we introduce "linear" approximations to the set Ω and to the continuous functions h and r at $\hat{x}$.

Definition 2: We shall say that a convex cone $C(\hat{x}, \Omega)$ is a conical approximation to the constraint set Ω at the point $\hat{x} \in \Omega$ with respect to the functions h and r, if there exist continuous linear functions $h'(\hat{x}): \mathcal{X} \to E^p$ and $r'(\hat{x})$: $\mathcal{X} \to E^m$ such that for any finite collection $\{x_1, x_2, \ldots, x_k\}$ of linearly independent vectors in $C(\hat{x}, \Omega)$, there exists a continuous map ζ_ε from $\varepsilon S \triangleq \text{co}\{\varepsilon x_1, \varepsilon x_2, \ldots, \varepsilon x_k\}$, into $\Omega - \hat{x}$, for each ε, $0 \leq \varepsilon \leq 1$, and continuous functions $o_{h,\varepsilon}$: $\mathcal{X} \to E^p$ and $o_{r,\varepsilon}: \mathcal{X} \to E^m$, which satisfy (1), (2), (3) and (4) below:

$$\|o_{h,\varepsilon}(\varepsilon x)\|/\varepsilon \to 0 \text{ as } \varepsilon \to 0 \text{ uniformly for } x \in S \tag{1}$$

$$\|o_{r,\varepsilon}(\varepsilon x)\|/\epsilon \to 0 \text{ as } \varepsilon \to 0 \text{ uniformly for } x \in S \tag{2}$$

$$h(\hat{x} + \zeta_\varepsilon(x)) = h(\hat{x}) + h'(\hat{x})(x) + o_{h,\varepsilon}(x),$$

$$\text{for all } x \in \varepsilon S,\ 0 \leq \varepsilon \leq 1 \tag{3}$$

$$r(\hat{x} + \zeta_\varepsilon(x)) = r(\hat{x}) + r'(\hat{x})(x) + o_{r,\varepsilon}(x),$$

$$\text{for all } x \in \varepsilon S,\ 0 \leq \varepsilon \leq 1 \tag{4}$$

Theorem 1: If $\hat{x}$ is a solution to the Basic Problem, if $C(\hat{x}, \Omega)$ is a conical approximation to Ω at $\hat{x}$, and if $J(h(\hat{x}))$ is the set of critical indices for $h(\hat{x})$, then there exist a vector μ in E^p and a vector η in E^m such that

(i) $\mu^i \leq 0$ for $i \in J(h(\hat{x}))$ and $\mu^i = 0$ for $i \in \bar{J}(h(\hat{x}))$;

(ii) $(\mu, \eta) \neq 0$;

(iii) $\langle \mu, h'(\hat{x})(x) \rangle + \langle \eta, r'(\hat{x})(x) \rangle \leq 0$ for all $x \in \overline{C(\hat{x}, \Omega)}$,

where $h'(\hat{x})$, $r'(\hat{x})$ are the linear continuous maps appearing in the definition of $C(\hat{x}, \Omega)$.

Proof: Let $\hat{x}$ be a solution to the Basic Problem. Let $J(h(\hat{x}))$ and $B(\varepsilon_0, h(\hat{x}))$ be, respectively, the critical index set and the critical neighborhood of $h(\hat{x})$ in E^p. Also, let q be the cardinality of $J(h(\hat{x}))$ and let f, $f'(\hat{x})$ be continuous functions from $\mathcal{X}$ into E^q defined by $f(x) = (f^1(x), \ldots, f^q(x))$, $f'(\hat{x})(x) = f'^1(\hat{x})(x), \ldots, f'^q(\hat{x})(x))$, where $f^j = h^{i_j}$, $f'^j(\hat{x}) = h'^{i_j}(x)$, with $i_j \in J(h(\hat{x}))$ for $j = 1, 2, \ldots, q$ and $i_\alpha > i_\beta$ when $\alpha > \beta$. Now let

$$A(\hat{x}) = \{y \in E^q \mid y = f'(\hat{x})(x), \ x \in C(\hat{x}, \Omega)\}, \tag{5}$$

$$B(\hat{x}) = \{z \in E^m \mid z = r'(\hat{x})(x), \ x \in C(\hat{x}, \Omega)\}, \tag{6}$$

$$K(\hat{x}) = \{u \in E^q \times E^m \mid u = (f'(\hat{x})(x), \ r'(\hat{x})(x)), \ x \in C(\hat{x}, \Omega)\} \tag{7}$$

$$R = \{(y, 0) \in E^q \times E^m \mid y = (y^1, y^2, \ldots y^q), \ y^1 < 0, \ y^2 < 0, \ldots, y^q < 0, \ 0 \in E^m\}. \tag{8}$$

Examining (i), (ii), and (iii), we observe that if we define $\mu^i = 0$ for $i \in \overline{J}(h(\hat{x}))$, the complement of $J(h(\hat{x}))$ in $\{1, 2, \ldots, p\}$, then the claim of the theorem is that the convex sets $K(\hat{x})$ and R are separated in $E^q \times E^m$.

We now construct a proof by contradiction. Suppose that $K(\hat{x})$ and R are not separated in $E^q \times E^m$. Then,

(I) The convex sets $K(\hat{x})$ and R are not disjoint, i.e., $R \cap K(\hat{x}) \neq \phi$, the empty set.

(II) The convex cone $B(\hat{x})$ in E^m contains the origin as an interior point and hence $B(\hat{x}) = E^m$.

Statement (II) follows from the fact that if 0 is not an interior point of the convex set $B(\hat{x})$, then by the separation theorem (12), there exists a nonzero vector η_0 in E^m such that

$$\langle \eta_0, z \rangle \leq 0 \text{ for all } z \in B(\hat{x}). \tag{9}$$

Clearly, the vector $(0, \eta_0)$ in $E^q \times E^m$ separates R from $A(\hat{x}) \times B(\hat{x})$ and hence from $K(\hat{x})$, since $K(\hat{x}) \subset A(\hat{x}) \times B(\hat{x})$, contradicting our assumption that R and $K(\hat{x})$ are not separated.

Since the origin in E^m belongs to the non-void interior of $B(\hat{x})$ we can construct a simplex Σ in $B(\hat{x})$, with vertices $z_1, z_2, \ldots, z_{m+1}$, such that

(i) 0 is in the interior of Σ;

(ii) there exists a set of vectors $\{x_1, x_2, \ldots, x_{m+1}\}$ in $C(\hat{x}, \Omega)$ satisfying:

$$\text{(a)} \quad z_i = r'(\hat{x})(x_i) \text{ for } i = 1, 2, \ldots, m+1; \tag{10}$$

$$\text{(b)}\quad \zeta_1(x) \in ((\Omega - \hat{x}) \cap N) \text{ for all } x \in co\{x_1, x_2, \ldots, x_{m+1}\} \tag{11}$$

where ζ_1 is the map entering the definition of a conical approximation and N is a neighborhood of 0 in $\mathcal{X}$ such that $h(\hat{x} + N) \subset B(\varepsilon_0, h(\hat{x}))$, where $B(\varepsilon_0, h(\hat{x}))$ is the critical neighborhood for $h(\hat{x})$. (Clearly, such an N exists since h is continuous).

$$\text{(c)}\quad y_i = f'(\hat{x})(x_i) < 0 \quad \text{for } i = 1, 2, \ldots, m+1. \tag{12}$$

Let $\ell_1, \ell_2, \ldots, \ell_m$ be any basis in E^m, and let $Z: E^m \to E^m$, $X: E^m \to \mathcal{X}$ be linear operators defined by $Z\ell_i = (z_i - z_{m+1})$, $X\ell_i = (x_i - x_{m+1})$, respectively, with $i = 1, 2, \ldots, m$. Since $0 \in \text{int } \Sigma$, the vectors $(z_i - z_{m+1})$, $i = 1, 2, \ldots, m$, are linearly independent and hence the operator Z is nonsingular. Let Z^{-1} denote the inverse of Z. Clearly the map $z \to XZ^{-1}(z - z_{m+1}) + x_{m+1}$ from Σ into $co\{x_1, x_2, \ldots, x_{m+1}\}$ is continuous.

For $0 < \alpha \leq 1$, we now define a continuous map G_α from the simplex $\alpha\,\Sigma$ into E^m by

$$G_\alpha(\alpha z) = r(\hat{x} + \zeta_\alpha(\alpha\, XZ^{-1}(z - z_{m+1}) + \alpha x_{m+1})), \tag{13}$$

where ζ_α is the map specified by Definition 1.

Since $r(\hat{x}) = 0$, $r'(\hat{x})\,X = Z$, and $r'(\hat{x})(x_{m+1}) = z_{m+1}$, (13) becomes

$$G_\alpha(\alpha z) = \alpha z + o_r(\alpha\, XZ^{-1}(z - z_{m+1}) + \alpha x_{m+1}). \tag{14}$$

It now follows from (2) and Brouwer's fixed point theorem (13) that there exists an $\alpha_0 \in (0, 1]$ such that for every $\alpha \in (0, \alpha_0]$ we can find a $z_\alpha \in \Sigma$ satisfying $G_\alpha(\alpha\, z_\alpha) = 0$. Since by construction

$$f'^{i}(\hat{x})(XZ^{-1}(z - z_{m+1}) + x_{m+1}) < 0 \text{ for all } z \in \Sigma \text{ and } i = 1, 2, \ldots, q, \tag{15}$$

there exist by (1) $\alpha_1 > 0$, $\alpha_2 > 0, \ldots, \alpha_q > 0$ such that

$$f^i(\hat{x} + \zeta_\alpha(\alpha XZ^{-1}(x - z_{m+1}) + \alpha\, x_{m+1})) < f^i(\hat{x}) \text{ for all } z \in \Sigma,$$

$$\alpha \in (0, \alpha_i], \text{ and } i = 1, 2, \ldots, q, \tag{16}$$

Let α^* be the minimum of $\{\alpha_0, \alpha, \ldots, \alpha_q\}$, and let $z^* \in \Sigma$ satisfy $G_{\alpha^*}(\alpha^* z^*) = 0$. Then, $x^* = \hat{x} + \xi_{\alpha^*}(\alpha^* XZ^{-1}(z^* - z_{m+1}) + \alpha^* x_{m+1})$ is in Ω, $r(x^*) = 0$, $h(x^*) \nless h(\hat{x})$, and $h(\hat{x}) \nless h(x^*)$, which contradicts our assumption that $\hat{x}$, is a solution. Hence the theorem is true.

II. An Application to Optimal Control

We now illustrate the theory developed in the preceding section by obtaining a Pontryagin type maximum principle for an optimal control problem with a vector valued cost function.

The Optimal Control Problem: Let $z = (y, x)$, with $y \in E^p$, $x \in E^n$. Given a differential system

$$\frac{dz(t)}{dt} = F(x(t), u(t), t \in [t_o, t_f], \tag{17}$$

where $u(t) \in E^m$ is the control and $F = (c, f)$ is a map from $E^n \times E^m$ into E^{p+n} ($c(x, u) \in E^p$, $f(x, u) \in E^n$), continuous in u and continuously differentiable in x. Find a control $\hat{u}(t)$ and corresponding trajectory $\hat{z}(t)$ determined by (17), such that

(i) For $t \in [t_o, t_f]$, $\hat{u}$ is a measurable, essentially bounded function whose range is contained in an arbitrary but fixed subset U of E^m,

(ii) The following boundary conditions are satisfied:
(a) $\hat{z}(t_o) = \hat{z}_o = (0, \hat{x}_o)$, where $\hat{x}_o$ is a given vector in E^n, and (b) $g(\hat{x}(t_f)) = 0$, where $g : E^n \to E^\ell$ is a continuously differentiable map whose Jacobian $\frac{\partial g(x)}{\partial x}$ has maximum rank for all x satisfying $g(x) = 0$.

(iii) For every control $u(t)$ and corresponding trajectory $z(t)$, $t \in [t_o, t_f]$, satisfying (i) and (ii) above, the relation $y(t_f) \leq \hat{y}(t_f)$ implies that $y(t_f) = \hat{y}(t_f)$.

To transcribe the optimal control problem into the form of the Basic Problem, we take $\mathcal{H}$ to be the product space $\mathcal{S}_{p+n} = \mathcal{S} \times \mathcal{S} \times \ldots \times \mathcal{S}$, where $\mathcal{S}$ is the space of all real valued functions on $[t_o, t_f]$, which are either upper or lower semi-continuous at each point $t \in [t_o, t_f]$, with the pointwise topology. We define Ω to be the set of all absolutely continuous functions $z = (y, x)$ from $[t_o, t_f]$ into E^{p+n}, which for some u satisfying (i) above, satisfy the differential equation (17) for almost all $t \in [t_o, t_f]$, with $z(t_o) = (0, x_0)$. Finally, we define $h(z) = y(t_f)$ and $r(z) = g(x(t_f))$. It is easy to show that both h and r are continuous.

Suppose the control $\hat{u}(t)$ and the corresponding trajectory $\hat{z}(t)$ solve the optimal control problem. To construct a conical approximation $C(\hat{z}, \Omega)$ to Ω, we follow L. W. Neustadt's derivation (8), which was based on a utilization of the cone of attainability given in (13) by Pontryagin et al. Let $I \subset [t_o, t_f]$ be the set of all points t at which $\hat{u}(t)$ is regular.

Let $\Phi(t, \tau)$ be the $(p+n) \times (p+n)$ matrix which satisfies the linear differential equation

$$\frac{d}{dt} \Phi(t, \tau) = \frac{\partial F}{\partial z} (\hat{x}(t), \hat{u}(t)) \Phi(t, \tau) \tag{18}$$

for almost all $t \in [t_o, t_f]$ with $\Phi(\tau, \tau) = I_{p+n}$, the (p+n) identity matrix.

For any $s \in I$ and $v \in U$ we define

$$\delta z_{s,v}(t) = \begin{cases} 0 & \text{for } t_o \leq t < s \\ \Phi(t, s) [F(\hat{x}(s), v) - F(\hat{x}(s), \hat{u}(s)] & \text{for } s \leq t \leq t_f \end{cases} \tag{19}$$

and

$$C(\hat{z}, \Omega) = \{\delta z \in \mathcal{X} \mid \delta z(t) = \sum_{i=1}^{k} \alpha_i \delta z_{s_i, v_i}(t),$$

$$\{s_1, s_2, \ldots, s_k\} \subset I, \{v_1, v_2, \ldots, v_k\} \subset U, \text{ and}$$

$$\alpha_i \geq 0 \text{ for } i = 1, 2, \ldots, k, \text{ where k is arbitrary finite}\} \tag{20}$$

Finally, for every $\delta z = (\delta y, \delta x) \in \mathcal{H}$, we define $h'(\hat{z})(\delta z) = \delta y(t_f)$ and $r'(\hat{z})(\delta z) = (g(\hat{x}(t_f)/\partial x) \delta x(t_f)$.

It now follows from theorem 1 that there exist a vector $\mu \leq 0$ in E^p and a vector $\eta \varepsilon E^{\ell}$, $(\mu, \eta) \neq 0$, such that

$$\langle \mu, \ \delta y(t_f) \rangle \ + \ \langle \eta, \ \frac{\partial g(\hat{x}(t_f))}{\partial x} \ \delta x(t_f) \rangle \leq 0$$

$$\text{for all } \delta z \in \overline{C(\hat{z}, \Omega)} \qquad (21)$$

Substituting for $\delta z(t_f)$ from (20) into (21) and making the usual identifications, we obtain the following maximum principle.

Theorem 2: If the control $\hat{u}(t)$ and the corresponding trajectory $\hat{z}(t) = (\hat{y}(t), \hat{x}(t))$ solve the optimal control problem, then there exist a vector $\psi_1 \leq 0$ in E^p and a vector valued function $\psi_2 : [t_o, t_f] \rightarrow E^n$, with $(\psi_1, \psi_2(t)) \not\equiv 0$ such that

$$\text{(i)} \quad \frac{d\psi_2(t)}{dt} = - \left(\frac{\partial c(\hat{x}(t), \hat{u}(t))}{\partial x} \right)^T \psi_1 - \left(\frac{\partial f(\hat{x}(t), \hat{u}(t))}{\partial x} \right)^T \psi_2(t),$$

$$t \in [t_o, t_f] \qquad (22)$$

$$\text{(ii)} \quad \psi_2(t_f) = \left(\frac{\partial g(\hat{x}(t_f))}{\partial x} \right)^T \eta \ \text{ for some } \eta \in E^\ell \qquad (23)$$

(iii) for every $v \in U$ and almost all $t \in [t_o, t_f]$,

$$\langle \psi_1, \ c(\hat{x}(f), \ \hat{u}(t)) \rangle \ + \ \langle \psi_2(t), \ f(\hat{x}(t), \ \hat{u}(t)) \rangle \geq$$

$$\langle \psi_1, \ c(\hat{x}(t), v) \rangle \ + \ \langle \psi_2(t), \ f(\hat{x}(t), \ v) \rangle \qquad (24)$$

III. Reduction of a Vector-Valued Criterion to a Family of Scalar-Valued Criteria

We now examine the possibility of solving the Basic Problem by weighting the components of the vector criterion function into a scalar criterion, thus reducing the problem to a family of scalar valued criterion problems. The weighting common in economics and in engineering is with strictly positive weights only. However, we shall also consider the degenerate case in which some of the weights can be zero.

In this section we restrict ourselves to the partial ordering defined as follows: Given y_1, y_2 in E^p, $y_1 \prec y_2$ if and only if $y_1^i \leq y_2^i$ for $i = 1, 2, \ldots, p$. With this ordering, for any vector y in E^p, the critical index set $J(y)$ is the set $\{1, 2, \ldots, p\}$.

In order to simplify our exposition, we combine the constraint set Ω with the set $\{x \in \mathcal{X} \mid r(x) = 0\}$ into a set $A = \Omega \quad \{x \in \mathcal{X} \mid r(x) = 0\}$.

Definition 3: We shall denote by P the problem of finding a point $\hat{x}$ in A such that for every x in A, the relation $h(x) \leq h(\hat{x})$ (componentwise) implies that $h(x) = h(\hat{x})$.

Definition 4: Given any vector λ in E^p, we shall denote by $P(\lambda)$ the problem of finding a point $\hat{x}$ in A such that $\langle \lambda, h(\hat{x}) \rangle \leq \langle \lambda, h(x) \rangle$ for all x in A.

Definition 5: Let Λ be the set of all vectors $\lambda = (\lambda^1, \ldots, \lambda^p)$ in E^p such that $\Sigma \lambda^i = 1$ and $\lambda^i > 0$ for $i = 1, 2, \ldots, p$; let $\bar{\Lambda}$ be the closure of Λ in E^p.

We shall consider the following subsets of $\mathcal{X}$:

$$L = \{x \in A \mid x \text{ solves } P\} \tag{25}$$

$$M = \{x \in A \mid x \text{ solves } P(\lambda) \text{ for some } \lambda \in \Lambda\} \tag{26}$$

$$N = \{x \in A \mid x \text{ solves } P(\lambda) \text{ for some } \lambda \in \bar{\Lambda}\}. \tag{27}$$

Remark: It is trivially verified that M is contained in L and in N. Furthermore, it is easy to show by example that if h is a continuous function, then the closure of the set M is contained in the set N and that this inclusion may be proper. (see (11). It can also be shown that (see(11)) if for each $\lambda \in \bar{\Lambda}$ either $P(\lambda)$ has a unique solution or else it has no solution, then the set L contains the set N.

Theorem 3: Suppose that h is a convex function (componentwise) and that A is a convex set. Then the set N contains the set L.

Proof: Let $\hat{x}$ be a point in L, i.e., $\hat{x}$ is a solution to the problem P. Let

$$\Delta = \{\alpha = (\alpha^1, \alpha^2, \ldots \alpha^p) \mid h^i(x) - h^i(\hat{x}) < \alpha^i,\ i = 1, 2, \ldots, p, \text{ for some } x \in A\}. \tag{28}$$

Since $\hat{x}$ is a solution to P, Δ does not contain the origin. Furthermore, since h is convex, Δ is a convex set in E^p. By the separation theorem (12) there exists a vector $\bar{\alpha}$ in E^p, $\bar{\alpha} \neq 0$ such that

$$\langle \bar{\alpha}, \alpha \rangle \geq 0 \text{ for all } \alpha \in \Delta. \tag{29}$$

Since each α^i can be made as large as we wish, we must have $\bar{\alpha}^i \geq 0$ and hence $\bar{\alpha} \geq 0$. For any positive scalar $\varepsilon > 0$, let $\alpha = h(x) - h(\hat{x}) + \varepsilon e$ for some x in A and e = (1, 1, ..., 1). The vector α is in Δ by definition, and hence, from (29)

$$\langle \bar{\alpha}, h(x) - h(\hat{x}) \rangle \geq -\varepsilon \langle \bar{\alpha}, e \rangle . \tag{30}$$

Relation (30) holds for every x in A, and since ε is arbitrary,

$$\langle \bar{\alpha}, h(x) - h(\hat{x}) \rangle \geq 0 \quad \text{for all } x \in A. \tag{31}$$

If we define $\bar{\lambda} = \bar{\alpha} / \sum_{i=1}^{P} \alpha^i$, then $\bar{\lambda} \in \bar{\Lambda}$ and,

$$\langle \bar{\lambda}, h(\hat{x}) \rangle \leq \langle \bar{\lambda}, h(x) \rangle \quad \text{for all } x \in A \tag{32}$$

But (32) implies that $\hat{x} \in N$.

Corollary: If A is convex and h is strictly convex (componentwise), then L = N.

Definition 6: We shall say that a solution $\hat{x}$ of the problem P is regular if the relation $h(\hat{x}) = h(y)$ implies that $\hat{x} = y$.

We shall say that the problem P is regular if every solution of P is a regular solution.

Remark: It is easy to verify that if h is convex and one of its components is strictly convex then P is regular.

Theorem 4: Suppose that the problem P is regular, that h is continuous and convex, and that the constraint set A is a closed convex subset of a Hausdorff, locally convex, linear topological space $\mathcal{X}$, with the property that for som closed convex neighborhood V of the origin, the set $A \cap (V + x$

is compact for every x in A. Then the set L is contained in the closure of the set M.

Proof: Let $\hat{x}$ be any point in L, let $A' = A \cap (V + \hat{x})$, and let L', M' be defined by (25), (26), with A' taking the place of A. First we show that $h(L') \subset \overline{h(M')}$. Since A' is compact and h is continuous, $h(A')$ is closed, and for every $\varepsilon > 0$, $y - \varepsilon\bar{\Lambda}$ is closed by construction. Let $\hat{y}$ be any point in $h(L')$. Then, clearly, the closed, convex sets $h(A')$ and $(\hat{y} - \varepsilon\bar{\Lambda})$ are separated for every $\varepsilon > 0$. Consequently, for every $\varepsilon > 0$, there exists a $\delta(\varepsilon) \in (0, \varepsilon]$ such that the closed convex sets $h(A')$ and $N(\hat{y} - \varepsilon\bar{\Lambda}, \delta(\varepsilon))$ are disjoint, where $N(\hat{y} - \varepsilon\bar{\Lambda}, \delta(\varepsilon)) = \{y = y' + y'' \mid y' \in (y - \varepsilon\bar{\Lambda}) \text{ and } \|y''\| \leq \delta(\varepsilon)\} \subset E^p$. Now, for every $\varepsilon > 0$, let $y_\varepsilon \in h(A')$ and $s_\varepsilon \in N(y - \varepsilon\bar{\Lambda}, \delta(\varepsilon))$ be such that $\|y_\varepsilon - s_\varepsilon\|$ is the minimum distance between these two closed and disjoint sets. Let λ be a normal to a separating hyperplane through y_ε, such that

$$\langle \lambda, y - y_\varepsilon \rangle \geq 0 \quad \text{for all } y \in h(A') \tag{33}$$

and

$$\langle \lambda, y - y_\varepsilon \rangle < 0 \quad \text{for all } y \in N(\hat{y} - \varepsilon\bar{\Lambda}, \delta(\varepsilon)) \tag{34}$$

then, from (33), $\langle \lambda, \hat{y} - y_\varepsilon \rangle \geq 0$, and hence for every $y \in \bar{\Lambda}$, $\varepsilon\langle \lambda, y \rangle > \langle \lambda, \hat{y} - y_\varepsilon \rangle > 0$. But this means that $\lambda = \alpha\lambda'$, with $\alpha > 0$ and $\lambda \in \Lambda$. Hence we may choose $\alpha = 1$, i.e., $\lambda = \lambda'$, thus proving that $y_\varepsilon \in h(M')$. We now show that $\lim_{\varepsilon \to 0+} y_\varepsilon = \hat{y}$, i.e., that $\hat{y} \in \overline{h(M')}$.

Indeed,

$$\|y_\varepsilon - \hat{y}\| \leq \|\hat{y} - s_\varepsilon\| + \|s_\varepsilon - y_\varepsilon\| \leq \|\hat{y} - s_\varepsilon\| + \|\hat{y} - s_\varepsilon\|$$

$$\leq 2(\varepsilon + \delta(\varepsilon)) \leq 4\varepsilon. \tag{35}$$

We now prove that $L \subset \bar{M}$. Again let $\hat{x}$ be any point in L, and let A', L', M', be defined as above. Then, from the above, $h(L') \subset \overline{h(M')}$ and, by inspection, $\hat{x} \in L'$. For $i = 1, 2, 3, \ldots$, let $y_i \in h(M')$ be such that $y_i \to h(\hat{x})$ and let $x_i \in A'$ be such that $h(x_i) = y_i$. Since A' is compact, $\{x_i\}$ contains a subsequence, $\{x_{i_j}\}$ which converges to a point $\bar{x} \in A'$. Since all subsequences of $\{y_i\}$ converge to $h(\hat{x})$, it follows from the continuity of h that $h(\bar{x}) = h(\hat{x})$, and from the regularity of the problem P that $\bar{x} = \hat{x}$. Now, since

$x_{i_j} \to \hat{x}$, there exists an integer n_0 such that $x_{i_j} \in \mathrm{int}(V + \hat{x})$ for all $i_j \geq n_0$. It now follows from the convexity of h that for $i_j \geq n_0$ $x_{i_j} \in M$ and hence $L \subset \overline{M}$.

Conclusion

We should like to point out that our results can easily be extended to other types of ordering. For example, consider cone orderings on R^p of the following type: $y_1 \prec y_2$ if and only if $(y_1 - y_2) \in C$, where C is a given convex cone. When C has an interior, we let q = p and modify (8) to read $R = \{(y, 0) \in E^p \times E^m | y \in \mathrm{int}\, C,\ 0 \in E^m\}$. We then find that theorem 4 remains valid for cone orderings provided we replace the statement "$\mu \leq 0$" by "μ is in the cone polar to C." The scalarization theorems remain valid for cone orderings provided we replace the set Λ by the set $D = \{\lambda \,|\, \langle \lambda, y \rangle < 0$ for all $y \in C$ with $y \neq 0\}$, assuming, of course, that D is not the empty set.

Acknowledgment

We acknowledge with pleasure several interesting discussions with Professor H. Halkin of the University of California, San Diego.

The research reported herein was supported wholly by the National Aeronautics and Space Administration under Grant NsG-354, Supplement 3.

References

1. Pareto, V., Cours d'Economie Politique, Lausanne, Rouge, 1896.

2. Karlin, S., Mathematical Methods and Theory in Games, Programming and Economics, 1, Addison-Wesley, Massachusetts, 1959.

3. Debreu, G., Theory of Value, John Wiley, New York, 1959.

4. Kuhn, H. W. and Tucker, A. W., "Nonlinear Programming," Proc. of the Second Berkeley Symposium on Mathematic Statistics and Probability, University of California Press, Berkeley, California, 1951, pp. 481-492.

5. Zadeh, L. A., "Optimality and Non-Scalar-Valued Performance Criteria," IEEE Transactions on Automatic Control, vol. AC-8, number 1, pp. 59-60, January 1963.

6. Chang, S. S. L., "General Theory of Optimal Processes," J. SIAM Control, Vol. 4, No. 1, 1966, pp. 46-55.

7. Da Cunha, N. O. and Polak, E., "Constrained Minimization under Vector-Valued Criteria in Finite Dimensional Spaces," Electronics Research Laboratory, University of California, Berkeley, California, Memorandum No. ERL-188, October 1966.

8. Neustadt, L. W. "An Abstract Variational Theory with Applications to a Broad Class of Optimization Problems II," USCEE Report 169, 1966.

9. Halkin, H. and Neustadt, L. W., "General Necessary Conditions for Optimization Problems," USCEE Report 173, 1966.

10. Canon, M., Cullum, C. and Polak, E., "Constrained Minimization Problems in Finite Dimensional Spaces," J. SIAM Control, Vol. 4, No. 3, 1966, pp. 528-547.

11. Da Cunha, N. O. and Polak, E., "Constrained Minimization under Vector-Valued Criteria in Linear Topological Spaces," Electronics Research Laboratory, University of California, Berkeley, California, Memorandum No. ERL-M191, November 1966.

12. Edwards, R. E., Functional Analysis Theory and Applications, Holt, Rinehart and Winston, New York, 1965.

13. Dieudonne', J., Foundations of Modern Analysis, Academic Press, New York, 1960.

SMOOTHING AND APPROXIMATING CONTROL PROBLEMS

by
Henry Hermes*
Department of Mathematics
University of Colorado
Boulder, Colorado

Introduction. In general, we will study a contingent equation of the form $\dot{x}(t) \in R(t,x(t))$ with fixed initial data $x(0) = x_o \in E^n$ (E^n denotes Euclidean n space) where R is a compact set valued function. Of particular concern will be the effect of replacing $R(t,x)$ by its convex hull, or by an ϵ neighborhood of its convex hull.

The implication of such approximations to optimal control problems are as follows. Consider, for example, a time optimal problem having equations of motion $\dot{x}(t) = f(t,x(t),u(t))$ with f continuous and the control function u restricted to take value at time t in a compact set $U(t)$. This can be formulated in terms of a contingent equation by defining $R(t,x) = \{f(t,x,v): v \in U(t)\}$. The existence of an optimal control is, among other things, dependent upon the convexity, for each t,x, of the set $R(t,x)$; see (1), (2). Let $p \in E^n - \{0\}$. For a time optimal problem, the maximum principle requires that the values $u^*(t,x,p)$ of an optimal controller satisfy $p \cdot f(t,x,u^*(t,x,p)) = \max.\{p \cdot f(t,x,v): v \in U(t)\}$ or letting $r^*(t,x,p) = f(t,x,u^*(t,x,p))$ this is equivalent to $p \cdot r^*(t,x,p) = \max \{p \cdot r: r \in R(t,x)\}$. It is clear that if the maximization on the right defines a function r^*, as indicated, the continuity properties of r^* will also depend on the geometric shape of the set $R(t,x)$. In (3), it is shown that r^* will be well defined and continuously differentiable if, among other things, $R(t,x)$ is strictly

*This research was supported by the Air Force Office of Scientific Research under grant AF-AFOSR 1243-67.

convex and furthermore has a smooth boundary, denoted $\partial R(t,x)$, on which the Gauss map (which assigns to each point of $\partial R(t,x)$ the unit outward normal at that point) has nonvanishing Jacobian. A natural question to ask is the following. What is the loss of generality in replacing the set valued function R of an arbitrary control problem by one which satisfies the conditions outlined above? We shall next proceed to answer this question.

I. Throughout, it will be assumed that the set valued function R satisfies the following properties.

a) $R(t,x)$ is a nonempty, compact, subset of E^n for each $(t,x) \in [0,\infty) \times E^n$.

b) R is continuous in the Hausdorff metric topology.

c) There exists a constant $c > 0$ such that for any point valued function r having value $r(t,x) \in R(t,x)$, the inner product inequality $x \cdot r(t,x) \le c[1 + |x|^2]$ is valid.

The notation coR will be used to denote the set valued function with value $coR(t,x)$ the closed convex hull of $R(t,x)$, while R^ϵ will denote the set valued function with value $R^\epsilon(t,x)$ a compact $\epsilon > 0$ neighborhood of $R(t,x)$. It is clear that properties a), b) and c) then also hold for coR and R^ϵ. Throughout, T will be a fixed real positive number.

We first consider the following three contingent equations.

$$\dot{x}(t) \in R(t,x(t)), \qquad x(0) = x_o \tag{1}$$
$$\dot{x}(t) \in coR(t,x(t)), \qquad x(0) = x_o \tag{2}$$
$$\dot{x}(t) \in R^\epsilon(t,x(t)), \qquad x(0) = x_o. \tag{3}$$

Property c) implies that for any solution x of Eq. (1) (or similarly of Eq. (2)) the inequality $|x(t)|^2 \le (1 + |x_o|^2)\exp. 2cT$, $0 \le t \le T$, is valid, thus we need only consider R defined on the compact "rectangle"

$$D = \{t,x: 0 \le t \le T, \quad |x|^2 \le (1 + |x_o|^2)\exp. 2cT\}.$$

For later convenience, the notation D^γ will be used to denote a compact γ neighborhood of D.

Theorem 1. Given any $\epsilon > 0$, if φ is a solution of Eq. (2) then there exists a solution ξ of Eq. (3) which satisfies $\max.\{|\xi(t) - \varphi(t)|: 0 \le t \le T\} < \epsilon$.

Proof. Let φ be an arbitrary solution of Eq. (2). Then the set valued function $R(t,\varphi(t))$, considered as a function of t on the interval $[0,T]$, is bounded, say by k, in the sense of the Hausdorff metric. (I.e. Its distance from the compact set $\{0\}$ is less than k.)

Subdivide the interval $[0,T]$ into m subintervals each of length T/m. (At this point m is an arbitrary positive integer.) Let I_j denote the jth subinterval, explicitly $I_j = \{t: jT/m \le t \le (j + 1)T/m\}$, $j = 0, \ldots,$ $m-1$. Since R is bounded, theorem 3, (4), applies to yield $\int_{I_j} R(t,\varphi(t))dt = \int_{I_j} coR(t,\varphi(t))dt$ which is to be interpreted that there exists a measurable function y^j defined on I_j with value at time t in $R(t,\varphi(t))$ such that $\int_{i_j} y^j(t)dt = \int_{I_j} \dot{\varphi}(t)dt$. Define y as that measurable function on $[0,T]$, with value at t in $R(t,\varphi(t))$, whose restriction to I_j is y^j for $j = 0, \ldots, m-1$. (Since the value of y at a finite set of points is immaterial, any ambiguity of this definition of y at endpoints of the intervals I_j is of no consequence.)

Define $\xi(t) = x_o + \int_o^t y(\tau)d\tau$. Then $\dot{\xi}(t) = y(t) \in R(t,\varphi(t))$ and $\xi(jT/m) = \varphi(jT/m)$ for $j = 0,\ldots,m-1$. Also since $|\dot{\xi}(t)|$ and $|\dot{\varphi}(t)|$ are bounded by k by virtue of being in $R(t,\varphi(t))$, it is clear that for any $t \in [0,T]$, $|\varphi(t) - \xi(t)| \le kT/m$. Now given any $\epsilon_1 > 0$ we may choose m sufficiently large so that $\max.\{\varphi(t) - \xi(t)|: 0 \le t \le T\} < \epsilon$.

Let $\gamma > 0$ be given. Since R is continuous in D^γ it is uniformly continuous. Thus given any $\epsilon > 0$ there exists a $\delta > 0$ such that $R(t,x)$ is contained in an ϵ neighborhood of $R(t,y)$ if $|x-y| < \delta$, (t,x), $(t,y) \in D^\gamma$. Now choose ϵ_1 as the minimum of δ and γ. Then for all $0 \le t \le T$, $(t,\varphi(t))$ and $(t,\xi(t))$ belong to D^γ and $R(t,\varphi(t)) \subset R^\epsilon(t,\xi(t))$. Since $\dot{\xi}(t) \in R^\epsilon(t,\xi(t))$ and by its definition $\xi(0) = x_o$, ξ is the required solution of Eq. (3). Q. E. D.

To relate solutions of Eqs. (1) and (2), we resort to a further condition on the set valued function R.

Definition. If there is a continuous mapping U of $[0,T]$ into the set of nonempty compact subsets of E^r, (with the Hausdorff topology) for some $0 \leq r < \infty$, such that

$R(t,x) = \{f(t,x,u) \in E^n: u \in U(t)\}$ where f is continuous in all arguments and Lipschitz continuous in x for fixed t,u, we shall say that R is representable (f,U).

Theorem 2. Assume R is representable (f,U). Then given any $\epsilon > 0$, there exists an (arbitrarily small) $\epsilon_1 > 0$ such that if ξ is a solution of $\dot{x}(t) \in R^{\epsilon_1}(t,x(t))$, $x(0) = x_o$, then there exists a solution ψ of (1) which satisfies $\max \{|\psi(t) - \xi(t)|: 0 \leq t \leq T\} < \epsilon$.

Proof. By the definition of R^{ϵ_1}, there exists a measurable function $\mu: [0,T] \to E^n$ with $|\mu(t)| \leq 2\epsilon_1$ and such that $\dot{\xi}(t) + \mu(t) \in R(t,\xi(t))$ for all $0 \leq t \leq T$. By Filippov's lemma (1), there exists a measurable function u^*, with values $u^*(t) \in U(t)$, such that $\dot{\xi}(t) + \mu(t) = f(t,\xi(t),u^*(t))$ almost everywhere in $[0,T]$. Consider the differential equation $\dot{x}(t) = f(t,x(t),u^*(t))$, $x(0) = x_o$; call its solution ψ. Then $\psi - \xi$ satisfies $\dot{\psi}(t) - \dot{\xi}(t) = f(t,\psi(t),u^*(t)) - f(t,\xi(t),u^*(t)) - \mu(t)$, $\psi(0) - \xi(0) = 0$. From this, the Lipschitz continuity of f, and standard theory of ordinary differential equations, given any $\epsilon > 0$ we can choose $\epsilon_1 > 0$ and sufficiently small so that $\max \{|\psi(t) - \xi(t)|: 0 \leq t \leq T\} < \epsilon$. Q. E. D.

An interesting question is whether such a result can be obtained without the assumed representation, i.e. where R merely satisfies conditions a), b) and c).

Let $\epsilon > 0$ and φ a solution of Eq. (2) be given. If we first choose $0 < \epsilon_1 < \epsilon/2$, by theorem 1 there is a solution ξ of $\dot{x} \in R^{\epsilon_1}(t,x)$, $x(0) = x_o$, which differs from φ by at most $\epsilon/2$. By theorem 2, if $\epsilon_1 > 0$ is sufficiently small, we are assured of a solution ψ of Eq. (1) which differs from ξ by at most $\epsilon/2$. Combining these gives

Corollary 2.1. Assume R is representable (f,U). Then given any $\epsilon > 0$, if φ is a solution of Eq. (2) there *exists a solution* ψ *of Eq. (1) which satisfies* $\max\{|\varphi(t) - \psi(t)|: 0 \le t \le T\} < \varepsilon$.

We next note that if R is representable (f,U) then there exist functions g,V such that coR is representable (g,V). Indeed, let $v = (u_o,u,w) = (u_o,u_1,\ldots,u_r,w_1,\ldots,w_r)$ and $V(t) = \{(u_o,u,w) \in E^{2r+1}: 0 \le u_o \le 1, u \in U(t), w \in U(t)\}$. Define $g(t,x,v) = u_o f(t,x,u) + (1-u_o) \cdot f(t,x,w)$. Then $coR(t,x) = \{g(t,x,v): v \in V(t)\}$ while the continuity properties of g and V are clearly inherited from f and U. Thus if R is representable (f,U) we can apply the results of corollary 2.1 to R and coR, and those of theorem 2 to coR and $(coR)^{\varepsilon_1}$ obtaining

Theorem 3. Assume R *is representable* (f,U). *If given any* $\varepsilon > 0$ *there exists an* $\varepsilon_1 > 0$ *such that if* φ *is any solution of* $\dot{x}(t) \in (coR)^{\varepsilon_1}(t,x)$, $x(0) = x_o$, *then there exists a solution* ψ *of* $\dot{x}(t) \in R(t,x(t))$, $x(0) = x_o$ *satisfying* $\max\{|\varphi(t) - \psi(t)|: 0 \le t \le T\} < 2\varepsilon$.

In words, theorem 3 shows that up to uniform approximation of trajectories over a finite time interval $[0,T]$ there is little loss of generality by replacing $R(t,x)$, in Eq. (1), by a compact neighborhood of its convex hull.

Assume there exists a smooth function r_o with values $r_o(t,x)$ in $R(t,x)$. (This is an additional assumption and does not follow from properties a), b) and c) of R.) For any $\varepsilon_1 > 0$, a result obtained in (5, pg. 38) shows that for each (t,x) there exists a set $R^*(t,x)$ and a twice continuously differentiable function $\Omega(t,x,\cdot): E^n \to E^1$ such that

(4) $coR(t,x) \subset R^*(t,x) \subset (coR)^{\varepsilon_1}(t,x)$,

(5) the $n \times n$ matrix of partial derivatives $\Omega_{rr}(t,x,r-r_o(t,x))$ is positive definite.

(6) $R^*(t,x) = \{r \in E^n: \Omega(t,x,r-r_o(t,x)) \le 1\}$.

Property (5) implies that the second fundamental form on $\partial R^*(t,x)$, in terms of local coordinates, is definite. But the second fundamental form is a representation of the differential of the Gauss map therefore the Jacobian determinant of the Gauss map does not vanish. Property (4) and theorem 3 show that for any $\epsilon > 0$ and solution φ of

$$\dot{x}(t) \in R^*(t,x(t)), \quad x(0) = x_o \tag{7}$$

there is a solution of Eq. (1) uniformly within ϵ of φ.

It is not very difficult to show, by a smoothing or mollifying technique (3, pgs. 416-420), that Ω can be chosen twice continuously differentiable in all arguments and that R^* is therefore representable (h, D^n) where D^n is the closed unit disc (ball) in E^n. The discontinuities usually produced by the maximum principle no longer occur for the approximating problem determined by R^*. This enables the attainable set for Eq. (7) to be discussed from an analytic viewpoint. For some results, see (6).

References:

1. Filippov, A. F., On Certain Questions in the Theory of Optimal Control (English trans.) J. Soc. Ind. Appl. Math., Control, Ser. A, 1 (1962) 76-84.
2. Roxin, E., On the Existence of Optimal Controls; Michigan Math. J., 9 (1962) 109-119.
3. Hermes, H., The Equivalence and Approximation of Optimal Control Problems; J. Diff. Eqs., 1, No. 4, (1965) 409-426.
4. Aumann, R. J., Integrals of Set-Valued Functions; J. Math. Anal. & Appl., 12, No. 1, (1965) 1-12.
5. Bonnesen, T. and W. Fenchel "Theorie der Konvexen Korper." Chelsea, New York, (1948).
6. Hermes, H., Attainable Sets and Generalized Geodesic Spheres, (To appear) J. Diff. Eqs.

ON THE TRAJECTORIES OF A DIFFERENTIAL SYSTEM*

by
P. P. Varaiya
Department of Electrical Engineering and Computer Sciences and Electronics Research Laboratory,
University of California, Berkeley, California

INTRODUCTION

In this paper we investigate in detail the so-called convexity assumption made by Marcus and Lee (1), Fillipov (2), Roxin (3), and Warga (4) in their studies relating to the existence of optimal control. We first show (Theorem 2.1) that the set of relaxed trajectories is compact in the topology of uniform convergence. It is interesting to note that this result is true without a "Lipschitz condition" on the differential system. The next result (Theorem 2.2) shows that the set of trajectories is dense in the set of relaxed trajectories. In proving this result, critical use is made of the Lipschitz condition. Finally in Theorem 2.3 we prove that the set of trajectories is closed if and only if the convexity assumption is satisfied, i.e., if and only if at each point in the phase space the set of permissible velocities form a convex set. Some of these assertions have been proved in a less general setting by Warga (4). Also, for the main part, our proofs are different and simpler than those presented by Warga. We also remark that as an immediate consequence of Theorem 2.1 we obtain the results on the existence of optimal controls given in References (1)-(4).

---

* The research reported herein was supported wholly by U.S. Army Research Office--Durham under Grant No. DA-ARO-D-31-124-G576.

In Sec. 3 we derive some interesting consequences of Theorem 2.3 for the class of control systems for which the right-hand side of the differential equation is separable in the state and the control vectors (Eq. 3.1). We show that for such systems, if the convexity condition is not satisfied, then the set of trajectories and the set of limit points of the trajectories which are not themselves trajectories, are dense in each other. Furthermore, these two disjoint sets are pathwise connected if the initial set is pathwise connected. This result is interesting in the light of a result of Neustadt (5) which states that for a linear system the set of attainable sets is closed even if the convexity condition is not satisfied. We remark that the relations between the attainable sets and the convexity conditions are investigated in detail in Reference (6).

1. STATEMENT OF THE PROBLEM

We shall study the control system

$$\dot{x}(t) = f(x(t), t, u(t)) \quad , \qquad (1.1)$$

where $x \in R^n$ is the state, $u \in R^m$ is the control, and $t \in R$ is the time; f is a continuous mapping of $R^n \times R \times R^m$ into R^n; and $\dot{x}$ as usual denotes dx/dt. For each $(x,t) \in R^n \times R$ we are given a compact subset $U(x,t)$ of R^m such that the mapping $(x,t) \to U(x,t)$ is upper semicontinuous. Let

$$U = \bigcup_{(x,t) \in R^n \times R} U(x,t) \quad .$$

Finally, the following additional conditions are imposed on the function f: there exists a locally integrable function k and finite numbers M and N such that

$$|f(x,t,u) - f(x',t,u)| \leq k(t)|x - x'| \quad , \qquad (1.2)$$

$$|f(x,t,u)| \leq k(t)\ (M + N|x|) \quad , \qquad (1.3)$$

for all x, x′ in R^n, $u \in U$, and $t \in R$. Here and throughout, if $z \in R^\ell$ then $|z|$ denotes the Euclidean norm of z in R^ℓ.

We are also given a fixed compact subset X_0 of R^n and

two finite numbers a and b with $a \leq b$. Let $I = [a,b]$.

Definition 1.1. For $x \in R^n$ and $t \in R$ let $F(x,t) = \{f(x,t,u) | u \in U(x,t)\}$, and let $G(x,t)$ be the convex closure of $F(x,t)$.

Definition 1.2. An absolutely continuous function $x: I \to R^n$ is said to be a trajectory if

$$x(a) \in X_0 \tag{1.4}$$

and there is a measurable function $u: I \to R^m$ with $u(t) \in U(x(t),t)$ for $t \in I$, such that

$$\dot{x}(t) = f(x(t), t, u(t)) \quad \text{a.e. in } I. \tag{1.5}$$

Note. By Fillipov's lemma (1), Eq. (1.5) is equivalent to

$$x(t) \in F(x(t),t) \quad \text{a.e. in } I. \tag{1.6}$$

Let $\mathcal{T}$ denote the set of all trajectories. Following Warga (4), we make

Definition 1.3. An absolutely continuous function $x: I \to R^n$ is said to be a relaxed trajectory if

$$x(a) \in X_0 \ , \tag{1.7}$$

$$\dot{x}(t) \in G(x(t),t) \quad \text{a.e. in } I. \tag{1.8}$$

Let $\mathcal{R}$ denote the set of all relaxed trajectories. It is clear that $\mathcal{T} \subset \mathcal{R}$. Let $\mathcal{C}$ denote the real Banach space of all continuous functions $x: I \to R^n$ with the norm of x given by

$$\|x\| = \max_{t \in I} |x(t)| \ .$$

We will consider $\mathcal{T}$ and $\mathcal{R}$ as subsets of $\mathcal{C}$. Our purpose is to investigate the relationship between $\mathcal{T}$ and $\mathcal{R}$. In particular, we will show that $\mathcal{R}$ is a compact subset of $\mathcal{C}$; $\mathcal{R}$ is equal to the $\mathcal{C}$-closure of $\mathcal{T}$; $\mathcal{T}$ is closed in $\mathcal{C}$ if $F(x,t)=G(x,t)$ for every (x,t), and if the mapping $(x,t) \to U(x,t)$ is continuous, the converse statement is also true.

2. THE RELATION BETWEEN $\mathcal{R}$ AND $\mathcal{T}$

Using Eq. (1.3), we make an elementary application of Gronwall's lemma to obtain

Lemma 2.1. $\mathcal{R}$ and a fortiori $\mathcal{T}$ are bounded subsets of $\mathcal{C}$. From Eq. (1.3) and the preceding lemma we immediately have

Corollary 2.1. There is an integrable function μ defined on I such that for every x in $\mathcal{R}$

$$|\dot{x}(t)| \leq \mu(t) \quad \text{a.e. in I.} \tag{1.9}$$

Corollary 2.2. $\mathcal{R}$ is an equicontinuous family of functions.

Proof. Let $\varepsilon>0$. Since the function μ in Eq. (1.9) is integrable, there is a $\delta=\delta(\varepsilon)>0$ such that if t_1, t_2 in I and $|t_1-t_2|<\delta$ then $\int_{t_1}^{t_2}\mu(t)dt\leq\varepsilon$. Hence for any x in $\mathcal{R}$,

$$|x(t_1) - x(t_2)| \leq \int_{t_1}^{t_2} |\dot{x}(t)|dt \leq \int_{t_1}^{t_2}\mu(t)dt \leq \varepsilon \quad .$$

Theorem 2.1. $\mathcal{R}$ is a compact subset of $\mathcal{C}$.

Proof. By Lemma 2.1, Corollary 2.2, and the Arzelà-Ascoli Theorem, it suffices to show that $\mathcal{R}$ is closed in $\mathcal{C}$. To this end, let $\{x_n\}$ be a sequence in $\mathcal{R}$ converging to an element x in $\mathcal{C}$.

We first prove that x is absolutely continuous. Indeed, let $\varepsilon>0$, and let $\delta=\delta(\varepsilon)>0$ be such that for every finite increasing sequence $a\leq t_1\leq t_1'\leq\cdots\leq t_m\leq t_m'\leq b$ with $\sum_{i=1}^{m} |t_i'-t_i|<\delta$ we have

$$\sum_{i=1}^{m}\int_{t_i}^{t_i'}\mu(t)dt \leq \frac{\varepsilon}{2} \quad ,$$

where μ is the function given in Corollary 2.1. Now given such a sequence, let n be sufficiently large so that $\|x-x_n\|\leq 1/4m\varepsilon$. Then,

$$\sum_{i=1}^{m} |x(t_i') - x(t_i)| \leq \sum_{i=1}^{m} \Big\{ |x(t_i) - x_n(t_i)|$$

$$+ |x(t_i') - x_n(t_i')| + |x_n(t_i) - x_n(t_i')| \Big\} \leq \varepsilon \quad .$$

Hence x is absolutely continuous. It remains to show that $\dot{x}(t) \in G(x(t),t)$ a.e. in I. We first show that $\dot{x}_n$ converges to $\dot{x}$ in the weak topology of $L_1(I)$. To this end, let E be any subset of I with positive measure. Then for any $\varepsilon > 0$, there is a finite disjoint union

$$H = \bigcup_{i=1}^{m} (t_i, t_i')$$

of internals such that the measure of the difference E-H is less than ε. Then

$$\left| \int_E (\dot{x}_n(t) - \dot{x}(t))dt \right| \leq \left| \int_H (\dot{x}_n(t) - \dot{x}(t))dt \right|$$

$$+ \int_{E-H} (|\dot{x}_n(t)| + |\dot{x}(t)|)dt \leq \sum_{i=1}^{m} \Big\{ |x_n(t_i') - x(t_i')|$$

$$+ |x_n(t_i) - x(t_i)| \Big\} + \int_{E-H} (|\dot{x}_n(t)| + |\dot{x}(t)|)dt \quad .$$

The first term can be made small by choosing n large, and the second term can be made small by choosing ε small. Thus for every measurable subset E of I we have

$$\lim_n \int_E \dot{x}_n(t)dt = \int_E \dot{x}(t)dt$$

so that $\dot{x}_n$ converges to $\dot{x}$ weakly in $L_1(I)$. From this we see that for every vector $z \in R^n$,

$$\overline{\lim_n} \langle z,\dot{x}_n(t)\rangle \geq \langle z,\dot{x}(t)\rangle \geq \underline{\lim_n} \langle z,\dot{x}_n(t)\rangle \qquad (2.1)$$

a.e. in I. Since the set function $G(x,t)$ is upper semi-continuous in x for every fixed t and since $\|x_n - x\| \to 0$, for every $z \in R^n$ and t in I we must have

$$\overline{\lim_n} \max_{y \in G(x_n(t),t)} \langle z,y\rangle \leq \max_{y \in G(x(t),t)} \langle z,y\rangle ,$$

$$\underline{\lim_n} \min_{y \in G(x_n(t),t)} \langle z,y\rangle \geq \min_{y \in G(x(t),t)} \langle z,y\rangle . \qquad (2.2)$$

From Eqs. (2.1) and (2.2) we deduce that for every $z \in R^n$ and almost all $t \in I$,

$$\max_{y \in G(x(t),t)} \langle z,y\rangle \geq \langle z,\dot{x}(t)\rangle \geq \min_{y \in G(x(t),t)} \langle z,y\rangle$$

so that since G is closed and convex,

$$\dot{x}(t) \in G(x(t),t) \quad \text{a.e. in I.}$$

Q.E.D.

Remarks 2.1. a) In the proof of Theorem 2.1 we have not used either the assumption of continuity of f in t or the Lipschitzian condition (1.2). Therefore Theorem 2.1 is true and the same proof holds, if f is merely required to be measurable in t for fixed (x,u) and if condition (1.2) is eliminated. The proof of Theorem 2.2, however, makes critical use of (1.2).

b) If the initial set X_0 is merely required to be closed instead of compact, an immediate consequence of Theorem 2.2 is that $\mathcal{R}$ is closed in $\mathcal{C}$.

c) If, instead of the finite interval $I=[a,b]$, we consider the interval $\tilde{I}=[a,\infty)$, then the set $\tilde{\mathcal{R}}$ of relaxed trajectories defined on $\tilde{I}$ is a compact subset of $\tilde{\mathcal{C}}$ --the Frechet space of all continuous function $\tilde{x}:\tilde{I}\to R^n$ with the topology of uniform convergence on finite intervals.

Definition 2.1. Let x be a fixed element of $\mathcal{R}$. Let $\mathcal{F}$ ($\mathcal{G}$) be the family of all measurable functions

$f(g):I \to R^n$ such that $f(t) \in F(x(t),t)$ $(g(t) \in G(x(t),t))$ a.e. in I.

We note that $\mathcal{F} \subset \mathcal{G}$ and $\mathcal{G}$ is a convex, closed, and bounded subset of $L_1(I)$.

Lemma 2.2. Let $\ell:I \to R^n$ be any bounded, measurable function. Then there exist functions $\overline{f}$ and $\underline{f}$ in $\mathcal{F}$, depending on ℓ, such that

$$\int_I \langle \ell(t), \overline{f}(t) \rangle dt = \max_{g \in \mathcal{G}} \int_I \langle \ell(t), g(t) \rangle dt \tag{2.3}$$

$$\int_I \langle \ell(t), \underline{f}(t) \rangle dt = \min_{g \in \mathcal{G}} \int_I \langle \ell(t), g(t) \rangle dt \ . \tag{2.4}$$

Proof. It is enough to prove Eq. (2.3). For each t in I let

$$M(t) = \max_{y \in G(x(t),t)} \langle \ell(t), y \rangle \ .$$

Since $F(x(t),t)$ is compact and $G(x(t),t)$ is its convex hull we have

$$M(t) = \max_{y \in F(x(t),t)} \langle \ell(t), y \rangle \ .$$

Clearly, M is measurable and $F(x(t),t)$ is upper semicontinuous in t. By mimicking the argument of Fillipov (1) it is easy to show that there is a function $\overline{f}$ in which satisfies Eq. (2.3).

Corollary 2.3. Let $g \in \mathcal{G}$, $t_1, t_2 \in I$ (with $t_1 \leq t_2$) be arbitrary. Then there exists $f \in \mathcal{F}$ (depending on g, t_1, t_2) such that

$$\int_{t_1}^{t_2} g(t)dt = \int_{t_1}^{t_2} f(t)dt \ .$$

Proof. Because of Lemma 2.2, it is enough to show that the set

$$L(t_1,t_2,\mathcal{F}) = \left\{ \int_{t_1}^{t_2} f(t)dt \;|\; f \in \mathcal{F} \right\}$$

is a convex subset of R^n. Let $f_1, f_2 \in \mathcal{F}$ and let $\lambda \in [0,1]$ be arbitrary. Then we must show that

$$\int_{t_1}^{t_2} \left(\lambda f_1(t) + (1-\lambda) f_2(t) \right) dt \in L\left(t_1,t_2,\mathcal{F}\right) . \tag{2.5}$$

For each Borel subset B of I let $f_B \in \mathcal{F}$ be defined by $f_B(t) = f_1(t)$ for $t \in B$ and $f_B(t) = f_2(t)$ for $t \notin B$. But then by Lyapunov's theorem (7) the set $L = \left\{ \int_{t_1}^{t_2} f_B(t)dt \;|\; B \text{ is a Borel subset of } I \right\}$ is a convex subset of R^n so that Eq. (2.5) is verified.

Q.E.D.

Theorem 2.2. $\mathcal{R}$ is the $\mathcal{C}$-closure of $\mathcal{T}$.

Proof. Let $x \in \mathcal{R}$ and let $\varepsilon > 0$. We will first show that there exists f_ε in $\mathcal{F}$ (see Def. 2.1) such that for every t and t' in I

$$\left| \int_{t}^{t'} \left(\dot{x}(\tau) - f_\varepsilon(\tau) \right) d\tau \right| \leq \varepsilon . \tag{2.6}$$

Indeed let $\delta > 0$ be so small that

$$\int_{t}^{t'} \mu(\tau) d\tau < \varepsilon/3 \tag{2.7}$$

whenever $|t-t'| < \delta$ (μ is defined in Corollary 2.1). Choose a sequence $a = t_0 < t_1 < \cdots < t_m = b$ such that $t_{i+1} - t_i < \delta$ for each i. By Corollary 2.3 there exists a function f_i in $\mathcal{F}$ such that

$$\int_{t_i}^{t_{i+1}} \left(\dot{x}(\tau) - f_i(\tau) \right) d\tau = 0 . \tag{2.8}$$

Let $f_\varepsilon \in \mathcal{F}$ be defined by $f_\varepsilon(t) = f_i(t)$ for $t_i \leq t < t_{i+1}$. It is clear from Eqs. (2.7) and (2.8) that f_ε satisfies Eq. (2.6). By Fillipov's lemma (1), there is a measurable function $u_\varepsilon : I \to R^m$ with $u_\varepsilon(t) \in U(x(t),t)$ such that

$f_\varepsilon(t)=f(x(t),t,u_\varepsilon(t))$ a.e. in I. Let x_ε be the element in $\mathcal{T}$ defined by

$$\dot{x}_\varepsilon(t) = f(x_\varepsilon(t),t,u_\varepsilon(t)), \quad x_\varepsilon(a) = x(a) \quad .$$

Then, using Eqs. (1.2) and (2.6), a simple application of Gronwall's lemma shows that $\|x-x_\varepsilon\| \leq K\varepsilon$ where K is a fixed number independent of ε.

Q.E.D.

Corollary 2.4. If $F(x,t)$ is convex for each (x,t), then $\mathcal{T}$ is closed in $\mathcal{C}$, and hence $\mathcal{T} = \mathcal{R}$.

Remark 2.2. This result shows that the "convexity assumption" on F is sufficient to insure compactness of $\mathcal{T}$. Theorem 2.3 states that if the mapping $(x,t)\to U(x,t)$ is continuous, then the convexity assumption is also necessary.

Henceforth we will assume that the function $(x,t)\to U(x,t)$ is continuous. The next lemma is immediate.

Lemma 2.3. The mappings $(x,t)\to F(x,t)$ and $(x,t)\to G(x,t)$ are continuous. The set of points (x,t) for which $F(x,t)$ is not convex is an open subset of $R^n \times R$.

Theorem 2.3. Let $x \in \mathcal{T}$ and suppose that for some $t^* \in I$ $F(x(t^*),t^*)$ is not convex. Then for every $\varepsilon>0$, there is an element $x_\varepsilon \in \mathcal{R}$ such that $\|x-x_\varepsilon\| \leq \varepsilon$ and $x_\varepsilon \notin \mathcal{T}$.

Proof. Because of Lemma 2.3 we can assume that $a<t^*<b$. Also there exist positive numbers δ and δ' such that if $|x-x(t^*)|\leq\delta$ and $|t-t^*|\leq\delta$, then $d_H(F(x,t),G(x,t))\geq\delta'$ where $d_H(A,B)$ is the Hausdorff distance between A and B. Therefore there exists a measurable function $g:[t^*,t^*+\delta]\to R^n$ such that for each t, $g(t)\in G(x(t),t)$ and $|g(t)-y|\geq\delta$ for every $y\in F(x(t),t)$. By Fillipov's lemma there exist measurable functions α_i and u_i, $1\leq i\leq n+1$, with $\alpha_i(t)\geq 0$,

$$\sum_{i=1}^{n+1} \alpha_i(t)=1, \quad u_i(t)\in U(x(t),t) \text{ for each } t, \text{ such that}$$

$$g(t) = \sum_{i=1}^{n+1} \alpha_i(t)f(x(t),t,u_i(t)) \text{ for } t\in [t^*,t^*+\delta]. \text{ Also}$$

from the definition of g we see that there are positive numbers β and β' such that if

$$t^* \leq t \leq t^* + \beta \quad \text{and} \quad |z - g(t)| \leq \beta , \quad \text{then} \tag{2.9}$$

$$|z - y| \geq \beta' \quad \text{for every} \quad y\in F(z,t) \quad . \tag{2.10}$$

Now since $x\in \mathcal{T}$, there is a measurable function $u:I\to R^n$

with $u(t) \in U(x(t),t)$ such that $\dot{x}(t)=f(x(t),t,u(t))$ a.e. in I. For each positive integer m let $x_m \in \mathcal{R}$ be defined by

$$\dot{x}_m(t) = \begin{cases} f(x_m(t),t,u(t)) & t \in I, \quad t \notin \left[t^*, t^* + \frac{\delta}{m}\right] \\ \sum_{i=1}^{n+1} \alpha_i(t) f(x_m(t),t,u_i(t)) & t \in \left[t^*, t^* + \frac{\delta}{m}\right] \end{cases}$$

and $x_m(a) = x(a)$.

Clearly, $\|x_m - x\| \to 0$ as $m \to \infty$. Also for each m, since x_m and f are continuous functions, there is a number $t_m > 0$, such that for almost every $t \in [t^*, t^* + t_m]$, $|\dot{x}_m(t) - g(t)| \leq \beta$. From Eqs. (2.9) and (2.10) we see that $x_m \notin \mathcal{T}$ and the theorem is proved.

Q.E.D.

Definition 2.2. A pair $(x',t') \in R^n \times R^1$ is said to be an <u>attainable phase</u> if there is a trajectory $x \in \mathcal{T}$ such that $x(t')=x'$.

Corollary 2.4. $\mathcal{T}$ is closed and a fortiori compact in $\mathcal{C}$ if and only if for every attainable phase (x',t') the set $F(x',t')$ is convex.

3. SOME CONSEQUENCES OF THEOREM 2.3

In this section we consider the class of control systems where Eq. (1.1) has the form:

$$\dot{x}(t) = w(x(t),t) + \hat{v}(u(t),t) \quad . \tag{3.1}$$

The functions w and $\hat{v}$ are assumed continuous, the control set $U(t,x)$ is assumed to be independent of x, i.e., $U(t,x) \equiv U(t)$, and the mapping $t \to U(t)$ is assumed to be continuous.

Let $V(t)=\{\hat{v}(u,t) \mid u \in U(t)\}$ and let $G(t)$ be the convex closure of $V(t)$. Let $\mathcal{T}$ and $\mathcal{R}$, respectively, denote the trajectories and relaxed trajectories of Eq. (3.1), defined on $I=[a,b]$ with $a<b$, and starting at time a, in some fixed closed subset X_0 of R^n. We note that $\mathcal{T}$ consists of those absolutely continuous functions $x: I \to R^n$ for which $x(a) \in X_0$ and $\dot{x}(t) \in w(x(t),t)+V(t)$* a.e., whereas $\mathcal{R}$ consists of

* For $q \in R^n$ and $Q \subset R^n$, $q+Q$ denotes the set $\{q+q' \mid q' \in Q\}$.

those absolutely continuous functions x for which $x(a) \in X_0$ and $\dot{x}(t) \in w(x(t),t)+G(t)$ a.e. in I.

Definition 3.1. a) Let $\mathcal{V}$ denote the set of all measurable functions $v: I \to R^n$ such that $v(t) \in V(t)$ a.e. in I.

b) Let $\mathcal{G}$ denote the set of all measurable functions $g: I \to R^n$ such that $g(t) \in G(t)$ a.e. in I.

c) Let $\mathcal{Q} = \mathcal{G} - \mathcal{V}$ denote the complement of $\mathcal{V}$ in $\mathcal{G}$.

Remark 3.1. We consider $\mathcal{V}$, $\mathcal{Q}$, and $\mathcal{G}$ as subset of the real Banach space L_1 consisting of all integrable functions $\ell: I \to R^n$ with the norm of ℓ given by $\|\ell\|_1 = \int_I |\ell(t)| dt$.

Definition 3.2. For $x_0 \in X_0$ and $g \in \mathcal{G}$, let $\tau(x_0,g)$ denote the element x of $\mathcal{C}$ given by

$$\dot{x}(t) = w(x(t),t) + g(t) \quad \text{a.e. in I} \quad ,$$

$$x(a) = x_0 \quad .$$

Lemma 3.1. The mapping $\tau: X_0 \times \mathcal{G} \to \mathcal{C}$ is continuous and one-to-one.

Proof. Let x_0, x_0' belong to X_0 and g, g' belong to $\mathcal{G}$. Let $x = \tau(x_0,g)$ and $x' = \tau(x_0',g')$. Then, for $a \leq t \leq b$,

$$|x(t) - x'(t)| \leq |x_0 - x_0'| + \int_a^t |\dot{x}(s) - \dot{x}'(s)| ds$$

$$\leq |x_0 - x_0'| + \int_a^t |w(x(s),s) - w(x'(s),s)| ds$$

$$+ \int_a^t |g(s) - g'(s)| ds \leq \int_a^t k(s)|x(s) - x'(s)| ds$$

$$+ \|g - g'\|_1 + |x_0 - x_0'|$$

by Eq. (1.2). By Gronwall's lemma we obtain

$$|x(t) - x'(t)| \leq \exp\left(\int_a^t k(s) ds\right) \left[|x_0 - x_0'| + \|g - g'\|_1 \right]$$

so that τ is continuous.

Now suppose that $x=\tau(x_0,g)=\tau(x_0',g')=x'$. Then certainly $x_0=x_0'$. Furthermore, $\dot{x}(t)=\dot{x}'(t)$ a.e., so that

$$w(x(t),t) + g(t) = w(x'(t),t) + g'(t)$$

$$= w(x(t),t) + g'(t) \quad \text{a.e.}$$

and hence $g=g'$. Therefore τ is one-to-one.

Lemma 3.2. The sets $\mathcal{V}$ and $\mathcal{Q}$ $(=\mathcal{G} - \mathcal{V})$ are pathwise-connected* in L_1.

Proof. Let v_0 and v_1 be in $\mathcal{V}$. For $t \in [0,1]$ let h_t in $\mathcal{V}$ be given by

$$h_t(\tau) = v_0(\tau) \quad \text{for} \quad \tau \geq t \quad ,$$

and

$$h_t(\tau) = v_1(\tau) \quad \text{for} \quad \tau < t \quad .$$

Clearly, the map $t \to h_t$ is continuous; $h_0=v_0$ and $h_1=v_1$ so that $\mathcal{V}$ is pathwise-connected.

Let q_0 and q_1 be in $\mathcal{Q}$. Since $q_0 \notin \mathcal{V}$, the set E of all points t for which $q_0(t) \notin V(t)$ has positive measure. Let χ_E be the indicator function of E, i.e., $\chi_E(t)=1$ if $t \in E$, and $\chi_E(t)=0$ if $t \notin E$. Let

$$\xi(t) = \int_a^t \chi_E(s)ds \quad \text{for} \quad a \leq t \leq b \quad .$$

Then ξ is a continuous, non-decreasing function of t and $\xi(t)=0$. Let $t^* \in I$ be such that $\xi(t)=0$ for $t \leq t^*$ and $\xi(t)>0$ for $t>t^*$. Since measure of E is positive, $t^*<b$. This implies that

$$\text{measure } (E \cap (t^*,t^* + \delta)) > 0 \quad \text{for} \quad \delta > 0 \quad . \quad (3.2)$$

Now for each $t \in [a,b]$ define the function h_t as follows:

(i) Let $a \leq t \leq t^*$. Then $h_t(\tau)=q_0(\tau)$ for $\tau \geq t$ and $h_t(\tau)=q_1(\tau)$ for $\tau<t$.

---

* A subset K of a topological space T is <u>pathwise-connected</u> if given k_0,k_1 in K there is a continuous mapping $h:[0,1] \to T$ such that $h(0)=k_0$, $h(1)=k_1$, and $h(t) \in K$ for each t.

(ii) Let $t^* < t \leq b$. Then $h_t(\tau) = q_1(\tau)$ for $\tau \leq t^*$ and for $\tau \geq b - t + t^*$; whereas $h_t(\tau) = q_0(\tau)$ for $t^* < \tau < b - t + t^*$.

It is easy to check that $t \to h_t$ is continuous and $h_0 = q_0$, $h_1 = q_1$; also Eq. (3.2) implies that $h_t \in \mathcal{Q}$ for each t in I.

Definition 3.3. Let $\mathcal{S} = \bar{\mathcal{T}} - \mathcal{T} = \mathcal{R} - \mathcal{T}$. Thus $\mathcal{S}$ is the set of limit points of $\mathcal{T}$ which are not themselves members of $\mathcal{T}$.

Theorem 3.1. Suppose that for some $t^* \in I$ the set $V(t^*)$ is not convex. Then

(i) $\mathcal{S} \neq \Phi$ (Φ denotes the empty set),

(ii) $\bar{\mathcal{S}} = \bar{\mathcal{T}} = \mathcal{R}$,

(iii) $(\mathcal{S} \cap \mathcal{T}) = \Phi$, and

(iv) $\mathcal{S}$ and $\mathcal{T}$ are pathwise-connected subsets of $\mathcal{C}$ if and only if the initial set X_0 is pathwise-connected.

Proof. Since $V(t^*)$ is not convex, the set $\{w(z,t^*) + V(t^*)\}$ is not convex for every z in R^n. By Theorem 2.3, for every x in $\mathcal{T}$ and every $\varepsilon > 0$, there is an element $x_\varepsilon \in \mathcal{S}$ such that $\|x - x_\varepsilon\| < \varepsilon$. This implies (i) and (ii). (iii) follows from the definition of $\mathcal{S}$.

By Lemma 3.1, since τ is one-to-one,

$$\mathcal{T} = \{\tau(x_0, v) \mid x_0 \in X_0, v \in \mathcal{V}\} ,$$

and

$$\mathcal{S} = \{\tau(x_0, q) \mid x_0 \in X_0, q \in \mathcal{Q}\} .$$

By Lemma 3.2 the sets $\mathcal{V}$ and $\mathcal{Q}$ are pathwise-connected; and by Lemma 3.1 τ is continuous so that (iv) follows.

REFERENCES

1. L. Marcus and E. B. Lee, Optimal Control for Nonlinear Processes, Arch. Ratl. Mech. Anal., 8 (1961), pp. 36-58.

2. A. F. Fillipov, On Certain Questions in the Theory of Optimal Control, J. SIAM Control, 1 (1962), pp. 76-84.

3. E. Roxin, The Existence of Optimal Controls, Michigan Math. J., 9 (1962), pp. 109-119.

4. J. Warga, Relaxed Variational Problems, J. Math. Anal. Appl., 4 (1962), pp. 111-128.

5. L. W. Neustadt, The Existence of Optimal Controls in the Absence of Convexity Conditions, J. Math. Anal. Appl., 7 (1963), pp. 110-117.

6. D. Eggert and P. Varaiya, Representation of a Differential System, University of California Electronics Research Laboratory Memorandum ERL-M177 (to be published).

7. P. Halmos, The Range of a Vector Measure, Bull. Amer. Math. Soc., 54 (1948), pp. 416-421.

ON CERTAIN EXTREMAL PROBLEMS INVOLVING LINEAR FUNCTIONAL DIFFERENTIAL EQUATION MODELS*

D. Chyung[+] and E. B. Lee[++]

[+]Department of Electrical Engineering
University of South Carolina, Columbia, South Carolina

[++]Center for Control Science, Institute of Technology
University of Minnesota, Minneapolis, Minnesota

Introduction

In this paper we consider extremal (optimal control) problems for a class of linear controlled systems as modeled by functional differential equations with convex cost functionals and side constraints. The results are primarily generalizations of those when the model is an ordinary linear differential equation, (1).

The system model is the linear functional differential equation

$$\dot{x}(t) = \int_{-\tau}^{0} d_s A(t,s)x(t+s) + B(t)u(t) \tag{1}$$

with a continuous initial function $x(t) = \phi(t)$ on $[t_0-\tau, t_0]$, where

1. $x(t)$ is an $(n\times 1)$ state vector.
2. $u(t) \in \Omega$ is an $(m\times 1)$ measurable (control) function.
3. $\Omega \subset R^m$ is a compact convex restraint set.
4. $B(t)$ is a continuous $(n\times m)$ matrix.
5. $\tau > 0$ is a constant.
6. $A(t,s)$, defined for $t \geq t_0$, $-\infty < s < \infty$, is an $(n\times n)$ matrix continuous in t uniformly with respect to s, $-\tau \leq s \leq 0$.

*Research sponsored by Air Force Office of Scientific Research, Office of Aerospace Research, United States Air Force, Grant No. AF-AFOSR-571-66.

7. Each element of $A(t,s)$ is of bounded variation with respect to s, $-\tau \leq s \leq 0$.

The integral is in the sense of Lebesgue-Stieltjes, R^k denotes the real number space of dimension k and $\cdot = \frac{d}{dt}$. It is obvious that (1) includes the differential difference equation

$$\dot{x}(t) = \sum_{i=0}^{\ell} A_i(t)x(t-h_i)+B(t)u(t)$$

with $0 = h_0 < h_1 < \ldots < h_\ell \leq \tau$.

Let $Y(s,t)$ be the $(n \times n)$ matrix solution of

$$Y(s,t)+\int_s^{s+\Delta} Y(\sigma,t)A(\sigma,s-\sigma)d\sigma = E \tag{2}$$

$$\Delta = \begin{cases} t-s\,, & t-\tau \leq s \leq t \\ \tau & t_0 \leq s \leq t-\tau \end{cases}$$

on $t_0 \leq s \leq t$, $t_0 \leq t$, where E is the $(n \times n)$ identity matrix. For $t-\tau \leq s \leq t$, (2) is a Volterra integral equation, and hence one can obtain the solution $Y(s,t)$ on $[t-\tau,t]$. Once $Y(s,t)$ is known on $[t-\tau,t]$, then one can solve (2) obtaining the solution on $t-2\tau \leq s \leq t-\tau$ because (2) is again a Volterra equation on the interval. Thus through a step-by-step method, $Y(s,t)$ can be obtained on $[t_0,t]$. $Y(s,t)$ is continuous in t for $t \geq t_0$ and in s for $t_0 \leq s \leq t$.

Let $x(t,\phi)$ be the solution of the equation

$$\dot{x}(t) = \int_{-\tau}^{0} d_s A(t,s)x(t+s) \tag{3}$$

with the continuous initial function $x(t) = \phi(t)$ on $[t_0-\tau,t_0]$. Again, this equation can be solved through a step-by-step method by solving it first on $[t_0,t_0+\tau]$ and then proceeding to the next interval $[t_0+\tau,t_0+2\tau]$. Since the initial function $\phi(t)$ is continuous, the solution $x(t,\phi)$ is continuous on $[t_0,t]$. The solution of Eq. (1) is given by

$$x(t) = x(t,\phi)+\int_{t_0}^{t} Y(s,t)B(s)u(s)ds \tag{4}$$

for all $t \geq t_0$. From (4) it follows that $x(t)$ is continuous in t and depends continuously on $u(s)$, $t_0 \leq s \leq t$, for each fixed $t \geq t_0$.

The extremal (optimal control) problem is: Find a measurable (control) function $u(t) \subset \Omega$ on $[t_o, t_1]$ for a given fixed $t_1 \geq t_o$ which steers the response $x(t)$ of (1) from a given initial function $\phi(t)$ on $[t_o - t, t_o]$ to a given convex closed set $G \subset R^n$ at $t = t_1$, and at the same time, minimizes the functional

$$C(u) = g(x(t_1)) + \int_{t_o}^{t_1} [f^o(x(t),t) + h^o(u(t),t)]\,dt \tag{5}$$

while satisfying the side constraint*

$$x^{n+1}(t_1) = \int_{t_o}^{t_1} [f^{n+1}(x(t),t) + h^{n+1}(u(t),t)]\,dt \leq d \tag{6}$$

where $g(x)$ is a C^1 convex function in $x \epsilon R^n$, $d > 0$ is a given constant, $f^o(x,t)$ and $f^{n+1}(x,t)$ are C^1 real non-negative convex functions in $x \epsilon R^n$ for all t and $h^o(u,t)$ and $h^{n+1}(u,t)$ are real non-negative convex continuous functions in $u \epsilon R^m$ for all t.

Let $\tilde{x}(t) = (x^o(t), x(t), x^{n+1}(t)) \epsilon R^{n+2}$ be a $(n+2)$ column vector, and define a new system

$$\begin{aligned} \dot{x}^o(t) &= f^o(x(t),t) + h^o(u(t),t) \\ \dot{x}(t) &= \int_{-\tau}^{0} d_s A(t,s) x(t+s) + B(t) u(t) \\ \dot{x}^{n+1}(t) &= f^{n+1}(x(t),t) + h^{n+1}(u(t),t) \end{aligned} \tag{7}$$

with initial function $\tilde{x}(t) = \tilde{\phi}(t) = (0, \phi(t), 0)$ on $[t_o - \tau, t_o]$. Also, let

$$\tilde{G} = \{\tilde{x} = (x^o, x, x^{n+1}) \mid -\infty < x^o < \infty, x \epsilon G, 0 \leq x^{n+1} \leq d\}$$

Then the extremal problem can be rephrased as follows: Find a measurable (control) function $u(t) \subset \Omega$ on $[t_o, t_1]$ such that

---

*Additional side constraints $x^{n+2}(t_1) \leq d_2, \ldots, x^{n+\ell-1}(t_1) \leq d_{\ell-1}$, $x^{n+\ell}(t_1) = d_\ell, \ldots, x^{n+r}(t_1) = d_r$ of the same type as $x^{n+1}(t_1)$ can be added, and require no essential modification to the results which are given here.

it steers the response $\tilde{x}(t)$ of (7) from $\tilde{\phi}(t)$ on $[t_o-\tau, t_o]$ to the set $\tilde{G} \subset R^{n+2}$ at $t = t_1$ and minimizes the functional $C(u) = g(x(t_1)) + x^o(t_1)$.

In the remainder of the paper we consider questions of existence of the optimal control function, necessary and sufficient conditions for optimal control, and discuss other problems to which the theory is applicable.

The Set of Attainability and the Existence of Optimal Controllers

Define the set of attainability $\tilde{K} \subset R^{n+2}$ at $t = t_1$ to be the set of endpoints $\tilde{x}(t_1)$ of the responses of the system (7) for all admissible control functions $u(t) \subset \Omega$ on $[t_o, t_1]$. A control function (controller) $u(t)$ on $[t_o, t_1]$ is called admissible if $u(t) \in \Omega$ for all $t \in [t_o, t_1]$ and is measurable. Also define the saturation set $\tilde{K}_s \subset R^{n+2}$ of $\tilde{K}$ to be the set of all points $\tilde{x} = (x^o, x, x^{n+1})$ in R^{n+2} for which there exists a point $\tilde{y} = (y^o, y, y^{n+1})$ in $\tilde{K}$ such that $y^o \leq x^o$, $y = x$, $y^{n+1} \leq x^{n+1}$. Since f^o, h^o, f^{n+1}, h^{n+1} are all non-negative, $\tilde{K}$ is in the subspace $x^o \geq 0$, $x^{n+1} \geq 0$ of R^{n+2}, and so $\tilde{K}_s$ is also in the same subspace. Obviously $\tilde{K} \subset \tilde{K}_s$.

Theorem 1. The saturation set $\tilde{K}_s$ is convex and closed in R^{n+2}.

Proof: To prove the convexity, let $\tilde{x}_1 = (x_1{}^o, x_1, x_1{}^{n+1})$ and $\tilde{x}_2 = (x_2{}^o, x_2, x_2{}^{n+1})$ be any two points of $\tilde{K}_s$ and let $u_1(t)$ and $u_2(t)$ be control functions on $[t_o, t_1]$ which steer $\tilde{\phi}$ to $\tilde{x}_1$ and $\tilde{x}_2$ respectively. (If $\tilde{x}_1$ and $\tilde{x}_2$ do not belong to $\tilde{K}$, then take two points $\tilde{y}_1$ and $\tilde{y}_2$ in $\tilde{K}$ such that $y_1{}^o \leq x_1{}^o$, $y_1 = x_1$, $y_1{}^{n+1} \leq x_1{}^{n+1}$, $y_2{}^o \leq x_2{}^o$, $y_2 = x_2$, $y_2{}^{n+1} \leq x_2{}^{n+1}$ and apply the subsequent analysis to $\tilde{y}_1$ and $\tilde{y}_2$ with the inclusion of $\tilde{x}_1$ and $\tilde{x}_2$ in their saturation.) It has to be shown that $\tilde{x} = \lambda\tilde{x}_1 + (1-\lambda)\tilde{x}_2$ is in $\tilde{K}_s$ for all $0 < \lambda < 1$.

Define $u_\lambda(t) = \lambda u_1(t) + (1-\lambda)u_2(t)$ on $[t_o, t_1]$. Since Ω is convex, $u_\lambda(t)$ is an admissible controller, and so $\tilde{x}_\lambda(t_1) \in \tilde{K}$ where $\tilde{x}_\lambda(t)$ is the response corresponding to $u_\lambda(t)$. From Eq. (4) it follows that

$$x_\lambda(t_1) = x(t_1, \phi) + \int_{t_o}^{t_1} Y(s, t_1)B(s)u_\lambda(s)\,ds$$

$$= \lambda x_1(t_1) + (1-\lambda)x_2(t_1) = x$$

Also, from the convexity of f^o, f^{n+1}, h^o, h^{n+1}

$$x_\lambda{}^o(t_1) \leq \lambda x_1{}^o(t_1)+(1-\lambda)x_2{}^o(t_1) = \lambda x_1{}^o+(1-\lambda)x_2{}^o = x^o$$

and

$$x_\lambda{}^{n+1}(t_1) \leq \lambda x_1{}^{n+1}(t_1)+(1-\lambda)x_2{}^{n+1}(t_1)$$
$$= \lambda x_1{}^{n+1}+(1-\lambda)x_2{}^{n+1} = x^{n+1}$$

Then, since $\tilde{x}_\lambda(t_1) \in \tilde{K}$, by the definition of $\tilde{K}_s$, $\tilde{x} = \lambda\tilde{x}_1 + (1-\lambda)\tilde{x}_2$ is in $\tilde{K}_s$. Thus $\tilde{K}_s$ is convex.

To establish that $\tilde{K}_s$ is closed, consider a sequence of points $\tilde{y}_j = (y_j{}^o, y_j, y_j{}^{n+1})$ in $\tilde{K}_s$ converging to a point $\tilde{y} = (y^o, y, y^{n+1})$ in R^{n+2}. Then there exists a corresponding sequence of points $\tilde{x}_j = (x_j{}^o, x_j, x_j{}^{n+1})$ in $\tilde{K}$ such that $x_j{}^o \leq y_j{}^o$, $x_j = y_j$, $x_j{}^{n+1} \leq y_j{}^{n+1}$ for each j. Let $u_j(t)$ on $[t_o, t_1]$ be the admissible control function with response $\tilde{x}_j(t)$ such that $\tilde{x}_j(t_1) = \tilde{x}_j$. Since Ω is a compact convex set, the family of all admissible controllers on $[t_o, t_1]$ is weakly compact (see (2)). Therefore there exists a subsequence $\{u_i(t)\}$ of $\{u_j(t)\}$ which converges weakly to an admissible controller $u(t) \subset \Omega$ on $[t_o, t_1]$. Let $\tilde{x}(t)$ be the response corresponding to $u(t)$. Then $\tilde{x}(t_1) \in \tilde{K}$. From (4) and the weak convergence

$$y = \lim y_i = \lim x_i = \lim x_i(t_1) = x(t_1)$$

From (7) and the convexity of f^o, f^{n+1}, h^o, h^{n+1}

$$y^o = \lim y_i{}^o \geq \lim\inf x_i{}^o = \lim\inf x_i{}^o(t_1) \geq x^o(t_1)$$

and

$$y^{n+1} = \lim y_i{}^{n+1} \geq \lim\inf x_i{}^{n+1} = \lim\inf x_i{}^{n+1}(t_1) \geq x^{n+1}(t_1)$$

This shows that $y^o \geq x^o(t_1)$, $y = x(t_1)$, $y^{n+1} \geq x^{n+1}(t_1)$. Then $\tilde{y} \in \tilde{K}_s$ for $\tilde{x}(t_1) \in \tilde{K}$. Hence $\tilde{K}_s$ is closed. Q.E.D.

Since Ω is compact and t_1 is fixed, it is apparent the response $\tilde{x}(t_1)$ of (7) is bounded for every admissible controller $u(t) \subset \Omega$ on $[t_o, t_1]$. Therefore the set $\tilde{K}$ is bounded, and

$$z^o = \sup_{\tilde{x} \in \tilde{K}} x^o \quad \text{and} \quad z^{n+1} = \sup_{\tilde{x} \in \tilde{K}} x^{n+1}$$

are finite. Furthermore the set K of end points $x(t_1)$ of responses $x(t)$ of (1) with $x(t) = \phi(t)$ on $[t_o-\tau, t_o]$ for all admissible controllers $u(t) \subset \Omega$ on $[t_o, t_1]$ is convex and compact. K is just the orthogonal projection of the set $\tilde{K}$, and hence $\tilde{K}_s$, on the x-space, R^n (the subspace $x^o = 0$, $x^{n+1} = 0$ in R^{n+2}). Thus the set

$$\tilde{M} = \{\tilde{x} = (x^o, x, x^{n+1}) | \tilde{x} \in \tilde{K}_s,\ 0 \leq x^o \leq z^o,\ 0 \leq x^{n+1} \leq z^{n+1}\}$$

is compact and convex in R^{n+2} and $\tilde{K} \subset \tilde{M}$.

Theorem 2. If there exists an admissible controller which steers the response $\tilde{x}(t)$ from the initial function $\tilde{\phi}(t)$ on $[t_o-\tau, t_o]$ to the target set $\tilde{G}$ at $t = t_1$, then there exists an optimal controller which steers the response to $\tilde{G}$ at $t = t_1$ and minimizes $C(u) = g(x)+x^o$ on $\tilde{K} \cap \tilde{G}$.

Proof: $\tilde{G} \cap \tilde{M} \neq \phi$ for $\tilde{G} \cap \tilde{K} \neq \phi$ by assumption. Therefore the continuous function $g(x)+x^o$ assumes a minimum on $\tilde{G} \cap \tilde{M}$. Let $\tilde{x}^* = (x^{o*}, x^*, x^{n+1*})$ be a point of $\tilde{G} \cap \tilde{M}$ where $g(x)+x^o$ is minimum. Then there exists a point $\tilde{y}$ in $\tilde{K}$ such that $x^{o*} \leq y^o$, $x^* = y$, $x^{n+1*} \leq y^{n+1}$ for $\tilde{x}^* \in \tilde{M} \subset \tilde{K}_s$. Obviously $\tilde{y} \in \tilde{G} \cap \tilde{K}$ and $g(x^*)+x^{o*} \geq g(y)+y^o$ for $y = x^* \in G$. But $g(x^*)+x^{o*}$ is a minimum on $\tilde{G} \cap \tilde{M}$, and $\tilde{K} \subset \tilde{M}$. Therefore $g(x^*)+x^{o*} = g(y)+y^o$ and is a minimum of $g(x)+x^o$ on $\tilde{G} \cap \tilde{K}$.

Q.E.D.

The results of this section apply to any system for which the input-output relationship can be expressed as in Eq. (4). For the next section we need the differential form (as in Eq. (7)) to establish a necessary and sufficient condition for steering to the boundary of the attainable set.

Conditions for Optimal Control

Since $\tilde{K}_s$ is closed and bounded below with respect to the x^o-axis and the cost functional is $C(u) = g(x)+x^o$, an optimum point where $C(u)$ assumes a minimum value must be a boundary point of $\tilde{K}_s$. Otherwise, there exists a point $\tilde{y}$ in $\tilde{K}_s$ such that $y^o < x^{o*}$, $y = x^*$, $y^{n+1} \leq x^{n+1*}$ and so $g(y)+y^o < g(x^*)+x^{*o}$ which contradicts the assumption that $g(x^*)+x^{*o}$ is minimum.

Define an admissible controller $u(t) \subset \Omega$ on $[t_o, t_1]$ to be a maximal controller if there exists a nontrivial response $\tilde{\eta}(t) = (\eta_o(t), \eta(t), \eta_{n+1}(t))$ of the equations

$$\eta_0(t) = \eta_0 = \text{constant} \leq 0$$

$$\eta_{n+1}(t) = \eta_{n+1} = \text{constant} \leq 0$$

$$\eta(t) + \int_t^{t+\Delta} \eta(s)A(s,t-s)ds + \int_{t_1}^{t} \eta_0 \frac{\partial f^0}{\partial x}(x(s),s)ds \tag{8}$$

$$+ \int_{t_1}^{t} \eta_{n+1} \frac{\partial f^{n+1}}{\partial x}(x(s),s)ds = \text{constant},$$

$$\Delta = \begin{cases} t_1 - t & t_1 - \tau \leq t \leq t_1 \\ \tau & t_0 \leq t \leq t_1 - \tau \end{cases}$$

such that

$$\eta_0 h^0(u(t),t) + \eta(t)B(t)u(t) + \eta_{n+1} h^{n+1}(u(t),t)$$
$$= \max_{u \in \Omega} \{ \eta_0 h^0(u,t) + \eta(t)B(t)u + \eta_{n+1} h^{n+1}(u,t) \} \tag{9}$$

almost everywhere on $[t_0,t_1]$. Here $x(t)$ is the response of (1) corresponding to the controller $u(t)$ with the initial function $x(t) = \phi(t)$ on $[t_0-\tau, t_0]$. Note that (8) is the same type of Volterra integral equation as (2), and hence it can be solved by the same step-by-step method. Also, the solution $\eta(t)$, and hence $\tilde{\eta}(t)$, is absolutely continuous.

Theorem 3 (Maximum Principle). If an admissible controller $u(t)$ on $[t_0,t_1]$ is a maximal controller, then it steers the response $\tilde{x}(t)$ to the boundary of $\tilde{K}_s$ at $t = t_1$. Conversely, if $\tilde{x}_1$ in $\tilde{K}$ is a boundary point of $\tilde{K}_s$, then the controller which steers the response to $\tilde{x}_1$ at $t = t_1$ is a maximal controller.

Proof: Let $u(t)$ be an admissible controller steering the corresponding response to a boundary point $\tilde{x}_1$ of $\tilde{K}_s$. Then, since $\tilde{K}_s$ is convex, there exists a supporting hyperplane π of $\tilde{K}_s$ at $\tilde{x}_1$. Choose a normal vector $\tilde{p}$ to π directed into the halfspace defined by π which does not contain $\tilde{K}_s$. Let $\tilde{\eta}(t)$ be the nontrivial solution of the Eq. (8) such that $\tilde{\eta}(t_1) = \tilde{p}$. Then $u(t)$ satisfies the maximal condition (9) with the response $\tilde{\eta}(t)$. To prove this, assume $u(t)$ does not satisfy the maximal condition (9). Let $\bar{u}(t)$ be an admissible controller which satisfies the maximal condition

(9). (For the existence of such a controller, see Chapter II of (3) or (4)), that is,

$$\eta_o h^o(\bar{u}(t),t)+\eta(t)B(t)\bar{u}(t)+\eta_{n+1}h^{n+1}(\bar{u}(t),t)$$
$$= \max_{u\in\Omega}\{\eta_o h^o(u,t)+\eta(t)B(t)u+\eta_{n+1}h^{n+1}(u,t)\}$$

almost everywhere on $[t_o,t_1]$. Then, since both $\bar{u}(t)$ and $u(t)$ are measurable, there exists a compact subset I of $[t_o,t_1]$ with positive measure whereon $\bar{u}(t)$ and $u(t)$ are continuous and

$$\begin{aligned}&\eta_o h^o(u(t),t)+\eta(t)B(t)u(t)+\eta_{n+1}h^{n+1}(u(t),t)+\delta\\&\quad<\eta_o h^o(\bar{u}(t),t)+\eta(t)B(t)\bar{u}(t)+\eta_{n+1}h^{n+1}(\bar{u}(t),t)\end{aligned} \tag{10}$$

for some $\delta > 0$ on I. Choose a T in I such that the set $(T,T+\varepsilon)\cap I$ has measure $\varepsilon(1+0(\varepsilon))$ for all small $\varepsilon > 0$, where $0(\varepsilon)/\varepsilon \to 0$ as $\varepsilon \to 0$.

Define a controller on $[t_o,t_1]$

$$u_\varepsilon(t) = \begin{cases}\bar{u}(t) & \text{on} \quad (T,T+\varepsilon)\cap I\\ u(t) & \text{elsewhere on} \quad [t_o,t_1]\end{cases} \tag{11}$$

Obviously $u_\varepsilon(t)$ is admissible, and so $\tilde{x}_\varepsilon(t_1)\in\tilde{K}$ where $\tilde{x}_\varepsilon(t)$ is the response corresponding to $u_\varepsilon(t)$. Using Eqs. (7) and (8), and integration by parts we found

$$\tilde{\eta}(t_1)\tilde{x}(t_1)-\tilde{\eta}(t_o)\tilde{x}(t_o) = \int_{t_o}^{t_1}\tilde{\eta}(t)\dot{\tilde{x}}(t)dt+\int_{t_o}^{t_1}d\tilde{\eta}(t)\tilde{x}(t)$$

$$= \int_{t_o}^{t_1}\eta_o\dot{x}^o(t)dt+\int_{t_o}^{t_1}\eta(t)\dot{x}(t)dt+\int_{t_o}^{t_1}\eta_{n+1}\dot{x}^{n+1}(t)dt$$
$$+\int_{t_o}^{t_1}d\eta(t)x(t)$$

$$= \int_{t_o}^{t_1}\{\eta_o(f^o(x(t),t)+h^o(u(t),t))$$
$$+\eta_{n+1}(f^{n+1}(x(t),t)+h^{n+1}(u(t),t))\}\,dt$$

$$+\int_{t_o}^{t_1} \eta(t)B(t)u(t)dt$$

$$-\int_{t_o}^{t_1}\left\{\eta_o \frac{\partial f^o}{\partial x}(x(t),t)+\eta_{n+1}\frac{\partial f^{n+1}}{\partial x}(x(t),t)\right\}x(t)dt$$

$$+\int_{t_o-\tau}^{t_o} d_t\left\{\int_{t_o}^{t+\tau}\eta(s)A(s,t-s)ds\right\}x(t) \tag{12}$$

For the controller $u_\varepsilon(t)$ with response $\tilde{x}_\varepsilon(t)$

$$\tilde{\eta}(t_1)\tilde{x}_\varepsilon(t_1)-\tilde{\eta}(t_o)\tilde{x}_\varepsilon(t_o)$$

$$=\int_{t_o}^{t_1}\{\eta_o(f^o(x_\varepsilon(t),t)+h^o(u_\varepsilon(t),t))$$

$$+\eta_{n+1}(f^{n+1}(x_\varepsilon(t),t)+h^{n+1}(u_\varepsilon(t),t))\}dt$$

$$+\int_{t_o}^{t_1}\eta(t)B(t)u_\varepsilon(t)dt-\int_{t_o}^{t_1}\left\{\eta_o\frac{\partial f^o}{\partial x}(x(t),t)\right.$$

$$\left.+\eta_{n+1}\frac{\partial f^{n+1}}{\partial x}(x(t),t)\right\}x_\varepsilon(t)dt$$

$$+\int_{t_o-\tau}^{t_o} d_t\left\{\int_{t_o}^{t+\tau}\eta(s)A(s,t-s)ds\right\}x_\varepsilon(t) \tag{13}$$

Since $x(t) = x_\varepsilon(t) = \phi(t)$ on $[t_o-\tau, t_o]$, substracting (12) from (13) yields

$$\tilde{\eta}(t_1)\tilde{x}_\varepsilon(t_1)-\tilde{\eta}(t_1)\tilde{x}(t_1)$$

$$=\int_{t_o}^{t_1}\{\eta_o h^o(x_\varepsilon(t),t)+\eta(t)B(t)u_\varepsilon(t)+\eta_{n+1}h^{n+1}(x_\varepsilon(t),t)$$

$$-\eta_o h^o(x(t),t)+\eta(t)B(t)u(t)+\eta_{n+1}h^{n+1}(x(t),t)\}dt$$

$$+\int_{t_0}^{t_1} \eta_0 \{ f^0(x_\varepsilon(t),t) - f^0(x(t),t) - \frac{\partial f^0}{\partial x}(x(t),t)(x_\varepsilon(t)-x(t))\} \, dt$$

$$+\int_{t_0}^{t_1} \eta_{n+1} \{ f^{n+1}(x_\varepsilon(t),t) - f^{n+1}(x(t),t) - \frac{\partial f^{n+1}}{\partial x}(x(t),t)(x_\varepsilon(t)-x(t))\} \, dt \qquad (14)$$

From (4) it is possible to show that, for small $\varepsilon > 0$

$$|x_\varepsilon(t) - x(t)| < c_1 \varepsilon \qquad (15)$$

for some $c_1 > 0$ on $[t_0, t_1]$. Then since $\frac{\partial f^0}{\partial x}$ and $\frac{\partial f^{n+1}}{\partial x}$ are continuous

$$|f^0(x_\varepsilon(t),t) - f^0(x(t),t) - \frac{\partial f^0}{\partial x}(x(t),t)(x_\varepsilon(t)-x(t))| < \varepsilon O(\varepsilon) \qquad (16)$$

on $[t_0, t_1]$. The same holds for $f^{n+1}(x,t)$. Therefore, for small $\varepsilon > 0$, from (10), (11), (16) and (14)

$$\tilde{\eta}(t_1)\tilde{x}_\varepsilon(t_1) - \tilde{\eta}(t_1)\tilde{x}(t_1) > \delta\varepsilon(1+O(\varepsilon)) + c_2\varepsilon O(\varepsilon) + c_3\varepsilon O(\varepsilon)$$

for some constants c_2 and c_3. Then for sufficiently small ε,

$$\tilde{\eta}(t_1)\tilde{x}_\varepsilon(t_1) > \tilde{\eta}(t_1)\tilde{x}(t_1)$$

But this is impossible for $\tilde{\eta}(t_1) = \tilde{p}$ is a normal vector to the supporting hyperplane π of $\tilde{K}_s$ at $\tilde{x}(t_1) = \tilde{x}_1$ directed into the halfspace defined by π which does not contain $\tilde{K}_s$ and $\tilde{x}_\varepsilon(t_1) \in \check{K} \subset \check{K}_s$. Hence $u(t)$ satisfies the maximal condition (9).

Conversely, assume $u^*(t)$ with response $\tilde{x}^*(t)$ satisfies the maximal condition (9) with a corresponding response $\tilde{\eta}(t)$. Let $\tilde{x}(t)$ be a response corresponding to any admissible controller $u(t)$. The same calculation as before gives the same Eq. (14) for

$$\tilde{\eta}(t_1)\tilde{x}^*(t_1) - \tilde{\eta}(t_1)\tilde{x}(t_1)$$

except that $\tilde{x}_\epsilon(t)$ and $u_\epsilon(t)$ are replaced by $\tilde{x}^*(t)$ and $\tilde{u}^*(t)$ respectively. Then, from the convexity of $f^o(x,t)$, $f^{n+1}(x,t)$, $h^o(u,t)$, $h^{n+1}(u,t)$ together with the fact that $u^*(t)$ satisfies the maximal condition (9), it follows that

$$\tilde{\eta}(t_1)\tilde{x}^*(t_1) \geq \tilde{\eta}(t_1)\tilde{x}(t_1)$$

for all $\tilde{x}(t_1) \in \tilde{K}$. Therefore $\tilde{x}^*(t_1)$ is an extremal point of $\tilde{K}$ in the $\tilde{\eta}(t_1)$ direction. But, since $\eta_o(t_1) = \eta_o \leq 0$ and $\eta_{n+1}(t_1) = \eta_{n+1} \leq 0$, from the definition of $\tilde{K}_s$, $\tilde{x}^*(t_1)$ must be on the boundary of $\tilde{K}_s$ and $\tilde{\eta}(t_1)$ is an outward normal vector to the convex set $\tilde{K}_s$ at $\tilde{x}^*(t_1)$. Q.E.D.

The following result is an immediate consequence of Theorems 3 and 4.

Theorem 4. Assume the target set $G = R^n$ (A free endpoint problem). If there exists an admissible controller $u(t)$ on $[t_o, t_1]$ with response $\tilde{x}(t)$ such that $x^{n+1}(t_1) \leq d$. Then there exists a solution $x^*(t), \eta^*(t)$ of

$$\dot{x}(t) = \int_{-\tau}^{o} d_s A(t,s)x(t+s) + B(t)u(t,\eta)$$

$$\eta(t) + \int_{t_t}^{t+\Delta} \eta(s)A(s,t-s)ds + \int_{t_1}^{t} \eta_o \frac{\partial f^o}{\partial x}(x(s),s)ds$$

$$+ \int_{t_1}^{t} \eta_{n+1} \frac{\partial f^{n+1}}{\partial x}(x(s),s)ds = C$$

with $\eta(t_1) = -\frac{\partial}{\partial x} g(x(t_1)$, $x(t) = \phi(t)$ on $[t_o - \tau, t_o]$ and either

$$\eta_o \leq 0 \qquad \eta_{n+1} < 0 \qquad x^{n+1}(t_1) = d$$

or

$$\eta_o \leq 0 \qquad \eta_{n+1} = 0 \qquad x^{n+1}(t_1) \leq d$$

where $C = \eta(t_1)$ is a constant and

$$\Delta = \begin{cases} t_1 - t, & t_1 - \tau \leq t \leq t_1 \\ \tau & t_o \leq t \leq t_1 - \tau \end{cases}$$

Here $u(t,\eta)$ is defined by the maximal condition

$$\eta_o h^o(u(t,\eta),t)+\eta(t)B(t)u(t,\eta)+\eta_{n+1}h^{n+1}(u(t,\eta),t)$$
$$= \max_{u\in\Omega}\{\eta_o h^o(u,t)+\eta(t)B(t)u+\eta_{n+1}h^{n+1}(u,t)\}$$

An optimal controller is given by $u^*(t) = u(t,\eta^*(t))$.

If one considers the case when we have steering to a target set G then the above Theorem 4 must only be modified to account for the direction of $\tilde{\eta}(t_1)$ with this further restriction (see (3)).

Other problems

The time optimal problem of steering from the initial function $\phi(t)$ to the target G in minimum time duration can be studied by extending the results of (5) in the above manner. In the above notation, let $f^o \equiv 1$, $h^o \equiv 0 \equiv g$, and consider the set of attainability in R^{n+1},

$$\hat{K}(t) = \{(x,x^{n+1}) \mid x = x(t),\ x^{n+1} = x^{n+1}(t),$$
$$u(s) \text{ admissible on } [t_o,t]\}$$

Define the saturation $\hat{K}_s(t)$ of $\hat{K}(t)$ as above in R^{n+1}. $\hat{K}_s(t)$ is the orthogonal projection of $\tilde{K}_s(t)$ on the plane $x^o = 0$ in R^{n+2}. $\hat{K}_s(t)$ is closed and convex in R^{n+1}. Moreover $\hat{K}_s(t)\subset R^{n+1}$ moves continuously with t in the sense that compact parts of it (near the origin) move continuously (see (5)). Let $\hat{G} = \{(x,x^{n+1}) \mid x\in G,\ 0 \le x^{n+1} \le d\}$. Then it can be shown that if $\hat{G}\subset R^{n+1}$ meets the interior of $\hat{K}_s(t_1)\subset R^{n+1}$ there exists $\delta > 0$ such that $\hat{G}$ meets $\hat{K}_s(t)$ for $|t-t_1| < \delta$. Thus the time optimal problem involves steering to the boundary of $\hat{K}_s(t_1)\subset R^{n+1}$ and the above Theorems 3 and 4 are then available, with the obvious reduction in dimension from R^{n+2} to R^{n+1}, to characterize controllers which steer to the boundary. Results on necessary and sufficient conditions for time optimal control then follow as in (5).

Sometimes it is essential to steer the response to a given final function $\psi(t)$ on $t_1-\tau \le t \le t_1$. This problem can be handled by solving the following problem: let

$$C_1(u) = \int_{t_o}^{t_1}\{f^{n+1}(x(t),t)+h^{n+1}(u(t),t)\}\,dt$$

$$f^{n+1}(x(t),t) = \begin{cases} 0 & t_o \leq t \leq t_1-\tau \\ |x(t)-\psi(t)|^2 & t_1-\tau \leq t \leq t_1 \end{cases}$$

$$h^{n+1}(u(t),t) \equiv 0$$

Then find a control function which minimizes

$$C(u) = g(x(t_1))+\int_{t_o}^{t_1} \{f^o(x(t),t)+h^o(u(t),t)\}\, dt$$

among the controllers which minimize $C_1(u)$. This problem can be solved by the method of this paper, and a more detailed result will be published later. If the minimum of $C_1(u)$ is zero then one has a solution. If the minimum $C_1(u)$ is not zero, then there are no admissible controls which steer the response to the given final function. Steering to an ε-neighborhood of ψ is handled by minimizing $C(u)$ among those controllers for which $C_1(u) \leq \varepsilon$. Other norms may be used when applying the above theory to such problems.

The problem of steering from an initial function to a final function in an optimum fashion can be formulated as a problem in function space. If the basic system is autonomous, in addition to being linear, the theory of semigroups (6) can be applied and there are results on controllability, etc. for this class of problems (7),(8) in function space.

References

1. E. B. Lee, "Linear optimal control problems with isoperimetric constraints," IEEE Trans. on Auto. Control, Vol. A.C.12 (1967).
2. N. Dunford and I. Schwartz, Linear Operators Part I, Interscience, New York 1958.
3. E. B. Lee and L. Markus, Foundations of Optimal Control Theory, John Wiley and Sons Inc., New York, 1967.
4. A. F. Filippov, "On certain questions in the theory of optimal control," SIAM J. on Control, Vol. 1, pp. 76-84 (1962).

5. E. B. Lee, "An approximation to linear bounded phase coordinate control problems," J. of Math. Anal. and Appl., Vol. 13, pp. 550-564 (1966).
6. J. K. Hale, "Linear functional differential equations with constant coefficients," Contributions to Diff. Eqs., Vol. II, pp. 291-317 (1963).
7. H. O. Fattorini, "Some remarks on complete controllability," SIAM J. on Control, Vol. 4, pp. 686-694 (1966).
8. A. V. Balakrishnan, "Optimal control problems in Banach spaces," SIAM J. on Control, Vol. 3, pp. 153-180 (1965).

FURTHER GEOMETRIC ASPECTS OF OPTIMAL PROCESSES: MULTIPLE-STAGE DYNAMIC SYSTEMS

A. BLAQUIÈRE
Laboratoire d'Automatique Théorique, Faculté des Sciences de Paris, Université de Paris, France

G. LEITMANN
Division of Applied Mechanics, University of California, Berkeley, U.S.A.

1. Introduction

This paper is a continuation of the work developed in (1) and summarized in (2). Here we shall consider a multiple-stage dynamic system, that is, one characterized by n real numbers $x_1, x_2, \ldots x_n$ and by the stage k of the process, where $k \in \{0,1,\ldots K\}$. It is convenient to think of the state of the system as a point $\tilde{x} = (x_1, x_2, \ldots x_{n+1})$ in E^{n+1}, its (n+1)-st component being the stage; that is, $x_{n+1}=k$.

As in (2) it is our purpose to discuss some geometric aspects of optimal processes rather than to present another derivation of necessary conditions derived earlier, e.g., see (3) - (5). However, to illustrate some consequences of geometric properties we shall indicate a derivation of necessary conditions for a restricted class of problems.

2. Transfer of the System

We shall consider the state as a function of stage k satisfying difference equations

$$x_j(k+1)-x_j(k) = f_j^k(x_1(k),\ldots x_n(k),u_1(k),\ldots u_m(k)) \qquad j = 1,2,\ldots n \qquad (1)$$

$$x_{n+1}(k+1)-x_{n+1}(k) = 1$$

The control $u = (u_1, u_2, \ldots u_m)$ is admissible if $u(k) \in U$ for all k, where U is a prescribed set in E^m. A control sequence $u_\ell = \{u(i), u(i+1), \ldots u(i+\ell-1)\}$, $0 \le i \le K-1$, $1 \le \ell \le K-i$, will be termed admissible if $u(i) \in U$ for all i. The set of all admissible control sequences will be denoted by $\mathcal{U}$.

For given u_ℓ and $\tilde{x}(i) = \tilde{x}^i$, Eqs. (1) define a unique sequence of states $\{\tilde{x}(i), \tilde{x}(i+1), \ldots \tilde{x}(i+\ell)\}$ called a path and denoted by p_ℓ. A subsequence

$$\{\tilde{x}(i+r), \tilde{x}(i+r+1), \ldots \tilde{x}(i+s)\} \quad r, s \in \{0, 1, \ldots \ell\}, \quad r \le s$$

will be called a subpath and denoted by p_{rs}; of course, $p_{rs} \subseteq p_\ell$ and $p_{0\ell} = p_\ell$.

In the subsequent discussion we shall be concerned with the paths generated by all admissible control sequences. In particular we shall be concerned with transferring the system from an initial state $\tilde{x}^i$ to a prescribed terminal state $\tilde{x}^K$.

3. Cost and Optimality

Given u_ℓ and $\tilde{x}^i$, the cost of transfer from $\tilde{x}(i+r) = \tilde{x}^{i+r}$ to $\tilde{x}(i+s) = \tilde{x}^{i+s}$ along subpath p_{rs} will be denoted by $V(\tilde{x}^{i+r}, \tilde{x}^{i+s}; u_\ell, p_{rs})$.

We shall call an admissible control sequence optimal for transfer from $\tilde{x}^i$ to $\tilde{x}^K$, and denote it by u_ℓ^* and the corresponding path by p_ℓ^*, if

$$V(\tilde{x}^i, \tilde{x}^K; u_\ell^*, p_\ell^*) \le V(\tilde{x}^i, \tilde{x}^K; u_\ell, p_\ell) \qquad \forall\, u_\ell \in \mathcal{U} \tag{2}$$

Since the minimum cost is unique, we write

$$V^*(\tilde{x}^i; \tilde{x}^K) = V(\tilde{x}^i, \tilde{x}^K; u_\ell^*, p_\ell^*) \tag{3}$$

4. Additivity Property

We shall restrict the discussion to systems for which the cost of transfer obeys an additivity property; that is, given $u_\ell \in \mathcal{U}$ and $\tilde{x}(i)=\tilde{x}^i$,

$$V(\tilde{x}^{i+r},\tilde{x}^{i+t}; u_\ell, p_{rt}) = V(\tilde{x}^{i+r},\tilde{x}^{i+s}; u_\ell, p_{rs}) + V(\tilde{x}^{i+s},\tilde{x}^{i+t}; u_\ell, p_{st}) \tag{4}$$

for all s, $r \leq s \leq t$, where $p_{rt} = p_{rs} \cup p_{st}$, and

$$V(\tilde{x}^{i+r}, x^{i+r}; u_\ell, p_{rr}) = 0$$

Eventually we shall consider systems for which the cost of transfer from $\tilde{x}^k$ to $\tilde{x}^{k+1}$ is given by $f_0^k(x_1(k),\ldots x_n(k),\ u_1(k),\ldots u_m(k))$, so that the additivity property holds; namely,

$$V(\tilde{x}^{i+r},\tilde{x}^{i+s}; u_\ell, p_{rs}) = \sum_{k=i+r}^{i+s} f_0^k(x_1(k),\ldots x_n(k), u_1(k),\ldots u_m(k)) \tag{5}$$

5. Augmented State, Trajectories and Limiting Surfaces

As in (2) we now introduce

(i) Cost variable x_0 and augmented state

$$x = (x_0, \tilde{x}) \in E^{n+2};$$

(ii) Trajectory

$$\Gamma_\ell = \{x^{i+r} : x_0^{i+r} + V(\tilde{x}^{i+r},\tilde{x}^{i+\ell}; u_\ell, p_{r\ell}) = C,\ p_{r\ell} \subseteq p_\ell,\ 0 \leq r \leq \ell\} \tag{6}$$

where C is a constant and $x_0(i+r) = x_0^{i+r}$;

(iii) Optimal trajectory

$$\Gamma_\ell^* = \{x^{i+r}: x_0^{i+r} + V(\tilde{x}^{i+r}, \tilde{x}^K; u_\ell^*, p_{r\ell}) = C,$$

$$p_{r\ell} \subseteq p_\ell^*, \; 0 \le r \le \ell = K-i\} \qquad (7)$$

(iv) Initial state sets

$$E = \{\tilde{x}^i : \exists \, p_\ell \text{ from } \tilde{x}^i \text{ to } \tilde{x}^K\}$$

$$E^* = \{\tilde{x}^i : \exists \, p_\ell^* \text{ from } \tilde{x}^i \text{ to } \tilde{x}^K\}$$

(v) Limiting surface Σ in $E^* \times x_0$, defined by

$$x_0 + V^*(\tilde{x}; \tilde{x}^K) = C \quad \forall \tilde{x} \in E^* \qquad (8)$$

Moreover we shall consider surface

$$\Sigma_k = \Sigma \cap P_k, \qquad P_k = \{x: x_{n+1} = k\} \qquad (9)$$

6. Some Global Properties of Limiting Surfaces

The results of our earlier work (2) concerning global properties of limiting surfaces apply here as well. Let us recall some of them.

A given Σ surface, corresponding to parameter C, separates $E^* \times x_0$ into two disjoint sets

$$A/\Sigma = \{x: x_0 > C - V^*(\tilde{x}; \tilde{x}^K) \;\; \forall \tilde{x} \in E^*\} \qquad (10)$$

$$B/\Sigma = \{x: x_0 < C - V^*(\tilde{x}; \tilde{x}^K) \;\; \forall \tilde{x} \in E^*\} \qquad (11)$$

A point $x \in A/\Sigma$ will be termed an A-point relative to Σ, and a point $x \in B/\Sigma$ a B-point relative to Σ.

As in (2) we can prove

Theorem 1. An optimal trajectory with one point on a limiting surface Σ lies entirely on Σ; that is, limiting surfaces are the loci of all optimal trajectories.

Theorem 2. A trajectory whose initial point belongs to a

given limiting surface Σ has no B-point relative to Σ.

Corollary 1. A trajectory whose initial point is an A-point relative to a given limiting surface Σ has no B-point relative to Σ nor, indeed, a point on it.

7. Interior Points of a Surface Σ_k

We shall say that $x \in \Sigma_k$ is an interior point of Σ_k if there exists an (n+1)-dimensional ball B(x) with center at x, such that

$$B(x) \subset P_k \cap (E^* \times x_0)$$

8. Some Local Properties of Σ_k Surfaces

A study of local properties of Σ_k surfaces involves arguments similar to those employed in (2) for the study of such properties of Σ surfaces. Here we shall mention only the modifications which should be introduced in order to make the earlier results applicable. Instead of S(x), $C_A(x)$ and $C_B(x)$, we shall define local cones $S^k(x)$, $C_A^k(x)$ and $C_B^k(x)$ at interior point x of Σ_k.

Consider the sets

$$A/\Sigma_k = (A/\Sigma) \cap P_k, \quad B/\Sigma_k = (B/\Sigma) \cap P_k$$

$$\widetilde{A/\Sigma_k} = (A/\Sigma_k) \cup \Sigma_k, \quad \widetilde{B/\Sigma_k} = (B/\Sigma_k) \cup \Sigma_k$$

Let η be a bound vector at interior point x of Σ_k, such that $x+\eta \in P_k$. As a first basic assumption, we shall assume that there exists $\sigma < 0$ such that for every ϵ, $0 < \epsilon < \sigma$, $x + \epsilon\eta$ belongs either to $\widetilde{A/\Sigma_k}$ or to B/Σ_k.

Next let us define local cones

$$C_A^k(x) = \{x+\eta \colon x \in \Sigma_k, \exists\, \alpha > 0 \ni \forall \epsilon, 0 < \epsilon < \alpha, \; x + \epsilon\eta \in \widetilde{A/\Sigma_k}\}$$

$$C_B^k(x) = \{x+\eta: x \in \Sigma_k, \exists\ \beta > 0 \ni \forall \epsilon, 0 < \epsilon < \beta, \\ x + \epsilon\eta \in B/\Sigma_k\}$$

We shall say that $x+\eta$ is an interior point of $C_A^k(x)$ $[C_B^k(x)]$ if

(i) $x + \epsilon\eta \in C_A^k(x)$ $[C_B^k(x)]$, $x \in \Sigma_k$; and

(ii) there exists an open (n+1)-dimensional ball $B(x+\eta)$ with center at $x+\eta$, such that $B(x+\eta) \subset C_A^k(x)$ $[C_B^k(x)]$.

The second basic assumption is the following. Let $x+\eta'$ be an interior point of $C_A^k(x)$ $[C_B^k(x)]$. We assume that there exists an open (n+1)-dimensional ball $B'(x+\eta')$ with center at $x+\eta'$, which belongs to $C_A^k(x)$ $[C_B^k(x)]$ and which has the property that for every point $x+\eta$ in $B'(x+\eta')$ there exists a positive number α (independent of η) such that for all ϵ, $0 < \epsilon \leq \alpha$, point $x+\epsilon\eta$ belongs to $\widetilde{A/\Sigma_k}$ $[B/\Sigma_k]$.

We shall now define local cone $S^k(x)$ by

$$S^k(x) = \bar{C}_A^k(x) \cap \bar{C}_B^k(x)$$

By invoking arguments similar to those of (2) one can show that $S^k(x)$ is not empty and prove

<u>Lemma 1.</u> If x is an interior point of Σ_k in P_k, then local cones $C_A^k(x)$ and $C_B^k(x)$ constitute a partition of P_k.

Now let η be a bound vector at interior point x of Σ_k. Then one can prove

<u>Lemma 2.</u> If $\eta = \eta(\epsilon)$ is a function of parameter ϵ with properties

(i) $\eta(\epsilon) \to \ell$ as $\epsilon \to 0$

(ii) $\exists\ \gamma > 0$ such that $\forall\ \epsilon$, $0 < \epsilon < \gamma$, $x + \epsilon\eta(\epsilon) \in \widetilde{A/\Sigma_k}$ then $x+\ell \in \bar{C}_A^k(x)$.

Lemma 3. If $\eta = \eta(\epsilon)$ is a function of parameter ϵ with properties

(i) $\eta(\epsilon) \to \ell$ as $\epsilon \to 0$

(ii) $\exists\ \gamma > 0$ such that $\forall \epsilon$, $0 < \epsilon < \gamma$, $x + \epsilon\eta(\epsilon) \in \widetilde{B/\Sigma_k}$

then $x + \ell \in \bar{C}_B^k(x)$.

9. The Trajectory Equation and a Linear Transformation

We shall now restrict the analysis to systems with cost given by (5) so that

$$x_0(k+1) - x_0(k) = f_0^k(x_1(k), \ldots x_n(k), u_1(k), \ldots u_m(k)) \tag{12}$$

Combining Eqs. (1) and (12) we write a single trajectory equation

$$x(k+1) - x(k) = f^k(x,u) \tag{13}$$

where $f^k = (f_0^k, f_1^k, \ldots f_n^k, 1)$. It should be noted that $f^k(x,u)$ is independent of x_0 and x_{n+1}.

We shall suppose that functions f_j^k and $\partial f_j^k / \partial x_i$, $j=0,1,\ldots n$, $i=1,2,\ldots n$, are defined and continuous on $E^n \times U$.

Consider now a bound vector $\eta^k = (\eta_0^k, \eta_1^k, \ldots \eta_{n+1}^k)$ at point $x^*(k)$ of optimal trajectory Γ_ℓ^*, such that $\eta^k = \eta(k)$ evolves according to

$$\eta(k+1) - \eta(k) = \left.\frac{\partial f^k(x, u^*(k))}{\partial x}\right|_{x=x^*(k)} \eta(k) \tag{14}$$

where $u^*(k)$ belongs to u_ℓ^*.

We shall assume that matrix $I + \left.\dfrac{\partial f^k(x, u^*(k))}{\partial x}\right|_{x=x^*(k)}$

is nonsingular for k=i, i+1,...K-1. Then the solution of (14) defines a nonsingular linear transformation A(i+r,i+s), $0 \le r \le \ell$, such that

$$\eta(i+s) = A(i+r,i+s)\ \eta(i+r) \quad 0 \le s \le \ell$$

Next we shall suppose that $x^*(i+r) + \eta(i+r) \in P_{i+r}$ so that $\eta_{n+1}(i+r) = 0$; consequently $\eta_{n+1}(i+s) = 0$.

The equation adjoint to (14) is

$$\lambda(k+1) - \lambda(k) = -\lambda(k) \left. \frac{\partial f^k(x,u^*(k))}{\partial x} \right|_{x=x^*(k)} \tag{15}$$

where $\lambda(k) = (\lambda_0(k), \lambda_1(k), \ldots \lambda_{n+1}(k))$. From (14) and (15) it follows that

(i) $\lambda(i) \neq 0 \Rightarrow \lambda(k) \neq 0 \quad i \le k \le K$

(ii) $\lambda(k+1) \cdot \eta(k+1) = \lambda(k) \cdot \eta(k) \quad i \le k \le K-1$ (16)

(iii) $\lambda_0(i) = \lambda_0(i+1) = \ldots = \lambda_0(K)$ (17)

$\lambda_{n+1}(i) = \lambda_{n+1}(i+1) = \ldots = \lambda_{n+1}(K)$ (18)

Now consider $\eta(i+s) = A(i+r,i+s)\ \eta(i+r)$, $0 \le r \le s \le \ell-1$. By arguments similar to those employed in (2) one can prove

Lemma 4. If $x^*(i+r) + \eta(i+r) \in \bar{C}_A^{i+r}$ then

$$x^*(i+s) + \eta(i+s) \in \bar{C}_A^{i+s}.$$

Lemma 5. If $x^*(i+s) + \eta(i+s) \in \bar{C}_B^{i+s}$ then

$$x^*(i+r) + \eta(i+r) \in \bar{C}_B^{i+r}.$$

10. Separating Hyperplane in P_k

A separating hyperplane $T_k(x)$ of $\bar{C}_A^k(x)$ [$\bar{C}_B^k(x)$] at an interior point x of Σ_k is an n-dimensional hyperplane through x, which belongs to P_k and is such that $\bar{C}_A^k(x)$

$[\bar{C}_B^k(x)]$ belongs to one of the closed half-planes determined by $T_k(x)$ in P_k. We shall let $R_A^k(x)$ $[R_B^k(x)]$ denote the corresponding half-planes. If there exists a separating hyperplane of $\bar{C}_A^k(x)$ $[\bar{C}_B^k(x)]$, we shall say cone $\bar{C}_A^k(x)$ $[\bar{C}_B^k(x)]$ is separable.

As in (2), at points $x^*(i+r)$ and $x^*(i+s)$, $0 \leq r \leq s \leq \ell-1$, of an optimal trajectory Γ_ℓ^*, we have

Theorem 3. If $\bar{C}_B^{i+r}$ is separable, then $\bar{C}_B^{i+s}$ is separable.

Theorem 4. If $\bar{C}_A^{i+s}$ is separable, then $\bar{C}_A^{i+r}$ is separable.

11. Regular Interior Points of Σ_k

We shall say that an interior point x of a surface Σ_k is a regular interior point of Σ_k, if both $\bar{C}_A^k(x)$ and $\bar{C}_B^k(x)$ are separable. As in (2) one can prove that

(i) $\bar{C}_A^k(x)$ and $\bar{C}_B^k(x)$ possess the same separating hyperplane $T_k(x) = S^k(x)$;

(ii) This separating hyperplane is unique; and

(iii) $\bar{C}_A^k(x) = \bar{R}_A^k(x)$ and $\bar{C}_B^k(x) = \bar{R}_B^k(x)$.

12. A Maximum Principle

For the remainder of this paper we shall restrict the discussion to a regular optimal trajectory Γ_ℓ^*, namely, one for which $x^*(k)$ is a regular interior point of Σ_k for all k, $i \leq k \leq K-1$.† Now consider the separating hyper-

† Since the terminal point of Γ_ℓ^* is an isolated point, it is not an interior point of Σ_k.

plane $T_i(x^i)$ of $\bar{C}^i_A(x^i)$ and $\bar{C}^i_B(x^i)$ at initial point $x^*(i) = x^i$. From Theorem 3 it follows that its transform $T_k(x^k)$, $x^*(k) = x^k$, $i \le k \le K-1$, due to linear transformation $A(i,k)$, is the separating hyperplane of $\bar{C}^k_B(x^k) = \bar{R}^k_B(x^k)$. Since x^k is a regular interior point of Σ_k, $T_k(x^k)$ is also the separating hyperplane of $\bar{C}^k_A(x^k) = \bar{R}^k_A(x^k)$. Moreover this separating hyperplane is unique.

Next let us consider the solution $\lambda(k)$, $i \le k \le K-1$, of adjoint equation (15) with initial condition $\lambda(i)=\lambda^i$ such that

$$\lambda^i \neq 0 \quad \text{with} \quad \lambda^i_{n+1} = 0 \tag{19}$$

and such that λ^i is normal to $T_i(x^i)$ and directed into $R^i_B(x^i)$; that is,

$$\lambda^i \cdot \eta^i \le 0 \;\; \forall\, x^i + \eta^i \in \bar{R}^i_A(x^i) \tag{20}$$

From Eq. (16) it follows that $\lambda(k)$ is normal to $T_k(x^k)$ for all k, $i \le k \le K-1$. As a consequence of Lemma 4, together with $\bar{C}^k_A(x^k) = \bar{R}^k_A(x^k)$ and $\bar{C}^k_B(x^k) = \bar{R}^k_B(x^k)$, we conclude that

$$x^i + \eta^i \in \bar{R}^i_A(x^i) \Rightarrow x^k + \eta^k \in \bar{R}^k_A(x^k) \text{ where } \eta^k = A(i,k)\,\eta^i \tag{21}$$

Since $A(i,k)$ is linear and nonsingular, it follows from (21) that

$$x^k + \eta^k \in \bar{R}^k_A(x^k) \Rightarrow x^i + \eta^i \in \bar{R}^i_A(x^i) \tag{22}$$

Finally it follows from Eqs. (16)-(22) that

$$\lambda(k) \cdot \eta^k \le 0 \;\; \forall\, x^k + \eta^k \in \bar{R}^k_A(x^k) \quad i \le k \le K-1 \tag{23}$$

Let us now consider the following set in P_k:

$$\Omega^k = \{x : x = x^*(k-1) + f^{k-1}(x^*(k-1), u(k-1)),$$
$$x^*(k-1) \in \Gamma^*_\ell, u(k-1) \in U\}$$

We shall make an assumption which is somewhat weaker than the assumption of x_0-directional convexity of Ω^k in-introduced in (4).

<u>Assumption</u>. For every $x \in \Omega^k$ there exists an $\alpha > 0$ such that for all ϵ, $0 < \epsilon < \alpha$, there exists a $\beta \leq 0$ such that

$$x^k + \epsilon(x - x^k) + \beta u_0 \in \Omega^k$$

where $x^k = x^*(k)$ and u_0 is a unit vector in the x_0-direction.

From Theorem 2 it follows that

$$x^k + \epsilon(x - x^k) + \beta u_0 \in \widetilde{A/\Sigma_k} \qquad i \leq k \leq K-1$$

for sufficiently small ϵ. This in turn implies that

$$x^k + \epsilon(x - x^k) \in \widetilde{A/\Sigma_k}$$

and hence by Lemma 2 that

$$x^k + (x - x^k) = x \in \bar{C}^k_A(x^k) = \bar{R}^k_A(x^k) \tag{24}$$

Finally it follows from Eqs. (23) and (24) that

$$\lambda(k) \cdot (x - x^k) \leq 0 \qquad i \leq k \leq K-1 \tag{25}$$

which may be rewritten

$$\lambda(k) \cdot [f^{k-1}(x^{k-1}, u(k-1)) - f^{k-1}(x^{k-1}, u^*(k-1))] \leq 0$$
$$\forall\, u(k-1) \in U \tag{26}$$

Finally, from (18) with (19) we have

$$\lambda_{n+1}(i) = \lambda_{n+1}(i+1) = \ldots = \lambda_{n+1}(K) = 0 \tag{27}$$

and invoking arguments similar to those used in (2) we obtain from (17) that

$$\lambda_0(i) = \lambda_0(i+1) = \ldots = \lambda_0(K) \leq 0 \tag{28}$$

Conditions (26) - (28) are summarized in

Theorem 5. If $u_\ell^* = \{u^*(i), u^*(i+1), \ldots u^*(K-1)\}$ is an optimal control sequence (for the problem stated above), then there exist nonzero vectors $\lambda(k)$, $i \leq k \leq K-1$, which satisfy adjoint equation (15), such that

(i) $$\max_{u(k-1) \in U} H^k(\lambda(k), x^*(k-1), u(k-1)) = H^k(\lambda(k), x^*(k-1), u^*(k-1))$$

for all k, $i \leq k \leq K-1$, where

$$H^k(\lambda(k), x^*(k-1), u(k-1)) = \lambda(k) \cdot f^{k-1}(x^*(k-1), u(k-1))$$

(ii) $\lambda_0(i) = \lambda_0(i+1) = \ldots = \lambda_0(K) \leq 0$

(iii) $\lambda_{n+1}(i) = \lambda_{n+1}(i+1) = \ldots = \lambda_{n+1}(K) = 0$

References

1. A. Blaquiere and G. Leitmann, On the Geometry of Optimal Processes, Parts I, II, III, Univ. of California, Berkeley, IER Repts. AM-64-10, AM-65-11, AM-66-1.

2. A. Blaquiere and G. Leitmann, On the Geometry of Optimal Processes, Chapter 7 of Topics in Optimization, G. Leitmann (editor), Academic Press, N.Y., 1967.

3. B.W. Jordan and E. Polak, Theory of a Class of Discrete Optimal Control Systems, Journal of Electronics and Control, Vol. 17, No. 6, p. 697, 1964.

4. J.M. Holtzman, Convexity and the Maximum Principle for Discrete Systems, IEEE Transactions on Automatic Control, Vol. AC-11, No. 1, p. 30, 1966.

5. J.M. Holtzman and H. Halkin, Directional Convexity and the Maximum Principle for Discrete Systems, J. SIAM Control, Vol. 4, No. 2, p. 263, 1966.

PERTURBATIONS AND APPROXIMATIONS OF CONTINUOUS OPTIMAL CONTROL PROBLEMS

J. Cullum
IBM Watson Research Center
Yorktown Heights, New York

1. INTRODUCTION

Let P be an optimal control problem describable by a system of ordinary differential equations and an integral cost functional. In (1) the question of the approximation of admissible trajectories and controls of problems $P(\epsilon)$, obtained from P by perturbations describable by a single parameter ϵ, to admissible pairs of P was considered. It was proved that under certain conditions approximations exist and that in certain cases, optimal solutions of the $P(\epsilon)$ approximate optimal solutions of P; that is, certain problems P are correctly-posed in a weak sense.

One purpose of this paper is to demonstrate that the requirements made in (1) that the differential equations associated with $P(\epsilon)$ for $(\epsilon > 0)$ be linear in the control variable and that the control sets be convex and monotonic are not necessary. A second purpose of this paper is to demonstrate that a generalization of Kirillova's result (6) that for certain families $P(\epsilon)$ $(0 \leq \epsilon \leq 1)$ of linear time optimal control problems, the optimal control of $P(\epsilon)$ converges in the strong L_2-topology to the optimal control of P_0, can be obtained from the presented results. Hence, the theorems presented in (1) and this paper generalize earlier results.

A third purpose of this paper is to demonstrate that the techniques used in studying the question of the correctness of the formulation of P can be used to study the numerical stability of P. If P is to be solved numerically, some step in the solution procedure involves a discretization. One possible procedure is to discretize P immediately, replacing it by a sequence P_m, $m = 1, 2, \ldots$

of finite dimensional discrete optimal control problems and then to solve P_m for some large m. The question considered for a particular discretization is, do admissible solutions of P_m approximate admissible solutions of P and in particular do optimal solutions of P_m approximate optimal solutions of P_0. It is demonstrated that for a linear, time optimal control problem, such approximations do exist.

2. CONTINUOUS PERTURBATIONS OF P

2.1 Statement of the problems. Let E^n denote n-dimensional Euclidean space. Let T be a fixed interval in E^1. For each ϵ, move from $G_0(\epsilon)$ along an absolutely continuous curve $(\hat{x}, \bar{I})$ ($\hat{x}(t) \in E^n$ and $\bar{I} = [t_0, t_1]$ is an interval contained in T) for which there exists a measurable function u, such that $u(t) \in U(t, \epsilon)$ a. e. in $\bar{I}$, $\dot{\hat{x}}(t) = \hat{f}(\epsilon, \hat{x}(t), u(t), t)$ a. e. in $\bar{I}$, $\hat{x}(t) \in A$ on $\bar{I}$, $\hat{x}(t_1) \in G_1(\epsilon, t_1)$, and the integral, the cost of $\hat{x}$, $C(\hat{x}) = \int_{\bar{I}} f_0^0(\hat{x}(t), u(t), t) dt$, is minimized.

This problem will be designated by $P(\epsilon) = P(f(\epsilon), G_0(\epsilon), G_1(\epsilon, t), U(t, \epsilon), T, A)$. It can be reformulated as a problem in E^{n+1} with $x = (x^0, \hat{x}) \in E^{n+1}$, where $\dot{x}^0 = f_0^0$. This formulation will also be denoted by $P(\epsilon)$ and will be the formulation used throughout the paper unless stated otherwise. An admissible pair for $P(\epsilon)$, that is, a trajectory and control that satisfy the differential system and the control and space variable constraints for $P(\epsilon)$, will be denoted by $(x(\epsilon), u(\epsilon), \bar{I}, a, b)$ where $\bar{I}$ is the domain of $x(\epsilon)$ and of $u(\epsilon)$, and a and b are, respectively, the initial and terminal values of $x(\epsilon)$.

The global assumptions are:

(1) f_0^0 is continuous on $(E^n \times \bar{\mathcal{U}} \times T)$ where $\bar{\mathcal{U}}$ denotes the closure of the union $\mathcal{U}$ over $(t, \epsilon) \in (T \times [0, 1])$ of the sets $U(t, \epsilon)$.

(2) for each ϵ, $f(\epsilon, \hat{x}, u, t) = (f_0^0(\hat{x}, u, t), \hat{f}(\epsilon, \hat{x}, u, t))$ is continuous in $(\hat{x}, u)$ for each t and measurable in t for each $(\hat{x}, u)$ for $(\hat{x}, u, t) \in (A \times \bar{\mathcal{U}} \times T)$.

(3) $G_0(t)$ and $G_1(\epsilon, t)$ $(0 \leq \epsilon \leq 1,\ t \in T)$ are families

of compact subsets of E^n that are upper semicontinuous in (ϵ, t) at each point $(0, t) \in \{0\} \times T$.

(4) A is a closed subset of E^n.

Let $U(t,0) = U(t)$, $f_0(x,u,t) = f(0,x,u,t)$, I denote an open interval, $\bar{I}$ denote a closed interval, and $\underset{\sim}{U}(F,\delta)$ denote the union of all closed spheres with centers in the set F and radius δ.

2.2 Counterexample. Before proceeding, consider the following example of a problem P (7) that is not well-posed.

Example 1. Let $P(\epsilon)$ $(\epsilon \geq 0)$ be the following time optimal control problem: $(P \equiv P(0))$

$$\begin{aligned} \dot{\hat{x}} &= \left(\frac{1}{1+\epsilon}\right) (\sin 2\pi u, \ \cos 2\pi u, \ -1) \\ \hat{x}(0) &= (0,0,1), \ x(t_f) = (0,0,0), \ |u| \leq 1 \end{aligned} \tag{1}$$

Clearly, the optimal time for $P(\epsilon)$ is $(1+\epsilon)$. Let $\epsilon_k = 1/k$ and set $u^k(t) = k(t - r/k)$ for $r/k \leq t \leq (r+1)/k$ $r = 0, 1, \ldots, k$. Clearly, u^k is an optimal control for $P_{1/k}$ and the corresponding optimal trajectory is

$$x^k(t) = \left(\frac{k}{k+1}\right)\left(\frac{1-\cos 2\pi kt}{2\pi k}, \ \frac{\sin 2\pi kt}{2\pi k}, \ \left(\frac{k+1}{k} - t\right)\right) \tag{2}$$

But observe that x^k does not approximate an optimal solution of P. Instead, on $[0,1]$, x^k converges pointwise to $x^0(t) \equiv (0, 0, 1-t)$ which is not even admissible for P. It should be observed that P satisfies all of the hypotheses of the theorems to be presented except the hypothesis of convexity.

2.3 Generalizations of (1). First, recall that a sequence $(x_n, u_n, \bar{I}_n, a_n, b_n)$ is an approximation of type 2 to $(x_0, u_0, \bar{I}_0, a, b)$ if and only if $I_n \to I_0$, $(a_n, b_n) \to (a, b)$, $x_n(t)$ converges to $x_0(t)$ for each $t \in I_0$, and there exist measurable extensions $\bar{u}_n$ of u_n to I_0 such that $\bar{u}_n$ converges to u_0 in the weak $L_2(I_0)$ topology. It is an approximation of type 3 if the extensions $\bar{u}_n$ are strongly convergent to u_0, and an approximation of type 1 if the reference to convergence of the controls is deleted.

The following theorem demonstrates that the restrictions made in theorem 2 (1) that the differential systems for the $P(\epsilon)$, $\epsilon > 0$ be linear in u and that the control sets $U(t, \epsilon)$ be convex and monotonic can be removed.

Theorem 1. Let $P(\epsilon)$ $(0 \leq \epsilon \leq 1)$ be a family of problems that satisfy the global assumptions and the following assumptions:

(a) For each $(x, t, \gamma) \in (E^{n+1} \times t \times R^{+})$ there exists $\delta = \delta(\hat{x}, t, \gamma) > 0$ such that for all $u \in \bar{\mathcal{U}}$, $||x - x_1|| + |\epsilon| < \delta$ implies that $||f(\epsilon, x_1, u, t) - f_0(x, u, t)|| < \gamma$.

(b) There exist functions μ and g mapping E^1 into E^1 such that $\mu \in L_1$, $g(s) = 0(s)$ as $s \rightarrow \infty$, g is bounded on bounded sets and for all $(\epsilon, \hat{x}, u, t) \in [[0,1] \times A \times \bar{\mathcal{U}} \times T]$, $||\hat{f}(\epsilon, \hat{x}, u, t)|| \leq \mu(t) g(||\hat{x}||)$.

(c) $f_0 = g(\hat{x}, t) + H(\hat{x}, t) u$, and is continuous on $A \times \bar{\mathcal{U}} \times T$.

(d) The sets $U(t, \epsilon)$, $(t, \epsilon) \in \{T \times [0,1]\}$, form a uniformly bounded family of sets of E^r that is upper semicontinuous in ϵ at $\epsilon = 0$, uniformly in t.

(e) For each t, the set $U(t)$ is convex and compact, and for each ϵ there exists a measurable function $u(\epsilon)$ defined on T such that $u(\epsilon, t) \in U(t, \epsilon)$ a. e.

If $(x(n), u(n))$ is any sequence of pairs admissible for the corresponding problems $P(\epsilon_n)$, $(\epsilon_n \rightarrow 0$ as $n \rightarrow \infty)$, then there exists a pair (x_0, u_0) admissible for P and a subsequence of $(x(n), u(n))$ that is an approximation of type 2 to (x_0, u_0).

Corollary 1. Under the hypotheses of Theorem 1, if the cost of $(x(n), u(n))$ converges to the optimal cost of P as $n \rightarrow \infty$, then $(x(n), u(n))$ contains a subsequence that is an approximation of type 2 to an optimal pair (x_0, u_0) of P.

Proof of theorem 1. The proof of Theorem 1 requires the following lemma. This is an analogue to Lemma 7 in (1).

Lemma 1. Let $U(t, \epsilon)$, $(t, \epsilon) \in (T \times [0, 1])$ be a uniformly bounded family of subsets of E^r that is upper semicontinuous in ϵ at $\epsilon = 0$, uniformly in t. For each t, let the set $U(t)$ be convex and compact. Let $S(\epsilon)$ be the set of all measurable functions u defined on T such that

$u(t) \in U(t, \epsilon)$ a.e. If $u(\epsilon_n) \in S(\epsilon_n)$ for all n and $u(\epsilon_n)$ converges weakly to a function u_0 as $\epsilon_n \to 0$, then $u_0 \in S_0$.

Proof. For $\delta \geq 0$ denote the set of all measurable functions u defined on T such that $u(t) \in \underset{\sim}{U}(U(t), \delta)$ a.e. by (S_0, δ). Since the $U(t)$ are convex and uniformly bounded, (S_0, δ) is a convex subset of $L_2(T)$. Furthermore, it is strongly closed and hence is weakly closed. (4)

By hypothesis, there exists $\epsilon(\delta) > 0$ such that for all $\epsilon < \epsilon(\delta)$ and all $t \in T$, $U(t, \epsilon) \subset \underset{\sim}{U}(U(t), \delta)$. Hence, there exists an N_δ such that for all $n > N_\delta$, $u(\epsilon_n) \in (S_0, \delta)$ so $u_0 \in \bigcap_{\delta>0} (S_0, \delta)$. But, $\bigcap_{\delta>0}(S_0, \delta) = S_0$ since for each t, $U(t)$ being compact implies that $\bigcap_{\delta>0} \underset{\sim}{U}(U(t), \delta) = U(t)$. Therefore, $u_0 \in S_0$.

In the following proof, all subsequences are denoted by the original sequence and are nested. By the Bolzano-Weierstrass theorem, there exists an interval $\bar{I}_0 = [t_0, t_1]$, points a and b, and a subsequence such that $I_n \to I_0$, and $(a_n, b_n) \to (a, b)$. Extend each control $u(n)$ to all of I_0, using hypothesis (e), and denote the extensions by $\bar{u}(n)$. It is clear that $I_0 \neq \{t_0\}$.

$$\begin{aligned} \text{Define } \phi^*(n, t) &= f(\epsilon_n, x(n, t), u(n, t), t) && t \in I_n \cap I_0 \\ &= f(\epsilon_n, x(n, t_n^1), u(n, t), t) && t \in [t_n^1, t_1] \quad (3) \\ &= f(\epsilon_n, x(n, t_n^0), u(n, t), t) && t \in [t_0, t_n^0] \end{aligned}$$

If $t_1 \leq t_n^1$ and/or $t_n^0 \leq t_0$, the obvious deletions should be made in the preceding definition. Then, as in the proof of Theorem 1 (1), hypothesis (b), the hypothesis of uniform domination, implies that there exists a subsequence (w.l.o.g. denoted by n) $\phi^*(n)$ and a $\phi_0 \in L_1$ such that $\phi^*(n)$ converges in the weak L_1-topology to ϕ_0. Hence, for $t \in I_0$, $x(n, t)$ converges to

$$x_0(t) = \int_{t_0}^{t} \phi_0(s)ds + a . \qquad (4)$$

So, x_0^* satisfies the boundary conditions and the state space constraints.

Consider the corresponding sequence $u(n)$ for the subsequence chosen. There exists a subsubsequence (w.l.o.g. denoted by n) and $u_0 \in L_2$ such that $u(n)$ converges in the weak L_2-topology to u_0. By Lemma 1, u_0 satisfies the control constraints. Define for $t \in I_0$

$$x_0^*(t) = \int_{t_0}^{t} f_0(x_0(s), u_0(s), s)ds + a . \tag{5}$$

Prove that $x_0^* \equiv x_0$. Given $t \in I_0$, there exists N such that for all $n > N$, $t \in I_n$ so

$$\begin{aligned} \|x(n,t) - x_0^*(t)\| &= \|\int_{t_0^n}^{t} f(\epsilon_n, x(n), u(n), s) - \\ &\int_{t_0}^{t} f_0(x_0, u_0, s) + a_n - a_0\| \leq \|\int_{t_0}^{t} h_n\| + \\ &\|\int_{t_0}^{t} [f_0(x_0, u(n), s) - f_0(x_0, u_0, s)]\| + \\ &\|\int_{t_0^n}^{t_0} \mu M\| + \|a_n - a_0\| \end{aligned} \tag{6}$$

where $h_n = [\phi_n^* - f_0(x_0, u(n), s)]$, and M is obtained from hypothesis (b). From hypotheses (b) and (c) and the construction, the last three terms vanish as $n \to \infty$. By hypothesis (a), h_n converges to zero pointwise and dominatedly on I_0. Therefore, $\int h_n$ also converges to zero.

Therefore, $x(n,t)$ converges to $x_0^*(t)$. Hence, $x_0 \equiv x_0^*$, and (x_0, u_0) is the desired pair. Q.E.D.

Remarks. (1) The result in Theorem 1 can be obtained for the problem originally considered in (1) by working with the convex hulls $V(t,\epsilon)$ of the sets $U(t,\epsilon)$ instead of $U(t,\epsilon)$, see (3). (2) The two sets of hypotheses on the control sets are not directly comparable. However, a generalization of Dini's theorem is valid (see (3)). (3) The conclusions of Theorem 1 (1) concerning approximations of type 1 are still valid if the hypotheses on the control sets are replaced by the weaker hypotheses, that each $U(t,\epsilon)$ is compact, $\mathcal{U}$ is bounded, the sets $U(t)$ are upper semicontinuous in t and for each t, $d_H(U(t,\epsilon), U(t)) \to 0$ as $\epsilon \to 0$. d_H denotes the Hausdorff metric distance. (4) Example 1 demonstrates that none of the results on approximations are extendable to a general problem P with a system that is linear in x but not linear in u.

2.4 Generalized Cost Functions. If only minimizing sequences are of interest, the linearity in u requirement on the cost functional made in Theorem 1 can be relaxed. A sequence $(x(n), u(n))$ is a minimizing sequence if $(\hat{x}(n), u(n))$ is admissible for $P(\epsilon_n)$, $(\epsilon_n \to 0$ as $n \to \infty)$ and the corresponding sequence of costs converges to the optimal cost for P.

Theorem 2. Let $P(\epsilon)$ $(0 \leq \epsilon \leq 1)$ be a family of problems whose unaugmented systems satisfy the hypotheses of Theorem 1. Let the cost $C(x, u)$ considered as a functional defined on $(C \times L_2)(I)$ where $I \subset T$ be weakly sequentially lower semicontinuous in u for each $x \in C(I)$. Then if $(x(n), u(n))$ is a minimizing sequence, the conclusion of Theorem 1 follows.

Proof. The proof of Theorem 1 applied to the unaugmented problem yields a subsequence $(\hat{x}(n), u(n))$ that is an approximation of type 2 to a pair $(\hat{x}_0, u_0)$, admissible for P. By hypotheses (a) and (b) of Theorem 1, the lower semicontinuity hypothesis, and the fact that $(x(n), u(n))$ is a minimizing sequence,

$$C(\hat{x}_0) = \int_{t_0}^{t_1} f_0^0(\hat{x}_0, u_0, s) \leq \underline{\lim} \int_{t_n^0}^{t_n^1} f_0^0(\hat{x}(n), u(n), s) = C^* \quad (7)$$

Hence, $C(\hat{x}_0) = C^*$. Q. E. D.

Remarks. $C(I)$ is the $(n+1)$-fold product of the space of all continuous functions from I into E^1 with itself with the product topology, and similar meaning is applied to $(C \times L_2)(T)$. As an example of a functional satisfying the hypotheses of Theorem 2, consider Lemma 3 (3).

Lemma 3. Let $f_0^0 = g(u, t) + h(\hat{x}, t)$ where g is a continuous map from $\overline{\mathcal{U}} \times T$ into E^1 and h is a continuous map from $E^n \times T$ into E^1 such that $|h(\hat{x}, t)| \leq \mu(t)$ for some $\mu \in L_1(T)$. Furthermore, let g be convex in u for each t, and h be convex in x for each t. Then the functional $\phi = \int_I f_0^0$ is weakly sequentially lower semicontinuous on the subset D of $(C \times L_2)(I)$ such that the range of u is in $\overline{\mathcal{U}}$.

Remark. Lemma 3 and Theorem 2 yield an existence theorem for a certain class of optimal control problems.

2.5 Approximations of Type 3. Theorem 1 demonstrates the existence of a subsequence that is an approximation of type 2. The natural questions to ask are, when is the original sequence itself an approximation and/or when is an approximation of type 3 obtained? Only minimizing sequences will be considered. The following theorem states that for minimizing sequences, subsequences do not have to be introduced if P has a unique optimal solution.

Theorem 3. Let $P(\epsilon)$ be a family of problems that satisfy the hypotheses of Theorem 1. If P has a unique optimal solution (x_0, u_0), then any minimizing sequence $(x(n), u(n))$ is itself an approximation of type 2 to (x_0, u_0).

Proof. The proof is trivial. By the proof of Theorem 1 and the uniqueness, every subsequence of $(x(n), u(n))$ contains a subsequence that is an approximation of type 2 to (x_0, u_0). Q. E. D.

To consider the question of strong convergence of the controls or approximations of type 3, recall that Kirillova (6) proved that for a certain family $P(\epsilon)$ $(0 \leq \epsilon \leq 1)$ of time optimal control problems with $\hat{f}(\epsilon) = A(t, \epsilon)\hat{x} + B(t, \epsilon)u$, $\hat{x}(0) = x_0$, $\hat{x}(t_f) = 0$, $A = E^n$ and $|u| = 1$, any sequence of optimal controls converges in the strong L_2-topology to the optimal control for P. It will be proved that a generalization of this result follows from Theorems 1 and 3 and several additional comments. For ease of notation, the hats will be omitted during this discussion.

The $P(\epsilon)$ considered by Kirillova satisfy the hypotheses in Theorem 1. Furthermore, the normality assumption that for each ϵ, if $\psi(t, \epsilon)$ is the inverse of the fundamental solution of the matrix equation $\dot{X} = A(t, \epsilon)X$, then for any nonzero vector λ, the vector function $(\psi B)^{\dagger}\lambda$ has all of its components nonzero except at most on a set of measure zero, implies that $P \equiv P(0)$ has a unique optimal solution (9). The proof given in (9) requires only the applicability of the maximum principle and the normality condition on P. Using a controllability hypothesis (5) which is weaker than the normality condition, one can easily prove the following lemmas. The proof of Lemma 4 is trivial.

Lemma 4: For each ϵ, $(0 \leq \epsilon \leq 1)$ and $[t_0, t_1]$ define

$$W(t_0, t_1, \epsilon) = \int_{t_0}^{t_1} [\psi(t,\epsilon)B(t,\epsilon)]\,[\psi(t,\epsilon)B(t,\epsilon)]^T dt$$

Then $W(t_0, t_1, \epsilon)$ is nonsingular if for each $\lambda \neq 0$, $[\psi(t,\epsilon)B(t,\epsilon)]^T\lambda \neq 0$ a. e. on $[t_0, t_1]$.

Lemma 5: Let each $P(\epsilon)$ $(0 \leq \epsilon \leq 1)$ be linear and completely controllable. Let t_0 and $t_1 - t_0$ be specified and let there exist $\sigma > 0$ and $\epsilon_0 > 0$ such that $\{u \,|\, |u| \leq \sigma\} \subseteq U(t, \epsilon)$ for all $\epsilon < \epsilon_0$. Then there exists an n-simplex with zero as an interior point such that for every $\epsilon < \epsilon_0$ every point in this simplex can be transferred to the origin by a control $u(\epsilon)$ admissible for $P(\epsilon)$ in time less than or equal to $(t_1 - t_0)$.

Proof. Let $I = [t_0, t_1]$. Choose $n+1$ points on the unit sphere in E^n, $x_1, \ldots, x_{n+1}$ such that the vectors $x_{j+1} - x_j$ $j = 1, 2, \ldots, n$ are linearly independent, and zero is an interior point of the n-simplex $S = \{x \,|\, x = \sum_1^{n+1} \alpha_i x_i, \alpha_i \geq 0$ $\Sigma \alpha_i = 1\}$. By Lemma 4, and the continuity of $W(t_0, t_1, \epsilon)$ in ϵ at $\epsilon = 0$, $W^{-1}(t_0, t_1, \epsilon)$ exists and is a continuous function of ϵ at $\epsilon = 0$. Therefore, there exists $\epsilon_0 > 0$ such that $\max_{1 \leq i \leq n+1} [\sup_{0 \leq \epsilon \leq \epsilon_0} \|W^{-1}(t_0, t_1, \epsilon)x_i\|] = M$ and $\sup_{0 \leq \epsilon \leq \epsilon_0} [\max_{t \in I} \|B^T(t,\epsilon)\Psi^T(t,\epsilon)\|] = Q$ exist and are non-zero and finite.

Set $\gamma_0 = \dfrac{\sigma}{QM}$ and consider the simplex $\gamma_0 S = Z$ with vertices $z_i = \gamma_0 x_i$. Then Z is the desired simplex. That is, let $z \in Z$ then $z = \gamma_0 (\sum_1^{n+1} \alpha_i x_i)$ where $\sum_1^{n+1} \alpha_i = 1$. Set $u(\epsilon) = -\gamma_0 \sum_{i=1}^{n+1} \alpha_i [\Psi(\epsilon)B(\epsilon)]^T W^{-1}(t_0, t_1, \epsilon)x_i$. Then $|u(\epsilon)| \leq \sigma$, and $z + \int_{t_0}^{t_1} \Psi(\epsilon)B(\epsilon)u(\epsilon) = 0$. Q. E. D.

But Lemma 5 is a statement of the uniform controllability of the $P(\epsilon)$ in a neighborhood of the origin. Therefore, by Theorem 4.13 (2), the optimal time for $P(\epsilon)$ converges to the optimal time for P as $\epsilon \to 0$. Therefore, any sequence of optimal solutions $(x(n), u(n))$ for $P(\epsilon_n)$, $(\epsilon_n \to 0$ as $n \to \infty)$ is a minimizing sequence and hence is itself an approximation of type 2 to the optimal solution (x_0, u_0) of P.

In particular for Kirillova's problems, $U(t,\epsilon) \equiv (|u| \leq 1)$ so that Pontryagin's maximum principle implies that $|u_0^i(t)| = 1$ a.e. $i = 1,\ldots, r$. Hence,

$$\sqrt{m(I_0)r} = ||u_0|| \leq \underline{\lim}_{n} ||u(n)|| \leq \overline{\lim}_{n} ||u(n)|| = \sqrt{m(I_0)r} \,. \quad (8)$$

That is, $||u(n)|| \to ||u_0||$. Consequently, $u(n) \to u_0$ in L_2 (4). Therefore, Kirillova's conclusions have been obtained. In fact, the following result has been established.

Theorem 4. Let $P(\epsilon)$ be a family of controllable, linear, time optimal control problems with $x_F = 0$ and $\sigma > 0$ such that $\{|u| \leq \sigma\} \subset U(t,\epsilon)$ for all $t \in T$, $\epsilon < \epsilon_0$. If P has a unique optimal solution, (x_0, u_0) and $||u_0||_{L_2(I_0)} = \sup_{0 \leq \epsilon \leq \epsilon_0} [\max_{u(t) \in U(t,\epsilon)} ||u||_{L_2(I_0)}]$ for some $\epsilon_0 > 0$, then any sequence $(x(n), u(n))$ of optimal solutions for $P(\epsilon_n)$ $(\epsilon_n \to 0$ as $n \to \infty)$ is itself an approximation of type 3 to (x_0, u_0).

3. DISCRETE APPROXIMATIONS TO P

3.1 Introduction. Let P denote a continuous optimal control problem satisfying the global assumptions given in section 2 and for which optimal solutions exist. In order to determine an optimal solution of P numerically, the solution procedure at some step must approximate the given infinite dimensional problem by finite dimensional problems. One conceivable way to accomplish this approximation is to discretize P directly in some manner, thereby obtaining a sequence P_m $m = 1, 2,\ldots$ of finite dimensional discrete optimal control problems which can be solved by programming techniques. Assuming that optimal solutions of such P_m $m = 1, 2,\ldots$ can be obtained exactly, the question to be considered is do these solutions approximate in some sense optimal solutions of P ? Only one particular form of discretization will be considered in this paper.

Definition 1. Let $(\bar{x}_m, \bar{u}_m)$ where $\bar{x}_m = (x_m^0, x_m^1, x_m^2, \ldots, x_m^{k_m})$ and $\bar{u}_m = (u_m^0, u_m^1, \ldots, u_m^{k_m - 1})$ be a sequence of pairs admissible for P_m $m = 1, 2,\ldots$ This sequence is an approximation of type 1 (2) (3) to a pair (x_0, u_0) admissible for P if the continuous function x_m

obtained from $\bar{x}_m$ by connecting successive components of $\bar{x}_m$ with straight line segments and the piecewise constant extensions u_m of $\bar{u}_m$ are an approximation of type 1 (2) (3) to (x_0, u_0) in the sense of section 2.

Before proceeding, consider the following example of a problem that is not numerically stable in the preceding sense.

Example 2. Let P_0 and P_m $m = 1, 2, \ldots$ be the following time optimal control problems. (The hats on the $\hat{x}$ are omitted.)

$$P_0 : \quad \begin{array}{l} \dot{x} = (\sin 2\pi u,\ \cos 2\pi u,\ -1) \\ x(0) = (0,0,1),\ x(t_f) = (0,0,0),\ |u| \leq 1 \end{array} \tag{9}$$

$$P_m : \quad \begin{array}{l} x^{k+1} - x^k = (\sin 2\pi u^k,\ \cos 2\pi u^k,\ -1)\frac{1}{m} \quad k = 0, 1, \ldots \\ |u^k| \leq 1,\ x^0 = (0,0,1),\ x^{k_f} = (0,0,0) \end{array} \tag{10}$$

Clearly, the optimal time for P_m, $m = 0, 1, 2, \ldots$ is 1. Set $u_m^k = (-1)^k \frac{1}{4}$, $k = 0, 1, \ldots, m-1$ and consider only even m. $\bar{u}_m$ is optimal and the corresponding optimal trajectory $\bar{x}_m$ has components x_m^k equal to $(0, 0, 1 - k/m)$ if k is even, and equal to $(1/m, 0, 1 - k/m)$ if k is odd. Hence, for $t \in [0,1]$, $x_m(t)$ converges to $x_0(t) = (0, 0, 1-t)$ which is not even admissible for P. Therefore, P is not approximable by the P_m.

3.2 Time Optimal Control. The discussion in this paper will be restricted to time optimal control problems P with linear differential systems.

Theorem 5. Let P be a completely controllable, linear, time optimal control problem

$$\dot{x} = A(t)x + B(t)u,\ x(0) = x_0,\ x(t_f) = 0,\ |u| \leq 1 \tag{11}$$

Let P_m $m = 1, 2, \ldots$ be the following discrete, time optimal control problems obtained from P by discretizing the Green's Formula for the differential equations associated with P.

$$x^{k+1} - x^k = C_k x^k + D_k u^k \qquad k = 0, 1, \ldots$$
$$x^0 = x_0, x^{k_f} = 0, \; |u^k| \leq 1 \qquad (12)$$

where

$$C_k = (X_{k+1} X_k^{-1} - I), D_k = X_{k+1} \int_{J_{k+1}} X^{-1} Bu$$
$$J_k = [\frac{k-1}{m}, \frac{k}{m}], X_k = X(t_k), t_k = \frac{k}{m}$$

Then (1) the optimal cost of P_m converges to the optimal cost of P as $m \to \infty$, (2) any sequence $(\bar{x}_m, \bar{u}_m)$ of pairs $m = 1, 2, \ldots$ optimal for the corresponding problems P_m contains a subsequence that is an approximation of type 2 to a pair (x_0, u_0) optimal for P. If P is normal, then the entire sequence is an approximation of type 3 to the optimal solution (x_0, u_0) of P.

Remarks. First, it is clear that the P_m represent an optimal discretization of the problem P. That is, a maximum amount of problem structure has been preserved. However, such a discretization requires complete knowledge of the fundamental solution of the differential system associated with P, knowledge which one probably would not have. Second, P_m is essentially the restriction of P to controls that are piecewise constant on successive subintervals of length $1/m$. That is, if a control is admissible for P_m, then the piecewise constant extension of it is admissible for P, the trajectory x_m of P generated by this extension has the property that $x_m(t_k) = x_m^k$ $k = 0, 1, \ldots$ and the cost for this control is the same for both problems.

Proof of Theorem 5. (1) Proved by Neustadt (8). (2) Let $(\bar{x}_m, \bar{u}_m, \bar{I}_m)$ be a sequence of optimal solutions corresponding to P_m, $m = 1, 2, \ldots$. Then $\bar{I}_m = [0, t_m]$, with $t_m \geq t^*$, since P_m is essentially a restriction of P to a subfamily of the family of admissible controls. From (1), $t_m \to t^*$.

Consider the sequence of piecewise constant functions $u_m(t) \equiv u_m^k$ for $t \in J_{k+1}^m$ $k = 0, 1, \ldots$ corresponding to $\bar{u}_m$. Each u_m is defined on $[0, t^*]$, therefore, there exists a control u_0 on $[0, t^*]$ admissible for P and a subsequence u_{m_k} that converges in the weak L_2-topology to u_0(4). (W.l.o.g. denote m_k by m). Define for $t \epsilon [0, t^*]$,

$$x_0(t) = X(t)[x_0 + \int_0^t X^{-1} Bu_0]$$
$$x^*_m(t) = X(t)[x_0 + \int_0^t X^{-1} Bu_m] \quad m = 1, 2, \ldots \tag{13}$$

Define for $m = 1, 2, \ldots$; $k = 0, 1, \ldots k_m$ and $t \epsilon [t_k^m, t_{k+1}^m] \cap [0, t^*]$

$$x_m(t) = x_m^k + (C_k^m x_m^k + D_k^m u_m^k) m(t - t_k^m) \tag{14}$$

Observe that $x_m(t_k^m) = x_m^k = x^*_m(t_k^m)$ for $m = 1, 2, \ldots$ and $k = 0, 1, \ldots k_m$; and that x^*_m converges pointwise to x_0 on $[0, t^*]$ (4). Furthermore, there exists a K such that the functions x_0, x_m defined above are pointwise uniformly bounded by K . This is clear since there exists a K such that $|x(t)| \leq K$ for all $t \epsilon [0, t^*]$ for any curve x generated by the differential equations associated with P and a control that satisfies the control constraints, and $x_m^k = x^*_m(t_k^m)$.

Let ϵ be given. Then there exists an M such that for all $m > M$, for all u such that $|u| \leq 1$ and all $t \epsilon J_{k+1}^m$,

$$||(X(t) X^{-1}(t_k^m) - I)(x_m^k)|| < \epsilon / 8$$
$$||X(t) \int_{t_k^m}^t X^{-1} Bu|| < \epsilon / 8 \tag{15}$$

Therefore, for any $t \epsilon [0, t^*]$ and $m > M$

$$|x_m(t) - x^*_m(t)| < \epsilon / 2 \tag{16}$$

Furthermore, given $t \epsilon [0, t^*]$, there exists $M_1 > M$ such that for $m > M_1$,

$$|x^*_m(t) - x_0(t)| < t/2 \tag{17}$$

Therefore, $x_m(t) \to x_0(t)$ on $[0, t^*]$, and x_0 satisfies the boundary conditions. Hence, it is an admissible and in fact an optimal trajectory for P . Therefore, (x_0, u_0) is the desired pair. If P is normal then P has a unique optimal solution (x_0, u_0) and $||u_0|| = 1$. Hence, the controls are strongly convergent (4). Q. E. D.

Remark. It has been verified that for a special type of problem, approximations of the type desired can be obtained. The question of approximations for more general discretizations, systems, and costs will be discussed in a later paper.

REFERENCES

1. Cullum, J., Perturbations of Optimal Control Problems," SIAM j. on Control, 4(1966).
2. ibid, "Continuous optimal control problems with phase space constraints," Tech. Report prepared under Contract Nonr 222(88), ONR (1965).
3. ibid, "Perturbations of Optimal Control Problems II," RC 1722, IBM Research, 1966.
4. Dunford, N., and Schwartz, J., Linear Operators, Vol. I, Interscience, N. Y., 1964.
5. Kalman, R. E., Ho, Y. C., and Narendra, K. S., "Controllability of linear dynamical systems," Contributions to Differential Equations, 1(2) (1965), pp. 189-213.
6. Kirillova, F. M., "On the correctness of the formulation of an optimal control problem," SIAM J. on Control, 1(1963) pp. 224-239.
7. Lee, E. B., and Markus, L., "Optimal control for nonlinear processes," Arch. Rational Mech. Anal. 8(1961), pp. 36-58.
8. Neustadt, L. W., "Discrete Time Optimal Control Systems," International Symp. on Nonlinear Differential Equations and Nonlinear Mechanics, Academic Press, 1963.
9. Pontryagin, L. S., et al, The Mathematical Theory of Optimal Processes, Interscience, N. Y., 1962.

This research was supported by IBM and the United States Office of Naval Research under contract Nonr 222(88).

A CONTROLLABILITY PROBLEM FOR NONLINEAR SYSTEMS

Ivin Tarnove
TRW Systems
Applied Mathematics Department
Redondo Beach, California

Abstract Sufficient conditions are obtained for the existence of a solution of the following problem in the mathematical theory of control systems: given a compact interval K in R, the class U of measurable mappings of K into a compact subset Q of R^r, a class A of continuous mappings of K into R^n and a continuous mapping $f: R^n \times Q \times K \to R^n$, find conditions under which there exists a $u \in U$ such that the differential equation $\dot{x} = f(x,u(t),t)$ has a solution in A.

This problem is formulated as a fixed point problem for a set-valued mapping Φ defined on a suitable subset B of A. Under the conditions that $f(\{x\} \times Q \times \{t\})$ be convex for every $(x,t) \in R^n \times K$, and that for each $b \in B$ there exist a $u \in U$ such that $\dot{x} = f(b(t),u(t),t)$ has a solution in B, it is proved that Φ satisfies appropriate conditions for application of an extension of Schauder's fixed point theorem to set-valued mappings. An example is provided to show that the convexity condition is essential. An extension is made permitting the set Q to depend on x and t.

Utilizing a similar fixed point formulation, an existence theorem for a general class of boundary value problems is obtained.

Introduction Several results for nonlinear systems have been obtained (6,9,11,12) which establish the existence of an optimal control under the assumptions that a certain convexity condition holds and that the system is controllable. Considerable effort has recently been directed toward the study of systems in which the convexity condition is relaxed. However, it is not at all obvious when a given system is controllable, particularly if it may operate only over a limited time interval. It is this condition with which we shall be concerned.

Let us consider a control system governed by a family F of differential equations

$$\dot{x} = f(x,u(t),t) \qquad u \in U \qquad (F)$$

satisfying the following assumptions: (i) the class U of admissible controls consists of all (Lebesgue) measurable mappings u of the fixed interval $K = [0,T]$ into a compact subset Q of R^r; (ii) f is a continuous mapping of $R^n \times Q \times K$ into R^n.

Each member of the family F has, for any $x^o \in R^n$ and any $t_o \in K$, at least one solution v with $v(t_o) = x^o$ which is defined in some neighborhood I of t_o in K. More precisely, Carathéodory's existence theorem (see for example (4)) guarantees that, whatever $u \in U$, there is an absolutely continuous mapping v of a neighborhood $I \subset K$ of t_o into R^n which satisfies at every $t \in I$

$$v(t) = x^o + \int_{t_o}^{t} f(v(s),u(s),s)\, ds$$

and hence, at almost every $t \in I$, $\dot{v}(t) = f(v(t),u(t),t)$.

We shall be interested in whether there is at least one member of F which has a solution that is defined in K and belongs to a given subset A of C, the set of all continuous mappings of K into R^n.

Controllability as a Fixed Point Problem for a Set-Valued Mapping

Let us introduce the following terminology.

Definition. Let A be a given subset of C. We shall say that F is A-controllable if at least one member of F has a solution belonging to A.

It is clear that the family F need not be A-controllable. However, if it is, and the mapping b is a solution of some member of F belonging to A, then the family F_b,

$$\dot{x} = f(b(t),u(t),t) \qquad u \in U \qquad (F_b)$$

is also A-controllable. This suggests that A-controllability of F may be deducible from the A-controllability of a suitable set of simpler families.

Indeed, let B be a nonempty subset of A. For each $b \in B$ let U_b denote the set of admissible controls $u \in U$ for which the family F_b has a solution in B, and let V_b denote the set of all such solutions. We define a mapping Φ of B into the set P(B) of subsets of B by $\Phi(b) = V_b$.

If Φ has a fixed point, that is, if there is a $b_o \in B$ for which $b_o \in \Phi(b_o)$ then F is A-controllable, indeed B-controllable. For if $b_o \in \Phi(b_o)$, then, by definition, there is a $u_o \in U_{b_o} \subset U$ such that b_o is a solution of $\dot{x} = f(b_o(t),u_o(t),t)$. Hence b_o is an absolutely continuous mapping in B which is a solution of $\dot{x} = f(x,u_o(t),t)$ so that F is B-controllable.

We have thus formulated the question of A-controllability of F as a fixed point problem for the set-valued mapping Φ.

We regard C as a Banach space under the norm $\|c\| = \sup\{\|c(t)\|:t\epsilon K\}$. Recall that the graph of a set-valued mapping Φ of a subset S of a Banach space X into the set P(Y) of subsets of a Banach space Y is the subset of the product space $X \times Y$ defined by $G(\Phi) = \{(x,y):x\epsilon S, y\epsilon\Phi(x)\}$. Evidently, $G(\Phi)$ is closed if and only if the relations $(x,y)\epsilon X \times Y, \lim x_n = x, \lim y_n = y$ with $x_n \epsilon S, y_n \epsilon \Phi(x_n)$ imply $x\epsilon S$ and $y\epsilon\Phi(x)$.

<u>The Main Theorem</u> Our main result reduces the problem of <u>A-controllability</u> of F to that of the simpler systems F_b.

<u>Theorem 1</u>. <u>Let</u> B <u>be a nonempty bounded closed convex subset of</u> C <u>and let</u> $f(\{x\} \times Q \times \{t\})$ <u>be convex for each</u> $(x,t)\epsilon R^n xK$. <u>If</u> F_b <u>is</u> B-<u>controllable for every</u> $b \in B$, <u>then</u> F <u>is</u> B-<u>controllable</u>.

The proof of this theorem will be based on properties of the set-valued mapping Φ which are established in the following lemmas.

<u>Lemma 1</u>. <u>Let</u> B <u>be a bounded subset of</u> C. <u>Then</u> $\Phi(B)$ <u>is relatively compact</u>.

<u>Proof</u>: By definition $\Phi(B) \subset B$ so that $\Phi(B)$ is bounded. Since Q,K, and every closed ball in R^n are compact, and f is continuous, there is an $L \geq 0$ such that $\|f(b(t),u(t),t)\| \leq L$ for every $b \in B, u \in U$, and $t \in K$. Hence, for any solution v we find $\|v(t)-v(\tau)\| \leq L\ |t-\tau|,\ t,\tau\epsilon K$. Thus $\Phi(B)$ is a bounded, equicontinuous set in C so that by Ascoli's theorem (<u>7</u>) $\Phi(B)$ is relatively compact.

<u>Lemma 2</u>. <u>Suppose</u> B <u>is convex and</u> $f(\{x\} \times Q \times \{t\})$ <u>is convex for each</u> $(x,t)\epsilon R^n xK$. <u>Then</u> V_b <u>is convex for every</u> $b \in B$.

Proof: Let $b \in B$, $v_1, v_2 \in V_b \subset B$, and let $\lambda \in [0,1]$. Since B is convex, $v = (1-\lambda)v_1 + \lambda v_2 \in B$. We must show that in fact $v \in \Phi(b)$.

By definition of $\Phi(b)$, there are u_1, u_2 in U_b such that

$$v_i(t) = v_i(0) + \int_0^t f(b(s),u_i(s),s)\, ds \qquad i = 1,2$$

so that

$$v(t) = v(0) + \int_0^t [(1-\lambda)\, f(b(s),u_1(s),s) + \lambda f(b(s),u_2(s),s)]ds.$$

Since $f(\{x\} \times Q \times \{t\})$ is convex for each $(x,t) \in R^n \times K$, $f(\{b(t)\} \times Q \times \{t\})$ is convex for each $t \in K$. Hence, for each $t \in K$, the integrand

$$y(t) \equiv (1-\lambda)f(b(t),u_1(t),t) + \lambda f(b(t),u_2(t),t)$$

belongs to $f(\{b(t)\} \times Q \times \{t\})$, and $y{:}K \to R^n$ is a measurable mapping. By Filippov's lemma (9), there exists a measurable mapping $u{:}K \to Q$ such that $y(t) = f(b(t),u(t),t)$ a.e. in K. Hence

$$v(t) = v(0) + \int_0^t f(b(s),u(s),s)\, ds$$

and this implies that V_b is a convex set.

Lemma 3. Let B be a closed subset of C and let $f(\{x\} \times Q \times \{t\})$ be convex for every $(x,t) \in R^n \times K$. Then the graph of Φ is closed.

Proof: Let $(b_o, v_o) \in \overline{G(\Phi)}$. Since B is closed it suffices to show that $v_o \in \Phi(b_o)$.

There exists a sequence $\{(b_n, v_n)\}$ in $G(\Phi)$ converging to (b_o, v_o). Since $v_n \in \Phi(b_n)$ there is a $u_n \in U_{b_n}$ such that

$$v_n(t) = v_n(0) + \int_0^t f(b_n(s),u_n(s),s)\, ds \qquad n \geq 1.$$

Since the sequence $\{b_n\}$ is bounded in C and since Q and K are compact, the sequence of functions

$$y_n(t) = f(b_n(t),u_n(t),t) \qquad t \in K, n \geq 1,$$

is bounded, say, by M. It is likewise bounded when considered as a sequence in $L_1(K)$ since K has finite measure. Thus we may regard $\{y_n\}$ as a sequence in the set N of functions z in $L_1(K)$ for which $\|z(t)\| \leq M$ a.e. in K. Since for every $z \in N$ and every measurable subset $E \subset K$, $\left|\int_E z d\mu\right| \leq M\mu(E)$ we deduce that $\lim_{\mu(E)\to 0} \int_E z d\mu = 0$ uniformly in N. By the weak sequential compactness of the set N in $L_1(K)$ (8, Corollary 8.11, p.294) there is a $y_o \in N$ and a subsequence of $\{y_n\}$ converging weakly to y_o. Hence, renumbering if necessary,

$$v_o(t) = \lim_{n\to\infty} v_n(0) + \lim_{n\to\infty}\int_0^t y_n(s)ds = v_o(0) + \int_0^t y_o(s)ds.$$

It remains to prove that there exists a $u_o \in U$ such that

$$y_o(t) = f(b_o(t),u_o(t),t) \text{ a.e. in } K.$$

By virtue of the weak convergence of $\{y_n\}$ to y_o, for any measurable set E in K and any $w \in R^n$, we have (10, p.114)

$$\int_E \liminf [w\cdot y_n(s)]\, ds \le \liminf [\int_E w\cdot y_n(s)\, ds]$$
$$= \int_E w\cdot y_o(s)\, ds = \limsup [\int_E w\cdot y_n(s)\, ds \le \int_E \limsup [w\cdot y_n(s)]ds.$$

Hence, for every $w \in R^n$,

$\liminf [w\cdot y_n(t)] \le w\cdot y_o(t) \le \limsup [w\cdot y_n(t)]$ a.e. in K.
Now $y_n(t)\epsilon f(\{b_n(t)\} \times Q \times \{t\}), t\epsilon K, n \ge 1$. Since f is continuous and $\{b_n(t)\}$ converges to $b_o(t)$, for each $t \in K$
$\inf \{[w\cdot f(b_o(t),q,t)]:q\epsilon Q\} \le w\cdot y_o(t)$
$\le \sup \{[w\cdot f(b_o(t),q,t)]:q\epsilon Q\}$, a.e. in K.
Since this inequality holds for every w in R^n and $f(\{b_o(t)\} \times Q \times \{t\})$ is a compact convex set for every $t \in K$, $y_o(t)\epsilon f(\{b_o(t)\} \times Q \times \{t\})$ a.e. in K. By the lemma of Filippov (9) there exists a $u_o \in U$ such that $y_o(t) = f(b_o(t),u_o(t),t)$ a.e. in K so that we have

$$v_o(t) = v_o(0) + \int_0^t f(b_o(s),u_o(s),s)\, ds.$$

Hence $v_o \epsilon \Phi(b_o)$, and the lemma is established.

Proof of Theorem 1: The B-controllability of F_b means that $\Phi(b)$ is nonempty for each $b \in B$. By the lemmas, $\Phi(b)$ is convex for each $b \in B$, $\Phi(b)$ is contained in a compact subset, namely its closure, and the graph of Φ is closed. By the Bohnenblust-Karlin theorem (3) the set-valued mapping Φ has a fixed point in B. Hence F is B-controllable.

Example One can produce examples which show that each of the hypotheses of Theorem 1 is essential in the sense that if any one of them is deleted the assertion of the theorem is in general false, even for linear systems. We confine ourself here to an example violating the convexity condition.

Consider the scalar equation

$$\dot{x} = \frac{x}{1+t} + u(t)$$

on $R \times Q \times K$. We take Q to be the fixed set $Q = \{1,-1\} \subset R$ so that for every $(x,t) \in R \times K, f(\{x\} \times Q \times \{t\})$ is a set consisting of two distinct points which of course is not convex. The class of admissible controls U is the set of measurable mappings $u:K \to Q$ for which $|u(t)| \equiv 1$, i.e., the class of "bang-bang" controls.

Let $B = \{c \in C: c(t) = \alpha(t+1), \alpha \in [-1,1]\}$ which is clearly nonempty, bounded, closed and convex. For each $b \in B$, F_b is $\dot{x} = \alpha + u(t)$, $u \in U$, which is B-controllable for every $b \in B$. Indeed, if $\alpha \geq 0$, F_b has the solution $t \to (\alpha - 1)(t + 1)$ in B corresponding to $u(t) \equiv -1$, and if $\alpha \leq 0$, F_b has the solution $t \to (\alpha + 1)(t + 1)$ in B corresponding to $u(t) \equiv 1$. Nevertheless, F is not B-controllable, for each $b \in B$ satisfies the equation

$$\dot{x} = \frac{x}{1+t}$$

but $u(t) = 0$ a.e. in K is not an admissible control.

We note that if Q is enlarged to $Q = [-1,1]$ than all of the hypotheses would be satisfied. Indeed, $u = 0$ is then an admissible control, and any element of B is a fixed point, which illustrates the lack of uniqueness of the fixed point. Observe moreover that with the more modest enlargement of Q to $Q = \{-1,0,1\}$, $u = 0$ is again an admissible control but the convexity condition is violated. This shows that the convexity requirement is not a necessary condition.

Likewise it can also be shown that none of the conditions on B is a necessary condition.

We now consider the situation in which the solutions are required to start at a fixed point x^o in R^n, and construct an appropriate subset B directly in terms of the data of the problem.

<u>Theorem 2. Let</u> $K = [0,T] \subset R$, <u>and let</u> $f(\{x\} \times Q \times \{t\})$ <u>be convex for every</u> $(x,t) \in R^n \times K$. <u>Let</u> A <u>be a nonempty closed convex subset of</u> C <u>and suppose that for every</u> $c \in A, c(o) = x_o$. <u>Let</u> $p: R^+ \times K \to R^+$ <u>be a continuous mapping for which</u>

$$\|f(x,q,t)\| \leq p(\|x - x_o\|,t)$$

<u>and let</u> p <u>be nondecreasing in</u> R^+ <u>for each fixed</u> $t \in K$. <u>Suppose the maximal solution</u> η <u>of the equation</u> $\dot{r} = p(r,t)$ <u>which vanishes at</u> $t = o$, <u>exists in</u> K. <u>Set</u>

$$S = \{c \in C: \|c(t) - x_o\| \leq \eta(t), t \in K\},$$

$B = A \cap S$ <u>and suppose</u> B <u>is nonempty</u>. <u>If</u> F_b <u>is</u> A-<u>controllable for every</u> $b \in B$, <u>then</u> F <u>is</u> B-<u>controllable, hence</u> A-<u>controllable</u>.

Proof: The set B is nonempty by hypothesis, closed and convex because both A and S are, and bounded because S is bounded. By Theorem 1, it suffices to show that F_b is B-controllable. By hypothesis, F_b is A-controllable; so that we need only show that for every $b \in B$, $\Phi(b) \subset S$.

Let $b \in B$, and $v \in \Phi(b)$. Then there is a $u \in U_b$ such that

$$v(t) = x_o + \int_0^t f(b(s),u(s),s)\,ds \qquad t \in K.$$

Then

$$\|v(t)-x_o\| \le \int_0^t \|f(b(s),u(s),s)\|\,ds \le \int_0^t p(\|b(s)-x_o\|,s)\,ds$$

$$\le \int_0^t p(\eta(s),s)\,ds = \eta(t).$$

Hence $v \in S$ and so $\Phi(b) \subset S$. Thus $\Phi(b) \subset B$ so that F_b is B-controllable.

Generalization of Class Admissible Controls It is of interest to observe that the preceding results may be generalized with respect to the class of admissible controls. In fact the fixed set Q may be replaced by a set-valued mapping $Q:R^n \times K \to P(R^r)$. We shall take the set U of admissible controls to be the set of measurable mappings $u:K \to R^r$ for which there is a $c \in C$ such that $u(t) \in Q(c(t),t)$ in K.

Let B be a subset of A, and corresponding to each $b \in B$, let U_b denote the set of $u \in U$ for which $u(t) \in Q(b(t),t)$ and for which the equation $\dot{x} = f(b(t),u(t),t)$ has solution in B. Let V_b denote the set of such solutions. Let $\Phi:B \to P(B)$ be defined by $\Phi(b) = V_b$. As before, the existence of a fixed point of Φ implies the existence of a solution of our problem. Our results on A-controllability carry over to this more general problem if we can extend the lemmas to this case. Such an extension is possible under the conditions that (1) $Q(x,t)$ be compact and $f(\{x\} \times Q(x,t) \times \{t\})$ be convex for every $(x,t) \in R^n \times K$, and that (2) Q be upper semicontinuous with respect to inclusion (9) in the sense that given any $(x_o,t_o) \in R^n \times K$ and $\epsilon > 0$, there exists a $\delta(x_o,t_o,\epsilon) > 0$ such that $Q(x,t)$ is contained in an ϵ-neighborhood of $Q(x_o,t_o)$ whenever $\|x-x_o\| < \delta$, $|t-t_o| < \delta$.

We note moreover, that a fixed point b_o of $\Phi(B)$ is a solution of $\dot{x} = f(b_o(t),u_o(t),t)$ with $u_o(t) \in Q(b_o(t),t)$ as required.

Systems of Special Form   More precise results can be obtained for systems of special form. Let $\Sigma(x,\epsilon)$ denote the closed ball in R^n under the Euclidean norm which has radius ϵ and center x. We shall also use the norm $\|x\|_\infty = \max\{|x_i|:1 \le i \le n\}$. We consider first the case in which the control appears linearly.

Theorem 3. Suppose $f(x,q,t) = g(x,t)q + h(x,t)$ where g is a continuous $n \times r$ matrix-valued mapping, and h is a continuous vector-valued mapping. Let $x^o, x^1 \epsilon R^n, \rho > o, \epsilon \ge o$ and take $Q = \{x \epsilon R^r: \|x\|_\infty \le \rho\}$. Set $A = \{c \epsilon C: c(o) = x^o, c(T) \epsilon \Sigma(x^1,\epsilon)\}$. Let $p: R^+ \times K \to R^+$ be continuous mapping for which

$$\rho\|g(x,t)\| + \|h(x,t)\| \le p(\|x-x^o\|,t)$$

and let p be nondecreasing in R^+ for each fixed $t \epsilon K$. Suppose the maximal solution η of the equation $\dot{r} = p(r,t)$ which vanishes at $t = o$ exists in K. Set $S = \{c \epsilon C: \|c(t)-x^o\| \le \eta(t), t \epsilon K\}, B = A \cap S$ and suppose B is nonempty. For each $b \epsilon B$, write

$$z_b(T) = x^1 - x^o - \int_o^T h(b(t),t)\,dt.$$

If for each $b \epsilon B$ and $x' \epsilon R^{n'}$

$$|\langle z_b(T), x' \rangle| - \epsilon\|x'\| \le \rho\int_o^T \|x' g(b(t),t)\|\,dt,$$

then F is A-controllable.

Remark: The A-controllability of this theorem, in the terminology introduced by H. A. Antosiewicz (1), coincides with the notions of approximate controllability when $\epsilon > 0$ and (strict) controllability when $\epsilon = 0$.

Proof: The hypotheses imply that $f(\{x\} \times Q \times \{t\})$ is convex for every $(x,t) \epsilon R^n \times K$. The set B is a nonempty, bounded, closed, convex subset of A. For each $b \epsilon B$, the last condition is the appropriate specialization of the necessary and sufficient condition in (1) for A-controllability of the linear system F_b. As in the proof of Theorem 2 $\Phi(b) \subset S$ so that F_b is B-controllable for every $b \epsilon B$. Hence, by Theorem 1, F is B-controllable.

We consider now the case in which the mapping f has the form

$$f(x,q,t) = A(t)\,x + g(x,q,t)$$

where $A(t)$ is an $n \times n$ matrix defined for each $t \epsilon K$. In such cases, instead of dealing with the systems

$$\dot{x} = A(t)\, b(t) + g(b(t),u(t),t) \quad u \in U \quad (F_b)$$

it may be more convenient to formulate our theorems in terms of the systems

$$\dot{x} = A(t)\, x + g(b(t),u(t),t) \quad u \in U \quad (G_b).$$

With obvious modifications in the meaning of U_b, V_b, and Φ analogues of the previous results may be obtained provided the mapping $t \to A(t)$ is Lebesgue integrable on K and the hypotheses on f are imposed on g.

The preceding results may be applied to the question of the existence of optimal controls. Indeed, it suffices to replace the controllability assumption in the theorems of (9,11,12) by the requirement that for some $K = [0,T] \subset R, F_b$ be B-controllable for each b in a suitable subset B of A, for the hypotheses of these theorems imply the convexity condition of Theorem 1.

Boundary Value Problems We consider here a (non-control) problem of considerable importance in the theory of ordinary differential equations, namely, given $g: R^n \times K \to R^n$ with K a compact interval of R, and a subset $B \subset C$, does there exist a solution of $\dot{x} = g(x,t)$ in B. Problems on the existence of periodic solutions when g is periodic in t, or more generally, questions on the existence of solutions satisfying general boundary conditions (2,5) can be formulated in this context. A sufficient condition for the existence of a solution to this class of problems is embodied in

Theorem 4. *Let B be a nonempty bounded closed convex subset of $C, g: R^n \times K \to R^n$ a continuous mapping and suppose that for each $b \in B$, the equation $\dot{x} = g(b(t),t)$ has a solution in B. Then the equation $\dot{x} = g(x,t)$ has a solution in B.*

Remark: The proof can be obtained by considering this theorem as the trivial special case of Theorem 1 in which f is independent of q. However, the result is easily obtained by direct application of the previously mentioned fixed point theorem.

Proof: Let $\Phi: B \to P(B)$ be defined by taking $\Phi(b)$ to be the set of solutions in B of the equation $\dot{x} = g(b(t),t)$. By hypotheses, $\Phi(b)$ is nonempty. It is also convex for every $b \in B$.

Moreover, Φ has a closed graph, for if $(v_o,b_o) \in \overline{G(\Phi)}$ there is a sequence $\{(v_n,b_n)\}$ in $G(\Phi)$ converging to (v_o,b_o). But
$$v_n(t) = v_n(0) + \int_0^t g(b_n(s),s)\, ds.$$

Since the convergence of $\{b_n\}$ to b_o is uniform, the above equation holds for n = o, so that $(v_o, b_o) \in G(\Phi)$. By the Bohnenblust-Karlin Theorem, Φ has a fixed point, which is a solution of $\dot{x} = g(x,t)$ in B.

Acknowledgment The author wishes to express his appreciation to Prof. H. A. Antosiewicz of the University of Southern California for the guidance and encouragement he provided during the preparation of the dissertation on which this material is based.

REFERENCES

1. H. A. Antosiewicz, Linear Control Systems, Arch. Rational Mech. Anal. 12 (1963), 313-324.
2. H. A. Antosiewicz, Boundary Value Problems for Nonlinear Ordinary Differential Equations, Pacific J. Math. 17 (1966), 191-197.
3. H. F. Bohnenblust and S. Karlin, On a Theorem of Ville, in "Contributions to the Theory of Games," Vol. I., Princeton University Press, Princeton, 1950.
4. E. A. Coddington and N. Levinson, Theory of Ordinary Differential Equations, McGraw-Hill, New York, 1955.
5. R. Conti, Equazioni Differeziale Ordinarie Quasilineari con Condezioni Lineari, Am. Mat. Pura Appl. 57 (1962), 49-62.
6. R. F. Datko, An Implicit Function Theorem with an Application to Control Theory, Michigan Math. Journ. 11 (1964), 345-351.
7. J. Dieudonné, Foundations of Modern Analysis, Academic Press, New York, 1960.
8. N. Dunford and J. T. Schwartz, Linear Operators Part I: General Theory, Interscience, New York, 1958.
9. A. F. Filippov, On Certain Questions in the Theory of Optimal Control, Vestnik Moskov. Univ., Ser. Math., Mekh., Astr., Fiz., Khim., No. 2 (1959), 25-32. English Translation in J. Soc. Ind. Appl. Math., Ser. A, 1 (1962), 72-84.
10. P. R. Halmos, Measure Theory, Van Nostrand, Princeton, 1950.
11. E. B. Lee and L. Markus, Optimal Control for Nonlinear Processes, Arch. Rational Mech. Anal. 8 (1961), 36-58.
12. E. Roxin, The Existence of Optimal Controls, Michigan Math. Journ. 9 (1962), 109-119.

ON OPTIMAL STABILIZATION OF NONLINEAR SYSTEMS

Pavol Brunovský, Institute of Technical Cybernetics of the Slovak Academy of Sciences, Bratislava, Czechoslovakia

We refer to a problem, frequently called also "Analytic regulator design problem" (1),(2), (4),(6) or "Optimal regulator problem" (3), which may be formulated as follows:

Given a control system

$$\dot{x} = f(x,u) \qquad (1)$$

(x being n-vector, u being m-vector) with $f(0,0) = 0$ and a positive definite real cost function $V(x,u)$ (i.e. $V(0,0) = 0$, $V(x,u) > 0$ for $(x,u) \neq (0,0)$), denote $\Omega_{\hat{x}}$ the set of all measurable functions $u(t)$, $t \in \langle 0,\infty)$ such that the solution of the system $\dot{x} = f(x,u(t))$ starting at $\hat{x}$ for $t = 0$ (denote it by $x(t,u,\hat{x})$) exists on $\langle 0,\infty)$, satisfies $\lim_{t\to\infty} x(t,u,\hat{x}) = 0$ and $I(u,\hat{x}) = \int_0^\infty V(x(t,u,\hat{x}), u(t))\,dt < \infty$, for a given $\hat{x}$ find a control $u_{\hat{x}}$ (the optimal control) such that $I(u_{\hat{x}},\hat{x}) = \min_{u\in\Omega_{\hat{x}}} I(u,\hat{x})$. Further, find a function $v(x)$ in a domain D containing the origin (the closed-loop optimal control in D) such that for every $\hat{x} \in D$, $u_{\hat{x}}(t) = v(x(t,u_{\hat{x}},\hat{x}))$.

This problem has been treated by several authors for f linear and V quadratic (cf.(1),(2),(3),(4),(5)) in which case one obtains a linear theory (i.e. v is linear). The appearantly most general sufficient conditions for the existence and uniquenes of optimal control and closed-loop optimal control in the linear case are proved in (4) and (5).

The case of f linear and V non-quadratic has been treated in (6). In (4), the case of f and V both analytic is considered, but another concept of control is used (by control is always meant an analytic closed-loop control). In this paper, we shall give sufficient conditions (of local nature in $\hat{x}$) for the existence and uniqueness of optimal control an closed-loop optimal control in general nonlinear systems;further, the inverse problem will be discussed. The full proofs of the greater part of results will be published in (7).

Let R^k denote the k-dimensional real euclidean space, $|\cdot|$ the euclidean norm, E the unity matrix, A^* the transpose of matrix A.

Hypotheses

(f1) f is defined, of class C^1 in $G \times R^m$, G being an open domain of R^n, containing the origin; $f(0,0) = 0$. The system (1) is locally controllable in the origin, i.e. if we denote $A = \frac{\partial f}{\partial x}(0,0)$, $B = \frac{\partial f}{\partial u}(0,0)$, then the rank of the matrix $(B, AB, \ldots, A^{n-1}B)$ is n.

(V1) $V(x,u)$ is defined, continuous and positive definite in $G \times R^m$ and $\inf\limits_{|x| \geq \delta} \liminf\limits_{|u| \to \infty} V(x,u) > 0$ for every $\delta > 0$

(fV1) The set $Q(x) = \{(y_0,\dots,y_n) : (\exists u)(u \in R^m)$ $(y_0 \geq V(x,u))\,(y_i = f_i(x,u))\,(1 \leq i \leq n)\}$ is closed and convex for all $x \in G$

(fV2) There is a nonnegative continuous function $\varphi(\xi)$ such that $\lim_{\xi \to \infty} \xi^{-1} \varphi(\xi) = \infty$, $\varphi(\xi) > 0$ for $\xi > 0$ and $V(x,u) \geq \varphi(|f(x,u)|)$ for $(x,u) \in G X R^m$.

It is not difficult to show that under hypotheses (f1),(V1),(fV2) from $I(u,\hat{x}) < \infty$ follows $\lim_{t \to \infty} x(t,u,\hat{x}) = 0$.

Theorem 1. Let hypotheses (f1),(V1),(fV1),(fV2) be valid. Then, for every $\hat{x}$ from a certain neighbourhood of the origin there is an optimal control.

As may be seen from the hypotheses, this is an existence theorem similar to those of (8). Thus, if we know that $\Omega_{\hat{x}}$ is non-empty, the existence of an optimal control may be proved by a technique similar to (8); some changes have to be done due to the infiniteness of the time interval. That $\Omega_{\hat{x}}$ is non-empty for $\hat{x}$ sufficiently close to the origin, follows from (9).

Hypotheses:

(f1') f satisfies (f1) and $\partial^2 f_i / \partial u_i \, \partial u_j \, (x,u)$ $i,j = 1,\dots,m$ are continuous for $|x| + |u|$ sufficiently small

(V1') (V1) is valid, V is of class C^1 for $|x|$ sufficiently small and of class C^2 for

$|x| + |u|$ sufficiently small. The quadratic form $V_0(x,u) = x^*Px + x^*Qu + u^*Ru$ with $P = \frac{1}{2}(\partial^2 V/\partial x_i\, \partial x_j(0,0))$, $Q = (\partial^2 V/\partial x_i\, \partial u_j(0,0))$, $R = \frac{1}{2}(\partial^2 V/\partial u_i\, \partial u_j(0,0))$ is positive definite

(V2) There are constants $L, 0 < p_1 < 1, p_2 > 0$ such that $|\partial V/\partial x| \leq LV^{p_1}$, $|\partial V/\partial u| \leq LV^{p_2}$ for $|x|$ sufficiently small and $|u|$ sufficiently large

(fV3) There are constants $K, 0 < r_1 < 1, r_2 > 0$ such that $|\partial f/\partial x| \leq KV^{r_1}$, $|\partial f/\partial x| \leq KV^{r_2}$ for $|x|$ sufficiently small and $|u|$ sufficiently large. For every $\delta > 0$ there is a $\mu > 0$ such that $|\partial V/\partial u| \geq \mu |\partial f/\partial u|$ for $|x| \leq \delta$ and $|u| \geq \delta$.

Theorem 2. Let hypotheses (f1'),(V1'),(V2), (fV3) be valid. Assume that for every $\hat{x}$ from a certain neighbourhood of the origin there is an optimal control. Then, for $\hat{x}$ sufficiently close to the origin the optimal control is unique and there is a unique closed-loop optimal control in a neighbourhood of the origin, which is of class C^1.

The proof of this theorem is based on the following

Lemma. Let $x(t)$ be a solution of the system

$$\dot{x} = (C + D(t))x + g(t) \qquad (2)$$

(x - n-vector), where C is constant, $\int_0^1 |D(t+s)|ds \to 0$, $\int_0^1 |g(t+s)|ds \to 0$ for $t \to \infty$. Let G_0 be a constant $m \times n$ matrix such that the pair C, G_0 is completely observable (i.e. the rank of the matrix $(G_o^*, C^*G_o^*, \ldots, C^{n-1*}G_o^*)$ is n). Let G(t) be an m×n - matrix function, integrable over every finite interval of the positive semiaxis. Let

$$\int_0^1 \alpha\big(G(t+s)x(t+s)\big)ds \to 0 \quad \text{and}$$
$$\int_0^1 \alpha\big(|G(t+s) - G_o|\big)ds \to 0 \text{ for } t \to \infty \qquad (3)$$

where $\alpha(\xi)$ is a continuous nonnegative function defined for $\xi \geq 0$ such that $\alpha(0) = 0$ and for every $\sigma > 0$ there is a positive $K_\sigma > 0$ such that $\alpha(\sigma\xi) \leq K_\sigma \alpha(\xi)$ for $\xi \in \langle 0, \infty)$. Then, $x(t) \to 0$ for $t \to \infty$.

The idea of the proof of Theorem 2 is now as follows:

From the maximum principle and (V1'), (V2), (fV3) we conclude that the adjoint vector $\psi(t)$ satisfies a system of type (2) with $C = -A^*$, $D = [A - \partial f/\partial x(x(t,u,\hat{x}), u_{\hat{x}}(t))]^*$, $g = \partial V/\partial x(x(t,u,\hat{x}), u_{\hat{x}}(t))$ and condition (3) is satisfied with $G_o = B^*$, $G(t) = \partial f/\partial u(x(t,u,\hat{x}), u_{\hat{x}}(t))$. From the Lemma follows $\psi(t) \to 0$ for $t \to \infty$. From (V1') follows that for x, ψ sufficiently small, u may be from the maximum principle condition uniquely expressed as a C^1 - function $w(x, \psi)$. Hence, $x(t,u,\hat{x})$, $\psi(t)$ is a solution of the system

$$\dot{x} = f(x, w(x,\psi))$$
$$\dot{\psi} = -\left[\partial f/\partial x(x, w(x,\psi))\right]^* \psi + \partial V/\partial x(x, w(x,\psi)) \qquad (4)$$

tending to zero for $t \to \infty$.

The solutions of the linearized system corresponding to (4) which tend to zero, form an n-dimensional linear subspace of R^{2n} (cf. (4)) the points of which satisfy a relation $\psi = Sx$. By the theorem of conditional stability (10) the solutions of (4) which tend to zero for $t \to \infty$ form in the neighbourhood of the origin a manifold $\psi = s(x) = Sx + o(x)$, where s is of class C^1. The unique closed-loop optimal control is then in a neighbourhood of the origin given by $v(x) = w(x, s(x))$.

Combining the results of Theorem 1 and Theorem 2, we obtain.

Theorem 3. Let hypotheses (f1'), (V1'), (V2), (fV1), (fV2), (fV3) be valid. Then, for every $\hat{x}$ from a certain neighbourhood D of the origin there is a unique optimal control and there is a unique optimal closed-loop control in D, which is of class C^1.

Let us note that under hypotheses of Theorem 3 the zero solution of the system

$$\dot{x} = f(x, v(x)) \qquad (5)$$

is asymptotically stable and the function $W(x) = \int_0^\infty V(x(t), v(x(t)))dt$ ($x(t)$ being the solution of (5) with $x(0) = x$) is a Ljapunov function of it.

For scalar u (i.e. m = 1), (V1') and (fV1) may be weakened and (V2) released. However, for this case f has to satisfy an additional condition.

Hypotheses:

(V1'') V1 is valid and V is of class C^2 for $|x| + |u|$ sufficiently small

(fV1') The set $f(x,R^1)$ is closed and convex for $x \in G$

(f2) There are positive constants η, δ such that $|f(x,u)| > \eta$ for $x \notin G$, $|u| > \delta$.

Theorem 4. If m = 1, then the assertion of theorem 4 is valid under hypotheses (f1'),(V1''), (fV2), (fV3).

For the proof a function $U(x,w)$, $w \in R^1$ is constructed such that if we denote $\tilde{V}(x,u) = U(x, |f(x,u) - f(x,0)| \text{ sign } u)$, then V satisfies the hypotheses of theorem 3, $\tilde{V}(x,u) = V(x,u)$ in a neighbourhood of the origin and $\tilde{V}(x,u) \leq V(x,u)$ for $|\hat{x}|$ sufficiently small and arbitrary u. Then, one proves that the closed-loop optimal control of V yields the unique optimal control for V for $|\hat{x}|$ sufficiently small.

Note that if f is linear in u, then (fV1) is trivially satisfied, (fV2) is a consequence of (f1'), (fV3) is a consequence of (V1''), (fV2') and (fV2) is equivalent with

Hypothesis (fV2'). There is a nonnegative continuous function $\varphi(\xi)$

such that $\varphi(\xi) > 0$ for $\xi > 0$,
$\lim_{\xi \to \infty} \xi^{-1}\varphi(\xi) = \infty$ and $V(x,u) \geq \varphi(|u|)$
for $(x,u) \in G \times R^m$.

Therefore, as an important consequence of Theorem 4 we obtain.

Theorem 5. Let m = 1 and f be linear in u (i.e. $f(x) = g(x) + h(x)u$). Then, the assertion of Theorem 4 is valid under (f1'), (V1''), (fV2).

As mentioned above, if v is a closed-loop optimal control for (1), then (5) is an asymptotically stable differential system. Now, we may ask, whether to every system of type (5) there is a positive definite cost function V such that v is an optimal closed-loop control for V.

By transformation $u = v(x) + w$ the problem may be reduced to the case

$$\dot{x} = f(x,0) \tag{6}$$

being asymptotically stable.

Let D be the domain of asymptotic stability of (6), $Y_{\hat{x}}(t)$ the solution of the matrix system

$$\dot{Y} = \partial f/\partial x\,(x_{\hat{x}}(t),\, 0)\,Y$$

with $Y_{\hat{x}}(0) = E$, $x_{\hat{x}}(t)$ being the solution of (6) with $x_{\hat{x}}(0) = \hat{x}$, $\hat{x} \in D$.

By dynamic programming approach we obtain

Theorem 6. Let all characteristic roots of the matrix A (cf. (f1)) have negative real parts and let $|\partial f/\partial x(x,0) - A| = \sigma(|x|)$. Let $\omega(x)$ be a real positive definite C^1 - function, defined in D. Denote

$$q(x) = -\int_0^\infty \left[\partial\omega/\partial x\,(x_{\hat{x}}(t))\right]^* Y_{\hat{x}}(t)\,dt$$

for $\hat{x} \in D$. Let $V(x,u)$ be defined in $D \times R^m$ and $V(x,0) = \omega(x)$. Then, v is the optimal closed-loop optimal control for V in D if and only if

$$q(x)\,f(x,u) \leq V(x,u)$$

for $\hat{x} \in D$.

In virtue of this theorem, for given ω an appropriate positive definite V may be constructed as follows

$$V(x,u) = q(x)f(x,u) + \gamma\sigma_1(u) +$$
$$+ \sigma_2\left(|f(x,u) - f(x,0)|\right).\ |q(x)|$$

where σ_1, σ_2 are positive and of class C^1, $\sigma_1(0) = \sigma_2(0) = 0$, $\sigma_2(\xi) \geq \xi$ for large ξ and $\gamma \geq 0$ is sufficiently large.

References:

1. Letov A.M.: Analytic controller design, Automat. Remote Control 21 (1960), 389 - 393

2. Zubov V.I.: Theory of optimal control. Sudpromgiz, Leningrad 1966 (in Russian)

3. Chang A.: An optimal regulator problem. J. SIAM Control Ser. A 2 (1965), 220 - 233

4. Kurzweil J.: On Analytic regulator design. Automat. Remote Control 22 (1961) No 6

5. Popov V.M.: Hyperstability and optimality of automatic systems with several control functions. Rev. Roum. Sci. Techn.-Electrotechn. et Energ. 9 (1964), 629 - 690

6. Brunovský P.: On analytic regulators design with a non-quadratic minimized functional. Čas. pěst. mat. 90 (1965), 290 - 310 (in Russian)

7. Brunovský P.: On optimal stabilization of nonlinear systems. Czech. math. journal (to appear)

8. Cesari L.: Existence theorems for optimal solutions in Pontrjagin and Lagrange problems. J. SIAM on Control 3 (1965), 475 - 498

9. Lee E.B., Markus L.: Optimal control for nonlinear processes. Arch.Rat.Mech. Anal. 8 (1961), No 1

10. Coddington Earl A.,Levinson N.: Theory of ordinary differential equations, W Mc.Graw Hill, New York 1955.

TIME-OPTIMAL SYNTHESIS FOR NON-LINEAR CONTROL SYSTEMS OF SECOND ORDER

V. G. Boltyanskii
V. A. Steklov Mathematical Institute
U. S. S. R. Academy of Sciences
Moscow, U. S. S. R.

We consider a control system described by the equation:

$$\ddot{x} = f(x, \dot{x}, u), \qquad |u| \leq 1, \tag{1}$$

or, in the phase coordinates $x^1 = x$, $x^2 = \dot{x}$,

$$\left.\begin{array}{l} \dot{x}^1 = x^2 \\ \dot{x}^2 = f(x^1, x^2, u) \end{array}\right\}, \quad |u| \leq 1 . \tag{2}$$

We shall suppose that

$$\frac{\partial f(x^1, x^2, u)}{\partial u} > 0 . \tag{3}$$

For this system, we consider the problem of reaching the origin in the shortest time.

The maximum principle gives us

$$\begin{cases} \dot{\psi}_1 = -\psi_2 \dfrac{\partial f}{\partial x^1}, \\ \dot{\psi}_2 = -\psi_1 - \psi_2 \dfrac{\partial f}{\partial x^2}, \end{cases} \tag{4}$$

and

$$u = \operatorname{sign} \psi_2(t) . \tag{5}$$

(see (3)). Thus, it is necessary for us to investigate the behavior of the function $\psi_2(t)$.

We shall describe two quite large classes of control systems described by Eq. (1) for which the behavior of the function $\psi_2(t)$ is quite clear. This will permit us to construct the synthesis of the optimal trajectories for these two classes of systems.

The following theorem describes the first class.

Theorem 1. Let Eq. (1) describe a control system which satisfies the conditions:

(A) There exists a function $\varphi(x^1, x^2, u)$ with continuous derivatives $\frac{\partial\varphi}{\partial x^1}, \frac{\partial\varphi}{\partial x^2}$, such that

$$x^2 \frac{\partial\varphi}{\partial x^1} + f\frac{\partial\varphi}{\partial x^2} + \varphi^2 - \varphi\frac{\partial f}{\partial x^1} - \frac{\partial f}{\partial x^1} \leq 0$$

for all x^1, x^2 and $u = \pm 1$;

(B) $f(x^1, 0, 1) > 0$ if $x^1 \leq 0$; $f(x^1, 0, -1) < 0$ if $x^1 \geq 0$.

Then, in an open set containing the origin, there exists a synthesis of the time-optimal trajectories. Moreover, the function $\psi_2(t)$ has at most one zero, which means that each optimal control function $u(t)$ is equal to ± 1 and has at most one switching point.

More precisely, let Γ^+ be the half-trajectory of system (2) with $u \equiv 1$, which terminates at the origin, and let Γ^- be the half-trajectory of system (2) with $u \equiv -1$, which ends at the origin (Fig. 1). The two half-trajectories Γ^+ and Γ^- together constitute a curve Γ which passes through the origin. Let us consider all the half-trajectories of system (2) with $u \equiv -1$ situated above the line Γ and terminating on points of the arc Γ^+, and all the half-trajectories of system (2) with $u \equiv +1$ situated below the line Γ and terminating on points of the arc Γ^-. All these trajectories generate an open set G which contains a segment of the x^1-axis. In G, the indicated trajectories give the time-optimal synthesis. Finally, if $x_o \notin G$, then it is impossible to reach the origin starting from x_o. Let us note that, in addition, either $x^1 \to \infty$ as $t \to -\infty$ along Γ^+, or the arc Γ^+ has a single α-limit point, which lies on the x^1-axis. A similar assertion can be made for the arc Γ^-.

Let us indicate two particular cases of Theorem 1. If we set $\varphi \equiv 0$, then condition (A) takes the form:

$$(A') \quad \frac{\partial f}{\partial x^1} \geq 0 \text{ for all } x^1, x^2 \text{ and } u = \pm 1.$$

Thus, we obtain the following assertion:

The conclusion of Theorem 1 is valid if the control system (2) satisfies the conditions (A') and (B). This particular case of Theorem 1 was published by E. Roytenberg and myself (1). The general case, with proofs, is to appear in "Mat. Zametki" in Moscow, and in the English translation of my book (2).

The second particular case of Theorem 1 is obtained if we set $\varphi = (1/2)(\partial f/\partial x^2)$ in condition (A). Then, we arrive at the condition

$$(A'') \quad 2x^2 \frac{\partial^2 f}{\partial x^1 \partial x^2} + 2f \frac{\partial^2 f}{(\partial x^2)^2} - \left(\frac{\partial f}{\partial x^2}\right)^2 - 4 \frac{\partial f}{\partial x^1} \leq 0$$

for all x^1, x^2 and $u \pm 1$.

Consequently, the conclusion of Theorem 1 is valid if the control system described by Eq. (2) satisfies conditions (A'') and (B). Let us observe that each linear control system

$$\ddot{x} = -2\delta\dot{x} - \omega^2 x + u; \quad |u| \leq 1, \quad \delta \geq 0, \quad \delta^2 - \omega^2 \geq 0$$

satisfies conditions (A'') and (B). Moreover, if the control system (2) is such that

$$\frac{\partial f}{\partial x^1} > -\frac{1}{4}\left(\frac{\partial f}{\partial x^2}\right)^2 \quad \text{for all } x^1, x^2 \text{ and } u = \pm 1,$$

and if the second derivatives $\partial^2 f/\partial x^i \partial x^j$ are sufficiently small, then condition (A'') is satisfied. As we shall soon see, this is closely related to the second class of control systems, to which we now pass.

Thus, consider the control system (2), (3), which satisfies the additional conditions

$$\frac{\partial f}{\partial x^1} < -\frac{1}{4}\left(\frac{\partial f}{\partial x^2}\right)^2 \text{ for all } x^1, x^2 \text{ and } u = \pm 1 \qquad (6)$$

$$f(0, 0, 1) > 0, \quad f(0, 0, -1) < 0, \qquad (7)$$

$$\left(\frac{\partial^2 f}{\partial x^1 \partial x^2}\right)^2 \leq \frac{\partial^2 f}{(\partial x^1)^2} \cdot \frac{\partial^2 f}{(\partial x^2)^2}, \quad \frac{\partial^2 f}{(\partial x^1)^2} + \frac{\partial^2 f}{(\partial x^2)^2} \leq 0$$

$$\text{for all } x^1, x^2 \text{ and } u = \pm 1. \qquad (8)$$

The condition (8) means that (for $u = \pm 1$ and all x^1, x^2) the quadratic form

$$\frac{\partial^2 f}{(\partial x^1)^2} \xi_1^2 + 2 \frac{\partial^2 f}{\partial x^1 \partial x^2} \xi_1 \xi_2 + \frac{\partial^2 f}{(\partial x^2)^2} \xi_2^2$$

is negative semidefinite. For example, the conditions (6)-(8) are valid for the linear system

$$\ddot{x} + x = u, \qquad |u| \leq 1, \qquad (9)$$

as well as for nonlinear systems which differ from system (9) by a sufficiently small convex term. More precisely, let $\varphi(x^1, x^2, u)$ be a convex function (i. e., one for which condition (8) is satisfied) with bounded first derivatives:

$$\left|\frac{\partial \varphi}{\partial x^1}\right| \leq M, \qquad \left|\frac{\partial \varphi}{\partial x^2}\right| \leq M, \qquad \left|\frac{\partial \varphi}{\partial u}\right| \leq M.$$

Then the control system (2), (3), where

$$f(x^1, x^2, u) = -x^1 + u + \mu\varphi(x^1, x^2, u),$$

satisfies conditions (6)-(8) when μ is sufficiently small.

The following theorem was obtained by my Uzbek pupil G. Nasritdinov and myself. It is to be published in Differentsial'ny Uravneniya.

Theorem 2. Let there be given a control system (2), (3) satisfying conditions (6)-(8). Then, in an open set containing the origin, there exists a synthesis of the time-optimal trajectories, and this synthesis is qualitatively the same as the one for the linear system (9).

More precisely, the vector $\{\psi_1(t), \psi_2(t)\}$ (see (4)), for each optimal process, always rotates in a clockwise direction, and consequently (see (5)) the optimal control function u(t) may have many switching points. There exists a sequence of arcs $L_1^+, L_2^+, \ldots$ in the fourth quadrant with end points on the x^1- axis, and a sequence of arcs $L^-_1, L^-_2, \ldots$ in the second quadrant with end points on the x^1 - axis (Fig. 2), such that $u \equiv -1$ above the curve $L = (L^+_1 \cup L^+_2 \cup \ldots) \cup (L^-_1 \cup L^-_2 \cup \ldots)$ and on the arc L^-_1, and $u \equiv +1$ below the curve L and on the arc L^+_1. The optimal trajectories go to the origin as spirals, and these spirals generate an open set G which contains a segment of the x^1-axis. Finally, if $x_o \notin G_o$, then it is impossible to reach the origin, starting from x_o.

Let us note that it follows from (6) that

$$\frac{d}{dt}\arctan\frac{\psi_2}{\psi_1} = \frac{-\psi_1^2 - (\partial f/\partial x^2)\psi_1\psi_2 + (\partial f/\partial x^1)\psi_2^2}{\psi_1^2 + \psi_2^2} < 0 .$$

If there exists a constant $c > 0$ such that the left-hand side is less than $-c$, then each spiral has infinitely many rotations as $t \to -\infty$. In the other case, the number of rotations may be finite, and it is even possible that the control system has the same behavior as the one described in Theorem 1.

Two words about the proofs. In both theorems, we prove that

(i) each indicated trajectory satisfies the maximum principle;

(ii) all these trajectories make up the regular synthesis in the open set G.

It then follows from (3) that all of the indicated trajectories are optimal. The verification of (i) and (ii) in

Theorem 2 is somewhat complicated.

Finally, let us recall that, in Theorems 1 and 2 (as is true for any control system (2), (3)), the notion of a regular synthesis means the following: There exists a countable (or finite) system of smooth arcs in G which do not accumulate within G, and which subdivide G into a number of two-dimensional cells, and

(ii') in each cell u = constant (+1 or -1),

(ii'') when an indicated trajectory leaves a two-dimensional cell, it makes a nonzero angle with the boundary of this cell.

References

1. V. G. Boltyanskii, E. Ya. Roytenberg, "An Example of the Synthesis of a Nonlinear Second Order System", Kibernetika, 1966, No. 4, pp. 52-56.
2. V. G. Boltyanskii, "Mathematical Methods of Optimal Control", Nauka, Moscow, 1966. English translation to be published by Holt, Rinehart and Winston, New York, 1967.
3. V. G. Boltyanskii, "Sufficient Conditions for Optimality and the Justification of the Dynamic Programming Method", J. SIAM on Control, Vol. 4, No. 2, 1966, pp. 326-361.

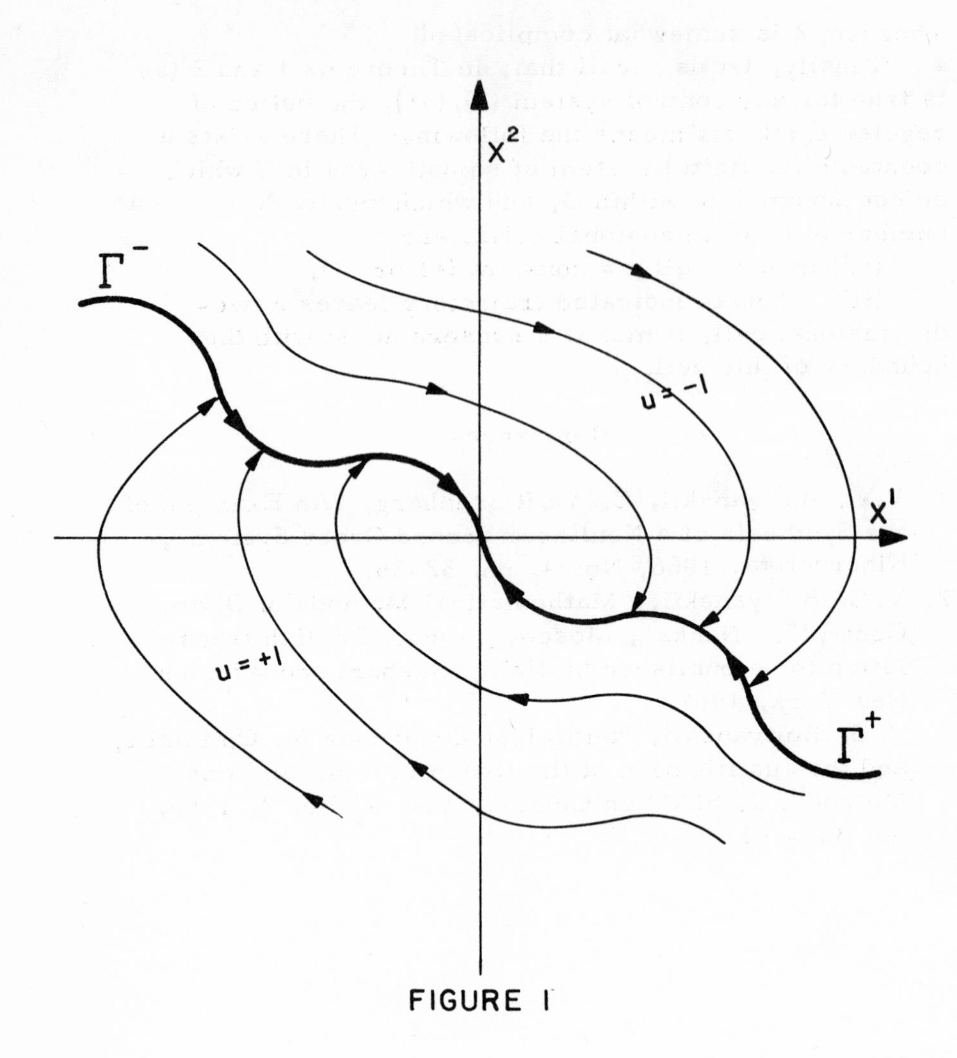

FIGURE 1

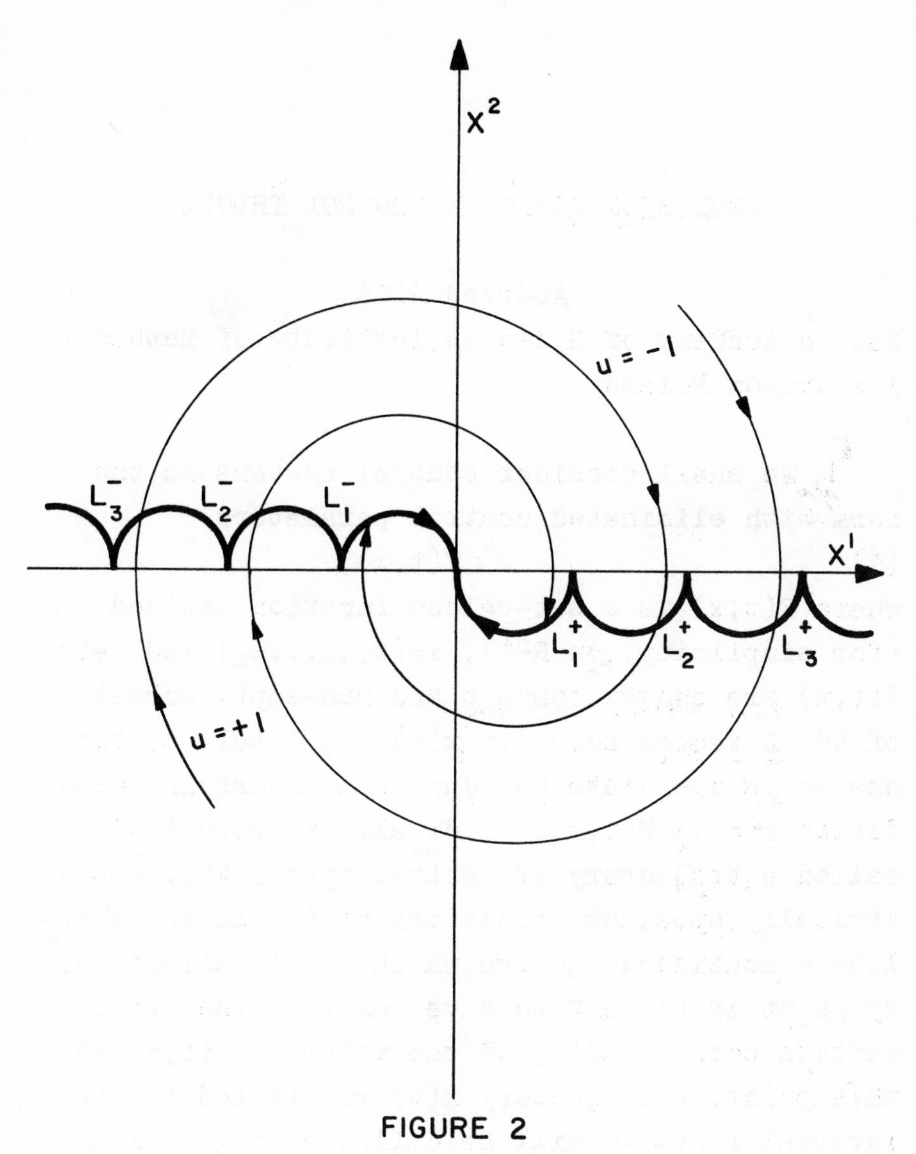

FIGURE 2

EMISSION ZONES IN CONTROL THEORY

Andrzej Pliś
Polish Academy of Sciences, Institute of Mathematics, Kraków, Poland

We shall consider control systems in the form with eliminated control parameters

(1) $$x' \in F(t,x),$$

where $F(t,x)$ is a set-valued function defined (for simplicity) on R^{n+1}, $x=(x_1,\dots,x_n)$ and sets $F(t,x)$ are convex compact and non-empty subsets of R^n. A vector function $x(t)$ absolutely continuous on an open interval $J \subset R$ and satisfying condition $x'(t) \in F(t,x(t))$ for almost every $t \in J$ is called a trajectory of control system (1). Geometrically speaking trajectory of (1) is an (absolutely continuous) curve which at its almost every point is tangent to a vector from the set of vectors corresponding to the value of $F(t,x)$ at this point. A trajectory $x(t)$ restricted to the interval $s \leqslant t < \infty$ will be called a (right) semi-trajectory starting from the point $(s,x(s))$.

In the following we shall assume that $F(t,x)$ is measurable bounded by an integrable function and upper semicontinuous in x on R^{n+1}. These assumptions imply that through every point of R^{n+1} passes at least one trajectory defined on R (1). If the set F(t,x) reduces at each point to a single vector the control system reduces to ordinary differential equation and we obtain as a special case the known Carathéodory's theorem on differential equations $x'=f(t,x)$ with $f(t,x)$ continuous in x and measurable in t .

If a control system is given in the form with control parameters

(2) $$x'=f(t,x,u), u \in U(t,x), U(t,x) \subset R^m ,$$

we can eliminate control parameters putting $F(t,x)=f(t,x,U(t,x))$. If this set is not convex we can take its convex envelope, what is equivalent to completing the space of trajectories in the topology of uniform convergence, provided F(t,x) satisfies the following condition

(3) $$r(F(t,x),F(t,y)) \leq l(t,|x-y|),$$

where r(S,Z) denotes the Hausdorff's distance of sets S,Z, the function $l(t,s)$ is continuous on R^2 and s=0 is the unique solution of the ordinary differential equation $s'=l(t,s)$ with the condition $s(r)=0$, where r is any number from R. The condition (3) is weaker than Lipschitz-continuity

(4) $$r(F(t,x),F(t,y)) \leq L |x-y| ,$$

where L is a given constant. Obviously to a given F(t,x) there correspond many possible functions f(t,x,u) but all give the same trajectories, therefore for a majority of problems including one I shall deal with, these differences are irrelevant. The relation between (1) and (2) is discussed in (2).

Now we pass to the main topics. Let S be a certain subset of R^{n+1} . For a given control system we shall call the union of all (right) semitrajectories starting from points of set S, the (right) emission zone of S (with respect to the control system). Similarly we define the left emission zone. These notions play an important role in the theory of optimal control.

There is a known theorem first proved for differential equations that to each point on the boundary of emission zone of S there exists a semitrajectory starting from $\bar{S}$ (closure of S) reaching this point and contained in the boundary. But in general even for ordinary differential equations there can be also other trajectories reaching this point and not contained in the boundary. I have proved that under assumption (3) the latter kind of trajectories does not exist (3). It follows that under suitable assumptions the optimal trajectories must be contained in the boundary of emission zone.

In general the boundary can be (even for ordinary differential equations) very irregular set. For instance the intersection of the boundary of the emission zone for the half-plane t=0, $x_1 \leq 0, x_2$ arbitrary (n=2), with the plane t=u can be for any positive number u a curve having no tangent at any point. I have proved that this is impossible for small u if F satisfies (4) (4) . Under suitable assumptions the boundary of the emission zone for the set $t=0, x_1 \leq 0, x_2, \ldots, x_n$ arbitrary is, for small t, Lipschitzian and therefore is differentiable (or has a tangent plane) at almost every point. In this theorem the constant L in (4) can be replaced by an integrable function (in this case the boundary must be Lipschitzian in x) but an essential weakening of (4) (or replacing it by (3)) is impossible.

To formulate another result we introduce the following notion. A set $S \subset R^n$ is called A-cone set if to each boundary point p of S there exists a (finite) n-dimentional cone contained in S with vertex at p and the angle at p equal to A. Now I give the idea of the result. Under assumption (4) if S is an A-cone set contained in the plane t=0 then the intersection of the emission zone of S with the plane t=u is a B-cone set, where B is near to A, for positive u from a neighbourhood of u=0. In proofs of last two results I use the following lemma. Under assumption (4) for any trajectory x(t) defined on R and any point $q \in R^{n+1}$ there exists a trajectory y(t) defined on R passing through q and satisfying the inequality $|y'(t)-x'(t)| \leq L\,|y(t)-x(t)|$, where L is the constant from (4), for almost every t .

References

(1) A.Pliś, Measurable orientor fields, Bull.Acad. Polon.Sci., Sér.sci.math., astr.et phys.13 (1965), p.565-569.

(2) T.Ważewski,On an optimal control problem,Proceedings of the Conference "Differential equations and their applications" held in Prague in September 1962.
(3) A.Pliś,On trajectories of orientor fields, Bull.Acad.Polon.Sci.,Sér.sci.math.astr.et phys.13(1965),p.571-573.
(4) A.Pliś,Emission zones for orientor fields, Coll.Math.16(1966),p.133-135.(To appear)

THEORY OF INEQUALITIES AND THE CONTROLLABILITY OF LINEAR SYSTEMS

Sanjoy K. Mitter
Systems Research Center
Case Institute of Technology
Cleveland, Ohio

The primary objectives of this paper are twofold: 1) to present a theory of controllability applicable to both finite and infinite dimensional linear control systems and 2) to show the relationship between the theory of inequalities of fundamental importance in mathematical programming, and controllability which is of fundamental importance in systems theory. It extends and generalises earlier results of Antosiewicz (1) and Conti (2).

Let X be a linear space with a locally convex Hausdorff topology $\mathcal{T}$ and let X^* be its topological dual. The natural pairing of X and X^* is represented as $\langle X,X^*\rangle$ and the fixed bi-linear functional by $\langle x,x^*\rangle$. The weak topology w for the linear space X with locally convex Hausdorff topology is the topology $w(X,X^*)$ of the natural pairing of X and X^* and the weak* topology for X^* is the topology $w(X^*,X)$ of the natural pairing of X^* and X [(3), Chapter 5: Sections 16 & 17].

Let U and X be linear speces with locally convex Hausdorff Topologies. Let $\langle U,U^*\rangle$ and $\langle X,X^*\rangle$ be their natural pairings. Let $T : U \to X$ be a continuous linear transformation and let $T^* : X^* \to U^*$ be the adjoint linear transformation.

Definition 1 [(4), p. 246]: The polar A^o in X^* of a subset A of X is defined by $A^o = \{x^* \in X^* : \langle x,x^*\rangle \leq 1\}$.

If A is equilibré then A^o is also given by

$$A^{o} = \{x^{*} \in X^{*} : |\langle x, x^{*} \rangle| \leq 1\} \quad .$$

Let U and X be locally convex Hausdorff topological spaces. U is to be thought of as the <u>control space</u> and X the <u>state space</u> of a control system. Consider a linear control system described by the operator equation

$$x = x_{o} + T(u) \quad , \tag{1}$$

where $x \in X$, $u \in U$, $x_{o} \in X$ is a fixed element and $T : U \to X$ is a continuous linear transformation. A wide variety of linear systems may be described by this abstract model.

As an example, we shall consider a linear differential system in a Banach space. Let U and X be real Banach Spaces.

Let $t > 0$ and $1 < p \leq \infty$. We define $L_{t}^{p}(U)$ to be the Banach Space of all U-valued strongly measurable functions defined on $[0, t]$ such that

$$\int_{o}^{t} \| u(\tau) \|_{U}^{p} \, d\tau < \infty \quad \text{if} \quad 1 < p < \infty$$

and ess. sup. $\{ \|u(\tau)\|_{U} , 0 \leq \tau \leq t\} < \infty$ if $p = \infty$.

The Banach Space $L_{t}^{p}(U)$ is normed by,

$$\|u\|_{p} = \left(\int_{o}^{t} \|u(\tau)\|_{U}^{p} \, d\tau \right)^{\frac{1}{p}} , \quad 1 < p < \infty$$

and $\|u\|_{\infty} = \text{ess. sup} \{ \|u(\tau)\|_{U} , \ 0 \leq \tau \leq t\}$ if $p = \infty$.

In the sequel we shall assume that the space $L_{t}^{p}(U)$, $1 < p < \infty$ to be reflexive. This will be the case if U is reflexive and separable or uniformly convex. The dual space $[L_{t}^{p}(U)]^{*}$ is isometrically isomorphic to $L_{t}^{q}(U^{*})$, $\frac{1}{p} + \frac{1}{q} = 1$.

Consider the linear differential system,

$$\dot{x}(t) = Ax(t) + Bu(t) \tag{2}$$

with initial condition $x(0) = x_o \in X$, where A is a linear closed operator with domain $D(A)$ which is the infinitesimal generator of a strongly continuous semi-group $T(t)$, $t \geq 0$, of linear bounded operators and B is a linear bounded operator mapping U into $D(A)$. We shall say that $x(\cdot)$ is a solution of Eq. (2) with initial condition $x(0) = x_o \in X$ if $x(\cdot)$ satisfies the integral equation

$$x(t) = T_t(x_o) + \int_o^t T_{t-\tau} \, Bu(\tau) \, d\tau \tag{3}$$

where the integral in the right hand side of Eq. (3) is in the sense of Bochner [(5), Section 3.7, p. 78].

For each $t > 0$, define a linear bounded transformation

$$R_t : u \to \int_o^t T_{t-\tau} \, Bu(\tau) \, d\tau$$

from $L_t^p(U)$ into X. Then Eq. (3) can be written as

$$x(t) = T_t(x_o) + R_t(u) \tag{4}$$

which fits our abstract model Eq. (1).

Necessary and Sufficient Conditions for Controllability

Consider the linear control system described by Eq. (1). Let $K \subseteq X$ be a closed convex set containing the null element and let $\Omega \subset U$ be a convex set which is compact with respect to the $w(U,U^*)$ - topology of U. Let K^o be the polar of K.

Definition 2: The system described by Eq. (1) is said to be controllable with respect to (x_o,Ω,K) if there exists a $\bar{u} \in \Omega$ such that $\bar{x} = x_o + T\bar{u} \in K$.

Our basic result is,

Theorem 1: The system described by Eq. (1) is

controllable with respect to (x_o,Ω,K) if and only if

$$\langle x_o,x^*\rangle - 1 \leq \mathrm{Max}[\langle u,T^*x^*\rangle : u\in\Omega] , \quad \forall\, x^*\in K^o \qquad (5)$$

The proof of the theorem will proceed via Propositions 1-4.

Proposition 1: The system described by Eq. (1) is controllable with respect to (x_o,Ω,K) if and only if there exists a $\bar{u}\in\Omega$ such that

$$\langle x_o + T\bar{u}, x^*\rangle - 1 \leq 0 , \quad \forall\, x^*\in K^o . \qquad (6)$$

Proof: Since $K \subseteq X$ is a closed convex set in a locally convex Hausdorff topological space it is closed with respect to the $w(X,X^*)$ - topology of X [(3), Chapter 5, Proposition 17.1]. Since K contains the null element, by the Bipolar theorem [(4), p. 248], $K = (K^o)^o$. Then from the definition of a polar set, $x_o + T\bar{u}\in K$ if and only if

$$\langle x_o + T\bar{u}, x^*\rangle \leqq 1 , \quad \forall\, x^*\in K^o .$$

The problem of controllability has thus been reduced to finding necessary and sufficient conditions for a feasible solution for an infinite system of linear inequalities to exist.

Let (X,T_1) be a real Hausdorff topological vector space and let R be the space of reals.

Definition 3: Let $C \subseteq X$ be a convex set. A function $f : C \to R$ is said to be quasi-convex on C if for any $r\in R$, the set

$$K = \{x\in C : f(x) \leq r\} \text{ is convex.}$$

The function f is said to be quasi-concave if the inequality is reversed.

The functions are said to be strictly quasi-convex (quasi-concave) if the inequalities are strict.

In a recent note Ky Fan (6) has proved certain geometric theorems regarding quasi-concave lower-semicontinuous functions. For our purposes we state one of the theorems in the following specialised form

Proposition 2: Let C_1,C_2 be non-empty compact convex subsets in a real Hausdorff topological vector space

X . Let $f_1 : C_1 \times C_2 \to R$ and $f_2 : C_1 \times C_2 \to R$ satisfy the following conditions:

(1) For every fixed $x_1 \in C_1$, $f_1(x_1,x_2)$ is a lower-semicontinuous function on C_2 and for every fixed $x_2 \in C_2$, $f_2(x_1,x_2)$ is a lower-semicontinuous function on C_1

(2) For every fixed $x_2 \in C_2$, $f_1(x_1,x_2)$ is a quasi-concave function on C_1 and for every fixed $x_1 \in C_1$, $f_2(x_1,x_2)$ is a quasi-concave function on C_2 .

Let $r_1, r_2 \in R$. If for every $x_2 \in C_2$, there exists an $x_1 \in C_1$ such that $f_1(x_1,x_2) > r_1$ and for every $x_1 \in C_1$, there exists an $x_2 \in C_2$ such that $f_2(x_1,x_2) > r_2$ then there exists a point $(\hat{x}_1,\hat{x}_2) \in C_1 \times C_2$ such that

$$f_1(\hat{x}_1,\hat{x}_2) > r_1$$

and

$$f_2(\hat{x}_1,\hat{x}_2) > r_2 \quad .$$

Proposition 3: Let C be a compact convex subset of a Hausdorff real topological vector space X . Let

$$P_n = \{\alpha = (\alpha_1, \ldots \alpha_n) : \alpha_i \geq 0 , i = 1,2,..n , \sum_{i=1}^{n} \alpha_i = 1\} .$$

Let g_i , $i = 1,2, \ldots n$ be a family of real-valued lower-semicontinuous functions on C such that

$$\sum_{i=1}^{n} \alpha_i \, g_i(x)$$

is quasi-convex on C for all $\alpha = (\alpha_1,\ldots\alpha_n) \in P_n$. Then the system of inequalities,

$$g_i(x) \leq 0 \ , \quad i = 1, 2, \ldots n \tag{7}$$

has a solution in C if and only if there exists an $x \in C$ such that

$$\sum_{i=1}^{n} \alpha_i \, g_i(x) \leq 0 \ , \tag{8}$$

for all $\alpha = (\alpha_1, \dots \alpha_n) \in P_n$.

Proof: The only if part is trivial.

To prove the if part, define two functions $\phi : C \times P_n \to R$ and $\psi : C \times P_n \to R$ by,

$$\phi(x,\alpha) = -\psi(x,\alpha) = -\sum_{i=1}^{n} \alpha_i g_i(x) \tag{9}$$

From the hypothesis of the theorem ϕ is quasi-concave on C. Also, clearly ϕ is a lower-semicontinuous function of α and ψ is a lower-semicontinuous function of x and a concave function of α. From condition Eq. (8) of the theorem, for any $\varepsilon > 0$ and any $\alpha \in P_n$ there exists an $x \in C$ such that $\phi(x,\alpha) > -\varepsilon$. Since $\phi(x,\alpha) = -\psi(x,\alpha)$ the two inequalities $\phi(x,\alpha) > -\varepsilon$ and $\psi(x,\alpha) > \varepsilon$ cannot be simultaneously satisfied. Hence by Proposition 2, for every $\varepsilon > 0$, there exists an $x_\varepsilon \in C$ such that $\psi(x,\alpha) \leq \varepsilon$, $\forall \alpha \in P_n$.

For a given $\varepsilon > 0$, consider the set $C_\varepsilon = \{x \in C : g_i(x) \leq \varepsilon, \ i = 1, 2, \dots n\}$. If we can prove that $\bigcap_{\varepsilon>0} C_\varepsilon \neq \emptyset$, where $\emptyset$ is the empty set, then the theorem is proved.

Since we have shown that for every $\varepsilon > 0$, there exists an $x_\varepsilon \in C$ such that $\psi(x_\varepsilon,\alpha) \leq \varepsilon$, $\forall \alpha \in P_n$, putting

$$\alpha = (1, 0, \dots. 0), \ (0, 1, 0, \dots 0)$$

etc. successively we obtain

$$g_i(x_\varepsilon) \leq \varepsilon, \quad i = 1, 2, \dots. n.$$

Hence $C_\varepsilon = \{x \in C : g_i(x) \leq \varepsilon$ is non-empty. Since each g_i has been assumed to be lower-semicontinuous C_ε is closed. C_ε is also bounded and hence it is compact. We also have for $0 < \varepsilon' < \varepsilon$, $C_{\varepsilon'} \subset C_\varepsilon$ and hence $\bigcap_{\varepsilon>0} C_\varepsilon \neq \emptyset$ [(4), p. 21]. Hence there exists an $x \in C$ such that Eq. (7) is satisfied.

Remark: If there exists an $x \in C$ such that Eq. (7) is satisfied, then there exists an $\hat{x} \in C$ such that

$$\operatorname*{Min}_{x \in C} \sum_{i=1}^{n} \alpha_i g_i(x) = \sum_{i=1}^{n} \alpha_i g_i(\hat{x}) \leq 0 \ , \ \forall \ \alpha = (\alpha_1, \ldots \alpha_n) \in P_n$$

Proposition 4: Let C be a compact convex subset of a real Hausdorff topological vector space X. Let I be an index set. For any $k > 0$, $I_k \subset I$ is the set $I_k = \{i : i = 1, 2, \ldots k\}$. Let $\{g_i\}_{i \in I}$ be an infinite family of real-valued lower-semicontinuous functions on C such that for any $k > 0$

$$\sum_{i \in I_k} \alpha_i \, g_i(x)$$

is quasi-convex for all $\alpha \in P_k$. Then the system of inequalities,

$$g_i(x) \leq 0 \ , \quad i \in I \tag{10}$$

has a solution in C, if and only if for any finite set of indices $k_1, k_2 \ldots . k_n \in I$ and for any $\alpha \in P_n$, there exists an $x \in C$ such that

$$\sum_{i=1}^{n} \alpha_i \, g_{k_i}(x) \leq 0 \ . \tag{11}$$

The proof of the theorem is omitted for the sake of brevity. Analogues of these theorems for finite dimensional spaces may be found in Berge (7).

Proof of Theorem 1

By assumption $\Omega \subset U$ is a convex set which is $w(U,U^*)$ - compact. The left hand side of Eq. (6) is continuous on Ω and hence it is $w(U,U^*)$ - continuous on Ω [(3), p. 154, Proposition 17.3]. Hence from Propositions 3 and 4 there exists a $u \in \Omega$ such that $x_o + T\,u \in K$ if and only if

$$\operatorname*{Min}_{u \in \Omega} \sum_{i=1}^{n} \alpha_i [\langle x_o, x_i^* \rangle + \langle u, T^*(x_i^*) \rangle - 1] \leq 0 \tag{12}$$

holds for any finite number of $x_i^* \in K^o$ and for any $\alpha = (\alpha_1, \ldots \alpha_n) \in P_n$. But

$$\sum_{i=1}^{n} \alpha_i [\langle x_o, x_i^* \rangle + \langle u, T^*(x_i^*) \rangle - 1]$$

$$= \sum_{i=1}^{n} [\langle x_o, \alpha_i x_i^* \rangle + \langle u, T^*(\alpha_i x_i^*) \rangle - 1$$

$$= [\langle x_o, \sum_{i=1}^{n} \alpha_i x_i^* \rangle + \langle u, T^*(\sum_{i=1}^{n} \alpha_i x_i) \rangle - 1]$$

Since K^o is convex, putting

$$x^* = \sum_{i=1}^{n} \alpha_i x_i^* \in K^o \quad ,$$

we obtain the desired result.

As a direct consequence of Theorem 1 the existance of minimum norm and best approximate controls can be established and moreover expressions for the minimum norm and minimum miss distance can be obtained in terms of the system data.

Controllability in the Presence of a Disturbance

Let U and W be reflexive Banach spaces and let X be a Hilbert Space. Consider the linear system

$$x = x_o + T(u) + S(w) \tag{13}$$

where $T : U \to X$ and $S : W \to X$ are continuous linear transformations and x_o is a given element in X. w is to be thought as a disturbance acting on the system. Let the controller restraint set be $\Omega_U = \{u \in U : ||u||_U \leq \rho\}$ and the disturbance set be

$$\Omega_d = \{d \in X : d = Sw, ||Sw||_X \leq \sigma\} \quad .$$

Let the target set be

$$K = \{x \in X : ||x - x_d||_X \leq \varepsilon\}$$

where x_d is the null element in X .

Theorem 2: Let the system (Eq. (13)) be controllable with respect to (x_o,Ω,K) in the absence of disturbances. Then the perturbed system is controllable with respect to (x_o,Ω,K) if and only if

$$\sigma \leq \varepsilon - \mathrm{Max}[0,\mathrm{Sup}\{|(x_d - x_o|x^*)| - \rho\,||T^*(x^*)||_{U^*} : ||x^*||_{X^*} = 1\}] \quad .$$

Proof: The perturbed system is controllable if and only if

$$\underset{u\in\Omega_u}{\mathrm{Min}} \; \underset{d\in\Omega_d}{\mathrm{Max}} \; [\,||Tu + d - (x_d - x_o)\,||_X] \leq \varepsilon \qquad (14)$$

$$\begin{aligned} ||\,Tu + d - (x_d - x_o)\,||_X &\leq ||d\,||_X + ||Tu - (x_d - x_o)\,||_X \\ &\leq \sigma + ||Tu - (x_d - x_o)\,||_X \end{aligned}$$

Let

$$\hat{d} = \frac{\sigma(Tu + x_o - x_d)}{||\,Tu + x_o - x_d\,||_X} \quad .$$

It is clear that $\hat{d}$ is the maximising d in Eq. (14) and

$$\underset{u\in\Omega_u}{\mathrm{Max}} \; [\,||Tu + d - (x_d - x_o)\,||_X] = \sigma + ||Tu + x_o - x_d\,||_X \quad .$$

Hence the perturbed system is controllable if and only if

$$\underset{u\;\Omega_u}{\mathrm{Min}} \; [\,||Tu + x_o - x_d\,||_X] + \sigma \leq \varepsilon \quad .$$

From the controllability conditions it may be shown that

$$\underset{u\in\Omega_u}{\mathrm{Min}} \; [\,||Tu + x_o - x_d\,||_X] = \mathrm{Max}[0,\mathrm{Sup}\{|(x_d - x_o|x^*)| - \rho\,||T^*(x^*)\,||_{U^*}\}]$$

and hence the theorem is proved.

References

1. H. A. Antosiewicz: Linear Control Systems, Archive for Rational Mechanics and Analysis, Vol. 12, No. 4, 1963, pp. 313-324.
2. R. Conti: Contributions to Linear Control Theory, Journal of Differential Equations 1, pp. 427-445 (1965).
3. J. L. Kelley, I. Namioka et al: Linear Topological Spaces, Van Nostrand, Princeton, 1963.
4. G. Köthe: Topologische Lineare Raume I, Springer-Verlag, Berlin, 1960.
5. E. Hille and R. S. Philips: Functional Analysis and Semi-Groups, American Mathematical Society, Providence, R. I., 1957.
6. Ky Fan: Sur un Theoreme Minimax: C. R. Acad. Sci. Paris t. 259 (30 Novembre 1964), Groupe 1, pp.3925-3928.
7. C. Berge: Topological Spaces, Macmillan, New York, 1963.

Acknowledgement

This research was partially supported by grant NSF GK-600.

ON THE EXISTENCE OF SATISFACTORY CONTROL

Y. Takahara
M.D. Mesarovic
Systems Research Center
Case Institute of Technology

Study of the sensitivity of optimal control have indicated a need for ensuring a sufficiently small variation of the performance over a given range of variations of the disturbances. This is provided by the so-called satisfaction approach to the control problem in which the objective consists in finding a control which will ensure a satisfactory performance over a range of disturbances.

In the present paper we shall give some conditions for the existance of the satisfactory control and will also indicate how these conditions can be used in a constructive way for a procedure to arrive at a strategy leading to a satisfactory control.

Consider at first the problem of controlling a system with disturbances.

Let X_1, X_2 and X_3 be real normed linear spaces and M, U and Y are subsets of X_1, X_2 and X_3, respectively. Let the system S be a mapping $S: M \times U \rightarrow Y$ and the behavior of S be evaluated by the performance functional $G: M \times Y \rightarrow R$ where R is the real line. Furthermore, let

$$S_m = S|\{m\} \times U \quad ; \quad G_m = G|\{m\} \times U$$

where $m \in M$. A mapping H_m can be then defined

$$H_m: U \rightarrow R, \text{ such that}$$

$$H_m(u) = G_m(S_m(u))$$

H_m gives the performance of the system for $u \in U$. In order to determine whether $H_m(u)$ is acceptable or not, there is given a mapping (tolerance function)

$$V: U \rightarrow R$$

The performance $H_m(u)$ is considered acceptable if $H_m(u) \leq V(u)$.

For any $m \in M$, there is defined a subset of U

$$U_m = \{u \mid u \in U \quad H_m(u) \leq V(u)\}$$

U_m is called satisfaction set in U.

Let S, G and V be continuous and assume the existence of a measure μ on U; let W_m be the characteristic function for U_m, i.e.,

$$W_m(u) = \begin{cases} 1 & \text{if } u \in U_m \\ 0 & \text{otherwise} \end{cases}$$

The global sensitivity of S for any given $m \in M$ is defined then by the integral:

$$\eta_m = \int_U W_m(u) \, d\mu \, (u)$$

If $\eta_m = \mu(U)$, then the sensitivity of S_m is called satisfactory and the respective control, m, is termed a satisfactory control.

The tolerance function V, just like the performance function G, has to be given in the definition of the control problem. In this paper we shall consider the case when

$$V(u) = G(o, S(o, u)).$$

Basically, such a tolerance function yields the largest set of disturbances in which the selected control is reasonable; any control which will violate such a tolerance function over the set of possible disturbances can not be accepted regardless how good performance the system yields at any particular point in the disturbance set. Furthermore, the results obtained for such a tolerance function could be extended to some classes of more general situations, in particular, when $V(u) = G(m^*,S(m^*,u))$, where m^* is a given control. The usefulness of this tolerance function for adaptive control and multi-level systems is discussed in[1].

The acceptability of an arbitrary control $m \in M$ is then measured by

$$\Delta_o(m,u) = G(m,S(m,u)) - G(o,S(o,u)) \qquad (1)$$

Assume that for each u_o in U there exists at least one optimal control m_o in M. In general, a set of pairs (u_o,m_o) is a relation on U x M but for the sake of simplicity, we assume that this relation is a mapping T such that $T: U \rightarrow M$ and for any $m' \in M$, $G(T(u_o),S(T(u_o),u_o)) \leq G(m',S(m',u_o))$. Then let M_o be

$$M_o = \{m | (\exists u)(u \in U \wedge m = T(u))\}$$

The following theorem gives a fundamental condition for the existance of the satisfactory control:

Theorem 1

Let U and M be compact and let $\Delta_o(m,u)$ be convex in m for each $u \in U$ and concave in u for each $m \in M$. Then, there exists a satisfactory control in M_o, which is not zero if and only if $\max_{u \in U} \min_{m \in M} \Delta_o(m,u) < o$. Note that in the present case the control m=o is trivially always a satisfactory control.

Proof

The following lemma is used.

Lemma 1[3]

Let X and Y be a real linear space, A and B non-void convex subsets of X and Y, respectively, and $\phi(x,y)$ a function on A x B to the reals that is concave in x for each y in B and convex in y for each x in A. Suppose there is a topology in A such that A is compact and ϕ is upper semi-continuous in x for each y in B. Then

$$\sup_{x\in A} \inf_{y\in B} \phi(x,y) = \inf_{y\in B} \sup_{x\in A} \phi(x,y)$$

Since Δ_o is continuous, let

$$\min_{u\in U} \max_{m\in M} \Delta_o(m,u) = \Delta_o(m^*,u^{**}) \qquad (2)$$

Let

$$\max_{u\in U} \min_{m\in M} \Delta_o(m,u) = \Delta_o(m^{**}, u^*) \qquad (3)$$

From the lemma we have

$$\Delta_o(m^*,u^{**}) = \Delta_o(m^{**},u^*) \qquad (4)$$

From (2),(3) and (4) we have

$$\Delta_o(m^*,u^{**}) \geq \Delta_o(m^*,u^*) \geq \Delta_o(m^{**},u^*) = \Delta_o(m^*,u^{**})$$

Consequently,

$$\Delta_o(m^*,u^{**}) = \Delta_o(m^*,u^*) = \Delta_o(m^{**},u^*) \qquad (5)$$

From (2),(3) and (5) we have

$$(\forall u)(\forall m)(u \in U \wedge m \in M \rightarrow \Delta_o(m^*,u) \leq \Delta_o(m^*,u^*) \leq \Delta_o(m,u^*)) \qquad (6)$$

If $\Delta_o(m^{**},u^*) < o$, $(\forall u)(u \in U \rightarrow \Delta_o(m^*,u) < o)$.

Consequently, m* is a satisfactory control. From (6), $(\forall m)(m \in M \rightarrow \Delta_o(m^*,u^*) \leq \Delta_o(m,u^*))$. Consequently, $m^* = T(u^*)$. Since $\Delta_o(m^*,u) < o, m^* \neq o$. Conversely, if $\Delta_o(m^{**},u^*) = o$ (notice that, generally, $\Delta_o(m^{**},u^*) \leq o$), since $T(u^*) = m^{**}$ from (3), $m^* = m^{**} = o$. The proof is complete.

Consider now a linear system with a quadratic performance. Let the system S be decided by

$$y = \Psi\,(m) + u + y_f \qquad (7)$$

where X_1, X_2 and X_3 are reflexive Banach spaces; $X_2 = X_3$, $y \in Y$, $y_f \in Y$, $m \in M$ and $u \in U$, and Ψ is a bounded linear operator from M into Y. $y_f \in Y$ represents, apparently, free motion of the system.

Suppose inner products are defined on X_1 and X_3. The inner products are assumed continuous. Let the performance functional be

$$q = G(m,y) = (y-r, A(y-r))_{X_3} + (m, Bm)_{X_1} \qquad (8)$$

where $q \in R$ and $r \in Y$; A and B are positive definite bounded linear operators such that $A: X_3 \rightarrow X_3$ and $B: X_1 \rightarrow X_1$: $(\ ,\ )_{X_3}$ and $(\ ,\ )_{X_1}$ are the inner products of X_3 and X_1, respectively. r represents the reference output. Let $F = B + \Psi^* A \Psi$ where Ψ^* is the adjoint of Ψ. Let $U = \{u \mid \|u\| \leq k_u\}$. Let $M \supseteq - F^{-1} \Psi^* A(y_f - r + U)$. (The existence of the continuous inverse of F can be proved(2)).

The conditions for the existence of the satisfactory control can be given in terms of the derivation of the free motion y_f from the reference output and the diameter of the set U. More specifically, the conditions will be given in terms of $\|y_f - r\|$ and k_u.

Lemma 2

An element m* of M can be defined by the following formula:

$$\min_{m \in M} \max_{u \in U} (G(m, S(m,u)) - G(o, S(o,u)))$$

$$= \max_{u \in U} (G(m^*, S(m^*,u)) - G(o, S(o,u))).$$

Moreover, m* is a satisfactory control and $m^* \in M_o$ i.e., there exists an element u* in U such that $m^* = T(u^*)$.

Proof:

Since X_2 is a reflexive Banach space, U is weakly compact and $G(m,S(m,u))$ can be proved weakly continuous[1]. Hence, since X_1 is a reflexive Banach space, also, the definition of m^* is valid.

Apparently, m^* is a satisfactory control[2]. It should be noticed that $(G(m,S(m,u))-G(o,S(o,u)))$ is convex in m for each u and concave in u for each m[2]. (Refer to (7) and (8)). Then from Lemma 1 it follows that

$$\min_{m\in M} \max_{u\in U} (G(m,S(m,u)) - G(o,S(o,u)))$$

$$= \max_{u\in U} \min_{m\in M} (G(m,S(m,u)) - G(o,S(o,u)))$$

$$= \min_{u\in U} (F^{-1} \Psi^*A(y_f - r + u), \Psi^*A(y_f - r + u))$$

$$\triangleq (F^{-1} \Psi^*A(y_f - r + u^*), \Psi^*A(y_f - r + u^*)). \tag{9}$$

Therefore, $m^* = T(u^*)$.

u^* is an element of the disturbance set such that m^* is the optimal control with respect to u^*.

The conditions for the existence of the satisfactory control are given now by the following theorems:

Lemma 3

Let $\|y_f - r\| \leq k_u$; then $u^* = -(y_f - r)$.

Proof:

Since $F = B + \Psi^*A\Psi$ is positive definite, F^{-1} is positive definite, also. Then, since (9) is non-negative for any u in U, we have the lemma.

Theorem 2:

Let $\|y_f - r\| \leq k_u$; then $m_o = o$ is the only

satisfactory control and furthermore, $o \in M_o$.

Proof:

From Lemma 3 and theorem 1 we have the result.

Theorem 3:

Let $\|y_f - r\| > k_u$ and $m^* = T(u^{**})$, where

$$u^{**} = - \frac{k_u}{\|y_f - r\|} (y_f - r).$$

then, m^* is a satisfactory control whenever

$$\min_{u \in U} (F^{-1} \Psi^* A(y_f - r + u), \Psi^* A(y_f - r + u))$$

$$= (F^{-1} \Psi^* A(y_f - r + u^{**}), \Psi^* A(y_f - r + u^{**}))$$

Moreover, $m^* \neq o$.

Proof:

The result follows from theorem 1 and Lemma 2. The derived existence conditions can be used as the basis for a strategy for satisfactory control in the following way:

Let the following be a dynamic system equation.

$$\frac{dy}{dt} = f(y, m, v)$$

where y is a state variable, m is a control variable and v is a disturbance.

Let m_r be a previously designed control. An important practical question is how to update m_r with the help of new information about v.

Let v_r be a predicted disturbance of v.

Let

$$\frac{dy_r}{dt} = f(y_r, m_r, v_r)$$

Set $y = y_r + \Delta y$, $m = m_r + \Delta m$ and $v = v_r + \Delta v$. Then

$$\frac{d(\Delta y)}{dt} = (\nabla_y f)\,\Delta y + (\nabla_m f)\,\Delta m + (\nabla_v f)\,\Delta v.$$

where $\nabla_y f$, $\nabla_m f$ and $\nabla_v f$ indicate gradient of f with respect to y, m and v, respectively. Consequently, we have the following model.

$$\frac{dz}{dt} = (\nabla_y f)\,z + (\nabla_m f)\,\Delta m$$

$$\Delta y = z + u$$

where u is an uncertainty and it consists of two parts; the first part comes from the disturbance Δv and the second part from inaccuracy of linear approximation of the model. k_u is estimated at regular time instances. Suppose the performance functional is approximated by a quadratic form with respect to Δy and Δm. Then, the adaptive policy is as follows; if $\|\Delta y_f - r\| \leq k_u$, no additional control is applied, i.e., $\Delta m = o$ and m_r is used; if $\|\Delta y_f - r\| > k_u$, the control $m_r + \Delta m^*$ is applied where Δm^* is given by theorem 3.

The proposed procedure shows an interesting fact that an appropriate measuring scale of the size of the disturbance set U in $\|y_f - r\|$, i.e., norm of the deviation of the free motion y_f from the desired value r of y. This fact supports the intuitive idea that an optimal control can be applied to a system under the disturbances, if that control affects the performance of the system more than the disturbance does. It should also be mentioned that u^* lies on the boundary of U if $\|y_f - r\| > k_u$.(1)

References

1. Takahara, Y., "Multilevel Systems and Uncertainties," Systems Research Center Report No. SRC 99-A-66-42, Case Institute of Technology, Cleveland, Ohio 1966.

2. Takahara, Y., and Mesarovic, M.D., "Global Sensitivity and Optimal Control," to be published.

3. Pettis, B.J., "Separations Theorems for Convex Sets," Mathematical Magazine, June 1956.

ON A THEOREM OF SCORZA-DRAGONI AND ITS APPLICATION TO OPTIMAL CONTROL

Gerald S. Goodman

Imperial College
Department of Mathematics
London S.W. 7, England

1. Scorza-Dragoni's Theorem and Some of its Consequences

In 1948, G. Scorza-Dragoni published a proof of the following theorem in the case where the domain of t, A_t, and the domain of x, $A_x(t)$ (which could conceivably depend upon t), were fixed closed intervals: $A_t = [t_o, t_1]$, $A_x(t) = [x_o, x_1]$ (6).

Scorza-Dragoni's Theorem   If a real-valued function $f(t,x)$ is measurable in t and continuous in x for all values of (t,x) in a set $A = A_t \times A_x(t)$, then, to every value of $\varepsilon > 0$, there can be assigned a perfect set $S \subset A_t$, of measure $m\,S > m\,A_t - \varepsilon$, in such a way that the function f will be continuous jointly in t and x when t is restricted to S.

We shall present his proof in the appendix.

As Scorza-Dragoni pointed out, there is no difficulty in extending his reasoning to the case in which t and x are vectors (and A_t and $A_x(t)$ are presumably fixed boxes) with f measurable in the one variable and continuous in the other.

An examination of his proof reveals that it is not necessary for A_t to be an interval: it can be any set of finite measure on the line.

This fact allows us to apply the theorem over again, taking for the domain of t the exceptional set S or its relative complement $A_t - S$. Using this procedure, we can establish that the theorem remains valid when f is vector valued by arguing on the successive components of f.

It also permits us to establish the following corollary.

Corollary Under the hypotheses of Scorza-Dragoni's theorem, there can be found a sequence of disjoint, perfect sets lying in A_t, whose union has full measure, and is such that the function f is continuous in (t,x) over each set in the sequence.

Here again, t and x can be vector variables, and f can be vector valued.

2. An Extension Theorem

For the applications to optimal control theory, it is desirable to have available a more general version of the theorem in which the set A is only supposed to be closed.

We can derive such a generalization once we know that the theorem holds for compact A. The case of compact A, however, can be reduced to the case already treated by appealing to the following theorem.

Extension Theorem Suppose f is measurable in t and continuous in x for all values of (t,x) in a compact set $A = A_t \times A_x(t)$. Then f can be extended to a function F which is measurable in t and continuous in x for t in A_t and all x, and F satisfies

$$\underline{f}(t) \equiv \min_{\bar{x} \in A_x(t)} f(t,\bar{x}) \leq F(t,x) \leq \max_{\bar{x} \in A_x(t)} f(t,\bar{x}) \equiv \bar{f}(t).$$

Before proving this theorem, we first require a lemma.

Lemma Suppose that the function $g(t,\bar{x})$ is measurable in t and continuous in $\bar{x}$ for all $(t,\bar{x})$ belonging to a closed set $A = A_t \times A_x(t)$ whose sections $A_x(t)$, for $t \in A_t$, are compact. Then the functions

$$\underline{g}(t) \equiv \min_{\bar{x} \in A_x(t)} g(t,\bar{x}) \quad \text{and} \quad \max_{\bar{x} \in A_x(t)} g(t,\bar{x}) \equiv \bar{g}(t)$$

are measurable in t for all t in A_t.

We remark that the closedness of A can certainly be replaced by a weaker hypothesis.

To prove the lemma, let

$$A_t(x) = \{t \in A_t : (t,x) \in A_t \times A_x(t)\};$$

then

$$\chi_{A_x(t)}(x) \equiv \chi_{A_t(x)}(t), \tag{1}$$

where χ denotes the characteristic function. Since $A_t(x)$ is closed, its characteristic function is measurable; hence the function standing at left above is a measurable function of t for t running over the set A_t.

Let A_x denote the union of the sets $A_x(t)$ when t ranges over A_t, and let $\{r_j\}$, $j = 1, 2, \ldots$, denote the set of rational points in A_x. From the preceding paragraph it follows that the functions

$$h(t,r_j) = \chi_{A_x(t)}(r_j)\, g(t,r_j)$$

are measurable in t on A_t for each value of j (if we assign to $g(t,r_j)$ the value 0 when $r_j \notin A_x(t)$). Hence the functions

$$\underline{g}(t) = \inf_{j \geq 1} h(t,r_j), \quad \sup_{j \geq 1} h(t,r_j) = \overline{g}(t)$$

are likewise measurable functions of t, for t in A_t, which proves the lemma.

Turning now to the proof of the extension theorem, we may assume that $f(t,x) \geq q > 0$ on A, for, if it is not, we may consider in its place the function

$$f(t,x) + |\underline{f}(t)| + q$$

which, by the lemma, is also measurable in t. This assumption allows us to adapt a line of reasoning used by F. Riesz ((1), p. 77f.) to prove Tietze's extension theorem in metric spaces.

Let $d(x,\bar{x})$ denote the (euclidean) distance from x to $\bar{x}$; then $d(x,A_x(t))$ can be defined in the usual way as $\inf d(x,\bar{x})$ over all $\bar{x}$ in $A_x(t)$.

Now for every value of t in A_t and every value of x set

$$F(t,x) = \inf_{\bar{x} \in A_x(t)} \left\{ \frac{f(t,\bar{x}) \cdot d(x,\bar{x})}{d(x,A_x(t))} \left(1 - \chi_{A_x(t)}(x)\right) + f(t,x) \cdot \chi_{A_x(t)}(x) \right\},$$

where we make the convention that $0/0 = 0$.

The function $F(t,x)$ reduces to $f(t,x)$ when $x \in A_x(t)$, and it can be shown by Riesz's argument that F is continuous for all values of x and satisfies the inequalities asserted in the theorem.

It therefore remains for us to show that F is also measurable in t. This will follow from the lemma once we know that the expression in braces above is measurable in t (for it is certainly continuous in $\bar{x}$ for $\bar{x}$ in $A_x(t)$). Because of (1) and the compactness of A, the characteristic function which appears there is measurable in t, so it is enough to show that the function $d(x, A_x(t))$ is measurable for all t in A_t, and then we can apply the lemma.

Suppose $\delta > 0$ and construct about each point $(\bar{t}, \bar{x})$ belonging to A the open neighborhood

$$N_\delta = \{(t,x): |t - \bar{t}| < \delta, \ |x - \bar{x}| < \delta\}.$$

For each fixed value of δ, the N_δ form an open covering of the set A. Hence, by the compactness of A, they can be reduced to a finite subcovering; we denote the open set comprised by the finite covering by $A(\delta)$, and any section $t = \text{const.}$ of $A(\delta)$ by $A_x(\delta; t)$. Now, the function $d(x, A_x(\delta; t))$ is a step-function. Moreover, it is readily seen that for each value of t in A_t

$$d(x, A_x(t)) = \lim_{\delta \to 0} d(x, A_x(\delta; t)),$$

since $A(\delta) \to A$ as $\delta \to 0$, and this is more than enough to prove the measurability of $d(x, A_x(t))$. Hence the lemma applies and the theorem is proved.

It is clear that the argument is sufficiently general to cover the case of t and x vectors, and the case of f vector valued results from treating each component of f separately.

3. An Extension of Scorza-Dragoni's Theorem

The validity of Scorza-Dragoni's theorem when A is a compact set is an immediate consequence of the foregoing extension theorem.

We may now treat the case when A is closed and A_t has finite measure by use of an exhaustion argument.

Let $\varepsilon > 0$ be given. We exhaust A by an increasing sequence of compact sets A_n, $n = 1, 2, \ldots$, *e.g.*,

$$A_n = \{(t,x) \in A: |x| \leq n\},$$

whose t-projections T_n will then converge to A_t as $n \to \infty$. Passing if necessary to a subsequence, we may suppose that

$$m(A_t - T_n) < \varepsilon/2^{n+1}, \qquad n = 1, 2, \ldots .$$

Applying Scorza-Dragoni's theorem to the compact sets A_n, we can find in each case a perfect subset $S_n \subset T_n$ with

$$m(T_n - S_n) < \varepsilon/2^{n+1}, \qquad n = 1, 2, \ldots,$$

over which f is continuous in (t,x) for x in $A_x(t)$, $|x| \leq n$. Now let

$$S^* = \bigcap_{n=1}^{\infty} S_n.$$

Then

$$m\, S^* = m\, A_t - m \bigcup_{n=1}^{\infty} (A_t - S_n) \geq m\, A_t - \sum_{n=1}^{\infty} m(A_t - S_n).$$

But

$$m(A_t - S_n) = m(A_t - T_n) + m(T_n - S_n)$$
$$< \varepsilon/2^{n+1} + \varepsilon/2^{n+1} = \varepsilon/2^n.$$

Hence,

$$m\, S^* > m\, A_t - \varepsilon \sum_{n=1}^{\infty} 1/2^n = m\, A_t - \varepsilon.$$

Clearly, f is continuous in that portion of A which lies over S*. S* need not be perfect, but it has a perfect subset S with

$$m(S^* - S) < m\, S^* - (m\, A_t - \varepsilon).$$

Hence,

$$m\, S > m\, A_t - \varepsilon,$$

and therefore S satisfies all the requirements of the theorem.

It is now an almost trivial matter to derive a corresponding theorem in the case when $m\, A_t = \infty$ by exhausting A_t by closed sets of finite measure and taking then the union of the exceptional sets. This union will be an open set, and we can achieve that its measure is $< \varepsilon$. Its complement will then be closed and will have a perfect subset of full measure, which then can be taken as the set S in the theorem.

All the remarks made previously about the case of t and x vector variables and f vector valued continue to hold in the present situation, as does the corollary to Scorza-Dragoni's theorem given at the end of section 1.

4. Application to Optimal Control: the Closure Problem

To illustrate the possibilities for applying the generalized Scorza-Dragoni theorem in optimal control theory, we turn to the closure theorem of A.F. Fillipov (3), as extended recently by L. Cesari (2).

These authors are concerned with control systems of the form

$$\dot{x} = f(t,x,u(t)) \text{ a.e.}, \tag{2}$$

where x is a vector variable and $f(t,x,u)$ is continuous in a closed set A, with $A_t = [t_0, t_1]$, while $u(t)$ is a vector valued measurable function on A_t whose range lies in a variable set $U(t,x)$ in u-space. They make different hypotheses concerning $U(t,x)$: for Fillipov it must be compact for each (t,x) in A and upper semi-continuous with respect to inclusion, while for Cesari it must satisfy his condition (U), *loc. cit.* p. 373. (This is, for us, a consequence of the set A being closed, just as Fillipov's conditions would be a consequence of the set A being compact. For the converse implications, see (2), § 4, (ii) and (vii), where the set A has a different meaning.) The image of the control region $U(t,x)$ under the differential equation, $Q(t,x) = f(t,x,U(t,x))$, is assumed to be convex. In Fillipov's case, it will also be compact and upper-semicontinuous; in Cesari's, it is assumed to satisfy

$$Q(t,x) = \bigcap_{\delta > 0} \operatorname{cl} \operatorname{co} Q(t,x,\delta), \tag{Q}$$

where $Q(t,x,\delta)$ is the union of the sets $Q(\check{t},\check{x})$ when the point $(\check{t},\check{x})$ roams over a δ-neighborhood of (t,x) and cl = closure, co = convex hull.

In its simplest form, the closure problem is to show that if $x_k(t)$, $k = 1, 2, \ldots$, is a sequence of trajectories of the control system (2) (with the associated control functions $u_k(t)$) which converges uniformly on A_t to an absolutely continuous function $x(t)$, then

$$\dot{x}(t) \in Q(t,x(t)) \text{ a.e. in } A_t. \tag{3}$$

A celebrated lemma of Fillipov (3), extended by Cesari in (2), then shows that

$$\dot{x}(t) = f(t,x(t),u(t)) \text{ a.e.},$$

for some measurable function $u(t)$ assuming values in

$U(t,x(t))$.

In Cesari's version of Fillipov's reasoning, the proof of the closure property (3) makes no use of the continuity of the function f, but is based rather upon the property (Q). The continuity of f intervenes, however, when one wants to show that Fillipov's assumptions imply that $Q(t,x)$ has property (Q) ((2), §4, (xiii)), and it intervenes also in the proofs of Fillipov's lemma given by these two authors. E. Roxin has shown in (5) that this reliance upon the joint continuity of f can be avoided in the proof of Fillipov's theorem (as well as in the lemma) by reasoning in a different way. (However, Roxin does not deal with the case of variable sets $U(t,x)$.) For him, it is enough for the function f to be measurable in t and continuous in (x, u). But, as we now know, this means that f will have the continuity properties stated in Scorza-Dragoni's theorem and its corollary. Thus we can be assured that if we make the remaining assumptions of Fillipov, but relax the continuity requirement in the above way, we can still achieve that $Q(t,x)$ has the property (Q) on each set of a sequence of perfect subsets of A_t whose union has full measure. The problem before us, then, is to see whether Cesari's reasoning can be modified to permit the set $Q(t,x)$ to have this property and still draw the conclusion that the closure property (3) is valid.

In the next section we shall show that the appropriate modifications can be made and a generalized closure theorem established provided the function f satisfies a growth condition of the form

$$|f(t,x,u)| \leq M(t,|x|) \tag{4}$$

for all (t,x,u) in A, where $M(t,y)$ is summable in t on A_t and monotone increasing in y for y in the range $[0,\infty)$, cf. (5). This condition is familiar from the theory of differential equations whose right members depend measurably upon t, where it gives the existence of local solutions. (It should be added that in view of this condition the mode of convergence in the statement of the closure problem can be weakened to convergence in measure and the absolute continuity of the limit function can be replaced by the assumption that it is essentially bounded without any change in the conclusion.)

As for Fillipov's lemma, our generalization of Scorza-Dragoni's theorem automatically provides what is needed to carry through the Fillipov-Cesari proof under the hypothesis that f is measurable in t and continuous in (x,u) the details may be left to the reader.

5. Proof of the Closure Theorem

In this section we show how to modify Cesari's reasoning and establish the closure property (3) under the hypothesis that f satisfies the growth condition (4) and $Q(t,x)$ has the property (Q) on each set in a sequence of (disjoint) measurable subsets of A_t whose union has full measure. The measurability properties of the function f come in only indirectly to insure that the integrals which we write down have a meaning.

The proof is based upon two facts from the theory of Lebesgue measure and integration, whose use in connection with Scorza-Dragoni's theorem is found already in (4).

If E is a measurable subset of A_t and $F = A_t - E$, we shall denote by $E_h(t)$ the intersection of E with the interval $[t, t+h]$, and similarly with F.

Proposition 1 For almost all points $\bar{t}$ in F there holds

$$\lim_{h \to 0} m E_h(\bar{t})/h = 0. \qquad (5)$$

This is a direct consequence of Lebesgue's density theorem, since

$$1 = m[\bar{t}, \bar{t}+h]/h = m F_h(\bar{t})/h + m E_h(\bar{t})/h$$

for all $h \neq 0$, and $m F_h(\bar{t})/h \to 0$ as $h \to 0$.

Proposition 2 Let $M(t)$ be a summable function of t on A_t. Then for almost all $\bar{t}$ in F there holds

$$\lim_{h \to 0} \frac{1}{h} \int_{E_h(\bar{t})} M(t)\, dt = 0. \qquad (6)$$

This proposition follows immediately from the fundamental theorem of calculus for Lebesgue integrals applied to the function $M(t)\chi_E(t)$.

To prove the closure theorem, we let G be any fixed subset of A_t over which property (Q) holds, and we let F denote the subset of G made up of points at which simultaneously (5) holds, (6) holds, and $\dot{x}$ exists. We shall show that at every point $\bar{t}$ in F $\dot{x}(\bar{t}) \in Q(\bar{t}, x(\bar{t}))$.

Since $mF = mG$ and the union of the sets G has measure equal to mA_t, the closure property (3) will therefore be completely established.

Fix $\bar{t}$ arbitrarily in F and let ε be >0. The trajectories $x_k(t)$ are uniformly bounded on A_t: $|x_k(t)| \leq Y$, and therefore it follows from the growth condition (4) that they all have the same modulus of continuity as the limit function $x(t)$. Hence it is possible to choose a positive $\delta < \varepsilon$ so small that for all $|h| < \delta$ and for all k there holds

$$|x_k(\bar{t}+h) - x_k(\bar{t})| < \varepsilon/4, \qquad |x(\bar{t}+h) - x(\bar{t})| < \varepsilon/4. \tag{7}$$

Now let $M(t,Y) \equiv M(t)$ of Proposition 2, and let $\bar{u}$ be an arbitrary point of $U(\bar{t}, x(\bar{t}))$. For any given value of $\eta > 0$ it is possible, by the two propositions given above, to fix a value of h, $0 < |h| < \eta, \delta$, so that

$$\frac{1}{h}\int_{E_h(\bar{t})} M(t)\,dt < \eta/4, \qquad |f(\bar{t}, x(\bar{t}), \bar{u})|\, m E_h(\bar{t})/|h| < \eta/4, \tag{8}$$

where $E = A_t - F$, and

$$\left| \dot{x}(\bar{t}) - \frac{x(\bar{t}+h) - x(\bar{t})}{h} \right| < \eta/4. \tag{9}$$

Having fixed h in this way, choose K so large that for all values of $k > K$

$$\left| \frac{x_k(\bar{t}+h) - x_k(\bar{t})}{h} - \frac{x(\bar{t}+h) - x(\bar{t})}{h} \right| < \eta/4 \tag{10}$$

and

$$|x_k(\bar{t}) - x(\bar{t})| < \varepsilon/4. \tag{11}$$

The triangle inequality then implies, by virtue of (7) and (11), that for all values of s such that $|s| \leq 1$ and for all $k > K$

$$|x_k(\bar{t}+sh) - x(\bar{t})| < \varepsilon/2. \tag{12}$$

Hence, if we define $\bar{Q}(\bar{t}, \bar{x}, \varepsilon)$ as the union of the sets $Q(t,x)$ when the point (t,x) roams over an ε-neighborhood of $(\bar{t}, \bar{x})$ subject to the restriction that t belongs to F, it follows from (12) that for every value of $\bar{t}+sh$ in $F_h(\bar{t})$

$$f(\bar{t}+sh, x_k(\bar{t}+sh), u_k(\bar{t}+sh)) \in \bar{Q}(\bar{t}, x(\bar{t}), \varepsilon). \tag{13}$$

If we now set

$$g_k(t) = \begin{cases} f(t, x_k(t), u_k(t)), & \text{for } t \text{ in } F_h(\bar{t}), \\ f(\bar{t}, x(\bar{t}), \bar{u}), & \text{for } t \text{ in } E_h(\bar{t}), \end{cases}$$

we then have from (13) and the definition of g_k, for $k > K$,

$$\frac{1}{h}\int_{\bar{t}}^{\bar{t}+h} g_k(t)\,dt = \int_0^1 g_k(\bar{t}+sh)\,ds \in \text{cl co}\,\tilde{Q}(\bar{t}, x(\bar{t}), \varepsilon). \qquad (14)$$

But

$$\frac{x_k(\bar{t}+h) - x_k(\bar{t})}{h} = \frac{1}{h}\int_{\bar{t}}^{\bar{t}+h} f(t, x_k(t), u_k(t))\,dt. \qquad (15)$$

Using the definition of g_k and the additivity of the integral, we see that (15) can be rewritten as

$$\frac{1}{h}\int_{\bar{t}}^{\bar{t}+h} g_k(t)\,dt + \frac{1}{h}\int_{E_h(\bar{t})}\left[f(t, x_k(t), u_k(t)) - f(\bar{t}, x(\bar{t}), \bar{u})\right]dt.$$

Estimating now the integral of each term in the second integral by use of (8) and taking into account (9), (10), (15) and (14) gives

$$\dot{x}(\bar{t}) \in \left[\text{cl co}\,\tilde{Q}(\bar{t}, x(\bar{t}), \varepsilon)\right]_\eta,$$

where the expression at right denotes the closure of the set of points whose distance from $\text{cl co}\,\tilde{Q}(\bar{t}, x(\bar{t}), \varepsilon)$ is at most equal to η. Since η is arbitrary and the set in brackets is closed, we conclude that

$$\dot{x}(\bar{t}) \in \text{cl co}\,\tilde{Q}(\bar{t}, x(\bar{t}), \varepsilon).$$

It now follows from the arbitrariness of ε and the fact that $Q(t,x)$ has property (Q) relative to $G \supset F$ that

$$\dot{x}(\bar{t}) \in Q(\bar{t}, x(\bar{t})).$$

Since $\bar{t}$ was an arbitrary point in F, this establishes the closure property a.e. in G, and therefore a.e. in A_t, because of the way in which G was chosen.

The proof of the closure theorem is thus completed.

References

(1) P. Alexandroff & H. Hopf, "Topologie," Springer Verlag, Berlin, 1935.
(2) L. Cesari, Existence theorems for weak and usual optimal solutions in Lagrange problems with unilateral constraints, Trans. Amer. Math. Soc. 124 (1966), 369-412.
(3) A.F. Fillipov, On certain questions in the theory of optimal control, Vestnik Moskov. Univ., Ser. Math. Mech. Astron. 2 (1959), 25-32 = J. SIAM Control 1 (1962), 76-84.

(4) Z. Opial, Sur l'équation differentielle ordinaire du premier ordre dont le second membre satisfait aux conditions de Carathéodory, Ann. Pol. Math. VIII (1960), 23-28.
(5) E. Roxin, The existence of optimal controls, Mich. Math. J. 9 (1962), 109-119.
(6) G. Scorza-Dragoni, Un teorema sulle funzioni continue rispetto ad una e misurabile rispetto ad un'altra variabile, Rend. Sem. Mat. Padova 17 (1948), 102-106.

Appendix: Demonstration of Scorza-Dragoni's Theorem

We present here a slightly abridged version of the proof put forward in (6) for the case in which $A_t = [t_o, t_1]$ and $A_x(t) \equiv A_x = [x_o, x_1]$.

For every positive integer n we divide the interval A_x into n equal parts by means of the points $x_o + j(x_1 - x_o)/n$, where $j = 1, \ldots, n$, and then set $\omega_{n,j}(t)$ equal to the oscillation of the function f on the interval $[x_{n,j-1}, x_{n,j}]$. By the lemma proved above in section 2, each function $\omega_{n,j}(t)$ will be measurable in t on A_t, and the same will therefore hold also for the functions

$$\Omega_n(t) = \max\,[\omega_{n,1}(t), \ldots, \omega_{n,n}(t)].$$

Furthermore, we have for each value of t in A_t

$$\lim_{n\to\infty} \Omega_n(t) = 0, \qquad (1)$$

because of the continuity of f in the variable x.

By successive applications of Luzin's theorem, we can produce a perfect set $S_n \subset A_t$ with $m\,S_n > m\,A_t - \varepsilon/2$ upon which each of the functions $f(t, x_{n,1}), \ldots, f(t, x_{n,n})$ is continuous; moreover, the sets $S_1, S_2, \ldots$ can be taken in such a way as to form a monotone decreasing sequence with respect to inclusion.

If we set

$$S^* = \bigcap_{n=1}^{\infty} S_n = \lim_{n\to\infty} S_n,$$

we then have

$$m\,S^* = \lim_{n\to\infty} m\,S_n \geq m\,A_t - \varepsilon/2.$$

We now apply Egoroff's theorem and find a perfect subset $S \subset S^*$, with

$$mS > mA_t - \varepsilon,$$

upon which the convergence in (1) is uniform.

We claim that <u>the function f is continuous in (t,x) in that portion of A which lies over S</u>. To confirm this, let $\eta > 0$ be given arbitrarily. Choose a value of n for which the inequality

$$\Omega_n(t) < \eta/3$$

holds throughout S. Having fixed n in this way, choose δ, $0 < \delta < (x_1 - x_0)/n$, so small that for any two values t', t" in S with $|t' - t''| < \delta$ there holds

$$|f(t', x_{n,j}) - f(t'', x_{n,j})| < \eta/3 \tag{2}$$

for $j = 1, \ldots, n$. This is possible because $S \subset S_n$. Now let x' and x" be any two values of x in A_x with $|x' - x''| < \delta$. There is a value of j such that for any t in S there holds

$$\begin{aligned} |f(t,x') - f(t,x_{n,j})| &\leq \Omega_n(t) < \eta/3, \\ |f(t,x'') - f(t,x_{n,j})| &\leq \Omega_n(t) < \eta/3. \end{aligned} \tag{3}$$

Thus if (t', x') and (t", x") are any two points in $S \times A_x$ with $|t' - t''| < \delta$ and $|x' - x''| < \delta$, it follows from (2) and (3), by use of the triangle inequality, that

$$|f(t', x') - f(t'', x'')| \leq \eta,$$

which establishes therefore the (uniform) continuity of f on $S \times A_x$ and thereby completes the proof of the theorem.

DEPARAMETRIZATION OF THE PONTRYAGIN MAXIMUM PRINCIPLE

By L.E. Zachrisson, Roy. Inst. Techn., Stockholm

The emphasis of the investigation sketchily reported below has changed since the abstract of my contribution was given the title above. A renaming: " A Hamiltonian Max-Min-problem and its Connections with the Pontryagin Maximum Principle" would give a better cover of the contents.

The parameter that we want to get rid of in the statement and proof of the Pontryagin max-principle is the control parameter or control variable (the vector u), as the parametrization by means of u of the possible directions of an admissible trajectory through a point (x, t) is to a large extent arbitrary but does not change the optimality of a given trajectory.

1. Generalities on deparametrization

A standard left point boundary value problem in control theory is the following:

Among all functions $x(t), u(t)$ such that

$$\begin{cases} u(t) & \in \quad U \text{ closed} \\ \dfrac{dx}{dt} & = \quad f(x, t, u) \quad \text{a. e.} \\ x(o) & = \quad \xi \end{cases}$$

find a pair $(\hat{x}(t), \hat{u}(t))$ that maximizes $g\left[x(T)\right]$. x and f are n-vectors, u is an m-vector.

The Pontryagin maximum principle states that - if certain regularity conditions on the function f are satisfied - necessary conditions for $(\ddot{x}(t), \ddot{u}(t))$ to be optimal are

$$\begin{cases} \max_{u \in U} y(t) f(\hat{x}, t, u) = y(t) f(\hat{x}, t, \hat{u}) & \text{(a)} \\ y(T) = \left[\operatorname{grad}_x g(x)\right]_{x=\hat{x}(T)} & \text{(b)} \\ \frac{dy}{dt} = -\left[\operatorname{grad}_x y(t) f(x, t, \hat{u})\right]_{x(t)=\hat{x}(t)} & \text{(c)} \end{cases} \quad (1)$$

The product of y and f in (a) and (c) is to be understood as a scalar product

$$y f = f y = \sum y_i f_i$$

Here (1a) can be translated into:

$\frac{d\hat{x}}{dt}$ should fulfill the condition

$$\frac{d\hat{x}}{dt} y(t) = \mathcal{H}(\hat{x}, y, t) \quad (2)$$

where $\mathcal{H}(x, y, t)$ is the support function of the set of admissible directions in (x, t): $F(x, t) = f(x, t, U)$

$$\mathcal{H}(x, y, t) = \sup_{f \in F(x,t)} y f \quad (3)$$

Therefore, the parametrization of the set $F(x, t)$ by means of u is irrelevant in (1a). In (1b) it does not occur at all, but in (1c) it seems essential, as the gradient in the right number is formed with the assumption that u is independent of x. It is easy to see that a reparametrization (dependent upon x) of F in general changes (1c).

Pursuing the thought of deparametrization the question then arises if it is possible to change (1c) into an equation of the form

$$\frac{dy}{dt} = -h(\hat{x}, y, \frac{d\hat{x}}{dt}, t) \quad (4)$$

from which the parameter u has disappeared.

In that case we would get a deparametrized version of the maximum principle having the following form (a "statement of Pontryagin type"):

"Necessary conditions that $\hat{x}(t)$ maximizes $g\left[x(T)\right]$ among all functions $x(t)$ fulfilling the conditions

$$\begin{cases} \frac{dx}{dt} \in F(x,t) \\ x(o) = \xi \end{cases} \tag{5}$$

are:

$$\begin{cases} \frac{d\hat{x}}{dt} \cdot y(t) = \mathcal{H}(\hat{x}, y, t) \quad \text{(defined in (3))} \\ y(T) = \left[\operatorname{grad}_x g(x)\right]_{x=\hat{x}(T)} \\ \frac{dy}{dt} = -h(\hat{x}, y, \frac{d\hat{x}}{dt}, t) \end{cases}$$

if the function $F : X \times T \to \left\{\text{Closed sets in } R^n\right\}$ is sufficiently regular."

The study of a certain Max-Min-problem on the support function $\mathcal{H}$ will lead to a more specified conjecture about what the correct form of such a statement would be. According to this conjecture eq. (4) should have a close connection with the second canonical equation of Hamilton:

$$\frac{dy}{dt} = -\left[\operatorname{grad}_x \mathcal{H}(x, y, t)\right]_{x(t)=\hat{x}(t)} \tag{6}$$

As a matter of fact, in the following simple case the Maximum Principle leads directly to this equation. Let $F(x,t)$ be the boundary of a compact and strictly convex set (hence having interior points), and let the F be parametrized by the exterior normal vectors u of the supporting hyperplanes. It is easy to see that Eq. (1a) and (1c) imply Eq. (6).

However, $\mathcal{H}$ is in general not differentiable. In the Max-Min-problem, $\mathcal{H}$ will be concave in x and hence super-differentiable, and the right hand member of the second canonical equation will be changed into "some supergradient with respect to x at $(\hat{x}, y, t)$".

2. Motivation of Max-Min-problem

The problem to be considered is the following:
Consider the functionsl from $X \times Y$ to R^1 :

$$A(x,y) = \int_o^T \left[-y\dot{x} + \mathcal{H}(x,y,t) \right] dt + \eta\, x(T) = \quad (a)$$

$$= y(o)\xi + \int_o^T \left[x\, dy + \mathcal{H}(x,y,t)\, dt \right] \quad (b) \qquad (10)$$

where $x(o) = \xi$; $y(T) = \eta$.
Here $\mathcal{H}(x,y,t)$ is concave in x and convex in y for each $t \in [o, T]$ and

$x(.) \in X$

$y(.) \in Y$

where X is some convex set in some locally convex linear topological space L_x and Y similarly in L_y.
Give conditions in order that there exist $\hat{x} \in X$; $\hat{y} \in Y$ such that

$$A(x,\hat{y}) \le A(\hat{x},\hat{y}) \le A(\hat{x},y)$$

or equivalently

$$\operatorname*{Max}_{x \in X} \operatorname*{Inf}_{y \in Y} A(x,y) = \operatorname*{Min}_{y \in Y} \operatorname*{Sup}_{x \in X} A(x,y)$$

We give a heuristic motivation for the relevance of the problem in the present context.

Motivation:

M1. If $\mathcal{H}(x,y,t)$ is the support function of the closed convex set $F(x,t)$ of admissible directions, and if y is allowed to take any value in R_n,

$$\text{then } \operatorname*{Inf}_{y} \left[-y\dot{x} + \mathcal{H}(x,y,t) \right] = \begin{cases} -\infty & \text{if } \dot{x} \notin F(x,t) \\ 0 & \text{if } \dot{x} \in F(x,t) \end{cases}$$

Hence the two problems

$$\begin{cases} \text{Max} \quad g\left[x(T)\right] \\ \text{when} \quad \frac{dx}{dt} \in F(x,t) \end{cases}$$

and

$$\underset{x}{\text{Max}} \left\{ \int_0^T \underset{y}{\text{Inf}} \left[-y\dot{x} + \mathcal{H}(x,y,t) \right] dt + g\left[x(T)\right] \right\} \tag{11}$$

are seen to be equivalent.

Specializing $g\left[x(T)\right]$ to the scalar product $\eta\, x(T)$ and hoping that it is allowed to put the "Inf" in (11) in front of the integral-sign, we get the task to solve the problem

$$\underset{x}{\text{Max}} \ \underset{y}{\text{Inf}} \ A(x,y)$$

M2. Convexity-concavity assumptions on $\mathcal{H}$.

$\mathcal{H}(x,y,t)$ is a closed convex function in y according to its definition as a support function (even if $F(x,t)$ is not convex. Convexity of F, however, is in general necessary for the existence of an optimal solution).

Now, if $\mathcal{H}$ is sufficiently differentiable and $A(x,y)$ takes on its Max-Min-value in an interior point, then this point is stationary. Stationarity implies according to classical variation calculus the truth of Hamilton's canonical equations:

$$\frac{d\hat{x}}{dt} = \left[\text{grad}_y \mathcal{H}(\hat{x},y,t)\right]_{y=\hat{y}}$$

$$\frac{d\hat{y}}{dt} = -\left[\text{grad}_x \mathcal{H}(x,\hat{y},t)\right]_{x=\hat{x}}$$

The symmetry of these equations show that if $\mathcal{H}(x,.,t)$ is the "Hamiltonian with respect to x" (first equation), then $-\mathcal{H}(.,y,t)$ should be the "Hamiltonian with respect to y". If $\mathcal{H}(x,.,t)$ ought to be convex, then $\left[-\mathcal{H}(.,y,t)\right]$ also should be convex, that is $\mathcal{H}(x,y,t)$ should be concave in x.

M3. Once the assumption concavity in x - convexity in y is made, it is seen that the functional A(x, y) also is concave - convex. And then we know according to general theorems, that this functional has a saddle-point at least if its domains in x and y are compact convex and if it is upper semicontinuous in x and lower semi-continuous in y. Then it is natural to ask if that saddle-point-property can be used with profit in the investigation. It is a rather old observation that the stationary points that occur in the "canonical problem" have saddle-point character. (See (5)).

Remark

The function

$$\sup_{y \in R^n} \left[y f - \mathcal{H}(x, y, t) \right] = \mathcal{H}_*(x, f, t)$$

which has occurred implicitly above, is the conjugate convex function of $\mathcal{H}$ (with respect to y) according to the definition of Fenchel (1).

(Conjugation with respect to y will be denoted by a sub-script star, with respect to x with a super-script star:

$$\inf_{x} \left[xg - \mathcal{H}(x, y, t) \right] = \mathcal{H}^*(g, y, t).)$$

$\mathcal{H}_*$ is the Lagrangian of the problem.

Rockafellar has made a thorough study of concave-convex functions (2). Cf also Moreau (4).

3. Comments on the formulation of the Max-Min-Problem

C1. The space L_x should contain absolutely continuous functions only, in order that $\dot{x}$ should exist a.e. and be measurable. The space L_y should contain functions of bounded variation only, in order that the integration by parts from (10a) to (10b) should be allowed. Subspaces of these maximal spaces might be considered as L_x or L_y.

C2. The Max-Min-problem remains meaningful even if $\mathcal{H}$ is not a support function (pos. homogenous of degree one in y). We had arrived at the more general formulation if we had started with the problem to maximize

$$-\int_0^T h(x(t), u(t), t)\, dt + g\left[x(T)\right]$$

and defined

$$\mathcal{H}(x, y, t) = \operatorname*{Sup}_{u \in U} \left[y\, f(x, u, t) - h(x, u, t)\right]$$

C3. The condition of concavity in x of $\mathcal{H}(x, y, t)$ in general makes it impossible that the x-domain is all R^n. For it is easy to show, that if $\mathcal{H}(x, ., t)$ is the support function of the bounded convex sets $F(x, t)$ defined for any $x \in R^n$, and if $\mathcal{H}$ is concave in x, then

$$\mathcal{H}(x, y, t) = \mathcal{H}_o(y, t) + \langle x, A(t)y \rangle$$

If the theory is to be extended from this almost trivial case, we are forced to introduce boundaries in state space (x or y). Therefore, the definition of the convex sets X and Y in functional space must in general include restrictions in state space of the form

$x(t) \in X(t)$ convex, closed

$y(t) \in Y(t)$ convex, closed.

C4. The specialization of $g\left[x(T)\right]$ to the form $\eta\, x(T)$ is made in order to introduce a perfect analogy between the expressions (10a) and (10b). For the following this is unnecessary if g is supposed to be concave. On the other hand, if g is concave there exists an y such that the optimal solution of the g-problem is also an optimal solution of the η-problem (separating hyperplanes).

C5. If the boundary of the convex set $F(x, t)$ contains a line segment l, then $\mathcal{H}(x, y, t)$ is not differentiable if y is the normal vector of a support plane containing l. Especially, if $F(x, t)$ has lower dimension than n, (which is the typical case in control theory, distinguishing it from classical variational calculus, if problems with side-conditions in the form of differential equations are disregarded) then $\mathcal{H}$ is not differentiable for y-vectors in the orthogonal complement to the minimal linear manifold containing F.

C6. The assumption that $\mathcal{H}$ is concave in x is equivalent to the assumption that F(x, t) is a concave family (parametrized by x) of convex sets (3), that is

$$r_1 \in F(x_1, t);\ r_2 \in F(x_2, t) \Rightarrow \lambda r_1 + (1-\lambda) r_2 \in F(\lambda x_1 + (1-\lambda) x_2, t)$$

$$(0 \leq \lambda \leq 1)$$

If $\mathcal{H}$ is a support-function, then $\mathcal{H}_*(x, r, t)$ is a function on X x F that is zero at (x, r) iff $r \in F(x, t)$ and $+\infty$ otherwise. It can thus be looked upon as a convex "cavity" in X x F - space.

That the restriction to x-concave $\mathcal{H}$-functions really excludes important cases can be seen by considering the example:

F(x, t) is the convex hull of the two points $(1, +x_2)$ and $(-1, -x_2)$ in two-dimensional space, which gives $\mathcal{H}(x, y, t) = |y_1 + x_2 y_2|$.

4. Sufficient conditions for a saddle-point

Theorem. The pair of functions $(\hat{x}, \hat{y})$ is a saddle-point of A(x, y) if

$$p(t) = \frac{d\hat{x}}{dt} \text{ is a (sub-gradient)}_y \text{ of } \mathcal{H} \text{ at } (\hat{x}, \hat{y}, t) \text{ and}$$

$$-q(t) = -\frac{d\hat{y}}{dt} \text{ is a (super-gradient)}_x \text{ of } \mathcal{H} \text{ at } (\hat{x}, \hat{y}, t)$$

(almost every t).

One half of the theorem is:

$$A(x, \hat{y}) \leq A(\hat{x}, \hat{y}) \tag{12}$$

if

$$-q(x-\hat{x}) \geq \mathcal{H}(x, \hat{y}, t) - \mathcal{H}(\hat{x}, \hat{y}, t)$$

or

$$qx + \mathcal{H}(x, \hat{y}, t) \leq q\hat{x} + \mathcal{H}(\hat{x}, \hat{y}, t) \tag{13}$$

for every $x \in X$; $x(o) = \hat{x}(o) = \xi$.

The proof is astonishingly simple.

As

$$A(x, \hat{y}) = \hat{y}(T)\,\xi + \int_{o}^{T} \left[x q + \mathcal{H}(x, \hat{y}, t) \right] dt$$

the inequality (13) immediately shows the truth of statement (12).

If functions of bounded variation are allowed as $y(.)$, the definition

$$q(t) = \frac{d\hat{y}}{dt}$$

should be understood in the distribution sense. Then q as well as qx and $q\hat{x}$, regarded as distributions, are equivalent to signed measures on R_1, and (13) should be interpreted as

$$\int_I x\, d\hat{y} + \mathcal{H}(x, \hat{y}, t) dt \leq \int_I \hat{x}\, d\hat{y} + \mathcal{H}(\hat{x}, \hat{y}, t)\, dt$$

for any sub-interval I of $\left[0, T\right]$.

A study of very simple examples, like the following:

$$\text{Max} \left[x_1(1) + x_2(1) \right]$$

when

$$x(o) = 0; \ \frac{dx_1}{dt} \leq 0; \ x_2 \leq 1$$

shows that the extension of y-space to that of functions of bounded variation generally becomes necessary in order to make the sufficient conditions of the theorem applicable in cases where the restrictions in state space are effective.

Condition (13) together with the subgradient condition can be summarized in the condition:

$(\hat{x}(t), \hat{y}(t))$ is almost everywhere (t) a saddle-point of the function

$$B(x, y, t) = q(t)x - p(t)y + \mathcal{H}(x, y, t). \tag{14}$$

We call this condition the local saddle-point condition, and the theorem states that the local saddle-point property implies the global saddle-point property. But also the reverse is true:

Theorem: The global saddle-point property implies the local saddle-point property.

The theorem is proved by making a sequence of local variations and using the Fatou lemma (unnecessary for y if the space is that of bounded variation).

5. Reinterpretation of the local saddle-point condition

A conjecture

The local saddle-point condition (see eq. (14)) can be translated into a condition expressed by means of the conjugate function

$$\mathcal{H}_*(x, r, t) = \operatorname*{Sup}_{y \in R^n} \left[y\, r - \mathcal{H}(x, y, t) \right]$$

where the value $+\infty$ is allowed. Cf Moreau (4).

It is easily seen that $\mathcal{H}_*$ is convex in the cartesion product space of x and r.

A little bit more difficult to prove is that

$$\left.\begin{array}{l} p \text{ is a (subgradient)}_y \text{ of } \mathcal{H} \text{ at } (\hat{x}, \hat{y}) \\ -q \text{ is a (supergradient)}_x \text{ of } \mathcal{H} \text{ at } (\hat{x}, \hat{y}) \end{array}\right\} \Rightarrow$$

$$\Rightarrow (q, \hat{y}) \text{ is a subgradient of } \mathcal{H}_*(x, r, t) \text{ at } (\hat{x}, p),$$

that is

$$q(x-\hat{x}) + \hat{y}(r-p) \leq \mathcal{H}_*(x, r, t) - \mathcal{H}_*(\hat{x}, p, t) \tag{15}$$

Under some precautions also the reverse implication is true.

If $\mathcal{H}(x, ., t)$ is the support function of $F(x, t)$ and if $(\hat{x}, p)$ is on the boundary of $F(x, t)$ (necessary for an optimum), then (15) is equivalent to the condition that $(q, \hat{y})$ is a support plane at $(\hat{x}, p)$ of the "convex cavity".

$$\mathcal{C}(t) = \{(x, r) : r \in F(x, t)\}$$

If $\hat{y}$ is a support plane of $F(\hat{x}, t)$, then the possible q's such that $(q, \hat{y})$ is a support plane of $C(t)$ form a closed convex set in q-space: $K(\hat{x}, \hat{y}, t)$. This means that the local saddle-point condition has been given the geometrical interpretation:

$$\frac{d\hat{y}(t)}{dt} = q(t) \in K(\hat{x}, \hat{y}, t) \tag{16}$$

which is a relationship of the same form as

$$\frac{d\hat{x}}{dt} \in F(\hat{x}, t)$$

expressing the main condition on the x-trajectories (Eq. (5)).

The interpretation (16) of Hamilton's second canonical equation in the concave case induces the following conjecture in the non-concave case.

Suppose that $F(x, t)$ is locally almost concave in the following sense:

The cone of admissible directions of $C(t)$ at the boundary point $(\hat{x}, p)$ is convex, closed and upper semi-continuous as a function of $(\hat{x}, p, t)$. Call it $C^1(\hat{x}, p, t)$. (Formal definition a few lines further on.) Let $\hat{y}$ be a support plane at p of $C^1(\hat{x}, p, t) \cap \{x: x=\hat{x}\}$ and let $K(\hat{x}, p, \hat{y}, t)$ be the set of q:s such that $(q, \hat{y})$ is a support plane of $C^1(\hat{x}, p, t)$ at $(\hat{x}, p, t)$. Then, (16) can be replaced by

$$\frac{d\hat{y}}{dt} = q(t) \in K(\hat{x}, p, \hat{y}, t)$$

in some "statement of Pontryagin type" still to be given a precise formulation.

C^1 is defined as $\cap \overline{C^1_\epsilon} (\hat{x}, p, t)$ where C_ϵ contains every half-line from $(\hat{x}, p)$ meeting an other point $(x, r) \in C(t)$ which satisfies the further restriction $\|x-\hat{x}\| \le \epsilon$.

6. Conclusion

Important points have been excluded in this short communication, for instance questions of topology and the use of a priori estimates. I intend to give a more detailed account in a paper to be published elsewhere.

References

(1) Fenchel, W.: On conjugate convex functions. Can. J. Math., 1(1949) 73-77

(2) Rockafellar, R. T.: Minimax theorems and conjugate saddle-functions. Math. Scand. 14(1964) 151-173

(3) Bonnesen, T. - Fenchel, W.: Theorie der konvexen Körper. p.33. Erg.d.Math.u.Grenzgeb., 3, Berlin 1934

(4) Moreau, J. J.: Théorèmes "inf-sup". C.R.Acad.Sc.Paris, 258(1964) 2720-2722

(5) Courant-Hilbert: Methods of Math. Physics, p.239. N.Y.1953

ON THE COST OF CONSTRAINTS IN DYNAMICAL OPTIMIZATION

R. PALLU DE LA BARRIERE

Laboratoire d'Automatique Théorique
Faculté des Sciences
CAEN (France)

The aim of the present communication is to give a general method for studying the influence of constraint parameters on the performance of an optimized dynamical system(+)

1-. Let us first give of the Pontrjagin maximum principle a version which we shall use in the following sections. We consider the system whose evolution is described by the following differential equation

$$\frac{dX(t)}{dt} = f(X(t), U(t), t)$$
$$t \in [0,T] \ , \ X(t) \in R^n \ , \ U(t) \in \mathcal{K} \qquad (1,1)$$

with the initial conditions

$$\varphi_i(X(0)) \begin{cases} = 0 \ , & \forall i \in I_0 \\ \leq 0 \ , & \forall i \in I_1 \end{cases} \qquad (1,2)$$

and the final conditions

$$\psi_k(X(T)) \begin{cases} = 0 \ , & \forall k \in K_0 \\ \geq 0 \ , & \forall k \in K_1 \end{cases} . \qquad (1,3)$$

The objective function to be maximized is

$$g_T(X(T)) - g_0(X(0)) \qquad (1,4)$$

All usual assumptions are made about continuity and differentiability of the functions $f, \varphi_i , \psi_k , \dots$.

(+) This research was supported by the Délégation Générale à la Recherche Scientifique et Technique under Contract n° 66-00-246.

Let $\tilde{U}$ be an optimal piecewise continuous control function and $\tilde{X}$ the corresponding trajectory. We define :

$$I_1' = \left\{ i \in I_1 \mid \varphi_i(\tilde{X}(0)) = 0 \right\}$$
$$K_1' = \left\{ k \in K_1 \mid \psi_k(\tilde{X}(T)) = 0 \right\} .$$

It is assumed that the derivatives $(\varphi_i)'(\tilde{X}(0))$ for $i \in I_0 \cup I_1'$ and $g_0'(\tilde{X}(0))$ are linearly independent as well as the derivatives $(\psi_k)'(\tilde{X}(T))$ for $k \in K_0 \cup K_1'$ and $g_T'(X(T))$.

Then there exists a non-zero function P defined for $t \in [0,T]$ with values in the dual $(R^n)'$ of R^n such that :

$$\frac{dP}{dt} = - P(t)\, f_x'(\tilde{X}(t), \tilde{U}(t), t) \qquad (1,5)$$

$$\left.\begin{aligned} P(T) &= \sum_{k \in K_0 \cup K_1'} \mu_k \psi_k'(\tilde{X}(T)) + \mu_0\, g_T'(\tilde{X}(T)) \\ &\text{with } \mu_k \geq 0 , \quad \forall k \in K_1' , \\ &\text{and } \mu_0 \geq 0 , \end{aligned}\right\} \qquad (1,6)$$

$$\left.\begin{aligned} P(0) &= \sum_{i \in I_0 \cup I_1'} \lambda_i\, \varphi_i'(\tilde{X}(0)) + \mu_0\, g_0'(\tilde{X}(0)) \\ &\text{with } \lambda_i \geq 0 , \quad \forall i \in I_1' ; \end{aligned}\right\} \qquad (1,7)$$

$$\max_{u \in \mathcal{K}} P(t)\, f(\tilde{X}(t), u, t) = P(t)\, f(\tilde{X}(t), \tilde{U}(t), t) \qquad (1,8)$$

for every value of t where $\tilde{U}$ is continuous.

The proof of this statement may be achieved by introducing an additional state vector Y(t) such that

$$\left\{ \begin{aligned} & Y(t) \in R^n \\ & \frac{dY(t)}{dt} = 0 \\ & X(0) - Y(0) = 0 \end{aligned} \right.$$

and applying the Pontrjagin maximum principle in the case of a final objective function. We shall say that P is <u>normalized</u> if $\mu_0 = 1$.

2-. The first constraint the influence of which we shall study, is a fixed initial state. Let us define :

$$h(\xi) = \sup \left\{ g_T(X(T)) \mid X(0) = \xi , U \in \mathcal{U} \right\}$$

where $\mathcal{U}$ is the set of all admissible control functions (i.e. piecewise continuous and such that for the corresponding trajectory the conditions (1,3) are fullfilled).

Let us assume the control function $\tilde{U}$ is optimal for $X(0) = \xi_0$, the final conditions (1,3) and the objective function $g_T(X(T))$. By virtue of the Pontrjagin maximum principle, there exists a non-zero function P such that Eqs. (1,6) and (1,8) are satisfied.

THEOREM. <u>If</u> h <u>is continuously differentiable in a neighbourhood of</u> ξ_0 <u>and if the function</u> P <u>satisfying Eqs.</u> (1,6) <u>and</u> (1,7) <u>is unique and normalized, then we have</u>

$$P(0) = h'(\xi_0).$$

Similar results may be stated if the initial values of some state variables are fixed and the other state variables are free or are functions of the former variables. It can be remarked that a similar result holds in the case of constraints involving both $X(t)$ and $U(t)$.

3-. Let us now study the influence of the coefficients c_j in the case of constraints of the form :

$$p_j(X(t),\ U(t)) \begin{cases} = c_j, & \forall j \in J_0 \\ \geq c_j, & \forall j \in J_1 \end{cases}. \qquad (3,1)$$

We get a new system by introducing an additional state vector :

$$Y(t) = \{Y_j(t)\},\quad j \in J_0 \cup J_1$$

satisfying the following conditions :

$$\frac{dY(t)}{dt} = 0$$

$$Y_j(0) = c_j,\quad \forall j \in J_0 \cup J_1 .$$

The conditions (3,1) may be rewritten in the following form :

$$p_j(X(t),\ U(t)) - Y_j(t)) \begin{cases} = 0, & \forall j \in J_0 \\ \geq 0, & \forall j \in J_1 \end{cases}.$$

Defining

$$h(c) = \sup \left\{ g_T(X(T)) \mid U \in \mathcal{U},\ (1,2)\ \&\ (1,3) \right\},$$

it is possible to determine $h'(c)$ by applying the theorem of the preceding section, because the coefficients c_j appear as initial state components in the new systems.

4-. The equation (1,1) itself may be considered as a constraint which limits the type of evolution of the system and may be modified by allowing discontinuities of the state variables at certain instants of time, the objective function being then allowed to depend on the discontinuities. Such is the case in mechanical systems (discontinuities of the velocity under the influence of impulses) and in economic systems (discontinuities of the capital under the influence of investment).

Let us consider the following typical case. The time t is varying from -1 to $+1$. For $t = 0$, the trajectory X has a 1st kind discontinuity given by the formula

$$X(+0) = \theta(X(-0), v)$$

where v is a decision vector (free or submitted to some constraints) and θ a continuously differentiable function.

By introducing the following functions for $t \in [0,1]$:

$$X^1(t) = X(t)$$
$$X^2(t) = X(-t)$$
$$X^3(t) = v$$
$$U^1(t) = U(t)$$
$$U^2(t) = U(-t)$$

we define a new dynamical system for $t \in [0,1]$:

$$\left.\begin{aligned} \frac{dX^1(t)}{dt} &= f(X^1(t), U^1(t), t) \\ \frac{dX^2(t)}{dt} &= -f(X^1(t), U^2(t), t) \\ \frac{dX^3(t)}{dt} &= 0 \end{aligned}\right\} \quad (4,2)$$

with the initial conditions :

$$X^1(0) = \theta(X^2(0), v)$$
$$X^3(0) = v \; .$$

Let us suppose that the objective function is $g_T(X(T)) + g_1(v)$. Then the influence of v on the maximum value of this objective function can be studied as the influence of some of the initial state components in the new system and therefore may be studied by means of the theorem of section 2.

Applying the Pontrjagin principle in his classical form to the new system (4,2) one gets a modified version of the Pontrjagin principle, taking into account relation (4,1). For instance, if v is free, the function P must satisfy the following relations :

$$P(-0) = P(+0)\,\theta'_x(X(-0),\,\tilde{v})$$

$$P(+0)\,\theta'_v(\tilde{X}(-0),\,\tilde{v}) + \mu_0 (g_1)'(\tilde{v}) = 0 \;,$$

where $\tilde{X}$ is a optimal trajectory corresponding to a control function $\tilde{U}$ and a particular value $\tilde{v}$ of v.

CONTROL PROBLEMS IN SYSTEMS DESCRIBED BY PARTIAL DIFFERENTIAL EQUATIONS

J. L. Lions
University of Paris

INTRODUCTION

This paper deals with control problems for systems described by evolution partial differential equations of several types (parabolic, hyperbolic, well set in the sense of Petrowski). We show how large classes of such problems—with fixed terminal time†—reduce to new families of boundary value problems of "unilateral type."

1. SYSTEMS DESCRIBED BY PARABOLIC EQUATIONS

1.1 A Boundary Control Problem

We consider a system described by a second order parabolic operator in a cylinder $Q = \Omega \times [o, T]$, Ω open set in R^n.

More precisely the control u is given on the lateral boundary of Q, $\Sigma = \Gamma \times [o, T]$ (Γ = boundary of Ω); the state of the system $y = y(x, t; u) = y(u)$ $(x \in \Omega, t \in [o, T])$ is given (when u is given) as the unique solution of the equation

$$\frac{\partial y}{\partial t} + A\left(x, t, \frac{\partial}{\partial x}\right) y = f, \text{ f given in } Q \tag{1.1}$$

subject to the boundary condition

$$y|_{\Sigma} = u \tag{1.2}$$

---

† For time optimal problems, see References (7) and (8).

and to the initial condition

$$y(x,o) = y_o(x), \ y_o \ \text{given in } \Omega. \tag{1.3}$$

In Equation (1.1) one has

$$A\left(x, t, \frac{\partial}{\partial x}\right) = -\sum_{i,j=1}^{n} \frac{\partial}{\partial x_i}\left(a_{ij}(x,t)\frac{\partial}{\partial x_j}\right) \tag{1.4}$$

we assume all functions a_{ij} to be real and C^{∞} in $\bar{Q}$, and to satisfy (ellipticity condition on A):

$$\sum_{i,j=1}^{n} a_{ij}(x,t)\xi_i\xi_j \geq \alpha(\xi_1^2 + \ldots + \xi_n^2), \ \alpha > 0, \ \forall \xi \in R^n \tag{1.5}$$

Assume for the time being (precise hypotheses will be given below) that for each u given in a (real Hilbert space $\mathcal{U}$ there exists a unique solution y of (1. 1), (1. 2) and (1. 3) which satisfies

$$y(u) \in L^2(Q) \tag{1.6}$$

Let N be given satisfying

$$N \in \mathcal{L}(\mathcal{U}, \mathcal{U}), \ N \text{ is positive definite in} \tag{1.7}$$

The cost function J(u) is given by

$$J(u) = \int_Q |y(u) - z_d|^2 \, dx\, dt + (Nu, u)_{\mathcal{U}}, \ u \in \mathcal{U} \tag{1.8}$$

where z_d is given in $L^2(Q)$. The problem is now to find u minimizing J(u) when u describes $\mathcal{U}_{ad}$ = given closed convex subset of $\mathcal{U}$.

Remark 1. 1: All that follows extends to general linear parabolic operators, of any order, and to general boundary conditions. See (12), (15).

Remark 1. 2: One can also consider more general cost

functions; see (12), (15). Other examples are given in Sections 1.5 and 1.6 below.

1.2 Precise Hypotheses. Adjoint Problem

We assume now (this hypothesis can of course be weakened)

$$\Omega \text{ is bounded with a } C^{\infty} \text{ boundary} \tag{1.9}$$

and we assume also that

$$\mathcal{U} = L^2(\Sigma) \tag{1.10}$$

One proves (see for instance References (14) and (15)) that under these hypotheses, problems (1.1), (1.2) and (1.3) admits a unique solution satisfying (1.6).

Remark 1.3: One can prove more: $y(u) \in H^{1/2, 1/4}(Q)$, which means that space derivatives of order $\leq 1/2$ of y(u) and time derivatives of order $\leq 1/4$ or y(u) belong to $L^2(Q)$. The space $H^{1/2, 1/4}(Q)$ is a "fractionnal" Sovolev space. See References (27) and (15).

The adjoint problem

For every $u \in \mathcal{U} = L^2(\Sigma)$ we define $p = p(u) = p(x,t,u)$ as the unique solution of

$$-\frac{\partial p}{\partial t} + A^* p = y(u) - z_d \text{ in } Q, \quad A^* = \text{adjoint of } A \tag{1.11}$$

$$p|_{\Sigma} = 0 \tag{1.12}$$

$$p(x, T; u) = 0, \quad x \in \Omega \tag{1.13}$$

The solution p belongs to Sobolev space $H^{2,1}(Q)$ which means:

$$p, \ \frac{\partial p}{\partial x_i}, \ \frac{\partial^2 p}{\partial x_i \partial x_j}, \ \frac{\partial p}{\partial t} \in L^2(Q)$$

1.3 The Generalization of the "Two-point Boundary Value Problem"

Thanks to (1.7) it is immediate to check that there exists one element u and only one in $\mathcal{U}_{ad}$ which minimizes J(u). This u (the optimal control) is characterized by

$$\int_Q \left(y(u) - z_d\right)\left(y(v)-y(u)\right) dx\, dt + (Nu, v-u)_{\mathcal{U}} \geq 0 \ \forall v \in \mathcal{U}_{ad} \tag{1.14}$$

As it is classical for systems described by ordinary differential equations we transform (1.14) using the Green's formula. The only difference (but the fundamental one!) is that there now appear surface integrals on Σ. Using (1.11), the first integral in (1.14) equals

$$\int_Q \left(-\frac{\partial p(u)}{\partial t} + A\, p(u)\right)\left(y(v) - y(u)\right) dxdt \tag{1.15}$$

and one can prove (see (14) and (15)) that the use of Green's formula is valid.† We set:

$$\begin{cases} \dfrac{\partial}{\partial \nu^*} = \sum a_{ji}(x) \cos(n, x_i) \dfrac{\partial}{\partial x_j}, \ n = \text{normal derivative} \\ \text{to } \sum \text{ directed toward the exterior of } Q; \end{cases} \tag{1.16}$$

then (1.15) equals

$$-\int_\Sigma \frac{\partial p}{\partial \nu^*}(u)\left(y(v) - y(u)\right) d\Sigma^{\ddagger}$$

---

† This has to be proved since y(u) is a generalized solution of (1.1), (1.2), (1.3). See a more difficult situation in Section 1.5 below.

‡ Remark that $\partial p/\partial \nu^*(u) \in H^{1/2, 1/4}(\Sigma)$ (see (14)) so that this integral makes sense.

and since $y(v) = v$ on Σ, we see that condition (1.14) is equivalent to

$$\left(Nu - \frac{\partial p}{\partial \nu^*}(u),\ v-u\right)_{\mathcal{U}} \geq 0 \ \forall v \in \mathcal{U}_{ad} \left(\mathcal{U} = L^2(\Sigma)\right) \qquad (1.17)$$

In other words:

$$\left(Nu - \frac{\partial p}{\partial \nu^*}(u), u\right)_{\mathcal{U}} = \operatorname*{Inf.}_{v \in \mathcal{U}_{ad}} \left(Nu - \frac{\partial p}{\partial \nu^*}(u), v\right)_{\mathcal{U}} \qquad (1.17\text{bis})$$

Summing up:

Theorem 1.1. We assume (1.5), (1.7), (1.9) to hold. The cost function is given by (1.8). There exists one and only one optimal control $u \in \mathcal{U}_{ad}$, $\left(\mathcal{U}_{ad} = \text{closed convex subset of } \mathcal{U} = L^2(\Sigma)\right)$. The optimal control u is given through the solution of systems (1.1), (1.2), (1.3), (1.11), (1.12), (1.13) and (1.17) (or (1.17 bis)).

Let us rewrite the system of equations satisfied by y, p, u:

$$\begin{cases} \frac{\partial y}{\partial t}(u) + A\, y(u) = f, & -\frac{\partial p}{\partial t}(u) + Ap(u) = y(u) - z_d \\ y(u)\big|_{\Sigma} = u & ,\ p(u)\big|_{\Sigma} = 0 \\ y(x, o; u) = y_o(x) & ,\ p(x, T; u) = 0 \end{cases} \qquad (1.18)$$

u being subject to (1.17) (or (1.17 bis)).

Systems (1.18), (1.17) is the generalization of the classical "two-point boundary value problem" one meets in similar problems for systems described by ordinary differential equations — (22). See also (30) and the bibliography of this paper.

1.4 A Simple Example

If

$$\mathcal{U}_{ad} = \mathcal{U} \qquad (1.19)$$

(no constraints) then (1.17) reduces to

$$Nu - \frac{\partial p}{\partial \nu^*}(u) = 0 \tag{1.20}$$

Since N is invertible, one can eliminate u in system (1.18) using (1.20) to get:

$$\begin{cases} \frac{\partial y}{\partial t} + Ay = f, \ \frac{\partial p}{\partial t} + A\ p = y - z_d, \ \text{in } Q = \Omega x[o,T] \\ y|_\Sigma = N^{-1}\left(\frac{\partial p}{\partial \nu^*}\Big|_\Sigma\right), \ p|_\Sigma = 0 \\ y(x,o) = y_o(x), \ \ p(x,T) = 0 \end{cases} \tag{1.21}$$

This system admits a unique solution $\{y, p\}$; the optimal control u is then given by

$$u = y|_\Sigma \tag{1.22}$$

Remark 1.4: As we saw in footnote at bottom of page 4, $\partial p/\partial \nu^* \in H\ 1/2, 1/4\ (\Sigma)$; if (as it is in general the case) $N = k$ (Identity), $k > 0$, then $N^{-1}\ \partial p/\partial \nu^* | \Sigma \in H\ 1/2, 1/4(\Sigma)$ and (1.22) proves that the optimal control $u \in H\ 1/2, 1/4(\Sigma)$; this is a regularity property of the optimal control.

Remark 1.5: Let us replace problem (1.21) in $Q = \Omega x[o,T]$ by a similar problem in $Q_s = \Omega x[o,s]$, $o < s < T$; more precisely, we consider the boundary value problem:

$$\begin{cases} \frac{\partial y}{\partial t} + Ay = f, \ -\frac{\partial p}{\partial t} + A\ p = y - z_d \ \text{in } Q_s \\ y = N^{-1}\ \frac{\partial p}{\partial \nu^*} \ \text{on } \sum_s = \Gamma\ x[o,s], \ p|_{\Sigma_s} = 0 \\ y(x,o) = y_o(x)\ , \ \ p(x,s) \ \ \underline{\text{given}} \end{cases} \tag{1.23}$$

One can check that this problem admits a unique solution; hence y(x, s) is uniquely defined when p(x, s) is given—and it is given by an affine transformation—therefore:

$$y(.,s) = X_{(s)}\Big(p(.,s)\Big) + r(.,s) \tag{1.24}$$

Using the Schwartz Kernel theorem (25), $X_{(s)}$ is represented by a Kernel $\mathcal{X}(x, \hat{x}; s)$ which satisfies a non-linear partial differential equation. Another approach to this question is due to (3) b.

1.5 Another Cost Function

Assume now that the state y(u) is still given by (1.1), (1.2), (1.3) but that the observation is

$$\frac{\partial y}{\partial \nu}(u)\Big|_{\Sigma} \tag{1.25}$$

1.5.1 If one assumes that $u = L^2(\Sigma)$, then $\partial y/\partial \nu\,(u)$ does not belong to $L^2(\Sigma)$. In fact, starting from Remark 1.3, one can prove that

$$\frac{\partial y}{\partial \nu}(u) \in H^{-3/2,-3/4}\Big(\Sigma\Big) \tag{1.26}$$

and then the cost function J(u) has to be taken of the form

$$J(u) = \left(M\frac{\partial y}{\partial \nu}(u) - z_d\right), \left(\frac{\partial y}{\partial \nu}(u) - z_d\right) + (Nu, u)_{\mathcal{U}} \tag{1.27}$$

where

$$M \in \mathcal{L}\left(H^{-3/2,-3/4}\Big(\Sigma\Big);\ H_0^{3/2,3/4}\Big(\Sigma\Big)\right)$$

and where in (1.27) the first parenthesis denotes the scalar product between $H^{-3/2,-3/4}(\Sigma)$ and its dual $H_0^{3/2,3/4}(\Sigma)$.

The adjoint problem is now (see (12))

$$\left.\begin{aligned} &-\frac{\partial p}{\partial t} + A\,p = 0 \\ &p\big|_{\Sigma} = M\ \frac{\partial y}{\partial \nu}(u) - z_d \\ &p(x,T) = 0 \end{aligned}\right\} \tag{1.28}$$

The optimal control u (which exists and is unique) is characterized by (1.19)

$$\left(M\left(\frac{\partial y}{\partial \nu}(u) - z_d\right), \frac{\partial y}{\partial \nu}(v) - \frac{\partial y}{\partial \nu}(u)\right) + (Nu, v-u)_{\mathcal{U}} \geq 0 \ \forall v \in \mathcal{U}_{ad} \tag{1.29}$$

Using again Green's formula (and one can prove that this formula is valid) condition (1.29) becomes

$$\left(\frac{\partial p}{\partial \nu^*}(u) + Nu,\ v-u\right)_{\mathcal{U}} \geq 0 \ \forall v \in \mathcal{U}_{ad} \tag{1.30}$$

The "optimality system" is now given by (1.1), (1.2), (1.3), (1.28) and (1.30).

Remark 1.6: The operator M plays the role of a regularization. The use of this operator cannot be avoided if $\mathcal{U} = L^2(\Sigma)$. One can (try to) escape this difficulty by considering more regular controls; see 1.5.2.

1.5.2 More regular controls: The simplest way to avoid M is to assume that $\partial y/\partial \nu\,(u) \in L^2(\Sigma)$, but this means [(14), (2), and (15)] that

$$y(u) \in H^{3/2,\,3/4}(\Sigma)$$

and then

$$u\left(= y(u)\big|_{\Sigma}\right) \in H^{1,\,1/2}(\Sigma) \tag{1.31}$$

Therefore, if we can assume that

$$\mathcal{U} = H^{1,\,1/2}(\Sigma) \tag{1.32}$$

then one can choose as cost function

$$J(u) = \int_{\Sigma} \left| \frac{\partial y}{\partial \nu}(u) - z_d \right|^2 d\Sigma, \quad z_d \text{ given in } L^2(\Sigma) \tag{1.33}$$

Then <u>if</u> $\mathcal{U}_{ad}$ <u>is bounded</u>, one has the existence of a (generally non-unique) optimal control. If we want to impose uniqueness, then we have to add to J(u) a term $(Nu, u)_{\mathcal{U}}$ where N is now more complicated than in (1.27): instead of being in $\mathcal{L}\left(L^2(\Sigma), L^2(\Sigma)\right)$, N has to belong to $\mathcal{L}\left(H^{1,1/2}(\Sigma), H^{1,1/2}(\Sigma)\right)$. Notice that after replacing $\mathcal{U} = L^2(\Sigma)$ by, say, (1.32), <u>condition</u> (1.14) <u>becomes much more difficult to handle</u>.

<u>Remark 1.7</u>: The situation is simpler in case the state y = y(u) is given as the solution of

$$\begin{cases} \frac{\partial y}{\partial t} + Ay = f \\ \frac{\partial y}{\partial \nu} = u \text{ on } \Sigma \qquad u \in \mathcal{U} = L^2(\Sigma) \\ y(x, o) = y_o(x) \end{cases}$$

and when the cost function is given by

$$J(u) = \int_{\Sigma} |y(u) - z_d|^2 d\Sigma + (Nu, u)$$

The adjoint problem is then $\left(p = p(u)\right)$

$$\begin{cases} -\frac{\partial p}{\partial t} + Ap = 0 \text{ in } Q \\ \frac{\partial}{\partial \nu^*} p = y(u) - z_d \text{ on } \Sigma \\ p(x, T) = 0 \end{cases}$$

The (unique) optimal control is characterized by

$$\left(p(u) + Nu, v - u\right)_{\mathcal{U}} \geq 0 \quad \forall v \in \mathcal{U}_{ad}$$

1.6 Distributed Control

We can also consider the case when the control $u \in \mathcal{U} = L^2(Q)$ (distributed control); the state $y(u)$ is given by

$$\frac{\partial y}{\partial t}(u) + Ay(u) = f + u \quad (\text{in } Q) \tag{1.34}$$

subject to

$$y(u)\big|_{\Sigma} = 0 \tag{1.35}$$

$$y(x, o; u) = y_o(x) \qquad x \in \Omega \tag{1.36}$$

Assume the cost function is still given by (1.8). We define the adjoint problem by

$$-\frac{\partial p}{\partial t}(u) + Ap(u) = y(u) - z_d \tag{1.37}$$

$$p(u)\big|_{\Sigma} = 0 \tag{1.38}$$

$$p(x, T; u) = 0\,, \quad x \in \Omega \tag{1.39}$$

The optimal control u (which exists and is unique) is characterized by

$$\left(p(u) + Nu,\ v - u\right)_{\mathcal{U}} \geq 0 \quad \forall v \in \mathcal{U}_{ad} \tag{1.40}$$

Remark 1.8: In case $\mathcal{U}_{ad} = \mathcal{U}$ (no constraints) (1.40) reduces to

$$p(u) + Nu = 0 \tag{1.41}$$

One can then eliminate u in (1.34)...(1.39) by using (1.41)

$$u = -N^{-1}\left(p(u)\right) \tag{1.42}$$

2. UNILATERAL BOUNDARY VALUE PROBLEMS

2.1 Example 1

We consider now the situation of Theorem 1.1, when $\mathcal{U}_{ad}$ is given by

$$\mathcal{U}_{ad} = \left\{ u \mid u \geq 0 \quad \text{a.e.} \quad \text{on } \Sigma \right\} \tag{2.1}$$

Then (1.17) is equivalent to the following conditions:

$$\begin{aligned} & u \geqq 0 \quad \text{on } \Sigma \text{ (a.e.)} \\ & Nu - \frac{\partial p}{\partial \nu^*}(u) \geq 0 \quad \text{on } \Sigma \text{ (a.e.)} \\ & u\left(Nu - \frac{\partial p}{\partial \nu^*}(u)\right) = 0 \quad \text{on } \Sigma \end{aligned} \tag{2.2}$$

We therefore obtain:

Theorem 2.1. We assume that the hypotheses of Theorem 1.1 hold true and we assume that $\mathcal{U}_{ad}$ is given by (2.1). The unique optimal control u is given by

$$u = y|_{\Sigma} \tag{2.3}$$

where y corresponds to the unique solution $\{y, p\}$ of the unilateral boundary value problem

$$\frac{\partial y}{\partial t} + Ay = f \text{ in } Q, \quad -\frac{\partial p}{\partial t} + Ap = y - z_d \text{ in } Q \tag{2.4}$$

$$y(x, o) = y_o(x), \quad p(x, T) = 0, \quad x \in \Omega \tag{2.5}$$

$$p|_{\Sigma} = 0 \tag{2.6}$$

$$\begin{cases} y|_\Sigma \geq 0, \; N\, y|_\Sigma - \dfrac{\partial p}{\partial \nu^*} \geq 0 \quad \text{on } \Sigma \\ y\left(N\, y - \dfrac{\partial p}{\partial \nu^*}\right) = 0 \quad \text{on } \Sigma \end{cases} \tag{2.7}$$

Remark 2.1: Unilateral boundary value problems were in (26), (23), (20). In the elliptic (stationnary) case, they were studied in (9) and (16).

System (2.4)...(2.7) was introduced in (12) (in a more general situation). Related problems are considered in (16) and (13).

Remark 2.2: Conditions (2.7) imply that, on Σ, either $y = 0$ either $Ny - \partial p/\partial \nu^* = 0$. It would be very interesting to obtain some information on the region of Σ where $y > 0$ (the boundary of this region is a "switching" curve).

Remark 2.3: The analogous of Remark 1.5 is open; in (1.24), $X_{(s)}$ is not linear.

2.2 Example 2

Consider now the situation of section 1.5.1, with $\mathcal{U}_{ad}$ still given by (2.1). The optimality system can be written:

$$\begin{cases} \dfrac{\partial y}{\partial t} + Ay = f, \; -\dfrac{\partial p}{\partial t} + Ap = 0 \quad \text{in } Q \\ y(x,o) = y_o(x), \quad p(x,T) = 0, \quad x \in \Omega \\ p = M\left(\dfrac{\partial y}{\partial \nu} - z_d\right) \quad \text{on } \Sigma \\ y \geq 0, \quad Ny + \dfrac{\partial p}{\partial \nu^*} \geq 0 \quad \text{on } \Sigma \\ y\left(Ny + \dfrac{\partial p}{\partial \nu^*}\right) = 0 \quad \text{on } \Sigma \end{cases} \tag{2.8}$$

This is still another "unilateral boundary value problem."

Remark 2.4: The "regularization" operator M can be taken to be the inverse of the Laplace-Beltrami operator on Σ.

2.3 Example 3

Consider now the situation of Section 1.6, assuming that $\mathcal{U}_{ad}$ is given by

$$\mathcal{U}_{ad} = \{u \mid u \in L^2(Q),\ u \geq 0 \text{ a.e. in } Q\} \tag{2.9}$$

Then the optimality system (1.34)...(1.40) becomes:

$$\frac{\partial y}{\partial t} + Ay - f \geq 0 \quad \text{a.e. in } Q \tag{2.10}$$

$$-\frac{\partial p}{\partial t} + Ap = y - z_d \quad \text{in } Q \tag{2.11}$$

$$y = 0 \quad \text{on } \Sigma, \quad p = 0 \quad \text{on } \Sigma \tag{2.12}$$

$$y(x, o) = y_o(x), \quad p(x, T) = 0, \quad x \in \Omega \tag{2.13}$$

$$p + N\left(\frac{\partial y}{\partial t} + Ay - f\right) \geq 0 \quad \text{a.e. in } Q \tag{2.14}$$

$$\left(\frac{\partial y}{\partial t} + Ay - f\right)\left(p + N\left(\frac{\partial y}{\partial t} + Ay - f\right)\right) = 0 \quad \text{a.e. in } Q \tag{2.15}$$

Remark 2.5: The systems (2.10)...(2.15) admits a unique solution. The (unique) optimal control is given by

$$u = \frac{\partial y}{\partial t} + Ay - f \tag{2.16}$$

Here again it would be very interesting to have some information on the region where $\partial y/\partial t + Ay - f > 0$;

the boundary of this (unknown) domain is a "switching surface."

Remark 2.6: The above problem is of the type "free boundary problem."

3. AN ITERATIVE METHOD OF SOLUTION

3.1 Statement of the Method

We consider here the very particular example which corresponds to Remark 1.8. The system of optimal equations, where we assume for simplicity $y_o = 0$, can be written

$$\begin{cases} \dfrac{\partial y}{\partial t} + Ay - N^{-1}p = 0 \\ -\dfrac{\partial p}{\partial t} + Ap - y = z_d \end{cases} \quad \text{in } Q \tag{3.1}$$

$$y|_{\Sigma} = p|_{\Sigma} = 0 \tag{3.2}$$

$$y(x,o) = 0, \quad p(x,T) = 0 \tag{3.3}$$

We define the following iterative method of solution (see (17) and (18)). Assuming that y^n, p^n is known, we define y^{n+1}, p^{n+1} in two steps.

1st Step: For ϵ, $k > 0$, we define $y^{n+1/2}$, $p^{n+1/2}$ as the solution of

$$\begin{cases} \dfrac{\epsilon}{k}\left(y^{n+1/2} - y^n\right) + A\,y^{n+1/2} - N^{-1}p^{n+1/2} = 0 \\ \dfrac{\epsilon}{k}\left(p^{n+1/2} - p^n\right) + A\,p^{n+1/2} - y^{n+1/2} = -z_d \end{cases} \quad \text{in } Q \tag{3.4}$$

subject to boundary conditions

$$y^{n+1/2} = p^{n+1/2} = 0 \quad \text{on } \Sigma \tag{3.5}$$

Remark 3.1: In (3.4) and (3.5) the time t appears as a parameter.

2nd Step: With the same ϵ, k than in the 1st step, we define y^{n+1}, p^{n+1} as the solution of

$$\begin{cases} \frac{\epsilon}{k}\left(y^{n+1} - y^{n+1/2}\right) + \frac{d\,y^{n+1}}{dt} = 0 \\ \frac{\epsilon}{k}\left(p^{n+1} - p^{n+1/2}\right) - \frac{d\,p^{n+1}}{dt} = 0 \end{cases} \tag{3.6}$$

subject to boundary conditions

$$y^{n+1}(o) = 0, \quad p^{n+1}(T) = 0 \tag{3.7}$$

Remark 3.2: This time it is x which appears as a parameter in (3.6) and (3.7). Notice, moreover, that Equations (3.6) and (3.7) are uncoupled (the explicit solution is trivial!).

One can prove the following (18):

Theorem 3.1: We assume that ϵ, $k \to 0$ in such a way that

$$\frac{k}{\epsilon} \to 0 \tag{3.8}$$

Let $S = Nk$ fixed. Then

$$\begin{cases} y_N = \frac{1}{N}\sum_{n=0}^{N-1} y^{n+1/2} \to y \quad \text{in } L^2(Q) \text{ weakly} \\ \frac{\partial y_N}{\partial x_i} \to \frac{\partial y}{\partial x_i} \quad \text{in } L^2(Q) \text{ weakly} \end{cases} \tag{3.9}$$

$$\begin{cases} p_N = \frac{1}{N}\sum_{n=0}^{N-1} p^{n+1/2} \to p \quad \text{in } L^2(Q) \text{ weakly} \\ \frac{\partial p_N}{\partial x_i} \to \frac{\partial p}{\partial x_i} \quad \text{in } L^2(Q) \text{ weakly} \end{cases} \tag{3.10}$$

3.2 Remarks

Remark 3.3: The iterative method (3.4), (3.5), (3.6), and (3.7) is a variant of the alternative direction method (5), (21) and of the fractional step method (19), (31), (28) and (29).

Remark 3.4: The present method extends to variational inequalities (17) and (18).

Remark 3.5: For other iterative methods for variational inequalities, see (10).

Remark 3.6: For the purpose of numerical analysis one can of course discretize (3.4). For variational inequalities, see (17). For other methods see (1) (and the bibliography of this work).

Remark 3.7: Under the hypotheses of Theorem 3.1, one has

$$\frac{1}{N}\sum_{n=0}^{N-1} y^{n+1} \to y \text{ in } L^2(Q) \text{ weakly (and same thing for p)}$$

4. OTHER EVOLUTION EQUATIONS

4.1 An Example

Let us consider now a system whose state $y = y(x,t;u) = y(u)$ is given as the solution of

$$\frac{\partial^2 y}{\partial t^2} + Ay = f \quad \text{in } Q \tag{4.1}$$

$$y|_\Sigma = u \tag{4.2}$$

$$y(x,o) = y_o(x)\,,\ \frac{\partial y}{\partial t}(x,o) = y_1(x),\quad x \in \Omega \tag{4.3}$$

In (4.1) we assume A to be given by (1.4) and (1.5) with the condition

$$a_{ij} = a_{ji} \quad (\text{hence } A = A) \tag{4.4}$$

Remark 4.1: The operator $\partial^2/\partial t^2 + A$ is now hyperbolic. But what follows extends to the case when A is a symmetric elliptic operator of any order 2m, and then $\partial^2/\partial t^2 + A$ is not hyperbolic anymore.

We assume the dates are such that

$$y(u) \in L^2(Q) \tag{4.5}$$

and we take the cost function J(u) to be (as in (1.8))

$$J(u) = \int_Q |y(u) - z_d|^2 dxdt + (Nu, u)_{\mathcal{U}} \tag{4.6}$$

4.2 The Generalization of the "Two-Point Boundary Value Problem."

We assume that

$$\mathcal{U} = L^2\left(\sum\right), \quad \mathcal{U}_{ad} = \text{closed convex set in} \tag{4.7}$$

We define the adjoint problem:

$$\frac{\partial^2 p(u)}{\partial t^2} + A\, p(u) = y(u) - z_d \quad \text{in } Q \tag{4.8}$$

$$p(u) = 0 \quad \text{on } \sum \tag{4.9}$$

$$\left.\begin{aligned} &p(x, T; u) = 0, \quad x \in \Omega \\ &\frac{\partial p}{\partial t}(x, T; u) = 0, \quad x \in \Omega \end{aligned}\right\} \tag{4.10}$$

Then the optimal control u is uniquely defined by

$$\left(Nu - \frac{\partial p}{\partial \nu}(u),\ v-u\right)_{\mathcal{U}} \geq 0 \ \forall v \in \mathcal{U}_{ad} \left(\mathcal{U} = L^2\left(\sum\right)\right)$$

Remark 4.2: The formal "proof" is trivial. The difficulty lies in justifying the use of Green's formula. See (15).

Remark 4.3: For more general results of this form, see (12), 3d note, Section 2, and (15).

Remark 4.4: The system of Equations (4.1), (4.2), (4.3), and (4.8)...(4.11) is the generalization to the present situation of the classical two-point boundary value problems.

Remark 4.5: See also (24).

4.3 An Example of Unilateral Boundary Value Problem

Let us choose, in the situation of Section 4.2:

$$\mathcal{U}_{ad} = \{u \mid u \geq 0 \quad \text{a.e. on } \Sigma\} \tag{4.12}$$

Then the unique control u is given by

$$u = y|_{\Sigma}$$

where $\{y, p\}$ is the unique solution of

$$\begin{cases} \dfrac{\partial^2 y}{\partial t^2} + Ay = f & \text{in } Q \\ \dfrac{\partial^2 p}{\partial t^2} + Ap - y = -z_d & \text{in } Q \end{cases} \tag{4.13}$$

$$\begin{cases} y(x, o) = y_o(x), \ \dfrac{\partial y}{\partial t}(x, o) = y_1(x), \quad x \in \Omega \\ p(x, T) = 0, \ \dfrac{\partial p}{\partial t}(x, T) = 0, \quad x \in \Omega \end{cases} \tag{4.14}$$

$$p = 0 \quad \text{on } \Sigma \tag{4.15}$$

$$\begin{cases} y \geq 0 \quad \text{on } \Sigma \\ Ny - \dfrac{\partial p}{\partial \nu} \geq 0 \quad \text{on } \Sigma \\ y\left(Ny - \dfrac{\partial p}{\partial \nu}\right) = 0 \quad \text{on } \Sigma \end{cases} \tag{4.16}$$

Remark 4.6: (Compare Remarks 2.2 and 2.5) It would be interesting to have some information on the region of Σ where $y > 0$.

Remark 4.7: No "splitting up" iterative method of the type presented in Section 3 is known for the present situation.

BIBLIOGRAPHY

(1) E.I. AXELBAND, The optimal control of linear distributed parameter systems, Thesis, Depart. Eng., University of California, Los Angeles, 1966.

(2) C. BAIOCCHI, Sui problemi ai limiti per la equizioni paraboliche del tipo del calore, B.U.M.I. 29 (1964), p. 407-422.

(3) A.V. BALAKRISHNAN, a) Optimal control problems in Banach spaces, Journal of SIAM, Control 3, (1965) p. 152-180. b) Personnal communication.

(4) L. CESARI, Existence theorems for multidimensional problems of optimal control. (To appear)

(5) J. DOUGLAS, JR., On the numerical integration of $\partial^2 u/\partial x^2 + \partial^2 u/\partial y^2 - \partial u/\partial t$ by implicit method, Journal of SIAM (1955), p. 42-65.

(6) A.I. EGOROV, Optimal processes for systems with distributed parameters. Isvestia Akad Nank, 29 (1965) p. 1205-1260. and Mat. Sbornik, 69 (1966) p. 371-421. (In Russian)

(7) Ju. V. EGOROV, Necessary conditions for optimal control in Banach spaces, Mat. Sbornik, 64(1964) p. 79-101. (In Russian)

(8) H.O. FATTORINI, Time optimal control of solutions of operational differential equations, Journal of SIAM, Control. Ser. A, vol 2 (1964) p. 54-59.

(9) G. FICHERA, Problemi elastostatici con vincoli unilaterali, Memorie dell'Accad. Naz. dei Lincei, S VIII, vol. VII (1964) p. 91-140.

(10) Y. HAUGAZEAU
C.R. Acad. Sc. Paris, November 1966.

(11) J.L. LIONS, Optimisation pour certaines classes d'équations d'évolution non linéaires. Annali di Mat. Para ed Applicata. Vol. LXXXII (1966) p. 275-294.

(12) J.L. LIONS, Sur le controle optimal de systèmes décrits par des équations aux dérivées partielles linéaires (I), (II), (III). C.R. Acad. Sc. Paris, 9, 16, 22 Novembre 1966.

(13) J.L. LIONS, Remarks on evolution inequalities, Journal of the Mathematical Society of Japan, Vol 18 (1966) p. 331-343.

(14) J.L. LIONS, E. MAGENES, Remarques sur les problèmes aux limites pour opérateurs paraboliques. C.R. Acad. Sc. Paris, 251(1960) p. 2118-2120.

(15) J.L. LIONS, E. MAGENES, Problèmes aux limites non homogènes et Applications, Vol 1, to appear in 1967.

(16) J.L. LIONS, G. STAMPACCHIA, Variational inequalities. To appear in the Comm. Pure Applied Math.

(17) J.L. LIONS, R. TEMAM, C.R. Acad. Sc. Paris, t.263 (1966) p. 563-565.

(18) J.L. LIONS, R. TEMAM, To appear.

(19) G.I. MARCHOUK, Numerical Methods...(In Russian) Novosibirsk, 1965.

(20) J.J. MOREAU, Principes extremaux pour le probleme de la naissance de la cavitation. Journal de Mecanique (1967).

(21) D.W. PEACEMAN, M.M. RACHFORD, The numerical solution of parabolic and elliptic differential equations. Journal SIAM (1965) p. 28-42.

(22) PONTRYAGIN, BOLTYANSKII, GAMKRELIDZE, MISCHENKO, The mathematical theory of optimal processes, Interscience, 1962.

(23) W. PRAGER, Unilateral constraints in mechanics of continua. Atti del Convegno Lagrangiano, Torino, Accad. delle Scienze (1964) p. 181-191.

(24) D.L. RUSSEL, Optimal regulation of linear symmetric hyperbolic systems with finite dimensional controls, Journal SIAM Control, Vol 4 (1966) p. 276-294.

(25) L. SCHWARTZ, Théorie des noyaux. Proc. of the Inter. Congress of Math. (1950) Vol 1, p. 220-230.

(26) A. SIGNORINI, Questioni di elasticità non linearizzata e semi linearizzata. Rendic Mat. 18 (1949) p. 95-139.

(27) S.L. SOBOLEV, Applications of functional Analysis to Mathematical Physics, Leningrad. 1950.

(28) R. TEMAM, C.R. Acad. Sc. Paris (1966)

(29) R. TEMAM, Thesis, Paris (1967).

(30) P.K.C. WANG, Control of distributed parameter systems, in Advances in Control Systems, ed. by C.T. Leondes, Vol 1, 1964, p. 75-172.

(31) N.N. YANENKO, Fractionnal steps method for the numerical solution of problems of Mathematical Physics. (in Russian) Novosibirsk (1966).

MULTIDIMENSIONAL LAGRANGE AND PONTRYAGIN PROBLEMS*

Lamberto Cesari
Department of Mathematics, University of Michigan
Ann Arbor, Michigan

In the present paper we consider multidimensional Lagrange problems of the calculus of variations of various forms, in particular, Lagrange problems where we seek the minimum of a functional of the form

$$I[x, u] = \int_G f_o(t, x, u)\, dt$$

in certain classes of pairs $x(t)=(x^1, \dots, x^n)$, $u(t)=(u^1, \dots, u^m)$, $t=(t^1, \dots, t^\nu) \in G \subset E_\nu$, satisfying (1) a system of partial differential equations each of the form

$$\partial^h x^i / \partial^{\alpha_1} t^1 \dots \partial^{\alpha_\nu} t^\nu = f_{i\alpha}(t, x, u),$$

$$\alpha = (\alpha_1, \dots, \alpha_\nu),\ h = \alpha_1 + \dots + \alpha_\nu,$$

(2) constraints of the form

$$(t, x(t)) \in A \subset E_\nu \times E_n, \quad x(t) \in U(t, x(t)) \subset E_m,$$

where A is a given fixed set, and $U(t, x) \in A$, is a given variable set depending on t and x, and (3) a suitable system of boundary conditions concerning the values of the functions x^i and of a number of their partial derivatives on the boundary ∂G of the fixed open set G.

For this problem and other analogous ones we state here existence theorems for optimal solutions $x(t), u(t)$, $t \in G$, with x in suitable Sobolev spaces and u measurable. Detailed proofs are given in [3], [4], and [5]. In the problems above, x is said to be the space variable and u the

* Research partially supported by AFOSR grant 942-65 at the University of Michigan.

control variable. These problems are called Pontryagin problems when the sets $U(t, x)$ are all compact and contained in a fixed bounded part of the u-space. When the sets $U(t, x)$ are closed and not necessarily compact, these problems are called Lagrange problems with unilateral constraints on the control variable u. If $U(t, x) = E_m$ for all t and x, then the problems are simply called Lagrange problems (or problems without unilateral constraints on u).

§ 1. General notations.

Let G be a bounded open subset of the t-space E_ν, $t = (t^1, \ldots, t^\nu)$, let $x = (x^1, \ldots, x^n)$ denote a vector variable in E_n, and $u = (u^1, \ldots, u^m)$ a vector variable in E_m. As usual, we shall denote by cl G and by bd $G = \partial G$ the closure and the boundary of G. We shall also denote by co H the convex hull of a set H, and thus cl co H is the closed convex hull of H. For every $t \in$ cl G, let $A(t)$ be a given nonempty subset of E_n, and let A be the set of all (t, x) with $t \in$ cl G, $x \in A(t)$. For every $(t, x) \in A$, let $U(t, x)$ be a subset of E_m, and let M be the set of all (t, x, u) with $(t, x) \in A$, $u \in U(t, x)$.

The set A defined above is a subset of $E_\nu \times E_n \times E_m$ and its projection on $E_\nu \times E_m$ is A.

We assume G to be bounded by a surface S, which is a regular boundary in the sense of Sobolev [9, Ch. 1, §10, p. 72, Remark], and for the sake of simplicity we shall say that G is of class K_ℓ. Thus, S can be decomposed into a finite number of manifolds $S_1, \ldots, S_J$ of dimension $\nu - 1$ (and corresponding boundaries), each S_j having the property that it can be mapped into a hyperplane π_j by means of a transformation of coordinates T_j defined on a part G_j of G and continuous with continuous derivatives up to the ℓth order, $j = 1, \ldots, J$.

We shall denote by $x(t) = (x^1, \ldots, x^n)$, $u(t) = (u^1, \ldots, u^m)$, $t \in G$, vector functions of t in G. For every $i = 1, \ldots, n$, we shall denote by $\{\alpha\}_i$ a given finite system of nonnegative integral indices $\alpha = (\alpha_1, \ldots, \alpha_\nu)$, $0 \leq |\alpha| \leq \ell_i \leq \ell$, with

$|\alpha| = \alpha_1 + \ldots + \alpha_\nu$. We shall assume each component $x^i(t)$ of $x(t)$ to be L_{p_i}-integrable in G and to possess the generalized partial derivatives $D^\alpha x^i(t)$ of the orders $\alpha \in \{\alpha\}_i$, all L_{p_i}-integrable in G for certain $p_i > 1$, $i = 1, \ldots, n$. We shall assume that each component $u^j(t)$ of $u(t)$ is measurable in G.

Let N denote the total number of indices α contained in the n systems $\{\alpha\}_i$, $i = 1, \ldots, n$, and let $f(t, x, u) = (f_{i\alpha})$ denote an N-vector function whose components are real-valued functions $f_{i\alpha}(t, x, u)$ defined on M. We shall consider the system of N partial differential equations in G:

$$D^\alpha x^i = f_{i\alpha}(t, x, u) \quad , \quad \alpha \in \{\alpha\}_i \, , \quad i = 1, \ldots, n \, ,$$

or briefly

$$Dx = f(t, x, u) \, .$$

We are interested in pairs x, u of vector functions $x(t)$, $u(t)$, $t \in G$, as above, satisfying the constraints

$$(t, x(t)) \in A \, , \quad u(t) \in U(t, x(t)) \, , \quad \text{a. e. in } G \, ,$$

and the system of partial differential equations

$$D^\alpha x^i(t) = f_{i\alpha}(t, x(t), u(t)), \quad \text{a. e. in } G, \quad \alpha \in \{\alpha\}_i, \; i = 1, \ldots, n,$$

or in short

$$Dx(t) = f(t, x(t), u(t)) \quad \text{a. e. in } G \, .$$

Given $\delta > 0$ and a point $(t_0, x_0) \in A$, we shall denote by closed neighborhood $N_\delta(t_0, x_0)$ of radius δ of (t_0, x_0) in A the set of all $(t, x) \in A$ at a distance $\leq \delta$ from (t_0, x_0). Also, we shall denote by U_ε the set of all points $u \in E_m$ at a distance $\leq \varepsilon$ from a given set U. We shall say that $U(t, x)$ is metrically upper semicontinuous at the point $(t_0, x_0) \in A$ provided, given $\varepsilon > 0$, there is some $\delta = \delta(\varepsilon, t_0, x_0) > 0$ such that $U(t, x) \subset [U(t_0, x_0)]_\varepsilon$ for all $(t, x) \in N_\delta(t_0, x_0)$. We shall say that $U(t, x)$ is metrically upper semicontinuous in A provided $U(t, x)$ has this property at every point $(t_o, x_o) \in A$. This concept of metric upper semicontinuity is most often used in Pontryagin problems.

For Lagrange problems we shall need analogous concepts more topological in character, which we shall call properties (U) and (Q).

First, given $\delta > 0$ and a point $(t_o, x_o) \in A$, let us denote by $U(t_o, x_o; \delta)$ the set

$$U(t_o, x_o; \delta) = \bigcup U(t, x) ,$$

where $\bigcup$ ranges over all $(t, x) \in N_\delta(t_o, x_o)$. We shall say that $U(t, x)$ satisfies property (U) at a point $(t_o, x_o) \in A$ provided

$$U(t_o, x_o) = \bigcap_{\delta > o} \text{cl}\, U(t_o, x_o, \delta) ,$$

that is,

$$U(t_o, x_o) = \bigcap_\delta \text{cl} \bigcup_{(t, x) \in N_\delta(t_o, x_o)} U(t, x) .$$

We shall say that $U(t, x)$ satisfies property (U) in A if $U(t, x)$ satisfies property (U) at every point $(t_o, x_o) \in A$. A set $U(t, x)$ satisfying property (U) is necessarily closed as the intersection of closed sets. Property (U) is the so-called property of upper semicontinuity used by C. Kuratowski [7], E. Michael [8], and G. Choquet [6].

Below we shall also consider the sets

$$Q(t, x) = f(t, x, U(t, x)) = [z \mid z = f(t, x, u), \ u \in U(t, x)] \subset E_N,$$

and other analogous ones, which we shall introduce as needed. We shall say that such a set $Q(t, x)$ satisfies property (Q) at a point $(t_o, x_o) \in A$ provided

$$Q(t_o, x_o) = \bigcap_{\delta > o} \text{cl co}\, Q(t_o, x_o; \delta) ,$$

that is,

$$Q(t_o, x_o) = \bigcap_{\delta} \text{cl co} \bigcup_{(t,x) \in N_{\delta}(t_o, x_o)} Q(t, x).$$

We shall say that $Q(t,x)$ satisfies property (Q) in A if $Q(t,x)$ satisfies property (Q) at every point $(t_o, x_o) \in A$. A set $Q(t,x)$ satisfying property (Q) is necessarily closed and convex as the intersection of closed and convex subsets of E_N.

§2. Boundary conditions and cost functional

Beside the N-vector $f(t,x,u) = (f_{i\alpha})$, we shall consider a scalar function $f_o(t,x,u)$ defined on M and we shall denote by $\tilde{f}(t,x,u)$ the (N+1)-vector function $\tilde{f}(t,x,u) = (f_o, f_{i\alpha})$ defined on M. Concerning the n-vector function $x(t) = (x^1, \dots, x^n)$ we shall require that each function $x^i(t)$, $t \in G$, belong to a Sobolev class $W^{\ell_i}_{p_i}(G)$ for given ℓ_i and p_i, $1 \le \ell_i \le \ell$, $p_i > 1$, $i = 1, \dots, n$. By force of Sobolev's imbedding theorems [9], each function x^i and each of its derivatives $D^{\alpha} x^i$ of order $\alpha = (\alpha_1, \dots, \alpha_{\nu})$, $o \le |\alpha| \le \ell_i - 1$, has boundary values ϕ^i_{α} defined almost everywhere on S, each of class L_{p_i} on S.

We shall now require a set $(B)^i$ of boundary conditions involving the boundary values of the functions x^i and of their generalized partial derivatives $D^{\alpha} x^i$, $o \le |\alpha| \le \ell_i - 1$. On these boundary conditions (B) we assume the following closure property: (P_1) if $x(t) = (x^1, \dots, x^n)$, $x_k(t) = (x^1_k, \dots, x^n_k)$, $t \in G$, $k = 1, 2, \dots$, are vector functions whose components x^i, x^i_k belong to the Sobolev class $W^{\ell_i}_{p_i}(G)$, if $D^{\beta} x^i_k(t) \to D^{\beta} x^i(t)$ as $k \to \infty$ strongly in $L_{p_i}(G)$ for every β with $o \le |\beta| \le \ell_i - 1$, if $D^{\beta} x^i_k(t) \to D^{\beta} x^i(t)$ as $k \to \infty$ weakly in $L_{p_i}(G)$ for every β with $|\beta| = \ell_i$, and if the boundary values $\phi^i_{k\alpha}$ of $x^i_k(t)$ on ∂G satisfy boundary conditions (B), $i = 1, \dots, n$, then the boundary values ϕ^i_{α} of $x^i(t)$ on ∂G satisfy conditions (B), $i = 1, \dots, n$.

For instance, if the boundary conditions (B) are defined by stating that some of the boundary values $\phi^i_{k\alpha}(t)$

coincide with preassigned continuous functions ϕ^i_α on certain parts of ∂S, then, by force of Sobolev's imbedding theorems [9], we know that property (P_1) is valid.

We shall need a further property of boundary conditions (B), say (P_2): If $x(t) = (x^1, \dots, x^n)$, $t \in G$, denotes any vector function satisfying boundary conditions (B), whose components $x^i(t) \in W^{\ell_i}_{p_i}(G)$, $p_i > 1$, $1 \leq \ell_i \leq \ell$, satisfy

$$\int_G |D^\beta x^i(t)|^{p_i} \, dt \leq N_{i\beta}$$

for all $\beta = (\beta_1, \dots, \beta_\nu)$ with $|\beta| = \ell_i$, $i = 1, \dots, n$, and constants $N_{i\beta}$, then there are constants $N_{i\alpha}$ such that

$$\int_G |D^\alpha x^i(t)|^{p_i} \, dt \leq N_{i\alpha}$$

for all $\alpha = (\alpha_1, \dots, \alpha_\nu)$ with $o \leq |\alpha| \leq \ell_i - 1, i = 1, \dots, n$, where the constants $N_{i\alpha}$ depend only on p_i, ν, all $N_{i\beta}$, G, and boundary conditions (B), but not on the vector function $x(t)$ above.

For instance, the boundary conditions (B) defined by preassigning continuous boundary value functions ϕ^i_α on ∂G of all derivatives $D^\alpha x^i(t)$, $\alpha = (\alpha_1, \dots, \alpha_\nu)$, $o < |\alpha| \leq \ell_i - 1$, $i = 1, \dots, \nu$, satisfy condition (P_2).

A pair $x(t) = (x^1, \dots, x^n)$, $u(t) = (u^1, \dots, u^m)$, $t \in G$, with $x^i \in W^{\ell_i}_{p_i}(G)$, u^j measurable in G, satisfying $(t, x(t)) \in A$, $u(t) \in U(t, x(t))$, $D^\alpha x^i(t) = f_{i\alpha}(t, x(t), u(t)), \alpha \in \{\alpha\}_i$, $i = 1, \dots, n$, a. e. in G, and $f_o(t, x(t), u(t)) \in L_1(G)$, is said to be <u>admissible.</u> A class Ω of admissible pairs is said to be <u>complete,</u> if, for any sequence x_k, u_k, $k = 1, 2, \dots$, of pairs all in Ω and any other admissible pair x, u such that $x_k \to x$ in the sense described under P_1, (x, u) belongs to Ω. The class of all admissible pairs is obviously complete.

The Lebesgue integral

$$I[x, u] = \int_G f_o(t, x(t), u(t)) \, dt ,$$

where x, u is an admissible pair and where $dt = dt^1 \, dt^2 \cdots dt^\nu$, is said to be the <u>cost functional</u> or performance index.

A problem of maximum for $I[x, u]$ in a class Ω reduces to a problem of minimum for the cost functional $-I[x, u]$ in Ω. Thus, existence theorems for a maximum can be obtained from existence theorems for a minimum by replacing f_o by $-f_o$, that is, by changing the sense of the corresponding inequalities.

§3. An existence theorem for multidimensional Pontryagin problems.

Existence Theorem 1. Let G be a bounded open set of class K_ℓ, $\ell \geq 1$, t-space E_ν, let $A(t)$ be a nonempty subset of the x-space E_n defined for every $t \in cl\, G$, and let us assume that the set A of all $(t, x) \in E_\nu \times E_n$ with $t \in cl\, G$, $x \in A(t)$, be compact. Let $U(t, x)$ be a nonempty compact subset of the u-space E_m defined for every $(t, x) \in A$, and let us assume that $U(t, x)$ be metrically upper semicontinuous in A. Let M be the set of all $(t, x, u) \in E_\nu \times E_n \times E_m$ with $(t, x) \in A$, $u \in U(t, x)$. For every $i = 1, \ldots, n$, let $\{\alpha\}_i$ be a given finite system of indices $\alpha = (\alpha_1, \ldots, \alpha_\nu)$, $0 \leq |\alpha| \leq \ell_i \leq \ell$, and let N be the total number of elements $\alpha \in \{\alpha\}_i$, $i = 1, \ldots, n$. Let $\tilde{f}(t, x, u) = (f_o, f_{i\alpha}, \alpha \in \{\alpha\}_i, i = 1, \ldots, n) = (f_o, f)$ be a continuous $(N+1)$-vector function on the set M, and let us assume that the set $\tilde{Q}(t, x)$ of all $\tilde{z} = (z^o, z) \in E_{N+1}$ with $z^o \geq f_o(t, x, u)$, $z = f(t, x, u)$, $u \in U(t, x)$, be a convex subset of E_{N+1} for every $(t, x) \in A$. Let (B) be a system of boundary conditions satisfying properties (P_1) and (P_2). Let Ω be a nonempty complete class of pairs $x(t) = (x^1, \ldots, x^n)$, $u(t) = (u^1, \ldots, u^m)$, $t \in G$, $x^i(t) \in W^{\ell_i}_{p_i}(G)$, $p_i > 1$, $1 \leq \ell_i \leq \ell$, $i = 1, \ldots, n$, $u^j(t)$ measurable in G, $j = 1, \ldots, m$, satisfying (a) the constraints $(t, x(t)) \in A$, $u(t) \in U(t, x(t))$, a. e. in G; (b) the system of partial differential equations

$$D^\alpha x^i(t) = f_{i\alpha}(t, x(t), u(t)), \text{ a. e. in } G, \ \alpha \in \{\alpha\}_i, i = 1, \ldots, n;$$

(c) the boundary conditions (B) on the boundary ∂G, concerning the boundary values of the functions $x^i(t)$ and of their generalized partial derivatives $D^\beta x^i(t)$ of orders β, $o \leq |\beta| \leq \ell_i - 1$, $i = 1, \ldots, n$; (d) the finite system of inequalities

$$\int_G |D^\beta x^i(t)|^{p_i} dt \leq N_{I\beta}, \quad \beta = \{\beta\}_i, \quad i = 1, \ldots, n,$$

where $N_{I\beta}$ are given numbers, and $\{\beta\}_i$ contains at least all indices $\beta = (\beta_1, \ldots, \beta_\nu)$ with $|\beta| = \ell_i$ which are not already in $\{\alpha\}_i$, $i = 1, \ldots, n$. Then the cost functional

$$I[x, u] = \int_G f_o(t, x(t), u(t))\, dt$$

possesses an absolute minimum in Ω. If for given i and $\beta \in \{\beta\}_i$ it happens that for any $L_o \geq 0$ sufficiently large there is some $N_{i\beta}$ such that $I[x, u] \leq L_o$ implies $\int_G |D^\beta x^i(t)|^{p_i} dt \in N_{i\beta}$, then the absolute minimum still exists, even if in defining Ω we disregard the corresponding requirement in (d); the absolute minimum, however, may change.

If the sets $\tilde{Q}(t, x) = \tilde{f}(t, x, U(t, x) = [\tilde{z} = (z^o, z) | \tilde{z} = \tilde{f}(t, x, u),$ $u \in U(t, x)]$ are known to be convex, then the cost functional $I[x, u]$ has both an absolute minimum and an absolute maximum in Ω.

Detailed proof of Theorem 1 is given in [3].

§4. Existence theorems for multidimensional Lagrange problems.

Existence Theorem 2. Let G be a bounded open set of class K_ℓ, $\ell \geq 1$, of the t-space E_ν, for every $t \in \mathrm{cl}\, G$, let $A(t)$ be a nonempty subset of the x-space E_n, and let us assume that the set A of all $(t, x) \in E_\nu \times E_n$ with $t \in \mathrm{cl}\, G$, $x \in A(t)$, be closed. For every $(t, x) \in A$ let $U(t, x)$ be a nonempty closed subset of the u-space E_m, and let us assume that $U(t, x)$ satisfies property (U) in A. Let M be the set of all $(t, x, u) \in E_\nu \times E_n \times E_m$ with $(t, x) \in A$, $u \in U(t, x)$. For every $i = 1, \ldots, n$, let $\{\alpha\}_i$ be a given finite system of indices $\alpha = (\alpha_1, \ldots, \alpha_\nu)$,

$o \le |\alpha| \le \ell_i \le \ell$, and let N be the total number of elements $\alpha \in \{\alpha\}_i$, $i = 1, \ldots, n$. Let $\tilde{f}(t, x, u) = (f_o, f_{i\alpha}, \alpha = \{\alpha\}_i, i = 1, \ldots, n) = (f_o, f)$ be a continuous $(N+1)$-vector function on M, and let us assume that the set $\tilde{Q}(t, x) = \tilde{f}(t, x, U(t, x))$ be a convex closed subset of E_{N+1} for every $(t, x) \in A$, satisfying property (Q) in A. Let (B) be a system of boundary conditions satisfying properties (P_1) and (P_2). Let Ω be a nonempty complete class of pairs $x(t) = (x^1, \ldots, x^n)$, $u(t) = (u^1, \ldots, u^m$, $t \in G$, $x^i(t) \in W^{\ell i}_{pi}(G)$, $1 \le \ell_i \le \ell$, $p_i > 1$, $i = 1, \ldots, n$, $u^j(t)$ measurable in G, $j = 1, \ldots, m$, satisfying (a) the constraints $(t, x(t)) \in A$, $u(t) \in U(t, x(t))$, a. e. in G; (b) the system of partial differential equations

$$D^{\alpha} x^i(t) = f_{i\alpha}(t, x(t), u(t)), \text{ a. e. in } G, \ \alpha \in \{\alpha\}_i, i = 1, \ldots, n;$$

(c) the boundary conditions (B) on the boundary ∂G of G concerning the boundary values of the functions $x^i(t)$ and of their generalized partial derivatives $D^\beta x^i(t)$ of orders β, $o \le |\beta| \le \ell_i - 1$, $i = 1, \ldots, n$; (d) the system of inequalities

$$\int_G |D^\beta x^i(t)|^{p_i} dt \le N_{i\beta} \quad \text{for all } \beta \text{ with } |\beta| = \ell_i, i = 1, \ldots, n,$$

$$\int_G | f_o(t, x(t), u(t)) |^{p_o} dt \le N_o,$$

where $N_{i\beta}$, N_o are given constants, and $p_o, p_i > 1$ are given. The cost functional

$$I[x, u] = \int_G f_o(t, x(t), u(t))\, dt$$

possesses an absolute minimum and an absolute maximum in Ω.

Detailed proof of Theorem 2 is given in [4].

Existence Theorem 3. Let G be a bounded open set of class K_ℓ, $\ell > 1$, of the t-space E_ν, for every $t \in \text{cl}\, G$, let $A(t)$ be a nonempty subset of the x-space E_n, and let us assume that the set A of all $(t, x) \in E_\nu \times E_n$ with $t \in \text{cl}\, G$, $x \in A(t)$, be closed. For every $(t, x) \in A$ let $U(t, x)$ be a nonempty closed subset of the u-space E_m, and let us assume that $U(t, x)$ satisfies property (U) in A.

Let M be the set of all $(t, x, u) \in E_\nu \times E_n \times E_m$ with $(t, x) \in A$, $u \in U(t, x)$. For every $i = 1, \ldots, n$, let $\{\alpha\}_i$ be a given finite system of indices $\alpha = (\alpha_1, \ldots, \alpha_\nu)$, $0 \leq |\alpha| \leq \ell_i \leq \ell$, and let N be the total number of elements $\alpha \in \{\alpha\}_i$, $i = 1, \ldots, n$. Let $\tilde{f}(t, x, u) = (f_o, f_{i\alpha}, \alpha \in \{\alpha\}_i, i = 1, \ldots, n) = (f_o, f)$ be a continuous $(N+1)$-vector function on M, and let us assume that the set $\tilde{\tilde{Q}}(t, x)$ of all $\tilde{z} = (z^o, z^1, \ldots, z^n) = (z^o, z) \in E_{N+1}$ with $z^o \geq f_o(t, x, u)$, $z = f(t, x, u)$, $u \in U(t, x)$, be a convex closed subset of E_{N+1} for every $(t, x) \in A$, and that $\tilde{\tilde{Q}}(t, x)$ satisfy property (Q) in A. Also, let us assume that $f_o(t, x, u) \geq -M_o$ for all $(t, x, u) \in M$ and some constant $M_o \geq 0$. Let $(\mathcal{B})$ be a system of boundary conditions satisfying properties (P_1) and (P_2). Let Ω be a nonempty complete class of pairs $x(t) = (x^1, \ldots, x^n)$, $u(t) = (u^1, \ldots, u^m)$, $t \in G$, $x^i(t) \in W^{\ell_i}_{p_i}(G)$, $1 \leq \ell_i \leq \ell$, $p_i > 1$, $i = 1, \ldots, n$, $u^j(t)$ measurable in G, $j = 1, \ldots, m$, satisfying (a) the constraints $(t, x(t)) \in A$, $u(t) \in U(t, x(t))$, a. e. in G, (b) the system of partial differential equations

$$D^\alpha x^i(t) = f_{i\alpha}(t, x(t), u(t)) \text{ a. e. in } G, \ \alpha \in \{\alpha\}_i, i=1, \ldots, n;$$

(c) the boundary conditions (B) on the boundary ∂G of G concerning the boundary values of the functions $x^i(t)$ and of their generalized partial derivatives $D^\beta x^i(t)$ of orders β, $0 \leq |\beta| \leq \ell_i - 1$, $i = 1, \ldots, n$; (d) the system of inequalities

$$\int_G | D^\beta x^i(t) |^{p_i} dt \leq N_{i\beta}$$

for all β with $|\beta| = \ell_i$, $\beta \notin \{\alpha\}_i$, $i = 1, 2, \ldots, n$, where $N_{i\beta}$ are given constants; (e) $f_o(t, x(t), u(t))$ is L_1-integrable in G. Finally, let us assume that, whenever

$$\int_G f_o(t, x(t), u(t)) \, dt \leq L_o$$

for some constants L_o and pairs $x(t)$, $u(t)$ in Ω, then, for the same pairs we also have

$$\int_G | D^\alpha x^i(t) |^{p_i} dt \leq L_{i\alpha}, \ \alpha \in \{\alpha\}_i, \ i = 1, \ldots, n,$$

for constants $L_{i\alpha}$ depending only on L_o, Ω, G, p_i, ℓ_i, (B), but not on the particular pair x, u. Then the cost functional

$$I[x, u] = \int_G f_o(t, x(t), u(t))\, dt$$

possesses an absolute minimum in Ω.

If for given i and β as in (d) it happens that for any $L_o \geq 0$ sufficiently large there is some $N_{i\beta}$ such that $I[x, u] \leq L_o$ implies $\int_G |D^\beta x^i(t)|^{p_i} dt \leq N_{i\beta}$, then the absolute minimum still exists, even if in defining Ω we disregard the corresponding requirement in (d); the absolute minimum, however, may change.

Detailed proof of Theorem 3 is given in [4].

Existence Theorem 4. Let G be a bounded open set of class K_ℓ, $\ell \geq 1$, of the t-space E_ν, for every $t \in$ cl G, let A(t) be a nonempty subset of the x-space E_n, and let us assume that the set A of all $(t, x) \in E_\nu \times E_n$ with $t \in$ cl G, $x \in A(t)$, be closed. For every $(t, x) \in A$ let U(t, x) be a nonempty closed subset of the u-space E_m, and let us assume that U(t, x) satisfy property (U) in A. Let M be the set of all $(t, x, u) \in E_\nu \times E_n \times E_m$ with $(t, x) \in A$, $u \in U(t, x)$. For every $i = 1, \ldots, n$, let $\{\alpha\}_i$ be a given finite system of indices $\alpha = (\alpha_1, \ldots, \alpha_\nu)$, $0 \leq |\alpha| \leq \ell_i \leq \ell$, and let N be the total number of elements $\alpha \in \{\alpha\}_i$, $i = 1, \ldots, n$. Let $\tilde{f}(t, x, u) = (f_o, f_{i\alpha}, \alpha \in \{\alpha\}_i, i = 1, \ldots, n) = (f_o, f)$ be a continuous (N + 1)-vector function on M, and let us assume that the set $\tilde{\tilde{Q}}(t, x)$ of all $\tilde{z} = (z^o, z^1, \ldots, z^n) = (z^o, z) \in E_{N+1}$ with $z^o \geq f_o(t, x, u)$, $z = f(t, x, u)$, $u \in U(t, x)$, be a convex closed subset of E_{N+1} for every $(t, x) \in A$, and $\tilde{\tilde{Q}}(t, x)$ satisfy property (Q) in A. Let us further assume that there exists a continuous scalar function $\Phi(\xi)$, $0 \leq \xi < +\infty$, with $\Phi(\xi)/\xi \to \infty$ as $\xi \to \infty$, such that $f_o(t, x, u) \geq \Phi(|u|)$ for all $(t, x, u) \in M$, and that $|f(t, x, u)| \leq C + D|u|$ for all $(t, x, u) \in M$ and some constants $C, D \geq 0$. Let (B) be a system of boundary conditions satisfying properties (P_1) and (P_2). Let Ω be a nonempty complete class of pairs $x(t) = (x^1, \ldots, x^n)$, $u(t) = (u^1, \ldots, u^m)$, $t \in G$,

$x^i(t) \in W^{\ell_i}_{p_i}(G)$, $1 \leq \ell_i \leq \ell$, $p_i > 1$, $i = 1, \ldots, n$, $u^j(t)$ measurable in G, $j = 1, \ldots, m$, satisfying (a) the constraints $(t, x(t)) \in A$, $u(t) \in U(t, x(t))$ a.e. in G; (b) the system of partial differential equations

$$D^\alpha x^i(t) = f_{i\alpha}(t, x(t), u(t)) \text{ a. e. in } G, \alpha \in \{\alpha\}_i, i = 1, \ldots, n;$$

(c) the boundary conditions (B) on the boundary ∂G of G concerning the boundary values of the functions $x^i(t)$ and of their generalized partial derivatives $D^\beta x^i(t)$ of orders β, $o \leq |\beta| \leq \ell_i - 1$, $i = 1, \ldots, n$; (d) the system of inequalities

$$\int_G | D^\beta x^i(t)|^{p_i} dt \leq N_{i\beta}$$

for all β with $|\beta| = \ell_i$, $\beta \notin \{\alpha\}_i$, $i = 1, \ldots, n$, where $N_{i\beta}$ are given constants; (e) $f_o(t, x(t), u(t))$ L_1-integrable in G. Then the cost functional

$$I[x, u] = \int_G f_o(t, x(t), u(t)) \, dt$$

possesses an absolute minimum in Ω.

If for given i and β as in (d) it happens that for any $L_o \geq 0$ sufficiently large there is some $N_{i\beta}$ such that $I[x, u] \leq L_o$ implies $\int_G | D^\beta x^i(t)|^{p_i} dt \leq N_{i\beta}$, then the absolute minimum still exists, even if in defining Ω we disregard the corresponding requirement in (d); the absolute minimum, however, may change.

Detailed proof of Theorem 4 is given in [5]. This theorem extends to multidimensional Lagrange problems an existence theorem proved by Nagumo and Tonelli for one dimensional free problems of the calculus of variations, which have been extended to one dimensional Lagrange problems in [1] and [2].

In Theorems 2, 3 and 4 requirement (d) for the class Ω can be well formulated in the stronger form stated for Theorem 1.

References

[1] L. Cesari, Existence theorems for optimal solutions in Pontryagin and Lagrange problems. SIAM J. Control 3, 1965, 475-498.

[2] L. Cesari, Existence theorems for weak and usual optimal solutions in Lagrange problems with unilateral constraints. I and II. Trans. Amer. Math. Soc. 124, 1966, 369-412, 413-429.

[3] L. Cesari, Existence theorems for multidimensional problems of optimal control. Symposium on Differential Equations and Control, (Mayaguez, Puerto Rico, Dec. 1965). Acta, 115-132.

[4] L. Cesari, Existence theorems for multidimensional Lagrange problems. Journal of optimization and applications. vol. 1, no. 1, 1967.

[5] L. Cesari, Sobolev spaces and multidimensional Lagrange problems. To appear.

[6] G. Choquet, Convergences, Annales de l'Université de Grenobles 23, 1947-48, 55-112.

[7] C. Kuratowski, Les functions semi-continues dans l'espace des ensembles fermés. Fund. Math. 18, 1932, 148-166.

[8] E. Michael, Topologies on spaces of subsets. Trans. Amer. Math. Soc. 71, 1951, 152-182.

[9] S. L. Sobolev, Applications of functional analysis in Mathematical physics, Transl. Math. Monogr. Vol. 7, Amer. Soc. Providence, R.I. 1963 .

[10] L. Tonelli, Fondamenti di calcolo delle variazioni, Zanichelli, Bologna, 1921-23, 2 vols.

ON SOME ASPECTS OF LINEAR CONTROL THEORY

By Roberto Conti (Florence, Italy)

1. This work deals with control systems whose behavior is described by a linear differential equation

$$(1.1) \qquad dx/dt - A(t)\, x = B(t)\, u(t) + c(t)$$

with inputs $u(t)$ and responses $x(t)$ defined for t in a compact interval $[0,T]$ of the real line and taking values in reflexive B-spaces U and X respectively.

Our treatment of (1.1) will be based on the assumption of the existence of an evolution operator generated by A. More precisely, let $A : t \to A(t)$ be a function of $t \in [0,T]$ into the space of linear (possibly unbounded) operators in X. We assume that A admits an evolution operator $G : (t,s) \to G(t,s)$ defined for $0 \leq s \leq t \leq T$, with values in the space $\mathcal{L}[X,X]$ of linear bounded operators in X, strongly continuous in (t,s), strongly absolutely continuous in t and such that

$$G(t,s)\, G(s,r) = G(t,r) , \quad 0 \leq r \leq s \leq t \leq T$$
$$G(s,s) = \text{ the identity of } \mathcal{L}[X,X]$$
$$\partial G(t,s)/\partial t = A(t)\, G(t,s)$$

where $\partial/\partial t$ denotes the strong derivative and, for each $s \in [0,T]$, the $=$ holds a.e. in $[s,T]$. Sufficient conditions for the existence of G are known (See for instance T. Kato [8], J. Kisinsky [9], E. T. Poulsen 14).

Let $1 \leq p \leq \infty$. Given a B-space E , $L^p(0,T;E)$ shall denote the B-space of all E-valued, strongly measurable functions f defined in $[0,T]$, such that

$$|f|_p = \left(\int_0^T |f(t)|_E^p \, dt \right)^{1/p} < \infty \quad , \text{ if } p<\infty,$$

$$|f|_\infty = \text{ess sup} \left\{ |f(t)|_E : 0 \leq t \leq T \right\} < \infty , \text{ if } p = \infty .$$

As usual $p' = p(p-1)^{-1}$ for $1 < p < \infty$; $p' = 1$ for $p = \infty$; $p' = \infty$ for $p = 1$, and $\mathcal{L}[U,X]$ will denote the space of linear bounded operators of U into X . Then, if G exists, and if $v \in X$, $u \in L^p(0,T;U)$, $B \in L^{p'}(0,T; \mathcal{L}[U,X])$, $c \in L(0,T;X)$, we may define

$$(1.2) \quad x(t,u,v) = G(t,0)\, v + \int_0^t G(t,s)\, B(s)\, u(s)\, ds + \int_0^t G(t,s)\, c(s)\, ds , \quad 0 \leq t \leq T ,$$

where the integrals are in the sense of Bochner. (1.2) can be considered as the (Bochner) integral form of (1.1) with initial conditions $x(0,u,v) = v$. Sufficient conditions in order that (1.2) actually yield (1.1) are known. (See for instance the references already quoted).

Finally, let V , W be two convex bounded closed subsets of X and let $\mathcal{U}$ be a convex bounded closed subset of $L^p(0,T;U)$.

Having given X , U , T , p , A (or rather G), B , c , V , W and $\mathcal{U}$ we say that Problem (P) has a solution u , v , if there are $u \in \mathcal{U}$, $v \in V$, such that $x(T,u,v) \in W$.

With the terminology of controls this means that there are initial states v of the system in the base set V and steering functions u in the admissible set $\mathcal{U}$ such that the corresponding state $x(t,u,v)$ defined by (1.2) will reach the target set W in a given transfer time T . Problem (P) is then a problem of controllability.

Our purpose is to transform the conditions for the solvability of (P) into an inequality involving all data (Sects. 2, 3) and then to use the inequality for studying some classical optimization problems, such as minimum time, minimum effort and final value problems (Sects. 4 to 11). Our work is essentially an extension of Antosiewicz's paper [1] from finite to infinite dimensional spaces.

2. Let us denote by Γ the linear operator $x \to G(T,0)\,x$ of X into X, and by Λ the linear operator

$$u \to \int_0^T G(T,s)\,B(s)\,u(s)\,ds$$

of $L^p(0,T;U)$ into X. Both are bounded, therefore ΓV, the image of V by Γ, and $\Lambda \mathcal{U}$, the image of $\mathcal{U}$ by Λ, are bounded convex sets of X ? Then also

$$S = \left\{\int_0^T G(T,s)\,c(s)\,ds\right\} - W + \Gamma V + \Lambda \mathcal{U}$$

is a bounded convex subset of X and we can define its supporting function

$$(2.1)\quad h_S(x') = \sup_{x \in S} \langle x, x'\rangle = \int_0^T \langle G(T,s)\,c(s), x'\rangle\,ds +$$

$$+ \sup_{w \in W} \langle w, -x'\rangle + \sup_{v \in V} \langle v, x'G(T,0)\rangle +$$

$$+ \sup_{u \in \mathcal{U}} \int_0^T \langle u(s), x'G(T,s)B(s)\rangle\,ds$$

for all $x' \in X'$, the dual of X.

Of the following implications :

$$\text{(P) has solutions} \Leftrightarrow o_X \in S \Rightarrow o_X \in \bar{S} \Leftrightarrow h_S(x') \geq 0, x' \in X'$$

(o_X the origin of X), the first two are obvious and the third one can be proved by using the strict separation theorem for convex sets.

On the other hand, from the reflexivity of X it follows that $S = \overline{S}$ iff $\Lambda\mathcal{U}$ is closed, hence
Theorem 1. The set is closed iff

(2.2) (P) has solutions $\Leftrightarrow h_S(x') \geq 0, \; x' \in X'$.

3. In this Section sufficient conditions are given for $\Lambda\mathcal{U}$ to be closed, i.e. for the validity of (2.2). For the proofs we refer to our paper [4].

We recall first that according to S. Bochner and A. D. Taylor [3] a B-space U is said to satisfy Condition (D) if all the functions of [0,T] into U of bounded strong variation have a strong derivative a.e. in [0,T] . We shall say for brevity that U satisfies Condition (BT) if i) it is reflexive and, ii) both U and U' satisfy (D). Then reflexivity of $L^p(0,T;U)$, $1 < p < \infty$, does not depend on p and it is characterized by the validity of Condition (BT) for U .(See S.Bochner and A.D.Taylor, loc. cit.). Condition (BT) is certainly satisfied when U is uniformly convex, or reflexive and separable, or Hilbert, or finite - dimensional.

a) $1 < p < \infty$.

It is easy to show that $\Lambda\mathcal{U}$ is closed if $\mathcal{U}$ is a convex bounded closed subset of a reflexive $L^p(0,T;U)$. In other words we have :

Theorem 2. The set $\Lambda\mathcal{U}$ is closed if $\mathcal{U}$ is a convex bounded closed subset of $L^p(0,T;U)$, $1 < p < \infty$, and U satisfies Condition (BT).

b) $p = \infty$.

Question : Is Theorem 2 true for $p = \infty$?
The answer is "yes" at least in two cases, namely :

Theorem 2'. The set $\Lambda\mathcal{U}$ is closed if $\mathcal{U}$ is the unit ball of $L^\infty(0,T;U)$, U satisfies Condition (BT) and $B \in L^{1+\alpha}(0,T; \mathcal{L}[U,X])$ for some $\alpha > 0$.

Theorem 2". The set $\Lambda\mathcal{U}$ is closed if $\mathcal{U}$ is the unit ball of $L^\infty(0,T;U)$ with $\dim U = m < \infty$ and $\dim X = n < \infty$.

Remarks. Theorem 2' takes care of the case of regular B's, in particular constant ones, and it is essentially due to P. L. Falb [5]. Theorem 2" covers the case of ordinary differential equations.

c) $p = 1$.

Theorem 2 is certainly false for $p = 1$, even with $U = R$ and a constant B, as examples show. However $p = 1$ corresponds to $B \in L^\infty(0,T;\mathcal{L}[U,X])$, so one can take u in $L^{1+\alpha}(0,T;U)$ with $\alpha > 0$ arbitrarily "small" and use Theorem 2. Or one can assume, more restrictively, $B \in C(0,T;\mathcal{L}[U,X])$, the subspace of continuous mappings of $[0,T]$ into $\mathcal{L}[U,X]$ with uniform norm, and replace (1.2) by

$$x(t,\omega,v) = G(t,0)\,v + \int_0^t G(t,s)\,B(s)\,d\omega(s) + \int_0^t G(t,s)\,c(s)\,ds$$

where the first integral is Bochner-Stieltjes (Cfr. S. Bochner-A.D.Taylor, loc. cit.) and $\omega \in BV(0,T;U)$, the space of functions of $[0,T]$ of bounded strong variation into a B-space U satisfying Condition (BT). The most recent applications of this procedure may be found in L. W. Neustadt [11] and in A. V. Balakrishnan [2], for the finite and the infinite diemsnional case respectively.

4. Given X, U, T, p, A (or G), B, c, V, W, $\mathcal{U}$ as in Sec. 1, we say that Problem (P_t) has solutions if there are $u \in \mathcal{U}$, $v \in V$ and $t \in [0,T]$, such that $x(t,u,v) \in W$. Clearly, $(P_T) = (P)$. Assume that Problem (P_t) has solutions for some $t \in [0,T]$ and let τ be the inf of such t. Does Problem (P_τ) have solutions ? This is a minimum

time problem. We want to show, by extending the argument used by H. A. Antosiewicz [1] in the finite dimensional case, that the answer is "yes" under the assumptions of each one of the Theorems 2, 2' and 2".

To this effect let us define for each $t \in [0,T]$ the two linear operators

$$\Gamma_t : x \to G(t,0)\, x \quad ; \quad \Lambda_t : u \to \int_0^t G(t,s)B(s)u(s)ds$$

and the set

$$S_t = \left\{ \int_0^t G(t,s)\, c(s)\, ds \right\} - W + \Gamma_t V + \Lambda_t \mathcal{U}.$$

We also note that the assumptions of any of the Theorems 2, 2', 2" insure the closedness of $\Lambda_t \mathcal{U}$ for each $t \in [0,T]$ so that we have

Lemma 1. Under the assumptions of any of the Theorems 2, 2', 2" the set S_t is closed for all $t \in [0,T]$.

Next define the supporting function of S_t :

$$(4.1) \quad h(t,x') \equiv h_{S_t}(x') \equiv \sup_{x \in S_t} \langle x, x' \rangle =$$

$$= \langle \int_0^t G(t,s)\, c(s)\, ds, x' \rangle + \sup_{w \in W} \langle w, -x' \rangle +$$

$$+ \sup_{v \in V} \langle v, x'G(t,0) \rangle + \sup_{u \in \mathcal{U}} \int_0^t \langle u(s), x'G(t,s)B(s) \rangle ds.$$

The following Lemma lists some of its properties we shall need later :

Lemma 2. The function h defined by (4.1) has the the following properties : a) for each $t \in [0,T]$, $x' \to h(t,x')$ is a positively homogeneous and convex function on X' . Moreover it is bounded for $|x'| < 1$. Hence it is continuous on X' . b) for each $x' \in X'$, $t \to h(t,x')$ is a continuous function on $[0,T]$, uniformly with respect to x' in each bounded subset of X' .

Proof of a). The first three statements are evi-

dent : continuity then follows by a known theorem.
Proof of b). Let us recall that G is continuous on $[0,T]\times[0,T]$, hence bounded and uniformly continuous. Let $|x'|$ be bounded ; further since $\mathcal{U}$ is bounded, $u\in\mathcal{U}$ implies that $|u|_p$ is also bounded. If $t_k\in[0,T]$, $t_k\to t$, it follows that to each $\varepsilon>0$ there corresponds an integer k_ε, <u>not</u> depending on u, such that $k>k_\varepsilon$ implies

$$\int_0^t\langle u(s),\ x'G(t,s)B(s)\rangle\ ds-\varepsilon\leq\int_0^t\langle u(s),\ x'G(t,s)B(s)\rangle ds\leq$$

$$\leq\int_0^t\langle u(s),\ x'G(t,s)B(s)\rangle\ ds\ +\varepsilon\ .$$

Taking the sup with respect to $u\in\mathcal{U}$ we obtain the continuity of

$$t\to\sup_{u\in\mathcal{U}}\int_0^t\langle u(s),\ x'G(t,s)B(s)\rangle\ ds$$

uniformly with respect to x' in each bounded set of X'. The same property is proved for

$$t\to\sup_{v\in V}\ \langle v,\ x'G(t,0)\rangle$$

using the fact that V is bounded (and the continuity of G).

We can now prove :

<u>Theorem 3. Under the assumptions of any one of the Theorems 2, 2', 2", if Problem (P_t) has solutions for some</u> $t\in\,]0,T]$, <u>then there is a minimum</u> $\tau\in[0,T]$ <u>for which Problem (P_τ) has solutions</u>.

Let $\tau\geq0$ be the inf of $t\in\,]0,T]$ for which Problem (P_t) has solutions. There is a sequence $\{t_k\}$ in $]\tau,T]$, $t_k\downarrow\tau$, such that Problem (P_{t_k}) has solutions, hence $h(t_k,x')\geq0$, $x'\in X'$. Since $t\to h(t,x')$ is continuous by Lemma 2, it follows

$$h(\tau,x')\geq0,\quad x'\in X' \tag{4.2}$$

and by Theorem 1 and Lemma 1 this means that Problem (P_τ) has solutions.

Remark. For particular cases of Theorem 3 we refer to : H. A. Antosiewicz [1] , A. V. Balakrishnan [2] , H. O. Fattorini [6] , W. L. Miranker [10] .

5. Let $\tau \geq 0$ be the minimum time. If $\tau = 0$ this means $0_X \in -W + V$ so that $W \cap V$ is non-empty, and conversely. If $\tau > 0$ let $\{t_k\}$ be any sequence in $[0, \tau[$, $t_k \uparrow \tau$ and let the assumptions of any of the Theorems 2, 2', 2" be satisfied. For each t_k there is an x'_k, $|x'_k| = 1$, such that $h(t_k, x'_k) < 0$.

Assume that

$$(5.1) \qquad \dim X = n < \infty$$

hence also $\dim X' = n$, or, equivalently, $|x'| = 1$ is a compact set, so that we may assume $|x'_k - x'_0| \to 0$ for some x'_0, $|x'_0| = 1$. Applying Lemma 2 in full we see that to each $\varepsilon > 0$ there corresponds an integer k_ε such that $k > k_\varepsilon$ implies $h(t_k, x'_k) - h(\tau, x'_0) = h(t_k, x'_k) - h(\tau, x'_k) + h(\tau, x'_k) - h(\tau, x'_0) > -\varepsilon/2 - \varepsilon/2$, i.e. $h(\tau, x'_0) < h(t_k, x'_k) + \varepsilon < \varepsilon$, hence $h(\tau, x'_0) \leq 0$. Comparing with (4.2) (for $x' = x'_0$) we have $h(\tau, x'_0) = 0$, i.e.

$$(5.2) \quad \left\langle \int_0^\tau G(\tau,s)c(s)ds,\ x'_0 \right\rangle + \sup_{w \in W} \langle w, -x'_0 \rangle + \sup_{v \in V} \langle v, x'_0 G(\tau,0) \rangle + \sup_{u \in \mathcal{U}} \int_0^\tau \langle u(s), x'_0 G(\tau,s)B(s) \rangle ds = 0.$$

On the other hand, if τ, $\bar{u}$, $\bar{v}$ is a solution of Problem (P_τ) then

$$\langle \int_0^\tau G(\tau,s)c(s)ds,\ x'\rangle + \langle x(\tau,\bar{u},\bar{v}),-x'\rangle +$$

$$+ \langle \bar{v},\ x'G(\tau,0)\rangle + \int_0^\tau \langle \bar{u}(s),\ x'G(\tau,s)B(s)\rangle\, ds$$

$$= 0$$

for all $x' \in X'$, hence, in particular, for $x' = x'_0$. Comparing with (5.2), since $x(\tau,\bar{u},\bar{v}) \in W$, $\bar{v} \in V$, $\bar{u} \in \mathcal{U}$ we have

Theorem 4. (Maximum principle). *Under the assumptions of any one of the Theorems 2, 2', 2", plus the assumption (5.1), if* τ, $\bar{u}$, $\bar{v}$ *is a solution of the minimum time problem,* $\tau > 0$, *then there exists* x'_0, $|x'_0| = 1$, *such that*

$$(5.3) \qquad \langle x(\tau,\bar{u},\bar{v}),\ -x'_0\rangle = \sup_{w \in W} \langle w,\ -x'\rangle$$

$$(5.4) \qquad \langle \bar{v},\ x'_0G(\tau,0)\rangle = \sup_{v \in V} \langle v,\ x'_0G(\tau,0)\rangle$$

$$(5.5) \int_0^\tau \langle \bar{u}(s),\ x'_0G(\tau,s)B(s)\rangle\, ds \geq$$

$$\geq \int_0^\tau \langle u(s),\ x'_0G(\tau,s)B(s)\rangle\, ds, \quad u \in \mathcal{U}.$$

Remark 1. Equations (5.3),(5.4) mean that $x(\tau,\bar{u},\bar{v})$ and $\bar{v}$ must belong to the boundaries of W and V respectively. They are the equations of supporting hyperplanes to W at $x(\tau,\bar{u},\bar{v})$ and to V at $\bar{v}$ respectively.

Inequality (5.5), when also $\dim U$ is finite is a particular case of inequality (2.8) of R. V. Gamkrelidze [7].

When $\tau = 0$ (5.5) is trivial while (5.3) and (5.4) would mean that $\bar{v}$ must be on the boundary of both W and V, which is false in general since $\bar{v}$ can be any point of $W \cap V$.

Remark 2. Whether Theorem 4 can be proved without

assumption (5.1) is an open question. In fact, when $\dim X$ is infinite then the unit ball X'_1 of X' is no longer compact. However, since X is reflexive, X'_1 is weakly compact and we can use weak lower semi-continuity of $x' \to h(t,x')$ instead of part a) of Lemma 2, to obtain $h(\tau,x'_o) < h(t_k,x'_k) + \varepsilon < \varepsilon$, hence $h(\tau,x'_o) = 0$. But x'_o is now a weak limit and since the boundary of X'_1 is not weakly closed we have only $|x'_o| \leq 1$, instead of $|x'_o| = 1$, which does not exclude $x'_o = o_{X'}$, and this would render Theorem 4 meaningless.

6. The final value problem is another typical optimization problem (Cfr. for instance A. V. Balakrishnan [2]). It consists of solving Problem (P) under the condition that $|x(T,u,v) - w_o|$ be minimum for a given $w_o \in X$.

Taking $W = \{w_o\} + \varepsilon X_1$, X_1 the unit ball of X, this amounts to minimizing $\varepsilon \geq 0$. Since $-W = \{-w_o\} + \varepsilon X_1$, the set S of Sec. 2 can be replaced by

$$S_\varepsilon = \left\{\int_o^T G(T,s)c(s)\, ds - w_o\right\} + \varepsilon X_1 + \Gamma V + \Lambda \mathcal{U}$$

whose supporting function is

$$h(\varepsilon,x') = h_{S_\varepsilon}(x') = \langle \int_o^T G(T,s)c(s)\, ds - w_o, x'\rangle +$$

$$+ \varepsilon|x'| + \sup_{v \in V} \langle v, x'G(T,0)\rangle + \sup_{u \in \mathcal{U}} \int_o \langle u(s), x'G(T,s)B(s)\rangle ($$

If ε is large enough then $h(\varepsilon,x') \geq 0, |x'| = 1$. Let ε_o be the inf of such ε and let $\varepsilon_k \downarrow \varepsilon_o$, $h(\varepsilon_k,x') \geq 0$, $|x'| = 1$. It follows $h(\varepsilon_o,x') \geq 0$, $|x'| = 1$, hence if $\Lambda\mathcal{U}$ is closed we have $\varepsilon_o =$

$= \min \; |x(T,u,v) - w_o|$, i.e. :

Theorem 5. Under the assumptions of any of the Theorems 2, 2', 2" the final value problem has solutions for every $w_o \in X$ and every convex bounded closed subset $V \subset X$.

Remark 1. The final value problem may not have solutions when $V = X$ and $\dim X = \infty$ (Cfr. W.L.Miranker [10]).

Remark 2. A more general problem would consist of solving (P) under the condition that the distance of $x(T,u,v)$ to a given subset $W_o \subset X$ be minimum.

(Cfr. H.A.Antosiewicz [1']). When W is convex bounded and closed this can be dealt with as the final value problem, simply by taking $W = W_o + \varepsilon X_1$.

7. If (5.1) holds and $\varepsilon_o > 0$, then by an argument similar to that used in Sec. 5 there will be x'_o, $|x'_o| = 1$, such that $h(\varepsilon_o, x'_o) = 0$, i.e. :

$$\langle \int_0^T G(T,s)c(s)\,ds - w_o,\; x'_o \rangle + \varepsilon_o + \sup_{v \in V} \langle v,\; x'_o G(T,0) \rangle +$$

$$+ \sup_{u \in \mathcal{U}} \int_0^T \langle u(s),\; x'_o G(T,s)B(s) \rangle\,ds = 0 .$$

On the other hand if $\bar{u}$, $\bar{v}$ is a solution then

$$\langle \int_0^T G(T,s)c(s)\,ds - w_o,\; x' \rangle + \langle -x(T,\bar{u},\bar{v}) + w_o, x' \rangle +$$

$$+ \langle \bar{v},\; x'G(T,0) \rangle + \int_0^T \langle \bar{u}(s),\; x'G(T,s)B(s) \rangle\,ds = 0$$

for all $x' \in X'$, in particular for $x' = x'_o$. By comparison we have thus :

Theorem 6. (Maximum principle). Under the assumptions of any one of the Theorems 2, 2', 2", plus the assumption (5.1), if ε_o, $\bar{u}$, $\bar{v}$ is a solution of the final value problem, $\varepsilon_o > 0$, then there exists x'_o, $|x'_o| = 1$, such that

(6.1) $\langle w_o - x(T,\bar{u},\bar{v}),\ x'_o \rangle = \varepsilon_o$

(6.2) $\langle \bar{v},\ x'_o G(T,0) \rangle = \sup_{v \in V} \langle v,\ x'_o G(T,0) \rangle$

(6.3) $$\int_0^T \langle \bar{u}(s),\ x'_o G(T,s)B(s) \rangle\, ds \geq$$

$$\geq \int_0^T \langle u(s),\ x'_o G(T,s)B(s) \rangle ds\ ,\ u \in \mathcal{U}.$$

Remark 1. Equation (6.1) gives

$$\langle w_o - x(T,\bar{u},\bar{v}),\ x'_o \rangle = |w_o - x(T,\bar{u},\bar{v})|\ |x'_o|$$

and (6.2) means that $\bar{v}$ must belong to the boundary of V. When $\varepsilon_o = 0$ (6.1) becomes trivial, while (6.2) and (6.3) are no longer true, in general.

Remark 2. The possibility of dropping assumption (5.1) is again an open question, similar to the one raised in Sec. 5, Remark 2.

8. By symmetry, the initial (instead of final) value problem, will consist in solving (P) under the condition that $|v - v_o|$ be minimum for a given $v_o \in X$. Taking $V = \{v_o\} + \sigma X_1$, this amounts to minimizing $\sigma \geq 0$. The set S is now replaced by

$$S_\sigma = \left\{\int_0^T G(T,s)c(s)\ ds\right\} + \{G(T,0)v_o\} - W + \sigma\Gamma X_1 + \Lambda\mathcal{U}$$

and its supporting function is

$$h(\sigma,x') = h_{S_\sigma}(x') = \left\langle \int_0^T G(T,s)c(s)\ ds,\ x' \right\rangle +$$

$$+ \sup_{w \in W} \langle w,\ -x' \rangle + \langle v_o, x'G(T,0) \rangle + \sigma |\ x'G(T,0)| +$$

$$+ \sup_{u \in \mathcal{U}} \int_0^T \langle u(s),\ x'G(T,s)B(s) \rangle\ ds\ .$$

If there are $\sigma > 0$, $u \in \mathcal{U}$ such that Problem (P) has solutions, then $h(\sigma, x') \geq 0$, $|x'| = 1$ for those σ.

Let σ_o be their infimum. If $\sigma_k \downarrow \sigma_o$, $h(\sigma_k, x') \geq 0$, $|x'| = 1$, then $h(\sigma_o, x') \geq 0$, $|x'| = 1$, hence, if $\Lambda \mathcal{U}$ is closed, $\sigma_o = \min |v - v_o|$ and we have :

<u>Theorem 8. Under the assumptions of any one of the Theorems 2, 2', 2" if Problem (P) has solutions for a pair of sets</u> V, W, <u>then the initial value problem has solutions for all</u> $v_o \in V$.

<u>Remark</u>. If $\dim X = \infty$ and W is reduced to a single point the initial value problem may not have solutions (Cfr. W. L. Miranker [10]).

9. Again by an argument similar to that used in Sec. 5 we can prove :

<u>Theorem 9. (Maximum principle). Under the assumptions of any one of the Theorems 2, 2', 2", plus assumption (5.1), if</u> $\sigma_o, \bar{u}, \bar{v}$, <u>is a solution of the initial value problem,</u> $\sigma_o > 0$, <u>then there exists</u> $x'_o, |x'_o| = 1$, <u>such that</u>

$$\langle x(T,\bar{u},\bar{v}),\ x'_o \rangle = \sup_{w \in W} \langle w,\ x'_o \rangle$$

$$\langle \bar{v} - v_o, x'_o G(T,0) \rangle = \sigma_o |x'_o G(T,0)|$$

$$\int_0^T \langle \bar{u}(s),\ x'_o G(T,s)B(s) \rangle\, ds \geq$$

$$\geq \int_0^T \langle u(s),\ x'_o G(T,s)B(s) \rangle\, ds\ ,\ u \in \mathcal{U}.$$

Remarks about the necessity of $\sigma_o > 0$ and the possibility of eliminating assumption (5.1) can be made, analogous to Remarks 1 and 2 of Sects. 5 and 7.

10. We conclude our review of optimization problems by considering the minimum effort problem : to solve (P) under the condition that $|u|_p$ or $|u|_\infty$ be minimum (Cfr. L. W. Neustadt [11] ; W.A.Porter-

J. P. Williams [12]).

Taking $\mathcal{U} = \rho\mathcal{U}_1$, $\rho \geq 0$, $\mathcal{U}_1$ the unit ball of $L^p(0,T;U)$, $1 < p \leq \infty$, we have to solve Problem (P) with minimum ρ. This time the set S is

$$S_\rho = \{\int_0^T G(T,s)c(s)\, ds\} - W + \Gamma V + \rho\Lambda\mathcal{U}_1$$

with supporting function

$$h(\rho,x') \equiv h_{S_\rho}(x') \equiv \langle \int_0^T G(T,s)c(s)\, ds,\ x'\rangle +$$

$$+ \sup_{w \in W} \langle w, -x'\rangle + \sup_{v \in V} \langle v, x'G(T,0)\rangle +$$

$$+ \rho(\int_0^T | x'G(T,s)B(s)|_{U'}^{p'}\, ds)^{1/p'}.$$

If $h(\rho,x') \geq 0, |x'| = 1$ for some $\rho > 0$ we can take the inf, ρ_0, of such ρ, then $\rho_k \downarrow \rho_0$, $h(\rho_k,x') \geq 0$, $|x'| = 1$, and if $\Lambda\mathcal{U}_1$ is closed we have :

Theorem 10. Under the assumptions of any one of the Theorems 2, 2', 2" if Problem (P) has solutions for some $\mathcal{U} = \rho\mathcal{U}_1$ and a pair of sets V , W , then the minimum effort problem has solutions for the same pair V, W.

Remark. A sufficient condition for the existence of solutions of (Problem (P) hence of) the minimum effort problem, when $\Lambda\mathcal{U}_1$ is closed, is represented by

$$|x'G(T,s)B(s)|_{U'} = 0, \text{ a.e. } [0,T] \Leftrightarrow x' = o_{X'},$$

which means that Λ is a mapping of $L^p(0,T;U)$ onto X . Difficulties arising when one removes this assumption were illustrated by W. A. Porter [13] .

11. When $\rho_0 > 0$ we have

Theorem 11. (Maximum principle). Let $\mathcal{U}_1$ be the unit ball either of $L^p(0,T;U)$, $1 < p < \infty$, with U satisfying Condition (BT), or of $L^\infty(0,T;U)$ with U satisfying Condition (BT) and $B \in L^{1+\alpha}(0,T;\mathcal{L}[U,X])$ for some $\alpha > 0$, or of $L^\infty(0,T;U)$ with $\dim U < \infty$ and let (5.1) hold. Then if ρ_0, $\bar{u}$, $\bar{v}$ is a solution of the minimum effort problem, $\rho_0 > 0$, there exists x'_0, $|x'_0| = 1$, such that

$$\langle x(T,\bar{u},\bar{v}),\ x'_0 \rangle = \sup_{w \in W} \langle w,\ x'_0 \rangle$$

$$\langle \bar{v},\ x'_0 G(T,0) \rangle = \sup_{v \in V} \langle v,\ x'_0 G(T,0) \rangle$$

$$\int_0^T \langle \bar{u}(s),\ x'_0 G(T,s)B(s) \rangle\, ds =$$

$$= \rho_0 \Big(\int_0^T |x'_0 G(T,s)B(s)|_{U'}^{p'}\, ds \Big)^{1/p'}.$$

Remarks. Analogous to Remarks at the end of Sects. 5, 7, 9.

REFERENCES

[1] H. A. Antosiewicz, Linear control systems, Archive Rat. Mech. & Anal., 12, 1963, 313-324 ;

[1'] H. A. Antosiewicz, To appear ;

[2] A. V. Balakrishnan, Optimal control problems in Banach spaces, Jour. SIAM, Control, 3, 1965, 152-180 ;

[3] S. Bochner - A. D. Taylor, Linear functionals on certain spaces of abstractly-valued functions, Annals of Math., (2) 39, 1938, 913-944 ;

[4] R. Conti, Problems in linear control theory, to appear in the Proceedings of Equadiff II, Bratislava, Sept. 1966 ;

[5] P. L. Falb, Infinite dimensional control problems, I : The closure of the set of attainable states for linear systems, Jour. Math. Anal.

& Appls., 9, 1964, 12-22 ;
[6] H. O. Fattorini, Time-optimal control of solutions of operational differential equations, Jour. SIAM,Control, 2, 1964, 54-59 ;
[7] R. V. Gamkrelidze,On some extremal problems in the theory of differential equations with applications to the theory of optimal control, Jour. SIAM, Control, 3, 1965, 106-127 ;
[8] T. Kato,Nonlinear evolution equations in Banach spaces, A.M.S. Symposia in Appl. Math.,vol.17, 1965, 50-67 ;
[9] J. Kisinsky, Sur les opérateurs de Green des problèmes de Cauchy abstraits, Studia Math., 23, 1964, 285-328 ;
[10] W. L. Miranker, Approximate controllability for distributed linear systems, Jour. Math. Anal. & Appls.,10, 1965, 378-387 ;
[11] L. W. Neustadt, Optimization, a moment problem and nonlinear programming, Jour. SIAM, Control, 2, 1964, 33-53 ;
[12] W. A. Porter - J. P. Williams, A note on the minimum effort control problem, Jour. Math. Anal. & Appls.,13, 1966, 251-264 ;
[13] W. A. Porter, On the optimal control of distributive systems, Jour. SIAM, Control, 4, 1966, 466-472 ;
[14] E. T. Poulsen,Evolutionsgleichungen in Banach-Räumen, Math. Zeitschrift, 90, 1965, 286-309.

CONTROLLABILITY OF HIGHER ORDER LINEAR SYSTEMS

H. O. Fattorini*

Consejo Nacional de Investigaciones Cientificas y Tecnicas

and

University of Buenos Aires, Buenos Aires, Argentina

Introduction. We consider in this paper a dynamical system whose evolution in time is described by a second-order linear differential equation in a complex Banach space $E = \{u,v,...\}$

$$u''(t) = Au(t) + Bf(t) \qquad (1)$$

Here A is a linear, possibly unbounded operator with domain $D(A) \subseteq E$ and range in E, B a bounded operator from another Banach space F to E. We assume $\rho(A)$, the resolvent set of A to be non-void, i.e. there exists a λ such that $R(\lambda;A) = (\lambda I-A)^{-1}$ exists and is bounded. The state of the system at time t is given by the pair $(u(t),u'(t))$ of elements of E; the F-valued function $f(\cdot)$ is the input or control by means of which we govern the system.

The problem of complete controllability consists, roughly speaking, in selecting a control f in a given class $\mathcal{L}$ in such a way that the systems evolutions from a given initial state to the vicinity of a given final state. If the initial state is taken to be $(0,0)$ then the problem is that of null controllability. We introduce in

*Present Address: Center for Dynamical Systems, Division of Applied Mathematics, Brown University, Providence, R.I.

This Research was supported in part by the National Aeronautics and Space Administration under Grant No. NGR 40-002 -015 and in part by the Air Force Office of Scientific Research, Office of Aerospace Research U.S. Air Force under AFOSR Grant No. 693-66.

Section 1 some results on the theory of the equation (1) and apply them in Section 2 to show that the problem of complete controllability of the system (1) can be reduced to the corresponding one for the first-order system $u' = Au + Bf$ if A satisfies a certain condition (Condition (2.6)). Finally, we examine in Section 3 the relation between null and complete controllability for first and second-order systems. We shall use without proofs some results on controllability of first-order systems $u' = Au + Bf$; we refer to (6) for proofs and further details.

§1. Let $g(\cdot)$ be a E-valued, strongly continuous function defined for $t \geqq 0$. We shall understand by a <u>solution</u> of

$$u''(t) = Au(t) + g(t) \tag{1.1}$$

an E-valued function $u(\cdot)$ defined and with two continuous derivatives in $t \geqq 0$, such that $u(t) \in D(A)$ and Eq. (1.1) is satisfied for all $t \geqq 0$.

We shall assume that the Cauchy problem for the homogeneous equation

$$u''(t) = Au(t) \tag{1.2}$$

is <u>uniformly well posed</u> in $t \geqq 0$, i.e. we shall suppose that

(a) There exists a dense subspace D of E such that if $u_0, u_1 \in D$ there exists a solution $u(\cdot)$ of (1.2) with $u(0) = u_0, u'(0) = u_1$.

(b) For each $t \geqq 0$ there exists a constant $K_t < \infty$ such that

$$|u(s)| \leqq K_t(|u(0)| + |u'(0)|), \quad 0 \leqq s \leqq t$$

for any solution $u(\cdot)$ of (1.2)

Let $u \in D$, $u(\cdot)$ (resp. $v(\cdot)$) be a solution of Eq (1.2) with $u(0) = u, u'(0) = 0$ (resp. $v(0) = 0, v'(0) = u$). Define

$$S(t)u = u(t) \quad (\text{resp. } T(t)u = v(t))$$

By virtue of (a) and (b) $S(t), T(t)$ are well defined and bounded for all $t \geqq 0$, at least in D. Thus they can be extended to bounded operators in E that we shall denote with the same symbols. It follows from a simple approximation argument that $S(\cdot)$, $T(\cdot)$ are strongly continuous functions of t. We shall call S,T the solution operators of Eq. (1.2)

We take from (4), Section 4 the following properties of $A, R(\lambda;A), S(\cdot), T(\cdot)$.

(c) For each $u \in E$, $t \geq 0$

$$T(t)u = \int_0^t S(s)u\,ds \tag{1.3}$$

(d) There exist constants $w < \infty$, $K < \infty$ such that

$$|S(t)| \leq Ke^{wt}, \quad |T(t)| \leq Ke^{wt}, \quad t \geq 0$$

(e) $\sigma(A)$, the spectrum of A is contained in the region $\{\lambda^2; \operatorname{Re}\lambda \leq w\} = \{\lambda; \operatorname{Re}\lambda \leq w^2 - (\operatorname{Im}\lambda)^2/4w^2\}$ and

$$R(\lambda^2;A)u = \lambda^{-1}\int_0^\infty e^{-\lambda t}S(t)u\,dt = \int_0^\infty e^{-\lambda t}T(t)u\,dt \tag{1.4}$$

for $\operatorname{Re}\lambda > w$.

With the help of $T(\cdot)$ we can construct solutions of the inhomogeneous equation (1.1). In fact, we have

LEMMA 1.1. *Let $g(\cdot)$ be continuously differentiable.* Then

$$u(t) = \int_0^t T(t-s)g(s)\,ds \tag{1.5}$$

is a solution of Eq. (1.1) with $u(0) = u'(0) = 0$.

The proof is substantially similar to the one for the analogous result in first order equations ((7), Lemma 6.1) and is therefore omitted. Let us observe that in computing the first derivative of $u(\cdot)$ we obtain

$$u'(t) = \int_0^t S(t-s)g(s)\,ds \tag{1.6}$$

We close this section with another result on the equation (1.2). Let $E^* = \{u^*, v^*, \ldots\}$ be the dual space of E; denote $\langle u^*, u\rangle$ the value of the functional u^* at the point $u \in E$.

LEMMA 1.2. *Let E be reflexive. Then the Cauchy problem for the equation*

$$(u^*)''(t) = A^*u^*(t) \tag{1.7}$$

is uniformly well posed. If $S^*(\cdot), T^*(\cdot)$ are the solution operators of Eq. (1.7) we have $S^*(t) = (S(t))^*$, $T^*(t) = (T(t))^*$, where S, T are the solution operators of (1.2).

The proof is a consequence of the characterization of operators A for which the Cauchy problem for (1.2) is well posed (4), Theorem 5.9). We shall assume throughout the rest of this paper that E is reflexive so that Lemma 1.2 applies.

§2. Let $E^2 = E \times E$ be the space of all pairs (u_o, u_1) of elements of E endowed with pointwise operations and any of its natural norms, for instance $|(u_o, u_1)| = |u_o| + |u_1|$. The dual space $(E^2)^*$ can be identified algebraically and topologically with the space $(E^*)^2$, application of the functional $u^* = (u_o^*, u_1^*)$ to the element $u = (u_o, u_1)$ being given by

$$\langle u^*, u\rangle = \langle u_o^*, u_o\rangle + \langle u_1^*, u_1\rangle$$

Let the linear control system

$$u''(t) = Au(t) + Bf(t) \tag{2.1}$$

(which we shall denote L) be given. We shall assume the class by $\mathcal{L}$ of controls to consist of all infinitely differentiable functions with values in F defined in $[0, \infty)$. Call $K_t(L)$, $t \geq 0$ the subspace of E^2 consisting of all pairs (u_o, u_1),

$$u_o = \int_0^t T(t-s)Bf(s)ds, \quad u_1 = \int_0^t S(t-s)Bf(s)ds \tag{2.2}$$

In view of Lemma 1, $K_t(L)$ can be described as the subspace of all pairs $(u(t), u'(t)), u(\cdot)$ a solution of Eq. (2.1) with $u(0) = u'(0) = 0$, $f \in \mathcal{L}$ or simply as the subspace of all possible states of the system at time t - the initial state being $(0,0)$ for $t = 0$. We also define $K(L) = \bigcup_{t>0} K_t(L)$. We shall say that the system L is <u>null controllable</u> if $\mathrm{Cl}\, K(L) = E^2$, <u>null controllable at time</u> t_o if $\mathrm{Cl}\, K_{t_o}(L) = E^2$. It is a consequence of the Hahn-Banach theorem that $\mathrm{Cl}\, K(L) = E^2$ if and only if $K(L)^{\perp} = \{(u_o^*, u_1^*) \in (E^*)^2;\ \langle (u_o^*, u_1^*), (u_o, u_1) \rangle = 0$ for all $(u_o, u_1) \in K(L)\} = 0$, $\mathrm{Cl}\, K_t(L) = E$ if $K_t(L)^{\perp} = 0$, $K_t(L)^{\perp}$ similarly defined.

Our first result is analogous to Proposition 2.1 in (6) and it is proved just in the same way.

<u>LEMMA 2.1</u>. $(u_o^*, u_1^*) \in K(L)^{\perp} (K_t(L)^{\perp})$ <u>if and only if</u>

$$B^*(T^*(s)u_o + S^*(s)u_1^*) = 0,\ 0 \leqq s\ (0 \leqq s \leqq t) \quad (2.3)$$

Let us denote $\rho_o(A)$ the connected component of $\rho(A)$ that contains the half-plane $\mathrm{Re}\, \lambda > w^2$ (w the constant in (d), Section 1)

<u>COROLLARY 2.2</u>. $(u_o^*, u_1^*) \in K(L)^{\perp}$ <u>if and only if</u>

$$B^* R(\lambda; A^*)(u_o^* + \lambda^{\frac{1}{2}} u_1^*) = 0 \quad \text{for} \quad \lambda \in \rho_o(A) \quad (2.4)$$

$(\arg \lambda^{\frac{1}{2}} = \frac{1}{2} \arg \lambda,\ -\pi < \arg \lambda < \pi$.

<u>Proof</u> We obtain (2.4) for λ real, $\lambda^{\frac{1}{2}} > w$ integrating $\exp(-\lambda^{\frac{1}{2}} t) B^*(T^*(s)u_o^* + S^*(s)u_1^*)$ in $(0,\infty)$ and applying (1.4) and Lemma 2.1. For $\lambda \in \rho_o(A)$ the result follows from an analytic continuation argument. The reverse implication is, as in (6), Corollary 2.2, a consequence of uniqueness of Laplace transforms.

We shall also consider in what follows the first order system M,

$$u'(t) = Au(t) + Bf(t) \quad (2.5)$$

Now $K_t(M)$ is defined as the subspace of E consisting of all values (at time t) of solutions of (2.5) such that $u(0) = 0$, $f \in \mathcal{L}, K(M), K(M)^{\perp}, K_t(M)^{\perp}$ are defined in a way similar to that for second-order systems (see (6) for more details)

THEOREM 2.3. *Assume A satisfies the condition*

$$\text{there exists a simple closed curve } C \text{ entirely contained in } \rho_o(A) \text{ and such that the origin is contained in the interior of } C \tag{2.6}$$

Then $K(L) = \{(u_o, u_1);\ u_o, u_1 \in K(M)\}$

Proof. Obviously we only have to prove $K(L)^{\perp} = \{(u_o^*, u_1^*); u_o^*, u_1^* \in K(M)\}$. We shall use the following characterization of the elements of $K(M)$ (see (6), Corollary 2.2); $u^* \in K(M)$ if and only if $B^*R(\lambda;A^*)u^* = 0, \lambda \in \rho_o(A)$. This makes clear that if $u_o^*, u_1^* \in K(M)^{\perp}$ then $(u_o^*, u_1^*) \in K(L)^{\perp}$. Conversely, assume $(u_o^*, u_1^*) \in K(L)^{\perp}$. Consider (2.4) for a given $\lambda \in C$. As λ turns once around the origin and returns to its original value, $\lambda^{1/2}$ changes sign. Adding up the two versions of (2.4) so obtained we get $B^*R(\lambda;A^*)u_o^* = B^*R(\lambda;A^*)u_1^* = 0$ for $\lambda \in C$; by analytic continuation this holds as well as for all $\lambda \in \rho_o(A)$, which ends the proof.

COROLLARY 2.4. *Assume A satisfies Condition (2.6). Then the control system L is null controllable if and only if M is null controllable.*

REMARK 2.5. If Condition (2.6) is not satisfied then Theorem 2.3 may fail to hold. We construct in what follows an example of this situation.

$L^2 = L^2_y(-\infty, \infty) = \{u(y), v(y), \ldots\}$. Recall that the space H^2 of the upper half-plane consists of all those functions in L^2 that are boundary values of functions $u(y+i\phi)$, holomorphic in the upper half-plane and such that

$$\sup_{\phi>0} \int |u(y+i\phi|^2 dy < \infty$$

(all integrals hereafter shall be taken on $(-\infty,\infty)$). By the Paley-Wiener theorem ((2), Chapter 8) H^2 consists of all those function in L^2 whose Fourier-Plancherel transform vanish for $t \geqq 0$, i.e. of those $u(\cdot)$ in L^2 such that

$$\hat{u}(t) = (2\pi)^{-\frac{1}{2}} \int u(y)e^{iyt}dy = 0 \quad \text{for} \quad t \geqq 0$$

We shall make use of the following

LEMMA 2.6. *Let* $m \in L^2$, $m \geqq 0$, $m \neq 0$. *There exists* $u \in H^2$ *such that* $|u(y)| = m(y)$ *if and only if*

$$\int |\log m(y)| \ (1+y^2)^{-1}dy < \infty.$$

For a proof for H^2 of the unit circle see (3), Theorem 7.33; it can be adapted to the case of the half-plane by using the results in (2), Chapter 8.

COROLLARY 2.7. Let $\{a_{ij}(y)\}$, $i,j = 1,2$ be a 2×2 matrix of functions in L^2. Assume

$$\int |\log |\det \{a_{ij}(y)\}|| \ (1+y^2)dy < \infty. \tag{2.8}$$

Then there exist v_1, v_2, both different from zero almost everywhere and such that

$$v_1 a_{i1} + v_2 a_{i2} \in H^2, \ i = 1,2 \tag{2.9}$$

Proof. Let $w_1 = (a_{22}-a_{12})b, w_2 = (a_{11}-a_{21})b$, where $b(y)^{-1} = \text{sgn} \det \{a_{ij}(y)\}$. We have

$$w_1 a_{11} + w_2 a_{12} = w_1 a_{21} + w_2 a_{22} = |\det \{a_{ij}\}|$$

In view of Lemma 2.6 there exists $u \in H^2$ such that $|\det \{a_{ij}(y)\}| = |u(y)|$. Thus if we set $v_i = w_i \text{ sgn } u$, $i = 1,2, v_1, v_2$ satisfy (2.9)

Let us now pass to the example. Let $E = L^2 =$

$=L^2(-\infty,\infty) = \{u(x),v(x),\ldots\}$ A_r, r real, the (self-adjoint) operator defined by

$$(A_r u)(x) = u''(x) + ru(x) \qquad (2.10)$$

$D(A_r) = \{u \in L^2; u'' \in L^2\}$ (u'' understood in the sense of distributions), $F = C^2 = \{(y_1,y_2),\ldots\}$ two dimensional unitary space, $f(t) = (f_1(t),f_2(t)), B(y_1,y_2)(x) = y_1 g_1(x) + y_2 g_2(x)$, g_1, g_2 elements of L^2 to be determined later.

The Fourier-Plancherel transform $u(x) \leftrightarrow \hat{u}(s)$ defines an isometric isomorphism of L^2 onto itself under which the operator A_r transforms in the multiplication operator

$$(\hat{A}_r u)(s) = (-s^2+r)u(s). \qquad (2.11)$$

Thus we may consider $E = L_s^2(-\infty,\infty) = \{u(s),v(s),\ldots\}$, A_r defined by (2.11), $B(y_1,y_2) = y_1 h_1(s) + y_2 h_2(s)$, $h_1 = g_1$, $h_2 = g_2$. The adjoint of B is given by $B^*u = (y_1(u), y_2(u))$,

$$y_i(u) = \int u(s)k_i(s)ds, \ i = 1,2$$

(here we have set $k_i = \bar{h}_i$). It is not difficult to see that the Cauchy problem for $u'' = A_r u$ is uniformly well posed for any r, the propagators being given by

$$S_r(t)u(s) = a(r,s,t)u(s), T_r(t)u(s) = b(r,s,t)u(s),$$

where $a(r,s,t) = \cosh (r-s^2)^{\frac{1}{2}}t$, $b(r,s,t) = (r-s^2)^{-\frac{1}{2}}\sinh (r-s^2)^{\frac{1}{2}}t$.

The spectrum of A_r consists of the half-line $(-\infty,r]$; thus if $r < 0$ condition (2.6) is satisfied. By Theorem 2.3 the system

$$u''(t) = A_r u(t) + Bf(t) \qquad (2.12)$$

is null controllable if and only if

$$u'(t) = A_r u(t) + Bf(t) \qquad (2.13)$$

is null controllable. For $r = 0$ the system (2.13) has been considered in (5), Section 4; it is null controllable when and only when

$$h_1(s)h_2(-s) - h_1(-s)h_2(s) \neq 0 \quad \text{a.e.} \tag{2.14}$$

It is easy to see that the result holds as well for any r (null controllability is "translation invariant" for first order systems). Condition (2.14) holds for instance when $g_1(x) = \exp(-|x|)$, $g_2(x) = \exp(-|x+1|)$; then $h_1(s) = 2(1+s^2)^{-1}$, $h_2(s) = 2(1+s^2)^{-1}\exp(-is)$ and the expression on the left-hand side of (2.14) reduces to $8i(1+s^2)^{-2}\sin s$.

Let us now examine the system (2.12) for $r \geq 0$ with the same choice of g_1, g_2. Let $u_o, u_1 \in L^2_s$. It is plain that Eq. (2.3) will hold for them if and only if

$$\int (a(r,s,t)u_1(s) + b(r,s,t)u_o(s))k_i(s)ds = 0 \tag{2.15}$$

$i = 1,2$, $t \geq 0$. It is easy to see by means of a simple change of variables that the part of the integral on the left-hand side of (2.15) extending over $|s| \geq r^{\frac{1}{2}}$ can be written

$$\int (\cos yt\tilde{u}_1(y) + y^{-1}\sin yt\tilde{u}_o(y))\tilde{k}_i(y)dy \tag{2.16}$$

where $u(s) \leftrightarrow \tilde{u}(y)$ is the isometric isomorphism of $L^2(|s| \geq r^{\frac{1}{2}})$ onto L^2_y given by

$$\tilde{u}(y) = |y|^{1/2}(y^2+r)^{-1/4}u((y^2+r)^{1/2}\operatorname{sgn} y) \tag{2.17}$$

If $\tilde{u}_o(y)/y$ is summable at the origin we can write (2.16) as follows:

$$\frac{1}{2}\int e^{iyt}(v_1(y)\tilde{k}_i(y) + v_o(y)\tilde{k}_i(-y))dy, \tag{2.18}$$

$v_1(y) = \tilde{u}_1(y) - i\tilde{u}_o(y)/y$, $v_2(y) = \tilde{u}_1(-y) - i\tilde{u}_o(-y)/y$. Call now $a_{ij}(y) = k_i((-1)^j y)$, $i,j = 1,2$. The matrix $\{a_{ij}\}$ so defined satisfies the assumptions in Corollary 2.7 and thus there exist v_1, v_2 in L^2, $v_1 \neq 0$ such that Eq. (2.9) holds. It is plain that Eq. (2.9) holds as well for $w_i(y) = v_i(y)(i+y)^{-1}$. If we now define $\tilde{u}_1(y) = \frac{1}{2}(w_1(y) + w_2(-y))$, $\tilde{u}_o(y) = \frac{1}{2}iy(w_1(y) - w_2(-y))$ then $\tilde{u}_o, \tilde{u}_1 \in L^2$ and Eq. (2.18) - a fortiori (2.16) vanishes for $t \geq 0$. Taking now u_o, u_1 to be the inverse images of $\tilde{u}_o, \tilde{u}_1$ under the map (2.17) and extending them to the entire real axis by setting $u_i = 0$ in $|s| \leq r^{\frac{1}{2}}$ we obtain two non-vanishing elements of L^2 such that Eq. (2.15) holds, which shows that the system (2.12) is not null controllable for $r \geq 0$.

REMARK 2.6. Our results on density of $K(L)$ generalize to other topologies. Let $m > 0$, let E_1, E_2 be Banach spaces contained in E, invariant with respect to S, T and such that $D(A^m) \subseteq E_1$, $D(A^{m-1}) \subseteq E_2$, the inclusions being continuous and with dense image ($D(A^m)$, $D(A^{m-1})$ endowed with the usual graph topologies). Assume, moreover, that $S(\cdot)$, $T(\cdot)$ are strongly continuous in E_i, $i = 0,1$ and that $B(F) \subseteq D(A^{m-1})$. Then it is not difficult to show that if the system (2.5) is null controllable (in the topology of E) and A satisfies Condition (2.6) then the system (2.1) is null controllable <u>in the topology of</u> $E_1 \times E_2$).

§3. Let us call the system (2.1) <u>completely controllable</u> if, given $u_o, u_1 \in D$, $v_o, v_1 \in E$, $\epsilon > 0$ there exists $f \in \mathcal{L}$ such that the solution of Eq. (2.1) with $u(0) = u_o$, $u'(0) = u_1$ satisfies

$$|u(t) - v_o| \leq \epsilon \quad |u'(t) - v_1| \leq \epsilon.$$

for some $t \geq 0$. It is plain that complete controllability of (2.1) implies null controllability. The reverse implication is also true; this follows from the fact that the solutions of Eq. (2.1) can be translated and inverted in time, i.e. if $u(\cdot)$ is a solution of Eq. (2.1) for some

$f(\cdot)$ then $v(t) = u(a-t)$ is also a solution of Eq. (2.1) for $g(t) = f(a-t)$. Thus to steer the system from (u_o, u_1) to the vicinity of (v_o, v_1) we only have to steer first to the vicinity of the origin (using null controllability and the inversion property just mentioned) and then from the origin to the vicinity of (v_o, v_1). The situation is different for first-order systems; in fact such a system may be null controllable without being completely controllable. There are, however, two important cases where the equivalence holds: these are (a) A generates an analytic semigroup and (b) A generates a group and $\rho_o(A) = \rho_o(-A)$, this last condition meaning that we can unite the points $-\infty$ and $+\infty$ of the real axis by means of a curve in the complex plane that does not meet the spectrum of A.

References

1. E. HILLE-R. S. PHILLIPS, Functional Analysis and Semigroups, American Mathematical Society Colloquium Publications, vol. XXXI, Providence, Rhode Island, 1957.

2. K. HOFFMAN, Banach space of analytic functions, Prentice-Hall, Englewood Cliffs, New Jersey, 1962.

3. A. ZYGMUND, Trigonometric series, second edition, vol. 1, Cambridge University Press, Cambridge, 1959.

4. H. O. FATTORINI, Ordinary differential equations in linear topological spaces, submitted for publication to J. Diff. Eq. Announcement of results in: Notices of the Amer. Math. Soc. Abstract 66T-474 (vol. 13) 734, Abstract 67T-41 (vol. 14), 140.

5. _______________, On complete controllability of linear systems, to appear in Journal of Differential Equations 3 (1967).

6. _______________, Some remarks on complete controllability, J. Soc. Ind. Appl. Math., ser. A: On Control, 4 (1966), 686-694.

7. R. S. PHILLIPS, Perturbation theory for semi-groups of linear operators, Trans. Amer. Math. Soc. 74 (1953), 199-221.

ON BOUNDARY-VALUE CONTROLLABILITY OF LINEAR SYMMETRIC HYPERBOLIC SYSTEMS*

David L. Russell

Department of Mathematics and Computer Sciences, University of Wisconsin, Madison, Wisconsin

§0. Introduction.

Many important systems arising in physics and engineering may be described by partial differential equations of the form

$$E(x)\frac{\partial u}{\partial t} = A(x)\frac{\partial u}{\partial x} + C(x)u \ . \tag{0}$$

Here u is an n-vector, x, t are scalar variables, while $E(x)$, $A(x)$, $C(x)$ are n by n matrices, $A(x)$ being symmetric and positive definite. These are linear symmetric hyperbolic systems in two independent variables.

In this paper we examine the question of controllability of such a system by means of forces applied at the boundaries $x = 0$ and $x = 1$ of the system. Our methods are constructive and corresponding numerical methods are available (see [3], [4]).

A very general treatment of systems of the form (0) is possible. Were this to be attempted here, however, notational and graphical complexities would probably create more confusion than clarification. We have chosen to deal with two systems familiar in applied mathematics; namely, the wave equation (vibrating string equation) and Timoshenko's equation for the vibrating beam. The results for the latter system are quite typical for systems (0) in general.

---

* Supported in part by N. S. F. Grant No. GP-6070 and in part by Honeywell, Inc., St. Paul, Minn.

Controllability of the Timoshenko Beam

Timoshenko's model of a vibrating beam consists of the partial differential equations

$$\frac{\partial}{\partial x}\left(E(x)I(x)\frac{\partial \psi}{\partial x}\right) + k(x)\left(\frac{\partial y}{\partial x} - \psi\right) - I\rho(x)\frac{\partial^2 \psi}{\partial t^2} = 0\ , \tag{1}$$

$$\rho(x)\frac{\partial^2 y}{\partial t^2} - \frac{\partial}{\partial x}\left(k(x)\left(\frac{\partial y}{\partial x} - \psi\right)\right) = 0\ .$$

A derivation of these equations and an explanation of the physical meaning of the various symbols may be found in [5], for example. Define a vector u with components

$$u_1 = \frac{\partial \psi}{\partial t},\quad u_2 = \frac{\partial \psi}{\partial x},\quad u_3 = \frac{\partial y}{\partial t},\quad u_4 = \frac{\partial y}{\partial x} - \psi\ , \tag{2}$$

and the equations (1) become equivalent to

$$\frac{\partial u}{\partial t} = \begin{pmatrix} 0 & \frac{EI}{I\rho} & 0 & 0 \\ 1 & 0 & 0 & 0 \\ 0 & 0 & 0 & \frac{k}{\rho} \\ 0 & 0 & 1 & 0 \end{pmatrix} \frac{\partial u}{\partial x} + \begin{pmatrix} 0 & \frac{(EI)'}{I\rho} & 0 & \frac{k}{I\rho} \\ 0 & 0 & 0 & 0 \\ 0 & 0 & 0 & \frac{k'}{\rho} \\ -1 & 0 & 0 & 0 \end{pmatrix} u\ . \tag{3}$$

Here $'$ denotes $\frac{d}{dx}$ and, for brevity, the argument x has been suppressed in the notation. There are four control functions $f_0(t)$, $g_0(t)$, $f_1(t)$, $g_1(t)$ corresponding to moments and laterally directed forces at each end of the beam, leading to the boundary conditions

$$u_2(0,t) \equiv f_0(t),\ u_4(0,t) \equiv g_0(t),\ u_2(1,t) \equiv f_1(t),\ u_4(1,t) \equiv g_1(t)\ . \tag{4}$$

The problem, given initial conditions

$$u(x,0) = u_0(x) \tag{5}$$

satisfying a Lipschitz condition on $[0,1]$, is to determine controls (4) so that the resulting solution $u(x,t)$ in $D = \{(x,t) \mid 0 \le x \le 1,\ 0 \le t \le T\}$ satisfies

$$u(x,T) \equiv 0. \tag{6}$$

If, for a given time $T > 0$, this is possible for all such initial conditions $u_0(x)$ the system (3) is controllable in time T.

There are four families C_1, C_2, C_3, C_4 of characteristic curves c_1, c_2, c_3, c_4 in the plane satisfying differential equations

$$\frac{dx}{dt} = c(x), \quad \frac{dx}{dt} = -c(x), \quad \frac{dx}{dt} = \tilde{c}(x), \quad \frac{dx}{dt} = -\tilde{c}(x) \tag{7}$$

where $c(x) = \left(\frac{E(x)I(x)}{I\rho(x)}\right)^{1/2}$, $\tilde{c}(x) = \left(\frac{k(x)}{\rho(x)}\right)^{1/2}$. Here $c(x)$ and $\tilde{c}(x)$ are strictly positive on $[0,1]$ and thus there are unique times $T_1, T_2 > 0$ such that the solutions $x(t), \tilde{x}(t)$ of $\frac{dx}{dt} = c(x)$, $\frac{dx}{dt} = \tilde{c}(x)$, respectively, satisfying $x(0) = \tilde{x}(0) = 0$, also satisfy $x(T_1) = \tilde{x}(T_2) = 0$. We are going to proceed under the assumption

$$c(x) > \tilde{c}(x), \quad x \in [0,1]. \quad (\text{Thus } T_2 > T_1 > 0.) \tag{8}$$

The case $\tilde{c}(x) > c(x)$ could be treated equally well.

Consider now the differential operators

$$D_1 = \frac{\partial}{\partial t} + c(x)\frac{\partial}{\partial x}, \; D_2 = \frac{\partial}{\partial t} - c(x)\frac{\partial}{\partial x}, \; D_3 = \frac{\partial}{\partial t} + \tilde{c}(x)\frac{\partial}{\partial x}, \; D_4 = \frac{\partial}{\partial t} - c(x)\frac{\partial}{\partial x}, \tag{9}$$

corresponding to differentiations with respect to t along characteristics in C_1, C_2, C_3, C_4, respectively, together with new variables

$$v_1 = u_1 - c(x)u_2, \; v_2 = u_1 + c(x)u_2, \; v_3 = u_3 - \tilde{c}(x)u_4, \; v_4 = u_3 + \tilde{c}(x)u_4. \tag{10}$$

The system (3) then assumes the "characteristic normal form"

$$D_1 v_1 = a_1(v_2 - v_1) + b_1(v_4 - v_3), \quad D_2 v_2 = a_1(v_2 - v_1) + b_1(v_4 - v_3)$$

$$D_3 v_3 = a_2(v_1 + v_2) + b_2(v_4 - v_3), \quad D_4 v_4 = -a_2(v_1 + v_2) + b_2(v_4 - v_3) \tag{11}$$

where a_1, a_2, b_1, b_2 are readily calculated expressions involving the entries of the matrices in (3).

We consider characteristic curves passing through the

vertices of the rectangle D, as shown in Figs. 1, 2. The domains D_1 and D_2 bounded by c_1, c_2, $t = 0$ and c_1^*, c_2^*, $t = T$, respectively are the domains of determinacy for the initial and terminal conditions (5) and (6), respectively. When $T < T_1$ (see Fig. 1) the domains D_1 and D_2 overlap in a domain $\hat{D}$. In general $u(x, t)$ as determined by (5) in D_1 and by (6) in D_2 will disagree in $\hat{D}$. Thus, in general, there is no solution $u(x, t)$ of (3) satisfying both (5) and (6) and we conclude the system (3) is not controllable in time $T < T_1$. Applying some results communicated to the author by J. L. Lions we can go further and show that this remains true for $T < T_2$. So we consider now only the cases $T \geq T_2$. Here, as in Fig. 2, we must concern ourselves with six domains $D_1, D_2, D_3, D_4, D_5, D_6$. When $T = T_2$ the line segment ℓ shown in Fig. 2 reduces to a point p. For clarity the characteristics in Fig. 2 are shown as straight lines. In general they are curves but the geometry is similar.

Again, given initial conditions (5) and terminal conditions (6) determining $u(x, t)$ uniquely in D_1 and D_2 respectively, our problem is to extend the solution into the remainder of the rectangle D, i. e. into D_3, D_4, D_5, D_6. The resulting values of $u_2(x, t)$, $u_4(x, t)$ on the lines $x = 0$, $x = 1$ will yield the control functions (4).

We will give here an indication as to how the solution may be extended into the domain D_3. The extension into D_4 is done in exactly the same way while the extensions into D_5 and D_6 require only minor changes in the method and are, in fact, simpler. The extension into D_3 will be described in terms of the variables v_i appearing in (11).

The domain D_3 is subdivided into smaller domains by means of characteristic curves as shown in Fig. 2. Given any $h > 0$ this subdivision can be carried out so that the maximum diameter of any subdomain so produced is $< h$. The solution is extended into these domains one at a time in the order indicated by the numbering in Fig. 2. We begin with the domain Δ_1, (numbered 1 in Fig. 2), shown enlarged in Fig. 3. The solution $u(x, t)$ is already known in D_1. On the line ℓ_1 (see Fig. 2) we select arbitrary (but absolutely continuous with respect to t) values of v_1 and v_2. Next we let p denote a point in Δ_1. Characteristic curves $c_1(p)$, $c_2(p)$, $c_3(p)$, $c_4(p)$ join p to points $\overline{p}_1, \overline{p}_2, \overline{p}_3, \overline{p}_4$, respectively on the boundary of D_1 or on ℓ_1 as indicated. This is done in such a way that $v_1(\overline{p}_1)$, $v_2(\overline{p}_2)$, $v_3(\overline{p}_3)$, $v_4(\overline{p}_4)$ are already known, either from the known solution in D_1 or the choice of v_1 and v_2 on ℓ_1. Points along the curves $c_i(p)$ are parametrized by t and written $p_i(t)$. Fig. 3 shows how this is done in the case of two different points, p and p'.

We now let W denote the space of all continuous four-dimensional vector valued functions $w(x, t)$ defined on Δ_1 with components w_i, $i = 1, 2, 3, 4$, such that

$$w_i(\overline{p}_i) = v_i(\overline{p}_i), \quad i = 1, 2, 3, 4. \tag{12}$$

Supplied with the familiar "sup" norm, W becomes a complete metric space. We take $u^0(x, t)$ to be an arbitrary element of W and define a sequence $\{v^k\}$ in W by

$$v_1^{k+1}(p) = v_1(\overline{p}_1) + \int_{c_1(p)} [a_1(x(t))(v_2^k(p(t)) - v_1^k(p(t))) + b_1(x(t))(v_4^k(p(t)) - v_3^k(p(t)))]\, dt$$

$$v_2^{k+1}(p) = v_2(\overline{p}_2) + \int_{c_2(p)} [a_1(x(t))(v_2^k(p(t)) - v_1^k(p(t))) + b_1(x(t))(v_4^k(p(t)) - v_3^k(p(t)))]\, dt$$

$$v_3^{k+1}(p) = v_3(\overline{p}_3) + \int_{c_3(p)} [a_2(x(t))(v_1^k(p(t)) + v_2^k(p(t))) + b_2(x(t))(v_4^k(p(t)) - v_3^k(p(t)))]\, dt$$

$$v_4^{k+1}(p) = v_4(\overline{p}_4) + \int_{c_4(p)} [-a_2(x(t))(v_1^k(p(t)) + v_2^k(p(t))) + b_2(x(t))(v_4^k(p(t)) - v_3^k(p(t)))]\, dt\,, \tag{13}$$

where the components of v^k are $v_1^k, v_2^k, v_3^k, v_4^k$.

If the diameter of Δ_1 is sufficiently small, application of the familiar contraction fixed point theorem readily shows the sequence $\{v^k\}$ converges uniformly in Δ_1 to a solution $v(x, t)$ of (11), which then provides the desired extensions of $u(x, t)$ from D_1 into Δ_1. This process may now be repeated in the other small subdomains of D_3, in the order indicated in Fig. 2. The equations (13) will remain the same in all cases and the points $\overline{p}_i$ will always lie on the boundary of a subdomain of D_3 in which $u(x, t)$ has already been constructed.

As remarked previously, the extension into D_5 and D_6 proceeds similarly with a different collection of subdomains. When $T > T_2$ one must arbitrarily assign values to all four functions v_1, v_2, v_3, v_4 on the line segment ℓ before this can be done.

Thus, to summarize, if $T < T_2$, the system (3) is not controllable in time T. If $T \geq T_2$ the system (3) is controllable in time T and the controls $f_0(t)$, $g_0(t)$, $f_1(t)$, $g_1(t)$ are given by the relations (4) after the solution $u(x, t)$ has been extended from the domains of determinacy D_1 and D_2 into the whole rectangle D as indicated above. Strangely enough, the controls, when they exist, are never unique. When $T = T_2$ they depend upon arbitrary values assigned to v_1 and v_2 on ℓ_1 and ℓ_2 and when $T > T_2$ they also depend upon arbitrary values assigned to v_1, v_2, v_3 and v_4 on ℓ.

If controls are applied at only one end of the beam, say by requiring

$$u_2(0, t) \equiv u_4(0, t) \equiv 0, \quad u_2(1, t) \equiv f(t), \quad u_4(1, t) \equiv g(t), \tag{14}$$

it can readily be shown that the system (3) is controllable in time T if and only if $T \geq 2T_2$ and the controls, when they exist, are, again, never unique.

The control situation for general linear symmetric hyperbolic systems of even dimension with paired characteristics is quite similar to that described above for the Timoshenko beam. The construction of controls requires the extension of the solution from the domains of determinacy of the initial and terminal conditions through a succession of V-shaped domains similar to D_3 and D_4 and finally to the boundaries $x = 0$, $x = 1$ through domains similar to D_5 and D_6. Variations of this approach may be expected to work even if characteristics are not paired. In the case of paired characteristics the system will, in general, be controllable in time $T = \hat{T}$, where $\hat{T}$ is the time required for the slowest waves in the medium to pass from $x = 0$ to $x = 1$.

Application to Optimization Problems.

The method for studying controllability described above can also be useful in optimization problems. We shall give an illustration of what we mean in the case of one boundary control of the vibrating string equation

$$\rho(x)\frac{\partial^2 w}{\partial t^2} - \frac{\partial}{\partial x}\left(p(x)\frac{\partial w}{\partial x}\right) = 0 . \tag{15}$$

The left end of the string is free while the right end is acted upon by a force $f(t)$. Thus the boundary conditions are

$$p(0)\frac{\partial w}{\partial x}(0, t) \equiv 0, \qquad p(1)\frac{\partial w}{\partial x}(1, t) \equiv f(t) . \tag{16}$$

Defining a vector u with components u_1, u_2 by

$$u_1 = \frac{\partial w}{\partial t}, \qquad u_2 = p(x)\frac{\partial w}{\partial x}, \tag{17}$$

(15) and (16) may be replaced by

$$\begin{pmatrix} \rho(x) & 0 \\ 0 & \frac{1}{p(x)} \end{pmatrix}\frac{\partial u}{\partial t} = \begin{pmatrix} 0 & 1 \\ 1 & 0 \end{pmatrix}\frac{\partial u}{\partial x}, \tag{18}$$

$$u_2(0, t) \equiv 0, \qquad u_2(1, t) \equiv f(t) . \tag{19}$$

There are two families of characteristics C_1 and C_2 consisting of curves c_1 and c_2 which obey

$$\frac{dx}{dt} = c(x) = \sqrt{\frac{p(x)}{\rho(x)}}, \qquad \frac{dx}{dt} = -c(x), \tag{20}$$

respectively. There is a unique positive number T_1 such that the solution of the first equation in (20) satisfying $x(0) = 0$ satisfies $x(T_1) = 1$. T_1 is the wave propagation time. It is easy to see that the system (18) is controllable in time $T > 0$ if and only if $T \geq 2T_1$. The geometry of the problem is exhibited by Fig. 4 for $T > 2T_1$. The domains of determinacy of the initial and terminal conditions are D_1 and D_2 respectively. On that segment, ℓ, of the line $x = 0$ lying between these domains the component $u_1(0, t)$ of the solution can be chosen arbitrarily. We require now, in addition to $u(x, T) \equiv 0$, that the least possible "energy" be used in controlling the string, i. e., that

$$C(u) = \int_0^T u_2(1, t)^2 dt = \int_0^T f(t)^2 dt \tag{21}$$

be as small as possible.

Let us suppose the function $u_1^*(0, t)$ on ℓ leads to an optimal solution $u^*(x, t)$ in D. If we make any other choice $u_1(0, t)$ on ℓ we will obtain a solution $u(x, t)$ such that $C(u) \geq C(u^*)$. Now, since the initial and terminal conditions are fixed beforehand, $u(x, t) - u^*(x, t) = \epsilon\, w(x, t)$ where $w(x, t)$ is a solution of (18) which is nonzero only in the domain D_3. If we require that $|\epsilon|$ be small the condition $C(u) \geq C(u^*)$ implies that

$$\int_0^T u_2^*(1, t) w_2(1, t) dt = 0 \tag{22}$$

for all $w_2(1, t)$ arising from the various choices of $u_1(0, t)$ on ℓ. We introduce now a solution $v(x, t)$ of (18) which satisfies at $x = 1$ the conditions

$$v_1(1, t) \equiv u_2^*(1, t), \qquad v_2(1, t) \equiv 0 \ . \tag{23}$$

The solution $v(x, t)$ exists and is unique in all of D_3. If we denote by $L(u) = 0$ the equation (18) and apply the divergence theorem to the integral in the equations

$$\iint_{D_3} [v^T(x, t) L(w(x, t)) + (L(v(x, t)))^T w(x, t)]\, dxdt = 0 \tag{24}$$

we arrive at

$$0 = \int_0^T u_2^*(1,t)w_2(1,t)dt = \int_\ell v_2(0,t)w_1(0,t)dt. \qquad (25)$$

(Some elementary theory of hyperbolic partial differential equations is used to show that the integrals over c_2 and c_1^* which arise when the divergence theorem is applied to (24) vanish.) Since this must be true for all $w_1(0,t)$ we conclude

$$v_2(0,t) \equiv 0 \quad \text{on } \ell . \qquad (26)$$

Thus the function $u_1^*(0,t)$ defined on ℓ leads to an optimal solution $u^*(x,t)$ in the sense that $C(u)$ is minimized only if the solution $v(x,t)$ of (18) determined by $u^*(x,t)$ through the relations (23) satisfies (26). In this case one readily verifies that this condition is also sufficient for optimality. When $p(x)$ and $\rho(x)$ are constant this information can be used in a fairly straightforward way to calculate $u_1^*(0,t)$ on ℓ explicitly in terms of the initial conditions imposed at $t = 0$.

REFERENCES

[1] R. Courant and D. Hilbert: "Methods of Mathematical Physics, Vol. II, Partial Differential Equations", Interscience Pub. Co., New York, 1962, Chap. V.

[2] D. Russell: "Optimal Regulation of Linear Symmetric Hyperbolic Systems with Finite Dimensional Controls" SIAM Jour. on Control, Vol. 4, No. 2, 1966.

[3] G. Forsythe and W. Wasow: "Finite-Difference Methods for Partial Differential Equations", Wiley New York, 1960.

[4] L. Collatz: "The Numerical Treatment of Differential Equations", Springer-Verlag, New York, 1966.

[5] Y. C. Fung: "Foundations of Solid Mechanics", Prentice-Hall, Englewood Cliffs, N. J., 1965, pp. 319 ff.

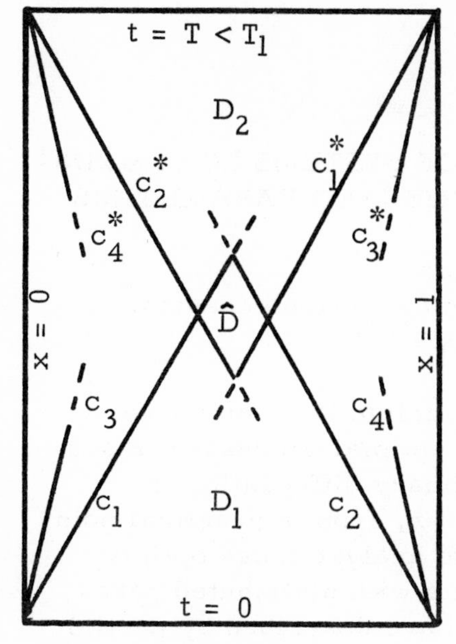

Fig. 1. The Case $T < T_1$

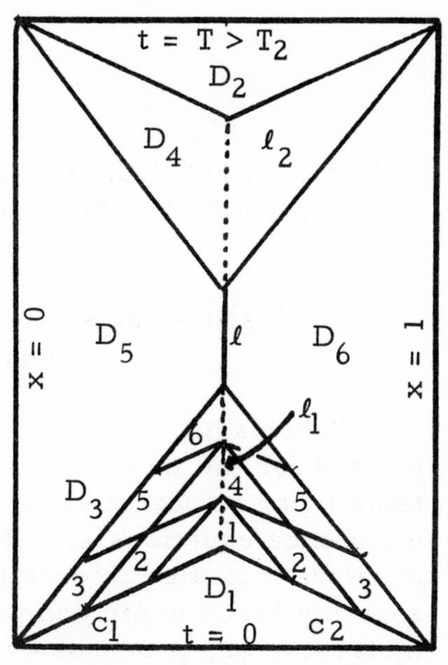

Fig. 2. The Case $T > T_2$

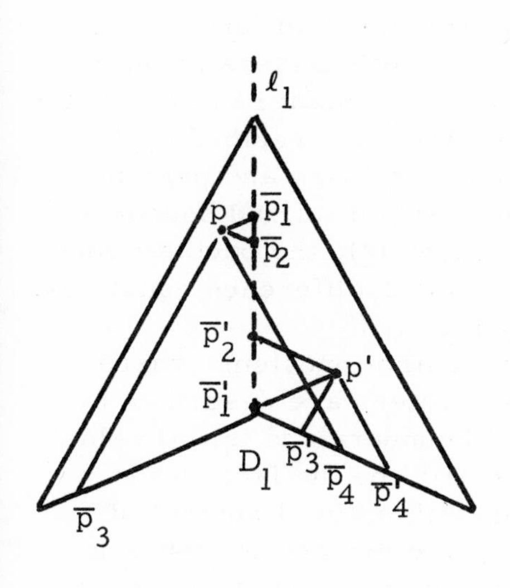

Fig. 3. The Domain Δ_1

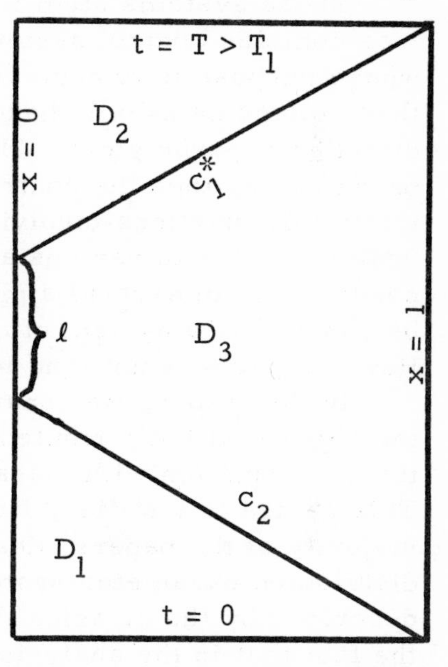

Fig. 4. 1-boundary control

OPTIMALITY CONDITIONS OF SYSTEMS CONTAINING COMPONENTS WITH DISTRIBUTED PARAMETERS

A. I. Egorov
Institute of Automation and Telemechanics,
Frunzé, U. S. S. R.

Pontryagin's Maximum Principle is an effective method for the investigation of optimal processes in systems that are described by ordinary differential or difference equations (1). However, from a practical point of view, it is also interesting to analyze those optimal systems that contain components with distributed parameters, i. e., processes which are described by partial differential equations.

These systems stem from the fact that any more or less complex control system contains auxiliary elements whose purpose is to control the system, and furthermore, these elements usually have lumped parameters as well as distributed parameters. Hence, if the plant has distributed parameters, then the control system is described by a totality of equations involving both ordinary and partial derivatives, with various additional (initial and boundary) conditions. In several simple cases (2), the problem may be reduced to a system of differential-difference equations. However, this is not true in general.

In this paper, we consider control problems where the objects with distributed parameters are described by the heat equation with classical boundary and initial values. This choice is justified, first of all, by the fact that a majority of the papers, dealing with optimal control of distributed parameter systems, are devoted to systems described by the classical heat equation, and secondly, by the fact that in the analysis of problems concerned with heat and mass transfer, equations of parabolic type are fundamental (3). Nevertheless, one may obtain similar results for other systems as well.

Let us assume that the process in the controlled plant is described by the boundary value problem:

$$u_{it} - a_i^2 u_{ixx} = f_i(t, x, u_1, \dots, u_n, u_{1x}, \dots, u_{nx}, \alpha), \quad 0 < t \leq T, \quad 0 < x < 1, \tag{1}$$

$$u_{ix}^o = \varphi_i^o(t, u_1^o, \dots, u_n^o, y_1^o, \dots, y_\ell^o, \beta^o), \quad u_{ix}^1 = \varphi_i^1(t, u_1^1, \dots, u_n^1, y_1^1, \dots, y_m^1, \beta^1), \tag{2}$$

$$u_i(0, x) = u_{io}(x), \quad i = 1, \dots, n, \tag{3}$$

where the a_i are real constants, $u_i^k = u_i(t, k)$, $u_{ix}^k = u_{ix}(t,k)$. We shall assume that the functions f_i and φ_i^k are continuous in t, continuously differentiable with respect to x, and possess continuous second order derivatives with respect to all their other arguments, and that the $u_{io}(x)$ are continuous over the interval $[0, 1]$. The control parameters α and β^k take on their values in certain open or closed sets A and B^k, which are contained in r and r^k-dimensional Euclidean spaces, respectively. The functions y_j^o and y_k^1 satisfy the differential equations

$$\left.\begin{aligned} \dot{y}_j^o &= \psi_j^o(t, u_1^o, \dots, u_n^o, y_1^o, \dots, y_\ell^o, \beta^o), \; j=1, \dots \ell, \\ \dot{y}_k^1 &= \psi_k^1(t, u_1^1, \dots, u_n^1, y_1^1, \dots, y_m^1, \beta^1), \; k=1, \dots, m, \end{aligned}\right\} \tag{4}$$

with initial conditions

$$y_j^o(0) = y_{jo}^o, \quad y_k^1(0) = y_{k1}^1, \quad j=1, \dots, \ell, \; k=1, \dots, m, \tag{5}$$

where the functions ψ_j^k satisfy the same conditions as the φ_i^k.

A function $w(t,x) = \{\alpha(t, x), \beta^1(t), \beta^2(t)\}$ will be called an admissible control function if it satisfies the following conditions

1) $\alpha(t, x)$ and the $\beta^k(t)$ take on their values in A and B^k, respectively,

2) the $\beta^k(t)$ are piecewise-continuous with at most a finite number of discontinuities,
3) it is possible to subdivide the rectangle $D = \{(t,x): 0 \leq x \leq 1,\ 0 \leq t \leq T\}$ into a finite number of regions by means of certain curves such that $\alpha(t,x)$ is continuous in each region. Further, the conditions of the problem may provide information on the form of the dependence of the function $\alpha(t,x)$ on t and x. For example, some of the components of the vector $\alpha(t,x)$ may depend only on x, and the rest may only depend on t.

In addition, we shall assume that all the functions in the boundary value problem (1)-(5) satisfy conditions which will insure that, for a given admissible control, the equations have a unique (classical or generalized) solution.

We shall say that an admissible control transfers the system from the state $\{(3),(5)\}$ to the state (6) if the solution of Eqs. (1)-(5) corresponding to this control satisfies the following conditions:

$$\left.\begin{cases} \Phi_\alpha(T,x,u(T,x)) = 0, \quad \alpha = 1,\dots,\nu \\ \int_0^1 \Psi_\beta(T,x,u(T,x)\,dx = C_\beta, \quad \beta=1,\dots,\mu, \\ y_\gamma^o(T) = y_{\gamma 1}^o, \quad \gamma=1,\dots,\alpha \leq \ell,\ y_\delta^1(T) = y_{\delta 1}^1, \quad \delta=1,\dots,\ell \leq m \end{cases}\right\} \quad (6)$$

where C_β, $y_{\gamma 1}^o$ are real constants; Φ_α and Ψ_β are functions which are continuous in x and have continuous first derivatives with respect to t and u_i.

The basic problem is: From among all the admissible controls that transfer the system from the state $\{(3),(5)\}$ to the state (6), find one such that the corresponding solution of the basic system Eqs. (1)-(5) assigns a minimum to the functional S given by

$$S = \sum_{i=1}^{n} \Big[\int_0^T (A_i^o(t)u_i^o + A_1^1(t)u_i^1)dt + \int_0^1 \beta_i(x)u_i(T,x)\,dx +$$

$$+\iint_D C_i(t,x)u_i(t,x)dxdt\Big] + \sum_{j=\alpha+1}^{\ell} C_j^o y_j^o(T) + \sum_{k=\ell+1}^{m} C_k^1 y_k^1(T),$$

and A_i^k, B_i, $C_i(t,x)$ are given continuous functions, C_i^k are real constants, and the value of T is not preassigned.

The particular case of this problem in which T was fixed and the terminal state was free was analyzed in (4).

If there exists only a finite number of admissible controls that transfer the system from the state {(3), (5)} to the state (6), then the above problem will not be a variational one. In order to employ variational methods one must assume that the class of admissible controls is sufficiently broad. Indeed, we shall assume that it is broad in the following sense:

Let us arbitrarily choose two admissible controls $w(t,x)$ and $w_1(t,x)$, defined in the rectangles $D = \{(t,x): 0 \leq t \leq T, 0 \leq x \leq 1\}$ and $D_1 = \{(t,x): 0 \leq t \leq T_1, 0 \leq x \leq 1\}$, respectively, which transfer the system from the state {(3), (5)} to the state (6). Then, for every sufficiently small $\varepsilon > 0$, there exists an admissible control function $w_\varepsilon(t,x)$ defined in the rectangle $D_\varepsilon = \{(t,x): 0 \leq t \leq T_\varepsilon, 0 \leq x \leq 1\}$ such that

1) $w_\varepsilon(t,x)$ transfers the system from the state {(3), (5)} to the state (6), where conditions (6) are satisfied at $t = T_\varepsilon$;

2) within the region $D \times D_\varepsilon$,

$$w_\varepsilon(t,x) = \begin{cases} w_1(t,x) \text{ for } (t,x) \in G_\varepsilon \\ w(t,x) \text{ for } (t,x) \in D - D_\varepsilon - G_\varepsilon, \end{cases}$$

where $G_\varepsilon (G_\varepsilon \subset D)$ is an arbitrarily given region of area ε;

3) $|T - T_\varepsilon| \leq L\varepsilon$, where L is a constant which is independent of ε but may depend on w and w_1.

Let us introduce the following notations:

$$H(t,x,u,v,\alpha) = \sum v_i f_i,$$

$$h^k(t, u^k, v^k, y^k, z^k, \beta^k) = \sum a_i^2 \; v_i^k \; \varphi_i^k + \sum z_j^k \; \psi_j^k \;, k=0, 1,$$

where $v^o = v(t, 0)$ and $v^1 = v(t, 1)$.

We shall define the auxiliary functions $v(t, x)$ and $z^k(t)$ by the boundary-value problem

$$v_{it} + a_i^2 v_{ixx} = -\frac{\partial H}{\partial u_i} + \frac{d}{dx}\left(\frac{\partial H}{\partial u_{ix}}\right) + C_i(t,x), 0 \leq t < T, 0 < x < 1,$$

$$v_i(T, x) = - B_i(x) - \sum_{\alpha=1}^{\nu} A_\alpha(x) \frac{\partial \Phi_\alpha(T, x, u(T, x))}{\partial u_i}$$

$$- \sum_{\beta=1}^{\mu} b_\beta \frac{\partial \Psi_\beta (T, x, u(T, x))}{\partial u_i} \quad ,$$

$$a_i^2 v_{ix}^o = \frac{\partial h^o}{\partial u_i^o} + \frac{\partial H}{\partial u_{ix}} \bigg|_{x=0} + A_i^o(t),$$

$$a_i^2 \; v_{ix}^1 = \frac{\partial h^1}{\partial u_i^1} + \frac{\partial H}{\partial u_{ix}} \bigg|_{x=1} - A_i^1(t) \; ,$$

$i = 1, \ldots, n,$

$$\dot{z}_j^o = - \frac{\partial h^o}{\partial y_j^o} \;, \; \dot{z}_k^1 = - \frac{\partial h^1}{\partial y_k^1} \;, \; j=1, \ldots, \ell \,; k=1, \ldots, m,$$

$$z_j^o(T) = -C_j^o \,, \; z_k^1(T) = C_k^1 \;, \; j=\alpha+1, \ldots, \ell; k=\ell+1, \ldots, m.$$

Here, $A_i^k(x)$, $B_i(x)$, $C_i(t, x)$ and C_j^k are the same as the ones that occur in the definition of the functional S, and $A_\alpha(x)$ and b_β are to be determined.

Let us assume that $w(t, x)$ is an arbitrary admissible control defined on the rectangle D which transfers the system from the state $\{(3), (5)\}$ to the state (6), and that $u(t, x)$, $y^k(t)$, and $v(t, x)$, $z^k(t)$ are the solutions of the boundary-value problems (1)-(5) and (7) corresponding to these control functions.

We shall say that $w(t, x)$ satisfies the maximum conditions if for any admissible control $w_1(t, x)=\{\alpha(t,x), \beta^o(t), \beta^1(t)\}$ defined on the rectangle $D_1=\{(t,x): 0 \leq t \leq T_1, 0 \leq x \leq 1\}$, the following inequalities are satisfied:

$$\iint_G \Big[H(t, x, u(t, x), v(t, x), \alpha_1) - H(t, x, u(t, x), v(t, x), \alpha)\Big] dxdt \leq 0,$$

$$\int_0^\tau \Big[h^k(t, u^k(t), v^k(t), z^k(t), \beta_1^k) - h^k(t, u^k(t), v^k(t), y^k(t), z^k(t), \beta^k)\Big] dt \leq 0,$$

$$k = 0, 1,$$

where $\tau = \min [T, T_1]$ and $G = D \times D_1$.

Theorem. Let us assume that $w(t, x)$ is an admissible control defined on the rectangle D which transfers the system from the state $\{(3), (5)\}$ to the state (6), and let $u(t, x)$, $y^k(t)$, and $v(t, x)$, $z^k(t)$ be the corresponding solutions of the boundary-value problems (1)-(5) and (7) which correspond to this solution for certain $A_\alpha(x)$ and b_β. Then for $w(t, x)$ to be an optimal control it is necessary that:

1) the control $w(t, x)$ must satisfy the above maximum conditions;

2)

$$\frac{dS}{dT} + \int_0^1 \Big[\sum_{\alpha=1}^{\nu} A_\alpha(x) \frac{d\Phi_\alpha}{dT} + \sum_{\beta=1}^{\mu} b_\beta \frac{d\Psi_\beta}{dT}\Big] dx - $$

$$- \sum_{j=1}^{\alpha} z_j^o(T) \dot{y}_j^o(T) + \sum_{k=1}^{\ell} z_k^1(T) \dot{y}_k^1(T) = 0.$$

It is easy to verify (2) that the necessary conditions of the theorem, by and large, isolate those controls among which the optimal controls must be chosen.

Similar results can be obtained if Eqs. 2 are replaced by the conditions $u_i^o = \varphi_i^o(y_1^o, \dots, y_\ell^o)$, $u_i^1 = \varphi_i^1(y_1^1, \dots, y_n^1)$, $i=1, \dots, n$.

If the functional S being minimized is replaced by the functional J, given by

$$J=\iint_D f_o(t, x, u_1(t,x), \dots, u_n(t,x), u_{1x}(t,x), \dots, u_{nx}(t,x), \alpha)dxdt,$$

then, in order to obtain necessary conditions for optimality, one may introduce the variable u_o in a manner similar to that employed in (4).

In problems where the time T is fixed and the terminal state of the system is free, we may obtain necessary conditions for optimality by making use of the above theorem. To do this, we should set

$$A_\alpha(x) = 0, \quad b_\beta = 0, \quad \alpha = 1, \dots, \nu; \ \beta = 1, \dots, \mu,$$

in Eqs. (7) and eliminate the second condition, involving the equality condition at the time $t = T$, from the theorem. In this case, the condition about the broadness of the class of admissible controls may be omitted (4). Furthermore, if the boundary-value problem is linear and the control parameters are additive, then the above necessary conditions of optimality are also sufficient. For the variation of a functional as a performance criterion one may obtain an explicit expression that makes it possible to solve certain linear problems concerning the theory of invariant systems with distributed parameters.

Since the necessary conditions for optimality require one to solve a boundary-value problem for a system of partial differential equations, then, even in the simplest cases, the solution of this problem cannot be obtained in closed form. As a rule, we may obtain the solution in the form of a series. As a result, shifting points coincide with the zeros of certain functionals. In some cases these points cannot be found, and we must be content with approximate methods.

One of the methods of finding an approximate solution to the optimal control problem is based upon a simplification of the basic equations and the side conditions that describe the process. For such a simplified problem we may formulate the optimality conditions, and then we may find an optimal control that is assumed to be an approximation to the unknown optimal control.

In (5) a linear case of the problem under consideration has been solved by the grid-point method. Necessary and sufficient conditions for optimality were obtained for linear discrete systems where the arguments change their values in a fixed region. These conditions are similar to the corresponding conditions obtained for continuous systems, and it is easy to establish that, as the grid-point spacing tends to zero, the optimal control of the discrete problem tends to the optimal control of the continuous problem.

References

1. L.S. Pontryagin, V.G. Boltyanskii, R.V. Gamkrelidze, E.F. Mishchenko, "The Mathematical Theory of Optimal Processes", John Wiley, New York, 1962.

2. Bessekersky V.A., Popov E.P., "Theory of Automatic Control Systems", Nauka, 1966.

3. Lykov A.V., Mikhahylov Yu.A., "Theory of Heat and Mass Transfer", Gosenergoizdat, 1963.

4. Egorov A.I., "Optimal Processes in Systems Containing Distributed Parameter Plants", Automation and Remote Control, July 1965, Vol. 26, No. 7, pp. 1178-1187.

5. Vostrova Z.I., "Optimal Processes in Sampled-Data Systems Containing Objects with Distributed Parameters", Automation and Remote Control, Vol. 27, No. 5, May 1966, pp. 767-779.

LINEAR DIFFERENTIAL GAMES

L. S. Pontryagin
V. A. Steklov Mathematical Institute
U. S. S. R. Academy of Sciences
Moscow, U. S. S. R.

During my previous visit to the U. S. A. in 1964, I presented (3) some results related to differential games described by differential equations of the form

$$\frac{dz}{dt} = Z(z, u, v).$$

At that time, these results were far from complete, and were formulated in a quite complicated manner. At the present time, they have been considerably simplified and have been published in (1).

Recently, on the basis of the results of (1), some essential progress has been made in the theory of linear differential games. Namely, Professor E. F. Mishchenko and I have obtained quite general, and yet simple conditions which are sufficient for a linear differential game to be completed. The present paper is devoted to the presentation of these results.

Let the motion of a vector z in an n-dimensional Euclidean space R be described by the vector differential equation

$$\frac{dz}{dt} = Cz + U(u) - V(v), \tag{1}$$

where u and v are control parameters that assume their values in a $(\nu-1)$-dimensional unit sphere K (such controls will be called admissible), C is a constant matrix, and U and V are analytic mappings of the sphere K into a space L. Let M be a given $(n-\nu)$-dimensional subspace of R. We shall say that the linear differential game is described by all these data.

We shall say that game (1) can be completed on some set $A \subset R$ if, for any initial value $z_o \in A$ for the vector z, there exists a number $T(z_o) \geq 0$ such that, for an arbitrary piecewise-continuous admissible control parameter v(t), it is possible to choose an admissible control parameter u(t) such that the point z reaches M (through the solution of (1)) in a time not exceeding $T(z_o)$. In addition, only the values of z(t) and v(t) at the current time t are employed in determining the value of u(t) for each t; the values of z and v at future times are not used.

We shall say that a theory for the differential game (1) has been constructed if, for any $z \in A$, where A is the above mentioned set on which the game can be completed, a function T(z) has been constructed.

I shall now describe the theory of the linear differential game (1) that was constructed by E. F. Mishchenko and myself, and I shall indicate the conditions that must be satisfied in order for this theory to be applicable.

Let L be the orthogonal compliment of M. We shall denote by $\pi[z]$ the orthognal projection onto L of any vector $z \in R$. The right-hand side of Eq. (1) determines the following two mappings of K into L:

$$y = \pi\left[e^{-\tau C} U(u)\right] \tag{2}$$

$$y = \pi\left[e^{-\tau C} V(v)\right] \tag{3}$$

Henceforth, we shall assume that τ is a negative number.

We shall assume that the following condition is satisfied:

a). The images of K under the mappings (2) and (3) are convex, locally-convex $(\nu - 1)$-dimensional hypersurfaces in L (the local-convexity is to be understood here in the differential-geometric sense, i. e., the second quadratic form is definite).

Let us consider the scalar products

$$\varphi \cdot \pi\left[e^{-\tau C} U(u)\right] \quad , \quad \varphi \cdot \pi\left[e^{-\tau C} V(v)\right] , \tag{4}$$

where φ is an arbitrary unit vector in L. We can consider φ to be a point in K, and K the unit sphere in L. Let $u = u(\tau, \varphi)$, $v = v(\tau, \varphi)$be the values of u and $v \in K$ that achieve the maximum for the corresponding scalar products (4) (for given φ and τ).

We set

$$w(\tau,\varphi) = \pi\left[e^{-\tau C}\Big(U\big(u(\tau,\varphi)\big) - V\big(v(\tau,\varphi)\big)\Big)\right] \qquad (5)$$

and define a mapping of K into L as follows:

$$y = w(\tau,\varphi) \,. \qquad (6)$$

This mapping, in general, is neither regular nor one-to-one. We shall denote the image of K under the mapping (6) by Σ_τ. It is easy to see that φ is a normal to the surface Σ_τ at $w(\tau,\varphi)$. We shall assume that the following condition is satisfied:

b). The surface Σ_τ is locally-convex, and φ is the outward normal to Σ_τ at $w(\tau,\varphi)$.

Finally, we shall assume that the following condition is satisfied:

c). The orthogonal projection of the subspace CM onto L is all of L:

$$\pi[CM] = L \qquad (7)$$

Then, the following theorem holds:

Theorem: If conditions a), b), and c) are satisfied, then the linear differential game (1) can be completed.

I shall not present the proof of this theorem here, since it is not simple. I shall only describe the theory of the game (1).

Let us consider the surface Δ_τ in L that is described by the equation

$$y = \int_0^\tau w(r,\varphi)\,dr \,. \qquad (8)$$

The surface Δ_τ is obtained by integrating the surface Σ_τ with respect to τ.

For $\tau = 0$, Δ_τ degenerates into a point. As τ varies from 0 to $-\infty$, Δ_τ expands, remaining convex (see Fig. (1)).

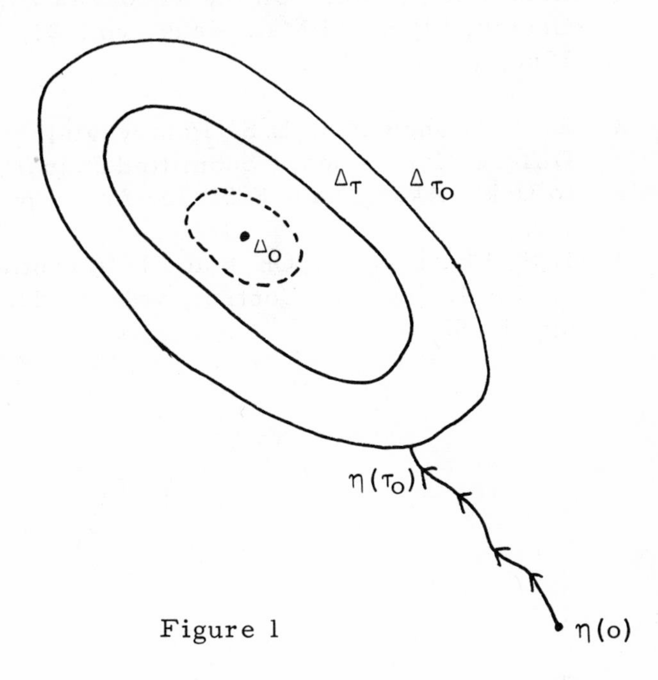

Figure 1

Let z_o be an arbitrary point in R. Then, for any τ, $0 \geq \tau > -\infty$,

$$\pi\left[e^{-\tau C} z_o\right] \epsilon \text{ L.}$$

We set

$$\eta(\tau) = \pi\left[e^{-\tau C} z_o\right] \tag{9}$$

Obviously, $\eta(0) \neq 0$ if $z_o \notin$ M. As τ varies, $\eta(\tau)$ varies within L (see Fig. 1).

<u>If, for some τ_o, the point $\eta(\tau_o)$ first reaches Δ_{τ_o}, then $z_o \epsilon$ A, and the minimum value of $T(z_o) = |\tau_o|$.</u>

This proposition is the theory of the linear differential game (1). It is easy to derive on the basis thereof a condition under which A = R.

References

1. L. S. Pontryagin, "On the Theory of Differential Games," Uspekhi Mat. Nauk, vol. 21, No. 4(1930), 1966, pp. 219-274.

2. E. F. Mishchenko, L. S. Pontryagin, "Linear Differential Games," Submitted January 26, 1967, to Dokl. Akad. Nauk SSSR for future publication.

3. L. S. Pontryagin, "On Some Differential Games," J. SIAM, Ser. A: Control, vol. 3, No. 1, 1965, pp. 49-52.

LINEAR DIFFERENTIAL GAMES

B. N. Pshenichniy
Institute of Cybernetics
Kiev, U. S. S. R.

Differential games constitute a new field in which there exist relatively few works. Among these works, I would like to mention, first, the book of R. Isaacs (1), which contains a qualitative analysis of the problem, and, second, the paper of L. S. Pontryagin (2). which apparently is the first paper in which a deep analysis of the analytical structure of the problem is given.

In the present paper, we consider a differential game described by the system of equations:

$$\dot{z} = Az + Bu + Cv, \tag{1}$$

and by a set M, where $z \in E^n$, $u \in U \subset E^r$, $v \in V \subset E^s$, and the matrices A, B, and C have dimensions (nxn), (nxr), and (nxs), respectively. We shall assume that the following conditions are satisfied: The sets U and V are bounded and closed, U is convex, and M is a closed and convex set in E^n. In addition, if

$$W_M(\psi) = \sup_{z \in M} (\psi, z), \quad K_M = \{\psi: W_M(\psi) < +\infty\}$$

then K_M is closed, and $W_M(\psi)$ is continuous on K_M.

Such conditions are satisfied, for example, by bounded convex closed sets or by sets defined by a system of linear inequalities.

We shall say that the game can be completed from an initial point z^o in the time $T(z^o)$ if, whatever the piecewise-continuous control $v(\cdot)$ employed by one of the players (E) such that $v(t) \in V$ for all $t \geq 0$, the second player (P) can choose a piecewise-continuous control $u(\cdot)$ with $u(t) \in U$ (where u(t) is determined soley by the values of the phase coordinates of z(t) and the control v(t) at the time t) such that $z(t_1) \in M$ for some time $t_1 \leq T(z^o)$.

1. By definition, we set

$$W(\psi, t, z) = \left(\Phi^*(t)\psi, z\right) + \int_0^t \max_{u \in U} \min_{v \in V} \left(\Phi^*(\tau)\psi, Bu+Cv\right) d\tau, \tag{2}$$

$$\lambda(z, t) = \min_{\|\psi\|=1} \left[W(\psi, t, z) + W_M(-\psi)\right], \tag{3}$$

$$\Gamma(z, t) = \left\{\psi: \|\psi\| = 1, W(\psi, t, z) + W_M(-\psi) = \lambda(z, t), \dot{\Phi} = A\Phi, \Phi(0) = I\right\} \tag{4}$$

Further, we shall denote by $T(z)$ the first non-negative root of the equation

$$\lambda(z, t) = 0.$$

If such a root does not exist, then we set $T(z) = \infty$. Let us observe that $T(z) \geq 0$ for all z, and that $T(z) = 0$ only when $z \in M$. This is not difficult to prove.

The following theorem gives the essence of the function $T(z)$.

Theorem 1. If $T(z^o) < +\infty$, then, whatever the measurable control $v(\cdot)$ with $v(t) \in V$ employed by E, there is, for P, a measurable control $u(\cdot)$ with $u(t) \in U$ such that $z(T(z^o)) \in M$, where $z(t)$ is the solution of system (1) for the chosen controls. For any $t_1 < T(z^o)$, there is a control $v(\cdot)$ for E such that $z(t_1) \notin M$, whatever the control employed by P.

Thus, $T(z^o)$ is the first time at which P can always bring $z(t)$ onto the manifold M, whatever the control employed by E.

Let us observe that it follows from the definition of $T(z)$ and the continuity of the function $\lambda(z, t)$ that $T(z)$ is lower semi-continuous.

The results formulated below are directed towards an investigation of conditions for $T(z)$ which will ensure that there is a termination time for the game.

2. The first approach to such a study consists in an investigation of the analytic properties of the function $T(z)$.

Definition. A point z, $z \notin M$, is called regular if the following conditions are satisfied:

a) $T(z) < \infty$,

b) $\max_{u \in U} \min_{v \in V} \left(\Phi^*(T(z))\,\psi,\ Az+Bu+Cv\right) > 0$

for all $\psi \in \Gamma\left(z, T(z)\right)$.

Theorem 2. The set Ω of regular points is open, and the function $T(z)$ is continuous on this set.

Theorem 3. At each regular point z, the function $T(z)$ has a directional derivative, and its derivative with respect to the direction e is given by the formula:

$$\frac{\partial T(z)}{\partial e} = \max_{\psi \in \Gamma\left(z, T(z)\right)} - \frac{\left(\partial_z W\left(\psi, T(z), z\right), e\right)}{\partial_t W\left(\psi, T(z), z\right)}, \tag{5}$$

where

$$\partial_z W(\psi, t, z) = \Phi^*(t)\psi,$$

$$\partial_t W(\psi, t, z) = \max_{u \in U} \min_{v \in V} \left(\Phi^*(t)\psi,\ Az+Bu+Cv\right). \tag{6a}$$

Remark. Let us recall that, by definition,

$$\frac{\partial T(z)}{\partial e} = \lim_{\tau \to 0^+} \frac{T(z+\tau e) - T(z)}{\tau}.$$

These theorems are proved by using methods that generalize those used in the usual proof of the implicit function theorem. It follows from condition (b) of the definition of a regular point that the function $\lambda(z, t)$ increases monotonically with respect to t in a neighborhood of the point $\{z, T(z)\}$. From this it follows that the equation

$$\lambda(z, t) = 0$$

has a solution $T(z)$ in a neighborhood of a regular point, and that this solution is continuous. The proof of Theorem 3 can be carried out by arguments slightly more complicated than those used to prove the existence of the derivative of an implicit function.

3. Let us now assume that $z(t)$ is the solution of system (1) for some controls $u(t)$ and $v(t)$ which are continuous from the right.

It then follows from theorem 3 that

$$\left(\frac{dT\left(z(t)\right)}{dt}\right)^{+} = \alpha\left(z(t);\, u(t),\, v(t)\right),$$

where

$$\alpha(z;u^o, v^o) = \max_{\psi\in\Gamma\left(z,\,T(z)\right)} - \frac{\left(\Phi^*\left(T(z)\right)\psi,\ Az+Bu^o+Cv^o\right)}{\max\limits_{u\in U}\min\limits_{v\in V}\left(\Phi^*\left(T(z)\right)\psi,\ Az+Bu+Cv\right)}$$

and $\alpha(z;u, v)$ is defined for each regular point z.

It is possible to show that $\alpha(z;u, v)$ is upper semi-continuous with respect to z and is continuous with respect to u and v.

Theorem 4. Suppose that every point z, for which $0< T(z)<+\infty$, is regular, and that at any such point, the system of linear inequalities

$$\left(\Phi^*\left(T(z)\right)\psi,\ Bu^o+Cv^o\right) \geq \max_{u\in U}\min_{v\in V}\left(\Phi^*\left(T(z)\right)\psi,\ Bu+Cv\right), \tag{6b}$$

$$\psi\in\Gamma\left(z,\,T(z)\right),\quad u^o\in U$$

can be solved for u^o, for arbitrary $v^o\in V$. Then, P can always complete the game beginning at the point z^o, where $T(z^o)<\infty$, in a time not exceeding $T(z^o)+\varepsilon$, where ε is an arbitrary positive number, whatever the continuous-from-the-right control $v^o(t)$ employed by E.

Let us indicate the general idea of the construction of the control $u^o(t)$ for the player P. Let

$$\delta = \frac{\varepsilon}{T(z^o)+\varepsilon}$$

From conditions (6b) of the theorem, it follows that there is a $u^1\in U$ such that

$$\alpha\left(z^o,\, u^1,\, v^o(0)\right) \leq -1.$$

P employs the control $u^o(t) = u^1$ until some time t_1 not violating the condition

$$\alpha\left(z^o(t),\, u^1,\, v^o(t)\right) < -1+\delta.$$

From the upper semi-continuity of the function $\alpha(z;u, v)$, it follows that $t_1>0$.

It is easy to see that $z^o(t)$ tends to some limit z^1 as $t\to t_1^-$. Beginning at the point z^1, one chooses the control $u^o(t)=u^2$, where u^2 satisfies the condition

$$\alpha\left(z^1;\ u^2,\ v^o(t_1)\right) \leq -1, \text{ etc.}$$

It is not difficult to see that if the trajectory $z^o(t)$ has already been constructed for some $t<\bar{t}$, then, in an analogous manner, the trajectory can be determined for some $t \geq \bar{t}$. Thus, the trajectory can be constructed so long as the point $z^o(t)$ does not leave the region of regularity. But this can occur only if the point reaches the boundary of M, since, because of the conditions under which the control was chosen, it follows that

$$\left(\frac{dT\left(z^o(t)\right)}{dt}\right)^+ = \alpha\left(z^o(t);u^o(t),\ v^o(t)\right) \leq -1+\delta<0,$$

i.e., $T\left(z^o(t)\right)$ decreases monotonically no slower than $T(z^o)-t(1-\delta)$, and therefore necessarily vanishes at a time not greater than

$$\bar{t} = \frac{T(z^o)}{1-\delta} = T(z^o) + \delta .$$

Let us note that, as was required by the conditions of the game, the choice of the control $u(t)$ is based only on $z(t)$ and $v(t)$.

Thus, Theorem 4 yields certain sufficient conditions under which it is possible to complete the game.

4. Theorem 4 was based on ideas ordinarily used in dynamic programming. In addition, the investigation of the analytic properties of the function $T(z)$ turned out to be basic. We shall now cite one result which is based on several other ideas.

Theorem 5. Suppose that at each point z^1 for which $0<T(z^1)<\infty$, the following conditions are satisfied:

a) The set $\Gamma(z,t)$ consists of a single vector $\psi(z,t)$ for all z and t in some neighborhood of $\{z^1, T(z^1)\}$;

b) The maximum value of the expression $\left(\Phi^*(t)\,\psi(z,t),\ Bu\right)$, with respect to $u \in U$, is attained at a unique point $u(z,t)$ for all points $\{z,t\}$ in the indicated neighborhood of $\{z^1, T(z^1)\}$. Then, P can always complete the game in a time not exceeding $T(z^o)$, where z^o is the initial position of the game, whatever the piecewise-continuous control used by E.

We shall denote the neighborhood indicated in the conditions of the theorem by $\Omega(z^o)$. It is possible to show that if the conditions of the theorem are satisfied, then $\psi(z, t)$ and $u(z, t)$ depend continuously on z and t in this neighborhood. Further, the function $\lambda(z, t)$ is continuously differentiable with respect to z and t, and

$$\partial_z \lambda(z, t) = \Phi^*(t)\, \psi(z, t), \tag{7}$$

$$\partial_t \lambda(z, t) = \max_{u \in U} \min_{v \in V} \left(\Phi^*(t)\, \psi(z, t), Az+Bu+Cv\right).$$

Let us write down the system of equations:

$$\begin{aligned} \dot{T} &= -1, \\ \dot{z} &= Az+Bu(z, T)+Cv(t), \\ z(0) &= z^o, \quad T(0) = T(z^o). \end{aligned} \tag{8}$$

Since the right-hand sides of equations (8) depend continuously on z and are piecewise-continuous with respect to t, then system (8) has a solution $z^o(t)$, $T(t)$ (which may not be unique), extendable up to the boundary of the region $\Omega(z^o)$. It easily follows from Eqs. (7) and (8) that, along this solution,

$$\frac{d}{dt} \lambda\left(z^o(t), T(t)\right) \geq 0.$$

Therefore,

$$\lambda\left(z^o(t), T(t)\right) \geq 0$$

and, hence,

$$T\left(z^o(t)\right) \leq T(t) = T(z^o) - t.$$

Thus, $T\left(z^o(t)\right)$ decreases no slower than $T(z^o) - t$.

If, at the time t_1, the point $z_1 = \lim_{t \to t_1^-} z^o(t)$ turns out to be on the boundary of $\Omega(z^o)$, then, for $t \geq t_1$, we define $z^o(t)$ as the solution of system (8) with the initial conditions

$$z^o(t_1) = z^1, \quad T(t_1) = T(z^1).$$

Let us note that, in addition, $T(z^1) \leq T(z^o) - t_1$.

We can, in an analogous manner, continue the construction. It is easy to see that if the trajectory $z^o(t)$ has been constructed for all $t<\bar{t}$, then it is possible to extend it, in a similar manner, for $t\geq\bar{t}$. In this connection,

$$T\left(z^{o}(t)\right) \leq T(t) \leq T(z^{o}) - t \quad \text{for all } t.$$

Thus, the point $z^{o}(t)$ comes out on the manifold M no later than the time $T(z^{o})$.

5. Theorems 4 and 5 give certain sufficient conditions under which the game can be completed. A simultaneous application of these theorems makes it possible to cover a sufficiently interesting class of problems. In particular, Theorem 5 allows one to deduce conditions under which such a pursuit problem has a solution (2). Suppose that the motion of P is described by the system of equations

$$\ddot{x} + \alpha\dot{x} = s\,u,$$

$$x \in E^{n}, \quad |u| \leq 1, \quad u \in E^{n},$$

while the motion of E is described by the system

$$\ddot{y} + \beta y = \sigma v,$$

$$y \in E^{n}, \quad |v| \leq 1, \quad v \in E^{n}.$$

The pursuit will be considered to have been completed if $x(t) = y(t)$.

If we apply Theorem 5, we obtain: The pursuit can be completed from the point $z^{o} = \{x^{o}, y^{o}\}$ in a time $T(z^{o})$ if $T(z^{o}) < \infty$ and

$$s \geq \sigma, \quad \frac{s}{\alpha} \geq \frac{\sigma}{\beta},$$

and if one of the inequalities is strictly satisfied. This coincides with the result obtained for this example in (2).

References

1. R. Isaacs, Differential Games, John Wiley, New York, 1965.

2. L. S. Pontryagin, On the Theory of Differential Games, Uspekhi Mat. Nauk. Vol. 21, 1966, pp. 219-274.

A Survey of Differential Games

Leonard D. Berkovitz*
Division of Mathematical Sciences
Purdue University
Lafayette, Indiana

Introduction

A differential game is a two-person zero-sum game that can be described somewhat imprecisely as follows. Let t denote time, let $x = (x^1, \ldots, x^n)$ be a vector in real euclidean n-space, E^n, and let $\mathcal{R}$ be a fixed region of (t, x) space. The position, or state, $x(t)$ of the game at time t is determined by a system of first order differential equations

$$(1.1) \qquad \frac{dx^i}{dt} = g^i(t, x, y, z)$$

$$x^i(t_o) = x^i_o \qquad i = 1, \ldots, n,$$

where $y = (y^1, \ldots, y^\sigma)$ is a vector chosen at each instant of time by Player I and $z = (z^1, \ldots, z^s)$ is a vector chosen at each instant of time by Player II. We shall call the system (1.1) the state equations.

It is assumed that both players know the present state of the game and that they know how the game proceeds; that is, the system of differential equations (1.1). At time t, when Player I chooses $y(t)$ he <u>does not</u> know the

*This work was supported in part by NSF Grant GP-06113

choice $z(t)$ of Player II. Similarly, when Player II chooses $z(t)$ at time t, he does not know the choice $y(t)$ of Player I. Each player can take the state of the game $x(t)$ into account in making his choice, since this information is available to him. Thus, Player I can let his choice of y be governed by a vector valued function Y of position and time

$$Y(t,x) = Y^1(t,x),\ldots,Y^\sigma(t,x)),$$

defined on $\mathcal{R}$; similarly, Player II can let his choice of z be governed by a vector valued function Z of position and time

$$Z(t,x) = (Z^1(t,x),\ldots,Z^s(t,x))$$

defined on $\mathcal{R}$. The functions Y and Z are called pure strategies and the variables y and z are called strategic variables. Player I selects his strategy from a class $\mathcal{Y}$ of permissible strategies and Player II selects his strategy from a class $\mathcal{Z}$ of permissible strategies. The classes $\mathcal{Y}$ and $\mathcal{Z}$ are prescribed in advance, and the choice of strategy is made by each player prior to the start of play. Therefore, in selecting a pure strategy a player selects a set of instructions for choosing his strategic variable in all possible situations (t,x).

Play begins at some initial time and position (t_o,x_o) in $\mathcal{R}$ and terminates whenever t and the position $x(t)$ are such that $(t,x(t))$ is a point of a previously specified set $\mathcal{T}$ in $\bar{\mathcal{R}}$, the closure of $\mathcal{R}$. If (t_1,x_1) denotes the point of termination of play of the game starting at (t_o,x_o), then the payoff to Player I is given by

$$(1.2)\quad P(t_o,x_o,Y,Z) = h(t_1,x_1) + \int_{t_o}^{t_1} f(t,x(t),y(t),z(t))dt.$$

where h is a real valued function on $\mathcal{J}$, f is a real valued function on (t,x,y,z) space, $y(t) = Y(t,x(t))$, and $z(t) = Z(t,x(t))$. The objective of Player I is to select a strategy Y that maximizes the payoff P; the objective of Player II is to select a strategy that minimizes P.

Usually, certain constraints are placed on the choice of strategy as follows. Two sets of functions

$$K^i(t,x,y) \qquad\qquad R^j(t,x,z),$$

$i = 1,\ldots,\pi$. $j = 1,\ldots,p$ are given, and the strategies Y and Z are required to be such that

$$K^i(t,x,Y(t,x)) \geq 0 \qquad R^i(t,x,Z(t,x)) \geq 0.$$

Differential games were first studied by Rufus Isaacs in a series of RAND Corporation memoranda that appeared in 1954 (1). Recently he has incorporated this work and his subsequent researches in a book (2). Isaacs studies many illuminating examples in this book and states some theorems about differential games. Some of the theorems are justified heuristically and some are established under very stringent conditions. The importance of this book stems from the examples. They illustrate solution methods and present phenomena that any general theory must take into account. Subsequent to Isaac's pioneering work, several authors have given more rigorous treatments of certain aspects of the theory. This work will be discussed and referenced below.

The only earlier work that this writer is aware of is that of Steinhaus who, in 1925, attempted to formulate a pursuit and evasion problem in general terms (3). While Steinhaus had the notion of strategy, he only considered a ''min-max'' problem and did not consider a game.

Zieba (4) has also attempted to develop a theory of differential games.

We close this introductory section by listing some notations and conventions that we shall use. Vector matrix notation will generally be used. Vectors and matrices will be denoted by single letters. Superscripts will be used to denote the components of a vector; subscripts will be used to distinguish vectors. Vectors will be written either as row matrices or as column matrices. It will be clear from the context how the vector is to be considered. The inner product of two vectors λ and μ, say, will be written $\lambda\mu$. A vector will be called positive if all of its components are positive. Similar definitions hold for negative, non-positive, and non-negative vectors. Let

$$g(t,x,y,z) = (g^1(t,x,y,z),\ldots,g^n(t,x,y,z))$$

be a vector valued function defined and differentiable on a region of (t,x,y,z) space. Then we shall denote the matrix of partial derivatives

$$\frac{\partial g^i}{\partial z^j} \qquad \begin{array}{l} i = 1,\ldots,n \\ j = 1,\ldots,s \end{array}$$

by g_z. The symbols g_x, g_y, g_t will have similar meanings.

PROBLEMS OF FORMULATION

In this section we shall discuss the problem of

giving a precise mathematical definition of a differential game. There are serious difficulties here.

The first task is to impose continuity and differentiability requirements on the functions f,g,h and the set $\mathcal{T}$ discussed in the introduction. The state equations (1.1) in vector notation are

$$(2.1) \qquad \frac{dx}{dt} = g(t,x,y,z) \qquad x(t_o) = x_o .$$

We assume that g is a $C^{(1)}$ function of (t,x,y,z). We assume that $\mathcal{T}$ is a piecewise $C^{(1)}$ manifold of dimension less than $n+1$; $\mathcal{T}$ may be a point. Finally we assume that h is defined and $C^{(1)}$ in a neighborhood of $\mathcal{T}$ and that the function f is a $C^{(1)}$ function of (t,x,y,z). We shall formulate the constraints in a more general fashion than we did in the introduction. Let Ω be a mapping from points (t,x) of $\mathcal{R}$ to subsets $\Omega(t,x)$ of E^s; let $\bar{\Omega}$ be a mapping from points of $\mathcal{R}$ to subsets of E^σ. Examples of such mappings are mappings defined by systems of inequalities

$$K^i(t,x,y) \geq 0 \qquad i = 1,\ldots,\pi$$

$$R^i(t,x,z) \geq 0 \qquad j = 1,\ldots,p.$$

The second task is to define the appropriate zero-sum two person game. In this connection we note that some authors use the term ''differential game'' to describe problems that are ''min-max'' problems but are not games in the sense used in the mathematical theory of games. We also note that some authors use an ''information pattern'' different from ours. Player I chooses a strategy Y that is a function of (t,x) and Player II chooses a strategy

Z that is a function of Y.

To define a two-person zero-sum game one needs to specify a set $\mathcal{A}$, called the strategy space for Player I, a set $\mathcal{B}$, called the strategy space for Player II, and a real valued function v defined on $\mathcal{A} \times \mathcal{B}$. If Player I chooses a in $\mathcal{A}$ and Player II chooses b in $\mathcal{B}$, then the payoff to Player I is v(a,b). We define the game to be the triple $(\mathcal{A},\mathcal{B},v)$. The game is said to have a value if

$$\sup \inf v(a,b) = \inf \sup v(a,b),$$

where a ranges over $\mathcal{A}$ and b ranges over $\mathcal{B}$. Assume that the game has a value, which we denote by v^*. If there exist strategies a^* in $\mathcal{A}$ and b^* in $\mathcal{B}$ such that

$$v^* = v(a^*,b^*),$$

then we say that a^* and b^* are optimal strategies. The pair (a^*,b^*) is also called a saddle point. Since we always have

$$\sup \inf v(a,b) \leq \inf \sup v(a,b),$$

it readily follows that a necessary and sufficient condition for $(\mathcal{A},\mathcal{B},v)$ to have a value and to have optimal strategies (a^*,b^*) is that there exist an $a^* \in \mathcal{A}$ and a $b^* \in \mathcal{B}$ such that for all $a \in \mathcal{A}$ and all $b \in \mathcal{B}$,

$$v(a,b^*) \leq v(a^*,b^*) \leq v(a^*,b).$$

It is well known that there exist games without values (even if mixed strategies are permitted), and that there exist games having a value, but not having optimal strategies. See Dresher (5) or Karlin (6).

From the discussion in the preceding paragraph and in

the introduction it is clear that in defining a differential game we will want to take $\mathcal{A} = \mathcal{Y}$, $\mathcal{B} = \mathcal{Z}$, and will want to take $v = P(t_o,x_o,y,z)$, where P is given by (1.2). A major difficulty arises when we try to specify the classes $\mathcal{Y}$ and $\mathcal{Z}$. One might think that for $\mathcal{Y}$ one should take the class of $C^{(1)}$ functions Y defined on (t,x)-space with range in E^{σ} such that for (t,x) in $\mathcal{R}$, we have $Y(t,x)$ in $\overline{\Omega}(t,x)$. Similarly for $\mathcal{Z}$ one might take the class of $C^{(1)}$ functions with range in E^s such that for (t,x) in $\mathcal{R}$, we have $Z(t,x) \in \Omega(t,x)$. If we let $y = Y(t,x)$ and $z = Z(t,x)$ in (2.1) we obtain

$$\frac{dx}{dt} = g(t,x,Y(t,x),Z(t,x)) \qquad x(t_o) = x_o. \tag{2.2}$$

Standard theorems guarantee a unique solution in a neighborhood of (t_o,x_o). For a given Y in $\mathcal{Y}$ and Z in $\mathcal{Z}$, however, the resulting solution of (2.2) need not reach the set $\mathcal{T}$. In this event, $P(t_o,x_o,Y,Z)$ is undefined.

From examples of differential games and from the calculus of variations we know that the class of $C^{(1)}$ functions will not suffice to yield maximizing and minimizing functions. One is led to consider piecewise $C^{(1)}$ functions. The difficulty encountered with $C^{(1)}$ functions is also present here. It is compounded by the discontinuities on the right hand side of (2.2). At points of discontinuity solutions may bifurcate or may coalesce. Thus $P(t_o,x_o,Y,Z)$ may be multi-valued. In summary, to define strategy spaces one must first find classes $\mathcal{Y}_1$ and $\mathcal{Z}_1$ of piecewise continuous functions on $\mathcal{R}$ (or a more general class of functions on $\mathcal{R}$) such that for Y in $\mathcal{Y}_1$ and Z in $\mathcal{Z}_1$ the differential equation (2.2) has a solution that reaches $\mathcal{T}$. Given a differential equation (2.1), it is generally not easy to determine maximal classes $\mathcal{Y}_1$ and $\mathcal{Z}_1$ with such properties.

Let us suppose that we can find strategy spaces $\mathcal{Y}$ and $\mathcal{Z}$ of piecewise $C^{(1)}$ functions, and therefore can define the game $(\mathcal{Y}, \mathcal{Z}, P)$. Such strategies will be called pure strategies. The following questions now arise. Does the game $(\mathcal{Y}, \mathcal{Z}, P)$ have a value? If the game has a value do optimal pure strategies exist? If the game has a pure strategy solution, can one characterize it in a reasonable way? We shall take up these questions in succeeding sections. We begin with the last question.

GAMES WITH SADDLE POINTS

Let P be given by (1.2). For each initial condition (t,x) in $\mathcal{R}$ let us suppose that we can define a game $(\mathcal{Y}, \mathcal{Z}, v)$, where $\mathcal{Y}$ and $\mathcal{Z}$ are classes of piecewise $C^{(1)}$ functions and where $v = P(t,x,Y,Z)$. Moreover, let us suppose that the classes $\mathcal{Y}$ and $\mathcal{Z}$ are independent of (t,x). We say that the game $(\mathcal{Y}, \mathcal{Z}, P)$ has a pure strategy solution Y^*, Z^* if $P(t,x,Y^*,Z^*)$ is single valued and if for all Y in $\mathcal{Y}$, for all Z in $\mathcal{Z}$, and all (t,x) in $\mathcal{R}$

$$(3.1) \qquad P(t,x,Y,Z^*) \leq P(t,x,Y^*,Z^*) \leq P(t,x,Y^*,Z).$$

We note that if $P(t,x,Y^*,Z)$ is multi-valued, then the inequality in (3.1) must hold for all values of $P(t,x,Y^*,Z)$. A similar remark holds concerning $P(t,x,Y,Z^*)$. We also remark that the requirement that $P(t,x,Y^*,Z^*)$ be single valued does not preclude the possibility of there being more than one trajectory from (t,x) resulting from (Y^*,Z^*);

it requires that P take on the same value along all such trajectories.

The functions (Y^*,Z^*) having the properties listed in the preceding paragraph will be called an optimal pair or saddle point. We shall set

$$W(t,x) = P(t,x,Y^*,Z^*).$$

Thus, $W(t,x)$ is the value of the game $(\mathcal{Y},\mathcal{Z},P)$ starting at (t,x). We shall call the function W the value function or simply the value of the game.

We remark that the developments that are to follow are applicable to a somewhat more general situation than that of the game. We saw that one of the difficulties in defining a game stems from the need to specify strategy spaces $\mathcal{Y}$ and $\mathcal{Z}$. We can partially overcome this difficulty by the following artifice. Let $\mathcal{Y}_1$ and $\mathcal{Z}_1$ be two classes of piecewise $C^{(1)}$ functions. We say that the triple $[\mathcal{Y}_1,\mathcal{Z}_1,P]$ determines a pseudo-game if there exists a Y^* in $\mathcal{Y}_1$ and a Z^* in $\mathcal{Z}_1$ such that some solution of (2.2) reaches $\mathcal{T}$. We say that the pseudo-game $[\mathcal{Y}_1,\mathcal{Z}_1,P]$ has a saddle point if (i) there exist a Y^* in $\mathcal{Y}_1$ and a Z^* in $\mathcal{Z}_1$ such that for all initial conditions $(t,x) \in \mathcal{R}$, all solutions of (2.2) corresponding to (Y^*,Z^*) reach $\mathcal{T}$; (ii) $P(t,x,Y^*,Z^*)$ is single valued in $\mathcal{R}$; (iii) for all Y in $\mathcal{Y}_1$, for all Z in $\mathcal{Z}_1$ and for all initial conditions (t,x) in $\mathcal{R}$, all solutions of (2.2) corresponding to (Y,Z^*) and (Z,Y^*) reach $\mathcal{T}$; (iv) the relation (3.1) holds. The functions (Y^*,Z^*) constitute the saddle point.

A Y in $\mathcal{Y}_1$ and Z in $\mathcal{Z}_1$ will be called a

<u>playable pair</u> if for all initial conditions (t_o,x_o) in $\mathcal{R}$ all solutions of (2.2) corresponding to (Y,Z) reach $\mathcal{J}$. A solution of (2.2) corresponding to a playable pair (Y,Z) will be called a trajectory and will be denoted by $\phi(t,t_o,x_o)$. A solution of (2.2) corresponding to a saddle point will be called an optimal trajectory and will be denoted by $\phi^*(t,t_o,x_o)$ or simply by ϕ^*.

Let us now focus our attention upon each of the two inequalities in (3.1). The right hand inequality suggests the following control problem.

PROBLEM 1. Find a control that minimizes

$$h(t_1,x_1) + \int_{t_o}^{t_1} f(t,x(t),Y^*(t,x(t)),z(t))dt \tag{3.2}$$

subject to

$$\frac{dx}{dt} = g(t,x,Y^*(t,x),z) \qquad x(t_o) = x_o \tag{3.3}$$

$$z(t) \in \Omega(t,x(t)) \tag{3.4}$$

$$(t_1,x(t_1)) \in \mathcal{J}. \tag{3.5}$$

If in (3.3) we take $z = Z(t,x)$, where $Z \in \mathfrak{Z}$, then we obtain a solution ϕ that reaches $\mathcal{J}$ at $(t_1,x_1) = (t_1,\phi(t_1))$. Corresponding to this solution we obtain a control function of time

$$z(t) = Z(t,\phi(t))$$

such that if we take $z = z(t)$ in (3.3) we again obtain ϕ. Moreover, since by hypothesis $Z(t,x) \in \Omega(t,x)$, it follows that $z(t)$ satisfies (3.4). Denote the class of control functions of time $z(t)$ obtained this way by $\mathfrak{Z}'(t_o,x_o)$. Let $z^*(t)$ denote the control function of time corresponding to $Z^*(t,x)$. It follows from (3.1) that z^* is a minimizing control for Problem 1 in the class $\mathfrak{Z}'(t_o,x_o)$.

A ''control law'' or ''control strategy'', or ''synthesis of control'' or ''feedback control'' for Problem 1 is defined to be a function $Z(t,x)$ defined on $\mathcal{R}$ such that if we set $z = Z(t,x)$ in (3.3), then for all (t_o,x_o) in $\mathcal{R}$, the corresponding solution $\phi(t,t_o,x_o)$ of (3.3) reaches $\mathfrak{T}$ and (3.4) holds. In other words a control law for Problem 1 is a function Z such that (Y^*,Z) is a playable pair. Clearly, Z^* furnishes a minimum in Problem 1 in the class of control laws Z or functions Z such that (Y^*,Z) is a playable pair.

A discussion analogous to the preceding can be carried out for the left hand inequality. Thus, corresponding to each of the inequalities in (3.1) we obtain a control problem. This suggests that one should be able to obtain necessary conditions that hold along a solution of (2.2) corresponding to a saddle point (Y^*,Z^*) by considering the two associated variational problems and using results and techniques from the calculus of variations.

The above program was first carried out by Berkovitz and Fleming (7) for problems in the plane and later by Berkovitz (8) for more general problems. These authors obtained a two sided Weierstrass condition or min-max principle and a multiplier rule that must hold along an optimal trajectory. They also presented a Hamilton-Jacobi theory. More detailed statements of the results will be given below. Some of these results had been previously stated by Isaacs (2), who derived them heuristically or under more stringent assumptions.

In (7) and (8) the field of trajectories is assumed to possess certain properties that can be roughly summarized as follows. (See Figure)

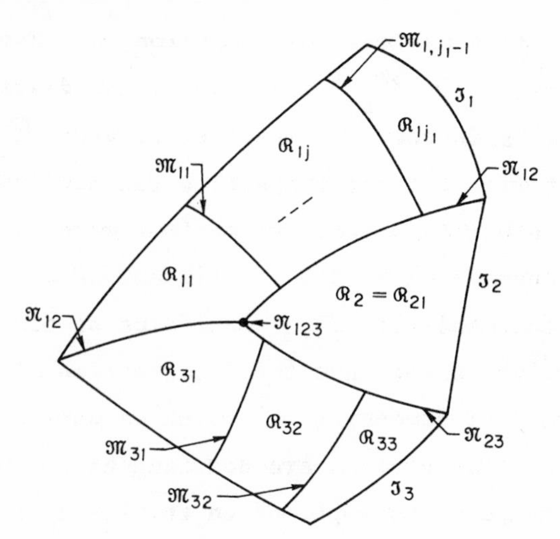

The region $\mathcal{R}$ can be written as

$$\mathcal{R} = \left(\bigcup_{i=1}^{n} \mathcal{R}_i\right) \cup \left(\mathcal{N}_{i_1 \ldots i_k}\right),$$

where the $\mathcal{R}_i$ are subregions each of which is simply covered by optimal trajectories and each $\mathcal{N}_{i_1 \ldots i_k}$ is a manifold of dimension $\leq n$ such that

$$\mathcal{N}_{i_1 \ldots i_k} = (\bar{\mathcal{R}}_{i_1} \cap \ldots \cap \bar{R}_{i_k}) \cap \mathcal{R}.$$

Moreover, from each point of a manifold $\mathcal{N}_{i_1 \ldots i_k}$, more than one trajectory can emanate. Each such trajectory, however, proceeds into the interior of only one of the regions $\mathcal{R}_{i_j}$, $j = 1, \ldots, k$. It is further assumed that each $\mathcal{R}_i$ can be written as the union of subregions $\mathcal{R}_{ij}$, $j = 1, \ldots, j_i$ such that in each $\mathcal{R}_{ij}$, the functions Y^* and Z^*

are $C^{(1)}$. If we set

$$\mathcal{M}_{ij} \equiv (\mathcal{R}_{ij} \cap \mathcal{R}_{i,j+1}) \cap \mathcal{R} \qquad j = 1,\ldots,j_i - 1,$$

then each $\mathcal{M}_{ij}$ is a manifold of dimension n that divides $\mathcal{R}_i$, and the manifolds $\mathcal{M}_{ij}$ are at positive distance from each other. It is further assumed that in each $\mathcal{R}_i$ the optimal trajectories are not tangent to the manifolds $\mathcal{M}_{ij}$. In (8) certain other technical assumptions were made, but they can be dispensed with, and so will not be listed here. We shall call the manifolds $\mathcal{M}_{ij}$ manifolds of discontinuity. Finally, we assume that the intersection of $\mathcal{T}$ and $\bar{\mathcal{R}}_i$ is a manifold of dimension n which we denote by $\mathcal{M}_{ij_i}$ and that optimal trajectories are not tangent to $\mathcal{M}_{ij_i}$.

The non-tangency assumptions on the field of trajectories are rather restrictive, as there exist problems in which these assumptions do not hold. In (8) the non-tangency restrictions and certain other restrictions arose from the need to guarantee that certain perturbations of Z*(t,x) will result in strategies that are still playable against Y*. This writer conjectures that the non-tangency restrictions are not essential in deriving the min-max principle and the multiplier rule, and merely arose from the particular perturbations used in (8). In establishing a Hamilton-Jacobi theory they probably are essential.

In (9) we established a Hamilton-Jacobi theory and the necessary conditions obtained in (8) by a somewhat different method. These results will be described below. The essential restrictions on the field of trajectories is the same as before; some of the more technical restrictions are removed, however. In (9) we first show that on each

$\mathcal{R}_i$ the function $W(t,x)$ is $C^{(1)}$, except perhaps at the manifolds of discontinuity $\mathcal{M}_{ij}$, $j = 1,\ldots,j_i - 1$ of Y^* or Z^* or both. A partial differential equation that W satisfies and a min-max relation are then deduced. It is then shown that W has continuous partial derivatives across those manifolds $\mathcal{M}_{ij}$ that are manifolds of discontinuity of only one of the functions Y^* or Z^*. A ''multiplier'' or ''adjoint variable'' is then introduced as a solution of the system adjoint to the equations of variation of (2.2), and this function is identified with W_x.

We now state some of the principal results concerning differential games with pure strategy solutions. The assumptions concerning the field of trajectories are essentially those stated above. For a more complete statement of the hypotheses and conclusions the reader is referred to (9).

THEOREM 1. *The value function W is continuous on $\mathcal{R}$. On each $\mathcal{R}_{ij}$, W_t and W_x exist, are continuous, and have continuous extensions to $\bar{\mathcal{R}}_{ij} \cap \mathcal{R}$. If $\mathcal{M}_{ij}$ is a manifold of discontinuity of only one of the functions Y^* or Z^*, then W_t and W_x are continuous at points of $\mathcal{M}_{ij}$. The function W satisfies*

$$\text{(3.6)} \qquad \max_y \min_z (f + W_x g) = \min_z \max_y (f + W_x g)$$

$$= f(t,x,y^*,z^*) + W_x G(t,x,y^*,z^*)$$

$$= -W_t,$$

where the following meanings are to be attached to the various symbols. The functions W_t and W_x are evaluated at (t,x); the arguments of f and G when not indicated are (t,x,y,z), and

$$
(3.7) \quad \begin{aligned} y &\in E[y \mid y = Y(t,x), \quad Y \in \mathcal{Y}] \\ z &\in E[z \mid z = Z(t,x), \; Z \in \mathcal{Z}\,], \end{aligned}
$$

$y^* = Y^*(t,x)$ <u>and</u> $z^* = Z^*(t,x)$. <u>At points of manifolds of discontinuity and at the terminal manifold the relations are to be interpreted as holding for the various one-sided limits.</u>

If we define a function H as follows,

$$H(t,x,y,z,\lambda) = f(t,x,y,z) + \lambda g(t,x,y,z),$$

then the last equation in (3.6) can be written as

$$H(t,x,Y^*(t,x),Z^*(t,x),W_x(t,x)) + W_t(t,x) = 0,$$

and so we have the following corollary.

<u>COROLLARY</u>. W <u>satisfies the Hamilton-Jacobi equation in</u> $\mathcal{R}$, <u>provided we interpret</u> Y^*, Z^*, W_x <u>and</u> W_t <u>as one sided limits at manifolds of discontinuity and at manifolds</u> $\mathcal{N}_{i_1 \ldots i_k}$.

Let $\phi^*(t) = \phi^*(t,\tau,\xi)$ be the optimal trajectory from a point (τ,ξ) in $\mathcal{R}_{ij}$. Let t_{ik}, $k = j, j+1, \ldots, j_i$ denote the time at which the trajectory intercepts the manifold $\mathcal{M}_{ik}$, $k = j, j+1, \ldots, j_i$. Recall that $\mathcal{M}_{ij_i}$ is part of the terminal set $\mathcal{T}$. We can define a function $\lambda(t,\tau,)$ corresponding to $\phi^*(t,\tau,\xi)$ as follows. On each interval $(t_{ik}, t_{i,k+1})$, $k = j-1, \ldots, j_i-1$ take λ to be the solution of the linear differential equation

$$
(3.8) \quad \frac{d\lambda}{dt} = -\frac{\partial H}{\partial x}(t,\phi^*(t), Y^*(t,\phi^*(t)), Z^*(t,\phi^*(t)), \lambda),
$$

where

$$\frac{\partial H}{\partial x} = H_x + H_y Y^*_x + H_z Z^*_x$$

and the left hand limits $\lambda(t_{ik} - 0)$ at points t_{ik}, $k = j, j+1, \ldots, j_i$, take on certain prescribed values. Note, that $\lambda(t_{ik} + 0)$ exists for $k < j_i$. For proper choice of $\lambda(t_{ik} - 0)$ we obtain that

$$\lambda(\tau,\tau,\xi) = W_x(\tau,\xi) \tag{3.9}$$

in $\mathcal{R}_{ij}$. Equations (3.8) together with (3.6) in which we replace W_x by λ now give a ''min-max principle'' or two sided Weierstrass condition. For more detailed statements, further results, and proofs the reader is referred to (9).

The relationship between games with saddle points and variational problems suggests a method for constructing saddle points when they exist. The method involves the construction of the analogue of a field in the calculus of variations, or equivalently, the solution of the Hamilton-Jacobi equation by the method of characteristics.

A region $\mathcal{R}$ and functions Y^*, Z^*, Λ are said to constitute a field $\mathcal{F}$ if the following hold. (i) The functions Y^* and Z^* satisfy the constraints; that is $Y^*(t,x) \in \bar{\Omega}(t,x)$ and $Z^*(t,x) \in \Omega(t,x)$. (ii) The set of solution trajectories of the differential equation

$$\frac{dx}{dt} = G(t,x,Y^*(t,x), Z^*(t,x)) \tag{3.10}$$

satisfies the assumptions made concerning the field of trajectories associated with a saddle point in the discussion of the necessary conditions, (iii). The function

$$W(\tau,\xi) = h(t_1,x_1) + \int_\tau^{t_1} f(t,\phi^*(t), Y^*(t,\phi^*(t)), Z^*(t,\phi^*(t))dt$$

is single valued in $\mathcal{R}$, where $\phi^*(t) \equiv \phi^*(t,\tau,\xi)$ is the solution of (3.10) satisfying the initial condition $\phi^*(\tau,\tau,\xi) = \xi$. On each $\bar{\mathcal{R}}_{ij} \cap \mathcal{R}$, the integral

$$(3.11) \qquad \int_C H(t,x,Y^*,Z^*, \ )dt - \Lambda\, dx$$

is independent of path. In addition to these conditions, a certain behavior is imposed on Λ at the terminal set $\mathcal{T}$ and at manifolds of discontinuity.

Let $\mathcal{F}$ be a field and let $\mathcal{Y}_1$ be the set of all Y that satisfy the constraints $Y(t,x) \in \bar{\Omega}(t,x)$, that are piecewise $C^{(1)}$ on $\mathcal{R}$, and are playable against Z^*. (In the definitions of playable we require here that the trajectories resulting from (Y,Z^*) lie in $\mathcal{R}$.) Let $\mathcal{Z}_1$ be similarly defined for a class of functions Z. By arguments similar to those used in the classical calculus of variations it can be shown (8) that if (3.6) holds with W_x replaced by Λ, where we replace $\mathcal{Y}$ by $\mathcal{Y}_1$ and replace $\mathcal{Z}$ by $\mathcal{Z}_1$ in (3.7), then (Y^*,Z^*) is a saddle point for the pseudo-game $[\mathcal{Y}_1, \mathcal{Z}_1, P]$. If $\mathcal{Y}_o$ is a subset of $\mathcal{Y}_1$ and $\mathcal{Z}_o$ is a subset of $\mathcal{Z}_1$ such that every pair (Y,Z) with $Y \in \mathcal{Y}_o$ and $Z \in \mathcal{Z}_o$ is playable (in $\mathcal{R}$), then (Y^*,Z^*) is a saddle point for the game $(\mathcal{Y}_o, \mathcal{Z}_o, P)$.

The question now arises as to how one constructs a field. Roughly speaking, the following procedure can be used. Integrate the equations (3.8) and

$$(3.12) \qquad \frac{dx}{dt} = G(t,x,y^*,z^*)$$

backwards from the terminal manifold, where y^* and z^* are chosen so that (3.6) holds with W_x replaced by λ. The values of λ at the terminal manifold are obtained from the transversality condition. The values of λ at points of discontinuity of y^* and z^* are the same as those used in the process of identifying the solution of (3.8) with W_x in the discussion of the necessary conditions. The solutions ϕ, λ, y^*, z^* so obtained will be parametrized by the coordinates of the points $u = (t_1, x_1)$ of the terminal manifold from which the emanate. (We assume for simplicity's sake that $\mathcal{T}$ is n-dimensional). Thus we write the solutions as $\phi(t,u)$, $\lambda(t,u)$, $y^*(t,u)$, $z^*(t,u)$. Along each path one can also compute the function

$$W(t,u) = h(u) - \int_{t_1}^{t} f(\tau, \phi(\tau,u), y^*(\tau,u), z^*(\tau,u))d\tau. \tag{3.13}$$

If the trajectories $\phi(t,u)$ simply cover $\mathcal{R}$, then we can invert the relation

$$x = \phi(t,u)$$

and obtain

$$u = U(t,x).$$

Moreover, if in the neighborhood of a point (t_o, u_o) ϕ is $C^{(1)}$ and $\det \phi_u(t,u) \neq 0$, it follows that U is $C^{(1)}$ in a neighborhood of (t_o, x_o), where $x_o = \phi(t_o, u_o)$. Thus, we obtain the field functions Y^*, Z^* and Λ by setting

$$\begin{aligned} Y^*(t,x) &= y^*(t, U(t,x)) \\ Z^*(t,x) &= z^*(t, U(t,x)) \\ \Lambda(t,x) &= \lambda(t, U(t,x)). \end{aligned}$$

From the conditions placed on λ at the terminal manifold and at the manifolds of discontinuity, and from the differential equations (3.8) and (3.12) it follows that the integral in (3.11) is independent of path.

Since the equations (3.12) and (3.8) are the characteristic equations for the Hamilton Jacobi equation

$$H(t,x,Y^*,Z^*,W_x) + W_t = 0,$$

it follows that the preceding construction of a field is equivalent to solving the Hamilton-Jacobi equation by the method of characteristics. For a more precise discussion and for details the reader is referred to (7), (8), (10). The procedure just outline for constructing fiels is essentially the same as the method used by Isaacs in solving many of his examples (2).

If the trajectories multiply cover $\mathcal{R}$, then the function $W(t,u)$ defined in (3.13) can be used to determine subregions $\mathcal{R}_i$ such that each $\mathcal{R}_i$ is simply covered by a family of trajectories, $\mathcal{R}$ is the union of the $\mathcal{R}_i$, and a field results in $\mathcal{R}$. This procedure is discussed for the problem in the plane and is illustrated by an example in (7). A more thorough and complete treatment for a class of max-min problems is given by Pontryagin in (11).

GAMES WITHOUT PURE STRATEGY SOLUTIONS

In this selection we shall discuss games that do not have pure strategy solutions We begin with a simple example of such a game in the plane Let $T > 0$ be fixed and let $\mathcal{R}$ be the strip $-\epsilon < t < T$, where $\epsilon > 0$. Player I chooses $y = Y(t,x)$, where Y is piecewise $C^{(1)}$ on $\mathcal{R}$ and $0 \leq Y(t,x) \leq 1$. Similarly, Player II chooses $z = Z(t,x)$, where Z is piecewise $C^{(1)}$ and $0 \leq Z(t,x) \leq 1$. The state x is determined by the system of differential equations

$$\frac{dx}{dt} = (y - z)^2 \qquad x(0) = x_o.$$

Play terminates at $t = T$. The function P is given by

$$P(0, x_o, Y, Z) = \int_0^T x \, dt.$$

We shall show that for this game, max min $\neq$ min max over pure strategies.

For a given choice of Y by Player I, Player II can choose the same strategy and thus guarantee $dx/dt = 0$ on $[0,T]$. Hence

$$\sup_y \inf_x \int_0^T x \, dt \leq x_o T.$$

But since $\int_0^T x \, dt \geq x_o T$ for any playable pair (Y,Z), it follows that

$$\max \min \int_0^T x \, dt = x_o T. \tag{4.1}$$

On the other hand, if Player II chooses a strategy Z, then Player I can choose a strategy Y as follows:

$$\begin{aligned} Y(t,x) &= 1 & \text{if } Z(t,x) &\leq 1/2 \\ &= 0 & \text{if } Z(t,x) &> 1/2. \end{aligned}$$

In so doing, Player I guarantees $dx/dt \geq 1/4$ on $[0,T]$. Hence

$$\inf_z \sup_y \int_0^T x \, dt \geq x_o T + T^2/8. \tag{4.2}$$

Let Player II now choose $Z(t,x) \equiv 1/2$. Then, for any Y, $dx/dt \leq 1/4$ on $[0,T]$. Hence upon integrating and comparing with (4.2), we get that

$$\min_z \max_y \int_0^T x \, dt = x_o T + T^2/8.$$

Comparing this result with (4.2) we see that the game does not have a value in pure strategies, and so a fortiori it does not have any pure strategy solutions.

We remark that the necessary conditions of Section 3 enable us to manufacture examples of differential games without a value in pure strategies. From (3.6) we see that for this purpose we should take functions g and f such that for all (t,x,λ) in the appropriate domain, the game with payoff

$$f(t, x, y, z) + \lambda g(t, x, y, z),$$

in which Player I chooses y as in (3.7) and Player II chooses z as in (3.7), does not have a value in pure strategies.

From a purely mathematical point of view the above discussion suffices to point out the need to consider differential games without a value in pure strategies. To emphasize the importance of this problem, however, we call attention to the so called ''tactical air games'' that arose in applications and do not have pure strategy solutions. These games differ from the games discussed in this survey in that time is discrete and the differential equations are replaced by difference equations. For a discussion of the applications and for the complete solution of these games, which involves the use of mixed strategies, see (12), (13), (14). In (15) it is shown that the differential game version of a tactical air game also cannot have a pure strategy solution.

Another interesting example of a differential game without a value in pure strategies is a pursuit and evasion game in the plane studied by Zieba (16).

The general question of characterizing games that have values in pure strategies has not as yet been treated with success. One of the difficulties stems from the problem of characterizing the classes of pure strategies for any given differential game. One result in this direction is due to Ryll-Nardzewski (17) who formulates an abstract pursuit and evasion game and gives sufficient conditions for this game to have a value. As yet, these results have not been interpreted for games of pursuit and evasion determined by systems of differential equations.

It is well known that matrix games that do not have pure strategy solutions always have solutions in mixed strategies. Also, ''games over the square'' whose payoffs have certain continuity properties always have solutions in mixed strategies. See (5) or (6). This leads one to consider the possibility of introducing the notion of mixed strategy for differential games. The mathematical difficulties that arise when this is attempted have not as yet been overcome. Fleming has attacked this problem by approximating the differential game by difference games with discrete time. We shall devote the remainder of this section to a survey of his results, (18), (19), (20).

A time discrete version of a differential game with terminal manifold given by $t = T$, where T is fixed, is defined as follows. Let Π be a partition of $(0,T)$ defined by points

$$0 = t_1 < t_2 < \dots < t_N < t_{N+1} = T.$$

Let $\delta_k = t_{k+1} - t_k$. The equations (2.1) are replaced by equations

$$(4.3) \qquad x_{k+1} = x_k + \delta_k g(x_k, y_k, z_k) \qquad y_k \in \mathcal{Y}, z_k \in \mathcal{Z},$$

where $\mathcal{Y}$ and $\mathcal{Z}$ are compact sets in E^σ and E^s respectively, and the initial position x_1 is specified. The payoff (1.2) is replaced by

$$(4.4) \qquad h(x_{N+1}) + \sum_1^N \delta_k f(x_k, y_k, z_k).$$

At move k, $k = 1,\ldots,N$ Player I chooses y_k and Player II chooses z_k. The choices are made with the knowledge of the position x_k of the game after $k - 1$ moves, but <u>without</u> knowledge of the opponents' choice of strategic variable at move k. For each (x,k) let $\eta(x,k)$ be a probability measure on $\mathcal{Y}$ such that $\eta(x,k)$ is carried by a finite set of points in $\mathcal{Y}$ and let $\zeta(x,k)$ be a probability measure on $\mathcal{Z}$ such that $\zeta(x,k)$ is carried by a finite set of points in $\mathcal{Z}$. A strategy for Player I is a function $\eta(x,k)$; a strategy for Player II is a function $\zeta(x,k)$. Let us call the discrete time game just described Δ.

If Δ has a value, it will depend on the intial point x, the duration T, and the partition Π. We denote the value, if it exists, by $V(x,T;\Pi)$. Consider the game over $\mathcal{Y} \times \mathcal{Z}$ with payoff $M(y,z)$, where M is continuous. This game has a value in mixed strategies (see (<u>6</u>)), which we denote by $\text{val } M(y,z)$.

Fleming has shown (<u>18</u>) that for the time discrete game Δ the following is true. For each initial x, each $T > 0$, and each partition Π, $V(x,T,\Pi)$ exists. V is continuous in x for each T and Π and satisfies

(4.5) $$V(x,T,\Pi) = \text{val}\,[\delta_1 f(x,y,z) + V(x + \delta_1 g(x,y,z),\ T - \delta_1;\ \Pi')],$$

where Π' is the partition of $(0, T - \delta_1)$ given by $t_1',\ldots,t_N'$ with $t_i' = t_{i+1}$ and

(4.6) $$V(x,\ T - \delta_1;\ \Pi') = h(x) \quad \text{if} \quad \delta_1 = T.$$

We now return to the differential game with continuous time. It is assumed that the functions f and g do not depend on t. We take the terminal manifold to be given by $t = T$, where T is fixed. Let $\mathcal{Y}$ be a compact set in E^σ and let $\mathfrak{Z}$ be a compact set in E^s. A strategy for Player I is taken to be a choice of partition Π_1 of the interval $[0,T]$ and a function $\mu(x,t)$ whose values are measures on $\mathcal{Y}$ carried by a finite number of points. A strategy for Player II is a partition Π_2 and a function $\zeta(x,t)$ whose values are measures on $\mathfrak{Z}$ carried by a finite number of points. Let Π be a partition that is the common refinement of Π_1 and Π_2, and let the partition points of Π be $\{t_i\}_{i=1}^{N+1}$. Play proceeds as in the discrete game with strategies $\mu(x,t_k)$, $\zeta(x,t_k)$. The payoff to Player I is given by (4.4). We shall call this version of the continuous game Γ.

Let $V(x,T,\Pi)$ be the value of the discrete game with duration T, initial position x and partition Π, where Π is as obtained in the preceding paragraph. In (18) Fleming shows that if there exists a continuous solution $V(x,T)$ of the partial differential equation

(4.7) $$V_T(x,T) = \underset{(y,z)}{\text{val}}\ [f(x,y,z) + V_x(x,T)g(x,y,z)] \qquad T \geq 0$$

(4.8) $$V(x,0) = h(x)$$

in a certain region $\mathcal{R}$, then

(4.9) $$\lim_{|\Pi| \to 0} V(x,T,\Pi) = V(x,T)$$

uniformly in $\mathcal{R}$, and the game Γ has the value $V(x,T)$ in $\mathcal{R}$.

The preceding result is somewhat unsatisfactory in that there is no accompanying existence theorem for (4.7) and (4.8). In (19) Fleming dispenses with the assumption that (4.7) has a smooth solution with initial data (4.8). Instead, he places restrictions on the functions f and g. Both functions are assumed to satisfy a uniform Lipschitz condition in x. The function f is assumed to be concave in y for each fixed (x,z) and is assumed to be convex in z for each (x,y). The function g is assumed to be bilinear in y and z for each fixed x. Finally, f and y are assumed to have the special forms

(4.10) $$\begin{aligned} f(x,y,z) &= a(x,y) + b(x,z) \\ g(x,y,z) &= c(x,y) + d(x,z) \end{aligned}$$

The continuous game Γ is defined essentially as before. Because of the convexity and concavity assumptions attention can be restricted to functions μ and ν whose values are measures concentrated at single points, i.e. pure strategies. Fleming shows that under the hypothesis listed, the value $V(x,T,\Pi)$ of the game Δ with discrete time, that corresponds as above to the game Γ, with continuous time, exists, satisfies (4.5) and (4.6), and converges uniformly on bounded sets as the norm of the partition tends to zero. Moreover, the limit $V(x,T)$ is the value of the game Γ with continuous time. No assertion is made that the limit $V(x,T)$ satisfies (4.7) and (4.8).

All of the preceding results were obtained by elementary arguments. In (20) Fleming uses deeper results from the theory of partial differential equations to prove that $V(x,T,\Pi)$, the value of the discrete time game Δ, converges uniformly on bounded sets, without placing any restrictive assumptions on f and g. All that is assumed concerning f and g is that they are continuous and satisfy a Lipschitz condition It is as yet not known whether now the limit function $V(x,T)$ is the value of the continuous game Γ. Also the question whether (4.7) and (4.8) hold is open.

DIFFERENTIAL GAMES OF SURVIVAL

A variant of the differential game considered heretofore is the so called ''differential game of survival'', or ''differential game of kind'', in the terminology of Isaacs (2). Here the state of the game is also given by a system of differential equations (2.1), and the strategies are chosen as before. The objective, however, is different. A set $\mathcal{J}$ in $\mathcal{R}$ is given. Player I wishes to choose a strategy Y_o in $\mathcal{Y}$ such that no matter what strategy Z in $\mathcal{Z}$ Player II chooses, the point $(t,x(t))$, $t_o < t < \infty$, will never belong to $\mathcal{J}$. Here, of course, $x(t)$ is the solution of

$$\frac{dx}{dt} = g(t,x,Y_o(t,x),Z(t,x)) \qquad x(t_o) = x_o.$$

If such a strategy Y_o exists, Player I is said to win. Similarly, Player II wishes to choose a strategy Z_o in $\mathcal{Z}$

such that no matter what strategy Y in $\mathcal{Y}$ Player I chooses, there will exist a time $t(Y)$ such that $t_o < t(Y) < \infty$ and such that $(t(Y), x(t(Y)))$ is a point of $\mathcal{J}$. If such a strategy Z_o exists, Player II is said to win. The problem is two-fold. First determine the set of initial conditions (t_o,x_o) for which Player I wins, the set of initial conditions for which Player II wins, and the set for which neither wins. Second, determine the winning strategies when they exist.

Games of survival usually arise from pursuit and evasion problems. Isaacs seems to have been the first to study these games; many examples of such games are discussed in his book (2).

Differential games of survival can be modified by assigning a payoff $M(x_1)$ to the position at which $\mathcal{J}$ is first reached, should this occur. Thus, for intial positions that result in a win for Player II, one has a differential game as defined in the preceding sections of this paper. We shall call such games ''survival games with payoff''.

Scarf (21) and Petrosjan (22), (23), (24), (25), seem to be the only authors other than Isaacs who have contributed to the problem of differential games of survival. Scarf (21) obtained some preliminary results for games in the plane with survival payoff. He discretized time and studied the limiting behavior of the value of the discrete game under rather restrictive assumptions. In (22) Petrosjan studies a survival game with payoff in the plane and shows that the game has a continuously differentiable value in pure strategies if and only if a certain partial differential equation has a solution.

In (23), (24), (25) the information pattern is one in which Player I (henceforth to be called the evader) chooses his strategy Y. Player II (henceforth to be called the pursuer) chooses his strategy Z, where Z is a function of Y. In (23) Petrosjan gives some properties of the set of initial states from which capture can occur. In (24) he considers survival games, survival games with payoff, and games with several pursuers and several evaders. For a survival game with n pursuers and one evader Petrosjan gives some restrictions on initial conditions that ensure capture and gives the forms of optimal strategies. For the survival game with payoff considered in (24) it is stated that a solution in pure strategies exists. Results are also stated for variants of this survival game and for survival games with payoff involving several pursuers and evaders. In (25) a survival game with payoff is studied for those initial conditions that result in capture. The investigation centers about the behavior of the value of time-discrete approximations as the norm of the approximation tends to zero.

FINAL REMARKS.

The reader will undoubtedly think of many problems that have not been treated in this survey. For these shortcomings we offer our apologies. We do, however, wish to mention some interesting games related to differential games that are not strictly within the scope of this survey. First is the Markov game studied by Zachrisson (26). Second, is the collection of tracking and evasion problems studied by

Grenander (27).

BIBLIOGRAPHY

1. Isaacs, R., ''Differential games I, II, III, IV'', The RAND Corporation, Research Memoranda RM-1391, RM-1399, RM-1411, RM-1486, 1954.

2. Isaacs, R., Differential Games, John Wiley and Sons, New York, London, Sydney, 1965.

3. Steinhaus, H., ''Definitions for a theory of games and pursuit'', Naval Res. Logist. Quart. 7(1960), 105-108. Transaltion of ''Definicje potrzebne do teorji gry i póscigo'', Myśl Akademicka, Lwów, 1925. nr. 1.

4. Zieba, A., ''Fundamental equations of the theory of pursuit'', Transactions of the 2nd Prague Conference on Information Theory, Statistical Decision Functions, Random Processes, Publishing House of the Czechoslovak Academy of Sciences, Prague, 1960.

5. Dresher, M., Games of Strategy: Theory and Applications, Prentice-Hall, Englewood Cliffs, 1961.

6. Karlin, S., Mathematical Methods and Theory in Games, Programming, and Economics. 2 Vols. Addison-Wesley, Reading, Mass. and London. 1959.

7. Berkovitz, L.D. and Fleming, W.H., ''On differential games with integral payoff'', Annals of Mathematics Study No. 39, Princeton University Press, Princeton, 1957, 413-433.

8. Berkovitz, L.D., ''A variational approach to differential games'', Annals of Mathematics Study No. 52, Princeton University Press, Princeton 1964, 127-174.

9. Berkovitz, L.D., ''Necessary conditions for optimal strategies in a class of differential games and control problems'', SIAM J. Control 5, (1967).

10. Berkovitz, L.D., ''Variational methods in problems of control and programming,'' J. Math. Anal. Appl. 3 (1961), 145-169.

11. Pontryagin, L.S., ''Towards a theory of differential games'', Uspehi Mat. Nauk. 21(1966), 219-274.

12. Berkovitz, L.D. and Dresher, M., ''A multimove infinite game with linear payoff'', Pacific J. Math. 10 (1960), 743-765.

13. Berkovitz, L.D. and Dresher, M., ''A game theory analysis of tactical air war,'' Operations Res. 7(1959), 599-620.

14. Berkovitz, L.D. and Dresher, M., ''Allocation of two types of aircraft in tactical air war: a game theoretic analysis'', Operations Res. 8(1960), 694-706.

15. Berkovitz, L.D., ''A differential game with no pure strategy solution'', Annals of Mathematics Study No. 52, Princeton University Press, Princeton 1964, 175-194.

16. Zieba, A., ''An example in pursuit theory'', Studia Math. 22 (1962), 1-6.

17. Ryll-Nardzewski, C., ''A theory of pursuit and evasion'', Annals of Mathematics Study No. 52, Princeton University Press, Princeton, 1964, 113-126.

18. Fleming, W.H., ''A note on differential games of prescribed duration,'' Annals of Mathematics Study No. 39, Princeton University Press, Princeton, 1957, 407-412.

19. Fleming, W.H., ''The convergence problem for differential games,'' J. Math. Anal. Appl. 3(1961), 102-116.

20. Fleming, W.H., ''The convergence problem for differential games II,'' Annals of Mathematics Study No. 52, Princeton University Press, Princeton, 1964, 195-210.

21. Scarf, Herbert E., ''Games with survival payoff,'' Annals of Mathematics Study No. 39, Princeton University Press, Princeton, New Jersey, 1957, 393-405.

22. Petrosjan, L.A., ''On the reduction of the solution of a game of pursuit and survival to the solution of the Cauchy problem for a first order partial differential equation'', Akad. Nauk Armjan. SSR Dokl. 40(1965), 193-196. (Russian).

23. Petrosjan, L.A., ''On a family of differential games of survival in the space R^n'', Dokl. Akad. Nauk SSSR 161 (1965), 52-54. (Russian).

24. Petrosjan, L.A., ''Differential games of survival with many participants'', Dokl. Akad. Nauk SSSR 161 (1965), 285-287. (Russian).

25. Petrosjan, L.A., ''A game of pursuit in the half-plane'', Akad. Nauk Armjan. SSR Dokl. 40(1965), 265-269. (Russian).

26. Zachrisson, L.E., ''Markov games'', Annals of Mathematics Study No. 52, Princeton University Press, Princeton 1964, 211-253.

27. Grenander, U., A Tactical Study of Evasive Manoeuvres, FOA P Report, A 126 Research Institute of National Defense, Stockholm, 1963.

ON LINEAR DIFFERENTIAL GAMES

Yoshiyuki Sakawa

Faculty of Engineering Science, Osaka University
Toyonaka, Osaka, Japan

1. Statement of the Problems

This paper treats a certain class of linear differential games, the state of which is specified by a state vector in an n-dimensional Euclidean space R^n. It is assumed that the state vector z(t) in R^n can be expressed as

$$z(t) = z_1(t) + \int_0^t F(t,s)u(s)ds + \int_0^t W(t,s)v(s)ds, \qquad (1)$$

where u(t) and v(t) are r-vectors called strategies or controls of the first and the second players, respectively, F(t,s) and W(t,s) are n×r matrix functions which are assumed to be continuous, and $z_1(t)$ is a known n-dimensional vector function. It is assumed that the strategies u(t) and v(t) are piecewise continuous and constrained as

$$u(t) \in U, \quad v(t) \in V, \qquad (2)$$

where U and V are certain sets in an r-dimensional Euclidean space. Such strategies u(t) and v(t) which satisfy above mentioned conditions are called admissible strategies. In this paper, we treat the case where the sets U and V are unit cube, respectively, i.e.,

$$U = V = \Omega = \left\{ u : |u_i| \leq 1 \ (i = 1, \cdots, r) \right\}. \qquad (3)$$

We consider two kinds of differential game problems stated as follows:

Problem 1. Determine a saddle point for

$$J(u,v) = (z(T),z(T)) + \int_0^T \left\{ (u(t),Cu(t)) - (v(t),Dv(t)) \right\} dt \qquad (4)$$

subject to the constraints (1) and (2), where (,) denotes the inner product in some finite-dimensional Euclidean space, C and D are r×r positive semidefinite diagonal matrices with nonnegative constant elements, and T is a fixed time. J(u,v) is called a payoff. A saddle point is defined as the pair

$u^o(t)$, $v^o(t)$ satisfying the relation

$$J(u^o,v) \leq J(u^o,v^o) \leq J(u,v^o) \tag{5}$$

for arbitrary admissible strategies u and v. Namely, the first player is to select a strategy that minimizes the payoff and the second player is to select a strategy that maximizes the payoff. If relation (5) can be realized, u^o and v^o are called the optimal strategies and $J(u^o,v^o)$ is called the value of the game.

Problem 2. Let $T_{u,v}$ be a time corresponding to the strategies $u(t) \in U$, $v(t) \in V$ and satisfying $z(T_{u,v}) = 0$. Determine a time T_{u^o,v^o} and a pair of admissible strategies $u^o(t)$, $v^o(t)$ such that

$$z(T_{u^o,v^o}) = 0, \quad T_{u^o,v^o} = \min_{u \in U} \max_{v \in V} T_{u,v}. \tag{6}$$

The second equation of (6) is equivalent to

$$T_{u^o,v} \leq T_{u^o,v^o} \leq T_{u,v^o}$$

Such differential game problems have been treated by several authors [1]-[7]. In this paper we consider the problems as an infinite-dimensional nonlinear programming problem [8]. By using the generalized Kuhn-Tucker theorem [9] in nonlinear programming, we derive a system of transcendental equations, the solution of which directly yields the optimal strategies.

We can mention two kinds of games describable in the form (1). One is a pursuit-evasion game governed by

$$\left.\begin{aligned} dx_p/dt &= A_p(t)x_p + B_p(t)u(t) + h_p(t), \quad x_p(0) = x_{po}, \\ dx_e/dt &= A_e(t)x_e + B_e(t)v(t) + h_e(t), \quad x_e(0) = x_{eo}, \end{aligned}\right\} \tag{7}$$

where x_p is an n-vector representing the state of the pursuer, $u(t) \in U$ is an r-vector representing the control of the pursuer, $A_p(t)$, $B_p(t)$, and $h_p(t)$ are $n \times n$, $n \times r$, and $n \times 1$ known matrices, respectively, continuous in t, and identical statements apply to the evader and x_e, $v(t) \in V$, $A_e(t)$, $B_e(t)$, and $h_e(t)$. x_{po} and x_{eo} are initial values. The state of the game is defined by

$$z(t) = Q[x_p(t) - x_e(t)], \tag{8}$$

where Q is an $n \times n$ positive semidefinite constant matrix. Then, the $z_1(t)$, $F(t,s)$, and $W(t,s)$ in Eq. (1) are given by

$$\begin{aligned} z_1(t) = Q[X_p(t)(x_{po} + \int_0^t X_p^{-1}(s)h_p(s)ds \\ -X_e(t)(x_{eo} + \int_0^t X_e^{-1}(s)h_e(s)ds)], \end{aligned}$$

$$\left.\begin{aligned} F(t,s) &= QX_p(t)X_p^{-1}(s)B_p(s), \\ W(t,s) &= -QX_e(t)X_e^{-1}(s)B_e(s), \end{aligned}\right\} \quad (9)$$

where $X_p(t)$ and $X_e(t)$ are n×n matrix functions satisfying

$$\left.\begin{aligned} dX_p(t)/dt &= A_p(t)X_p(t), \quad X_p(0) = I \text{ (the identity)}, \\ dX_e(t)/dt &= A_e(t)X_e(t), \quad X_e(0) = I. \end{aligned}\right\}$$

The other game describable in the form (1) is a control system subject to unpredictable disturbances. The state of the control system is governed by

$$dz/dt = A(t)z + B_1(t)u(t) + B_2(t)v(t) + h(t), \quad z(0) = z_0, \quad (10)$$

where $z(t)$ is an n-vector describing the state of the system, $u(t)\in U$ is an r-vector representing the control, $v(t)$ is an r-vector representing unpredictable disturbance functions, $A(t)$, $B_1(t)$, $B_2(t)$, and $h(t)$ are n×n, n×r, n×r, and n×1 known matrices, respectively, which are continuous in t. The known information concerning $v(t)$ is only the fact that $v(t)\in V$. In this case, the $z_1(t)$, $F(t,s)$, and $W(t,s)$ in Eq. (1) are given by

$$\left.\begin{aligned} z_1(t) &= X(t)[z_0 + \int_0^t X^{-1}(s)h(s)ds], \\ F(t,s) &= X(t)X^{-1}(s)B_1(s), \\ W(t,s) &= X(t)X^{-1}(s)B_2(s), \end{aligned}\right\} \quad (11)$$

where $X(t)$ is an n×n matrix function satisfying

$$dX(t)/dt = A(t)X(t), \quad X(0) = I.$$

2. Fundamental Theorem and its Application to the Problem 1

Since the solution of the Problem 2 is obtained from the solution of the Problem 1, we consider the Problem 1 first. Let H be a real Hilbert space of r-dimensional functions square integrable over [0,T]. Then, the strategies $u(t)$ and $v(t)$ $(0 \leq t \leq T)$ can be taken in H. Define the inner product of two vectors u^1 and u^2 in the Hilbert space H by

$$[u^1, u^2] = \int_0^T u^{1*}(t)u^2(t)dt = \int_0^T (u^1(t), u^2(t))dt,$$

where * denotes the transpose of a vector or a matrix. We define linear operators P and R, respectively, by

$$Pu = \int_0^T F(T,s)u(s)ds, \quad Rv = \int_0^T W(T,s)v(s)ds, \quad (12)$$

which map the Hilbert space H into the n-dimensional Euclidean space R^n. Then, from Eq. (1) it follows that

$$z_T = z_1 + Pu + Rv, \tag{13}$$

where $z_T = z(T)$ and $z_1 = z_1(T)$. The payoff (4) is rewritten as

$$J(u,v) = (z_T, z_T) + [u,Cu] - [v,Cv]. \tag{14}$$

By using Eq. (13), it follows that

$$(z_T, z_T) = (Pu,Pu) + 2(Pu, Rv + z_1) + (Rv + z_1, Rv + z_1). \tag{15}$$

Let P* now be the adjoint operator of P, then P* maps R^n into H and satisfies the relation

$$(x,Pu) = [P^*x,u],$$

where $x \in R^n$ and $u \in H$. From Eq. (12), it can be easily seen that

$$P^*x = F^*(T,t)x, \tag{16}$$

where F* denotes the transposed matrix of F. Then, the payoff (14) can be written as

$$\begin{aligned} J(u,v) &= [u,(P^*P + C)u] + 2[u,P^*(Rv + z_1)] \\ &\quad + (Rv + z_1, Rv + z_1) - [v,Dv] \\ &= [v,(R^*R - D)v] + 2[v,R^*(Pu + z_1)] \\ &\quad + (Pu + z_1, Pu + z_1) + [u,Cu]. \end{aligned}$$

Since $[u,(P^*P + C)u] = (Pu,Pu) + [u,Cu] \geq 0$, it can be seen that J(u,v) is convex with respect to $u \in H$. The concavity of J(u,v) with respect to $v \in H$ can be asserted under fairly strong condition stated as follows. Let $k_i(T,t)$ $(i = 1,\cdots,n)$ be r-dimensional row vectors of the matrix W(T,t). Denoting the norm of a vector v in H by $\|v\|$, we obtain

$$(Rv,Rv) = \sum_{i=1}^{n} [k_i, v]^2 \leq \|v\|^2 \sum_{i=1}^{n} \|k_i\|^2 .$$

Further, we obtain the following relation

$$(Rv,Rv) - [v,Dv] \leq \|v\|^2 \left(\sum_{i=1}^{n} \|k_i\|^2 - d\right),$$

where $d = \min(d_1, \cdots, d_r)$, and d_i are elements of the diagonal matrix D. Hence, if the relation

$$\sum_{i=1}^{n} \|k_i\|^2 \leq d \tag{17}$$

holds, then it is clear that J(u,v) is concave with respect to $v \in H$.

Define a mapping g, which maps H into H, by

$$g(u) = \begin{pmatrix} 1 - u_1^2(t) \\ \vdots \\ 1 - u_r^2(t) \end{pmatrix} . \tag{18}$$

Then, the constraints $u(t), v(t) \in \Omega$ can be expressed as

$$g(u) \geq 0, \quad g(v) \geq 0. \tag{19}$$

Define a closed bounded convex subset X of H by

$$X = \{u \in H : g(u) \geq 0\}.$$

Since J(u,v) is continuous and convex with respect to u on X, from [11, Theorem 2.1] there exists an element u^o in X such that

$$\inf_{u \in X} J(u,v) = J(u^o,v).$$

Furthermore, if J(u,v) is concave with respect to v, there exists an element v^o in X such that

$$\sup_{v \in X} J(u,v) = J(u,v^o).$$

In the following, assuming the existence of v^o, necessary conditions for the optimal strategies will be derived.

First, we show a theorem which corresponds to a special case of the Theorem V.3.3.2 in [9] and is available for our problem.

Theorem 1. Let f be a real-valued differentiable functional on the Hilbert space H. Let $x^o \in H$ maximize f(x) subject to the constraint $g(x) \geq 0$, where g(x) is defined by Eq. (18). Then there exists a $\lambda^o \in H$ such that

$$\lambda^o \geq 0, \tag{20}$$

and that the Lagrangian expression

$$\Phi(x, \lambda) = f(x) + [\lambda, g(x)] \tag{21}$$

satisfies the following relations:

$$\delta_x \Phi((x^o, \lambda^o); \xi) = 0 \quad \text{for all} \quad \xi \in H, \tag{22}$$

$$[\lambda^o, g(x^o)] = 0, \tag{23}$$

where $\delta_x \Phi((x^o,\lambda^o); \xi)$ represents the partial Fréchet differential of Φ with respect to x at (x^o,λ^o) with increment ξ, which is defined by

$$\delta_x \Phi((x^o, \lambda^o); \xi) = \lim_{\varepsilon \to 0} \frac{\Phi(x^o + \varepsilon\xi, \lambda^o) - \Phi(x^o, \lambda^o)}{\varepsilon}. \tag{24}$$

Now we apply Theorem 1 to our problem. Let $u^o \in H$ minimize J(u,v) subject to the constraint $g(u) \geq 0$, and $v^o \in H$ maximize J(u,v) subject to the constraint $g(v) \geq 0$. Then, there exist $\lambda^o \in H$ and $\mu^o \in H$ such that

$$\lambda^o \geq 0, \quad \mu^o \geq 0, \tag{25}$$

and that the Lagrangian expression

$$K(u,\lambda,v,\mu) = J(u,v) - [\lambda, g(u)] + [\mu, g(v)] \tag{26}$$

satisfies the following relations:

$$\delta_u K((u^o,\lambda^o,v^o,\mu^o); \xi) = 0 \quad \text{for all} \quad \xi \in H, \Big\}$$

$$\left.\delta_v K((u^o,\lambda^o,v^o,\mu^o);\xi)=0 \quad \text{for all} \quad \xi\in H,\right\} \tag{27}$$

$$[\lambda^o, g(u^o)] = 0, \quad [\mu^o, g(v^o)] = 0. \tag{28}$$

Henceforth, u^o, v^o, λ^o, and μ^o which satisfy these relations are simply written as u, v, λ, and μ. By evaluating the partial Fréchet differentials of $K(u,\lambda,v,\mu)$ with respect to u and v at (u,λ,v,μ) with increment ξ, it follows from Eq. (27) that

$$\left.\begin{aligned} &(P^*P + C)u + P^*Rv + P^*z_1 - \frac{1}{2}\frac{\partial g(u)}{\partial u}\lambda = 0, \\ &(R^*R - D)v + R^*Pu + R^*z_1 + \frac{1}{2}\frac{\partial g(v)}{\partial v}\mu = 0, \end{aligned}\right\} \tag{29}$$

where $\partial g(u)/\partial u$ denotes an r×r matrix defined by

$$\frac{\partial g(u)}{\partial u} = \left(\frac{\partial g_i(u)}{\partial u_j}\right) = -2\begin{pmatrix} u_1 & 0 & \cdots & 0 \\ 0 & u_2 & & \vdots \\ \vdots & & \ddots & \vdots \\ 0 & \cdots & & u_r \end{pmatrix}.$$

Define new vectors x and y in H by

$$\left.\begin{aligned} x &= Cu - \frac{1}{2}\frac{\partial g(u)}{\partial u}\lambda = \begin{pmatrix} c_1u_1 + \lambda_1 u_1 \\ \vdots \\ c_r u_r + \lambda_r u_r \end{pmatrix}, \\ y &= Dv - \frac{1}{2}\frac{\partial g(v)}{\partial v}\mu = \begin{pmatrix} d_1 v_1 + \mu_1 v_1 \\ \vdots \\ d_r v_r + \mu_r v_r \end{pmatrix}, \end{aligned}\right. \tag{30}$$

where c_i and d_i $(i = 1,\cdots,r)$ are elements of the nonnegative diagonal matrix C and D, respectively. Then, Eq. (29) can be written, respectively, as

$$\left.\begin{aligned} P^*(Pu + Rv + z_1) + x = 0, \\ R^*(Pu + Rv + z_1) - y = 0. \end{aligned}\right\} \tag{31}$$

Since $\lambda(t) \geq 0$ and $g(u(t)) \geq 0$ on the interval $[0,T]$, it follows from Eq. (28) that the equation

$$(\lambda(t), g(u(t))) = \lambda^*(t)g(u(t)) = 0$$

holds for almost all $t\in[0,T]$. Therefore,

$$\left.\begin{aligned} \lambda_i(t) &= 0 \quad \text{if} \quad -1 < u_i(t) < 1, \\ \lambda_i(t) &\geq 0 \quad \text{if} \quad u_i(t) = 1. \end{aligned}\right\}$$

Thus, the relation between $u_i(t)$ and $\lambda_i(t)$ can be shown as

Fig. 1 (a). The relation between $u_i(t)$ and $\lambda_i(t)u_i(t)$ and then the relation between $u_i(t)$ and $c_i(t)u_i(t) + \lambda_i(t)u_i(t)$ can also be obtained successively from Fig. 1 (a) as shown in Fig. 1 (b) and (c), respectively. Hence, the relation between $x \in H$ and $u \in H$, which is defined by Eq. (30), can be expressed as

$$u(t) = \varphi(x(t)), \quad \text{or} \quad u_i(t) = \varphi_i(x_i(t)) \ (i = 1, \cdots, r), \tag{32}$$

where the nonlinear function φ_i is shown in Fig. 2 (a), which can be obtained from Fig. 1 (c) directly.

Analogously, the relation between $y \in H$ and $v \in H$ can be expressed as

$$v(t) = \psi(y(t)), \quad \text{or} \quad v_i(t) = \psi_i(y_i(t)) \ (i = 1, \cdots, r), \tag{33}$$

where the nonlinear function ψ_i is shown in Fig. 2 (b). If we use a notation such that

$$\text{sat}\,\alpha = \alpha \ \text{ if } |\alpha| \le 1, \quad \text{sat}\,\alpha = \text{sgn}\,\alpha \ \text{ if } |\alpha| \ge 1,$$

then,

$$\varphi(x) = \begin{pmatrix} \text{sat}(x_1/c_1) \\ \vdots \\ \text{sat}(x_r/c_r) \end{pmatrix}, \qquad \psi(y) = \begin{pmatrix} \text{sat}(y_1/d_1) \\ \vdots \\ \text{sat}(y_r/d_r) \end{pmatrix}.$$

Substituting Eqs. (32) and (33) into Eq. (31) yields

$$\left.\begin{aligned} P^*(P\varphi(x) + R\psi(y) + z_1) + x = 0, \\ R^*(P\varphi(x) + R\psi(y) + z_1) - y = 0. \end{aligned}\right\} \tag{34}$$

Equation (34) is a system of nonlinear integral equations from which $x \in H$ and $y \in H$ can be determined. This system can be reduced to a system of transcendental equation as follows.

By setting

$$P\varphi(x) + R\psi(y) + z_1 = \alpha, \tag{35}$$

we obtain

$$x = -P^*\alpha, \quad y = R^*\alpha, \tag{36}$$

where α is a vector in R^n. In view of Eq. (13), it is clear that th α defined by Eq. (35) represents $z_T = z(T)$. Substituting Eq. (36) into Eq. (35) yields a transcendental equation:

$$-P\varphi(P^*\alpha) + R\psi(R^*\alpha) + z_1 = \alpha. \tag{37}$$

Let $f_i(T,t)$ and $w_i(T,t)$ $(i = 1, \cdots, r)$ be n-dimensional column vectors of the matrices $F(T,t)$ and $W(T,t)$, respectively. Then since

$$P^*\alpha = F^*(T,t)\alpha = \begin{pmatrix} f_1^*(T,t)\alpha \\ \vdots \\ f_r^*(T,t)\alpha \end{pmatrix},$$

$$R^*\alpha = W^*(T,t)\alpha = \begin{pmatrix} w_1^*(T,t)\alpha \\ \vdots \\ w_r^*(T,t)\alpha \end{pmatrix},$$

defining a mapping A from R^n into R^n by

$$A\alpha = \sum_{i=1}^{r} \int_0^T [w_i(T,t)\psi_i(w_i^*(T,t)\alpha) - f_i(T,t)\varphi_i(f_i^*(T,t)\alpha)]dt + z_1, \tag{38}$$

Eq. (37) can be rewritten as

$$A\alpha = \alpha . \tag{39}$$

3. Solution of the Transcendental Equation

Let $(A\alpha)_j$, f_{ij}, w_{ij}, and z_{1j} denote the jth component of n-vectors $A\alpha$, f_i, w_i, and z_1, respectively. Since $|\varphi_i| \leq 1$, $|\psi_i| \leq 1$ $(i = 1, \cdots, r)$, it follows that

$$\left. \begin{aligned} |(A\alpha)_j| \leq \sum_{i=1}^{r} \int_0^T [|w_{ij}(T,t)| + |f_{ij}(T,t)|]dt + |z_{1j}| \\ (j = 1, \cdots, n). \end{aligned} \right\} \tag{40}$$

Since the functions f_{ij}, w_{ij} are assumed to be continuous on the closed interval $[0,T]$, (40) shows that the mapping A maps a closed bounded convex subset of R^n into itself. Furthermore, the mapping is continuous. Therefore, by Brouwer's fixed-point theorem [12], we can conclude that there exists a point α such that $A\alpha = \alpha$. Namely,

Theorem 2. Let the vector functions f_i and w_i $(i=1,\cdots,r)$ be continuous on the closed interval $[0,T]$. Then, there exists a solution of Eq. (39).

The solution of Eq. (39) may be computed by the method of successive approximations:

$$\alpha_n = A\alpha_{n-1} \quad (n = 1, 2, \cdots). \tag{41}$$

As to the convergence of the successive approximations (41), we can propose:

Theorem 3. Let the nonnegative constants c_i, d_i $(i = 1, \cdots, r)$ be all positive. Further, let us assume that

$$\sum_{i=1}^{r} \int_0^T [\frac{1}{c}\|f_i(T,t)\|^2 + \frac{1}{d}\|w_i(T,t)\|^2]dt < 1, \tag{42}$$

where $c = \min(c_1, c_2, \cdots, c_r)$, $d = \min(d_1, d_2, \cdots, d_r)$, and $\| \ \|$ denotes the Euclidean norm in R^n. Then, the successive approximations (41), starting with an arbitrary α_0, converge to a unique solution of Eq. (39).

Proof. Let α and β be arbitrary points in R^n. By using the Schwarz inequality and the relations:

$$\begin{aligned} |\varphi_i(f_i^*(T,t)\alpha) - \varphi_i(f_i^*(T,t)\beta)| &\le \frac{1}{c}|f_i^*(T,t)(\alpha-\beta)| \\ &\le \frac{1}{c}\| f_i(T,t)\|\|\alpha-\beta\|, \end{aligned} \tag{43}$$

$$|\psi_i(w_i^*(T,t)\alpha) - \psi_i(w_i^*(T,t)\beta)| \le \frac{1}{d}\| w_i(T,t)\|\|\alpha-\beta\|,$$

it follows that

$$\begin{aligned} |(A\alpha)_j - (A\beta)_j| &\le \sum_{i=1}^r \int_0^T [\frac{1}{c}|f_{ij}(T,t)|\| f_i(T,t)\| \\ &\quad + \frac{1}{d}|w_{ij}(T,t)|\| w_i(T,t)\|]dt \ \|\alpha-\beta\| \end{aligned}$$

$$\begin{aligned} &\le [\frac{1}{c}\sqrt{\int_0^T \sum_{i=1}^r f_{ij}^2(T,t)dt}\sqrt{\int_0^T \sum_{i=1}^r \| f_i(T,t)\|^2 dt} \\ &\quad + \frac{1}{d}\sqrt{\int_0^T \sum_{i=1}^r w_{ij}^2(T,t)dt}\sqrt{\int_0^T \sum_{i=1}^r \| w_i(T,t)\|^2 dt}\ ] \|\alpha-\beta\|. \end{aligned}$$

Hence,

$$\begin{aligned} \|A\alpha - A\beta\| &\le [\frac{1}{c}\int_0^T \sum_{i=1}^r \|f_i(T,t)\|^2 dt \\ &\quad + \frac{1}{d}\int_0^T \sum_{i=1}^r \|w_i(T,t)\|^2 dt]\|\alpha-\beta\|. \end{aligned} \tag{44}$$

Inequality (44) shows that the mapping A defined by Eq. (38) is a contraction mapping under the condition (42) [13]. Thus, the theorem is proved.

4. Solution to the Problem 2

If $C = D = 0$ in Eq. (4), the payoff becomes

$$\hat{J}(u,v) = (z(T), z(T)). \tag{45}$$

In this case, Eq (39) which determines the vector α becomes

$$\begin{aligned} \alpha = \sum_{i=1}^r \int_0^T &[w_i(T,t)\,\mathrm{sgn}(w_i^*(T,t)\alpha) \\ &- f_i(T,t)\,\mathrm{sgn}(f_i^*(T,t)\alpha)]dt + z_1. \end{aligned} \tag{46}$$

Let us introduce a real number ε and a vector β in R^n such that

$$\alpha = \varepsilon\beta, \quad \varepsilon > 0, \quad \|\beta\| = 1.$$

Then, Eq. (46) can be rewritten as

$$\varepsilon\beta = \sum_{i=1}^{r} \int_0^T [w_i(T,t)\operatorname{sgn}(w_i^*(T,t)\beta) - f_i(T,t)\operatorname{sgn}(f_i^*(T,t)\beta)]dt + z_1. \quad (47)$$

As mentioned before, the vector α defined by Eq. (35) represents $z(T)$. Hence, if there exists a time T such that the value $J(u^o,v^o)$ of the game vanishes,then there exists a solution of the Problem 2. Letting $\varepsilon \to 0$ in Eq. (47) yields a equation

$$\sum_{i=1}^{r} \int_0^T [w_i(T,t)\operatorname{sgn}(w_i^*(T,t)\beta) - f_i(T,t)\operatorname{sgn}(f_i^*(T,t)\beta)]dt + z_1 = 0. \quad (48)$$

The time T and the n-vector β ($\|\beta\|=1$) which satisfy Eq. (48) give a solution to the Problem 2, i.e.,

$$T_{u^o,v^o} = T. \quad (49)$$

Furthermore, from Eqs. (32), (33), and (36) it follows that

$$u^o(t) = -\begin{bmatrix} \operatorname{sgn}(f_1^*(T,t)\beta) \\ \vdots \\ \operatorname{sgn}(f_r^*(T,t)\beta) \end{bmatrix}, \quad v^o(t) = \begin{bmatrix} \operatorname{sgn}(w_1^*(T,t)\beta) \\ \vdots \\ \operatorname{sgn}(w_r^*(T,t)\beta) \end{bmatrix}. \quad (50)$$

References

[1] L. D. Berkovitz and W. H. Fleming, On differential games with integral payoff, in M. Dresher, A. W. Tucker, and P. Wolfe (Eds.), Contributions to the Theory of Games III, Princeton U. P., 1957, pp.413-435.
[2] L. D. Berkovitz, A variational approach to differential games, in M. Dresher, L. S. Shapley, and A. W. Tucker (Eds.), Advances in Game Theory, Princeton U. P., 1964, pp. 127-174.
[3] R. Isaacs, Differential Games, John Wiley, 1965.
[4] D. L. Kelendzheridze, A pursuit problem, in Pontryagin et al., The Mathematical Theory of Optimal Processes, Interscience Publishers, 1962, pp. 226-237.
[5] D. L. Kelendzheridze, On a problem of optimum tracking, Avtomat. i Telemek., Vol. 23, 1962, pp. 1008-1013.
[6] L. S. Pontryagin, On some differential games, Dokl. Akad. Nauk SSSR, Vol. 156, 1964, pp. 738-741.
[7] Y. C. Ho, A. E. Bryson, and S. Baron, Differential games and optimal pursuit-evasion strategies, IEEE Trans. on Auto-

matic Control, Vol. AC-10, No. 4, 1965, pp. 385-389.
[8] Y. Sakawa, On a solution of an optimization problem in linear systems with quadratic performance index, J. SIAM Control , Vol. 4, No. 2, 1966, pp. 382-395.
[9] L. Hurwicz, Programming in linear spaces, in K. J. Arrow, L. Hurwicz, and H. Uzawa, Studies in Linear and Non-linear Programming, Stanford U. P., 1958, pp. 38-102.
[10] A. V. Balakrishnan, An operator theoretic formulation of a class of control problems and a steepest descent method of solution, J. SIAM Control, Vol. 1, No. 2, 1963, pp. 109-127.
[11] A. V. Balakrishnan, Optimal control problems in Banach spaces, J. SIAM Control, Vol. 3, No. 1, 1965, pp. 152-180.
[12] T. L. Saaty and J. Bram, Nonlinear Mathematics, McGraw-Hill, 1964.
[13] A. N. Kolmogorov and S. V. Formin, Elements of the Theory of Functions and Functional Analysis, Graylick Press, 1957.

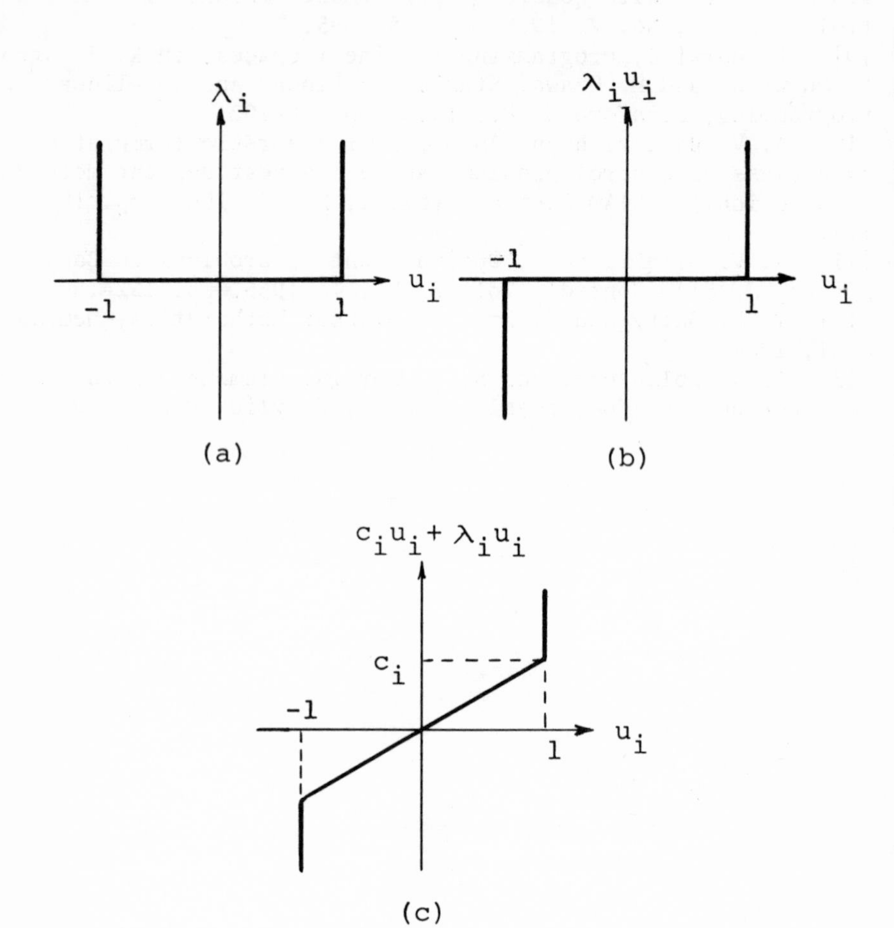

Fig. 1. Relations between the Variables.

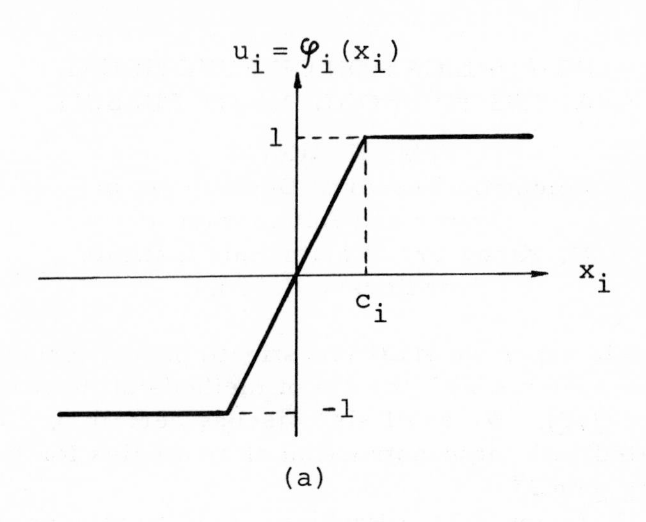

(a)

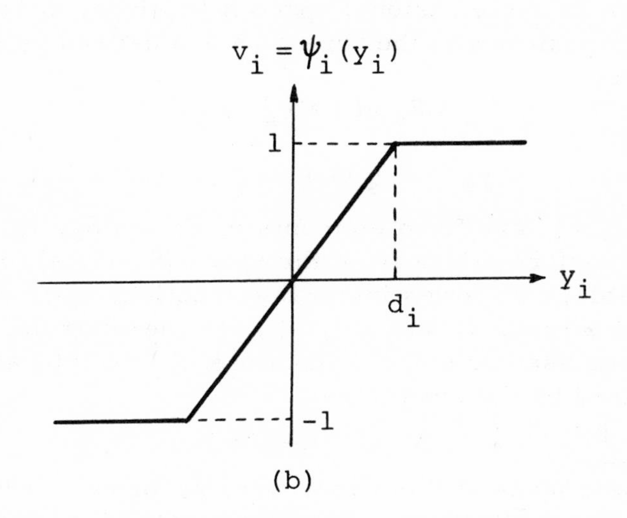

(b)

Fig. 2. Nonlinear Characteristics.

THE APPLICATION OF FUNCTIONAL ANALYSIS TO PROBLEMS OF PURSUIT

F. M. Kirillova
Scientific Research Department of
Power and Automation
S. M. Kirov Ural Polytechnic Institute
Sverdlovsk, U. S. S. R.

In this paper we shall investigate pursuit problems in linear systems with the aid of methods of functional analysis (1, 2). We shall also discuss certain problems associated with the construction of strategies for the pursuing point.*

1. Statement of the Problem. Let two moving points x and y in an n-dimensional space X be given, and suppose that their positions at the time $\tau = s$ are defined by the equations:

$$x_s = S_s u(\cdot) + c_s^1 \ ,$$
$$y_s = - P_s v(\cdot) - c_s^2 \ . \tag{1}$$

Here c_s^1, c_s^2 are fixed elements in X, and S_s, P_s are linear transformations from the space $\mathcal{L}_p (t_o, s)$ (of measurable, p-th power integrable functions $w(\cdot)$, where $1 < p \leq +\infty$) into X, and $u(\cdot)$, $v(\cdot)$ are the controls.

Let us assume that the functions $u(\cdot)$ and $v(\cdot)$ are constrained by the conditions:

$$\|u(\cdot)\| \leq \ell_1 \ , \quad \|v(\cdot)\| \leq \ell_2 \ . \tag{2}$$

---

* The basic ideas of this paper were reported in 1962 in the Sverdlovsk division of The Mathematical Institute of the Academy of Sciences of the U. S. S. R. A different approach to the study of some pursuit problems was independently suggested by N. N. Krasovskii in (3).

If, from the time t, the points x and y employ the controls $u(t, \theta)$ and $v(t, \theta)$, $t \leq \theta \leq s$, then we shall denote the positions of x and y at the time s by the symbols $x(t, s, u(\cdot))$ and $y(t, s, v(\cdot))$, respectively.

Let $x(t, t, u(\cdot)) = x(t)$ and $y(t, t, v(\cdot)) = y(t)$.

Problem A. Find the smallest value of $s = T^1$, and the controls $u^1(\cdot), v^1(\cdot)$ for which

$$\| x(t, T^1, u^1(\cdot)) - y(t, T^1, v^1(\cdot)) \| =$$

$$= \min_{s \geq t} \max_{\| v^1(\cdot)\| \leq \ell_2} \min_{\|u(\cdot)\| \leq \ell_1} \| x(t, s, u(\cdot)) - y(t, s, v(\cdot)) \| . \tag{3}$$

Problem B. Determine the smallest value for T^2, and the controls $u^2(\cdot)$, $v^2(\cdot)$ for which

$$\| x(t, T^2, u^2(\cdot)) - y(t, T^2, v^2(\cdot)) \| =$$

$$= \min_{s \geq t} \min_{\|u(\cdot)\| \leq \ell_1} \max_{\| v(\cdot)\| \leq \ell_2} \|x(t, s, u(\cdot)) - y(t, s, v(\cdot)) \|. \tag{4}$$

We shall call the solutions of these problems, i. e., the functions $u^i(\cdot)$ and $v^i(\cdot)$, the optimal controls.

Let us introduce the sets:

$$\Omega_x(t,s) = \{x : x(t, s, u(\cdot)) / x(t, t, u(\cdot)) = x(t), \ \| u(\cdot)\| \leq \ell_1\},$$

$$\Omega_y(t,s) = \{y : y(t, s, v(\cdot)) / y(t, t, v(\cdot)) = y(t), \ \| v(\cdot)\| \leq \ell_2\}.$$

We set

$$\| x(t, s, u(\cdot)) - y(t, s, v(\cdot)) \| = \rho_s (x, y) ,$$

$$\beta(s) = \beta_s(\Omega_y, \Omega_x) = \sup_{y \in \Omega_y(t,s)} \inf_{x \in \Omega_x(t,s)} \rho_s(x, y) ,$$

$$\delta_x(s) = \sup_{y \in \Omega_y(t,s)} \rho_s(x, y) .$$

The term $\beta(s)$ is the semi-distance (4) from the set

$\Omega_y(t,s)$ to the set $\Omega_x(t,s)$. The term $\delta_x(s)$ is the semi-distance of the set $\Omega_y(t,s)$ from the point x.

Consequently, Problem A is that of determining the earliest time for which the semi-distance from $\Omega_y(t,s)$ to $\Omega_x(t,s)$ is minimal. Problem B is that of determining the earliest time and the function $u(\cdot)$ for which the semi-distance from $\Omega_y(t,s)$ to the point x is minimal.

2. Optimal Controls. The vector $z = x-y$ at the time s satisfies the relation

$$z_s = S_s u(\cdot) + P_s v(\cdot) + c_s, c_s = c_s^1 + c_s^2 . \tag{5}$$

Theorem 1. The minimal semi-distance from $\Omega_y(t,s)$ to $\Omega_x(t,s)$ is equal to

$$\begin{aligned} \beta^o(T^1) &= \min_{s\geq t} \max_{\|g\|\leq 1} \{(g, c_s) + \ell_2 \| P_s^* g\| - \ell_1 \| S_s^* g\| \} = \\ &= (g_{T^1}, c_{T^1}) + \ell_2 \|P_{T^1}^* g_{T^1}\| - \ell_1 \| P_{T^1}^* g_{T^1}\|. \end{aligned} \tag{6}$$

If $\beta^o(T^1) > 0$, then the functions $u^1(\cdot)$ and $v^1(\cdot)$ for which the semi-distance $\beta(s)$ is minimal are defined by the relations

$$\begin{aligned} (S_{T^1}^* g_{T^1}, u^1(\cdot)) &= \min_{\|u(\cdot)\|\leq \ell_1} (S^*_{T^1} g_{T^1}, u(\cdot)), \\ (P_{T^1}^* g_{T^1}, v^1(\cdot)) &= \max_{\|v(\cdot)\|\leq \ell_2} (P^*_{T^1} g_{T^1}, v(\cdot)) . \end{aligned} \tag{7}$$

Proof. Let us fix $v(\cdot)$ and let us find

$$\beta(s, v(\cdot)) = \min_{x\in\Omega_x(t,s)} \rho_s(x, y) .$$

By virtue of the results of (5) we have, from Eqs. (2) and (5), that

$$\beta(s, v(\cdot)) = \max_{\|g\|=1} \{(g, c_s + P_s v(\cdot)) - \ell_1 \| S_s^* g\| \}.$$

Now it follows from Eq. (3) that, at each fixed time s,

$$\beta(s) = \max_{\|g\|=1} \{(g, c_s) + \ell_2 \| P_s^* g\| - \ell_1 \| S_s^* g\| \}. \tag{8}$$

Hence formula (6) is correct. Relations (7) follow from Eq. (8). Q. E. D.

Let us introduce the sets

$$Q(s, \ell_1) = \{ \xi_s : \xi_s = -S_s u(\cdot) - c_s, \; s \geq t, \|u(\cdot)\| \leq \ell_1 \}.$$

Let

$$\max_{\|v(\cdot)\| \leq \ell_2} \|P_s v(\cdot) - \xi_s\| = \Psi(s, \xi_s) \tag{9}$$

and

$$\min_{\xi_s} \Psi(s, \xi_s) = \Psi(s, e_s) = d_s. \tag{10}$$

Theorem 2. If $e_s \notin \text{int } Q(s, \ell_1)$ for all $s \geq t$, then the minimal semi-distance from $\Omega_y(t, s)$ to x equals

$$\delta_x^o(T^2) = \min_{s \geq t} \min_{\xi_s} \max_{\|g\| \leq 1} \{ \Psi(s, \xi_s) + (g, \xi_s + c_s) - \ell_1 \|S_s^* g\| \} =$$
$$= \Psi(T^2, \xi_{T^2}) + (g_{T^2}, \xi_{T^2} + c_{T^2}) - \ell_1 \| S_{T^2}^* g_{T^2} \|. \tag{11}$$

The following estimates are valid:

$$d_s \leq \min_{x \in \Omega_x(t, s)} \delta_x(s) \leq d_s + \max_{\|g\| \leq 1} \{(g, c_s + e_s) - \ell_1 \| S_s^* g\| \}. \tag{12}$$

The function $u^2(\cdot)$ is defined by the relation

$$(S_{T^2}^* g_{T^2}, u^2(\cdot)) = \min_{\|u(\cdot)\| \leq \ell_1} (S_{T^2}^* g_{T^2}, u(\cdot)),$$

and the function $v^2(\cdot)$ satisfies the condition

$$\| P_{T^2} v^2(\cdot) - \xi_{T^2} \| = \Psi(T^2, \xi_{T^2}).$$

Proof. We set $S_T u(\cdot) + c_T = - z_T$. According to Eq. (9), we have that $\delta_x(\tau) = \Psi(\tau, z_T)$. Since $\Psi(\tau, z_T)$ is convex with respect to z_T, then, by virtue of (6), we have that

$$\min_{x \in \Omega_x(t,\tau)} \delta_x(\tau) =$$

$$= \max_{\|g\| \leq 1} \min_{z_T} \{\Psi(\tau, z_T) + (g, c_T + z_T) - \ell_1 \| S_T^* g \|\},$$

from which Eq. (11) follows.

It is clear that

$$\max_{\|g\| \leq 1} \min_{z_T} \{\Psi(\tau, z_T) + (g, c_T + z_T) - \ell_1 \|S_T^* g\|\} \leq$$

$$\max_{\|g\| \leq 1} \{\Psi(\tau, e_T) + (g, c_T + e_T) - \ell_1 \|S_T^* g\|\}.$$

Consequently, the right-hand inequality in (12) is valid. The left-hand inequality in (12) follows from Eq. (10).

The relations for $u^2(\cdot)$ and $v^2(\cdot)$ are obtained from Eqs. (9) and (11).

Remark 1. In case $e_T \in \operatorname{int} Q(\tau, \ell_1)$, we decrease ℓ_1 so that $e_T \notin \operatorname{int} Q(\tau, \ell)$, $\ell < \ell_1$.

The following problems are closely related to the previous ones. Let ε_1 and ε_2 be positive numbers.

Problem A'. Determine the earliest time $s = T^1(\varepsilon_1)$ and functions $\tilde{u}^1(\cdot)$ and $\tilde{v}^1(\cdot)$ for which the semi-distance $\beta(s) = \varepsilon_1$.

Problem B'. Determine the earliest time $s = T^2(\varepsilon_2)$ and the functions $\tilde{u}^2(\cdot)$ and $\tilde{v}^2(\cdot)$ for which the semi-distance $\delta_x(s) = \varepsilon_2$.

Remark 2. It follows from Theorem 1 that the solution of the problem gives the smallest number $s = \tau^0$ satisfying the inequality

$$\max_{\|g\| = 1} \{(g, c_s) + \ell_2 \|P_s^* g\| - \ell_1 \|S_s^* g\| - \varepsilon_1 \|g\|\} \leq 0. \tag{13}$$

A method for solving Problem B' is given in Theorem 2.

Problem A', for $\varepsilon_1 = 0$, was examined by L. S. Gnoenskii (7). N. N. Krasovskii (3) called the latter variant of Problem A' the "absorption problem." In the sequel, we shall adhere to the latter term. As we shall establish, the absorption problem is related to the follow-in problem (8).

Problem C. Let $T(u(\cdot), v(\cdot))$ be the time at which the point $x(t, s, u(\cdot))$ overtakes $y(t, s, v(\cdot))$.

Determine functions $u^o(\cdot)$, $v^o(\cdot)$ for which

$$T(u^o(\cdot), v^o(\cdot)) = T^o = \max_{\|v(\cdot)\| \leq \ell_2} \min_{\|u(\cdot)\| \leq \ell_1} T(u(\cdot), v(\cdot)).$$

Remark 3. Another group of pursuit problems arises when one takes into consideration a group of points y^i, moving, for example, according to the equations

$$y_s^i = S_s^i v^i(\cdot) + c_s, \quad i = 1, \ldots, m, \quad \|v^i\| \leq \ell_i .$$

Let α_i be positive numbers.

We shall call the quantity $\alpha_i \| x_s - y_s^i \|$ the "protection" of the point y^i. The quantity

$$\sum_{i=1}^{m} \alpha_i \|x_s - y_s^i\|$$

naturally characterizes the protection of the group $\{y^i\}$.

Questions associated with the solution of problems of the optimal pursuit program of a group were considered in (9), and are not discussed here.

3. Conditions under which the solutions of Problems A, B, and A', C coincide. It is not difficult to see that

$$\text{a)} \ \beta^o(T^1) \leq \delta_x(T), \qquad \text{b)} \ T^o \leq T^1(0). \qquad (14)$$

At this point, we assume that

$$\| S_s^* g\| > 0, \ \| P_s^* g\| > 0 \ \text{for all} \ g \in X^*, \ \|g\| \neq 0. \qquad (15)$$

Let the values $\beta(T)$ and $\delta_x(T)$ of the semi-distances

$\beta(s)$ and $\delta_x(s)$ at the time $s = T$ be attained through the functions $u_T^1(t, \theta)$, $v_T^1(t, \theta)$ and $u_T^2(t, \theta)$, $v_T^2(t, \theta)$, respectively.

Theorem 3. If

$$\max_{y \in \Omega_y(t, T)} \rho_T(x(t, T, u_T^1(\cdot)), y(t, T, v(\cdot))) = \beta(T),$$

then $\beta(T) = \delta_x(T)$ and

$$\rho_T(x(t, T, u_T^1(\cdot)), \; y(t, T, v(\cdot))) \leq$$

$$\leq \rho_T(x(t, T, u_T^1(\cdot)), \; y(t, T, v_T^1(\cdot))) \leq$$

$$\leq \rho_T(x(t, T, u(\cdot)), \; y(t, T, v_T^1(\cdot))) \tag{16}$$

for all admissible $u(\cdot)$, $v(\cdot)$.

If

$$\min_{x \in \Omega_x(t, T)} \rho_T(x(t, T, u(\cdot)), \; y(t, T, v_T^2(\cdot))) = \delta_x(T),$$

then $\delta_x(T) = \beta(T)$ and

$$\rho_T(x(t, T, u_T^2(\cdot)), \; y(t, T, v(\cdot))) \leq$$

$$\leq \rho_T(x(t, T, u_T^2(\cdot)), \; y(t, T, v_T^2(\cdot))) \leq$$

$$\leq \rho_T(x(t, T, u(\cdot)), \; y(t, T, v_T^2(\cdot))) \tag{17}$$

for all admissible $u(\cdot)$, $v(\cdot)$.

Proof. It is not difficult to see that

$$\max_{y \in \Omega_y} \min_{x \in \Omega_x} \rho_T(x, y) \leq \min_{x \in \Omega_x} \max_{y \in \Omega_y} \rho_T(x, y) \leq$$

$$\leq \max_{y \in \Omega_y} \rho_T(x(t, T, u_T^1(\cdot)), \; y(t, T, v(\cdot))).$$

Therefore,

$$\max_{y \in \Omega_y(t, T)} \min_{x \in \Omega_x(t, T)} \rho_T(x, y) = \min_{x \in \Omega_x(t, T)} \max_{y \in \Omega_y(t, T)} \rho_T(x, y)$$

i. e., $\beta(T) = \delta_x(T)$, and (16) is valid.

Let us prove the second part of the assertion. Since

$$\min_{x\in\Omega_x} \max_{y\in\Omega_y} \rho_T(x, y) \geq \max_{y\in\Omega_y} \min_{x\in\Omega_x} \rho_T(x, y) \geq$$

$$\geq \min_{x\in\Omega_x} \rho_T(x(t, T, u(\cdot)), y(t, T, v_T^2(\cdot))),$$

then we have

$$\delta_x(T) \geq \max_{y\in\Omega_y(t, T)} \min_{x\in\Omega_x(t, T)} \rho_T(x(t,T,u(\cdot)), y(t(T,v(\cdot))) \geq \delta_x(T).$$

Hence, $\delta_x(T) = \beta(T)$, and inequality (17) is valid.

The theorem has been proved.

Let us denote the solution of the absorption problem by $\tilde{u}(t, s)$, $\tilde{v}(t, s)$.

Theorem 4. Let $T^1(0) < +\infty$ and

$$\Lambda(s, \tilde{v}(\cdot)) = \max_{\|g\|=1} \{(g, c_s + P_s v(\cdot)) - \ell_1\|S_s^* g\|\} > 0,$$

$$t \leq s \leq T^1(0).$$

Then $T^1(0) = T^0$ and $\tilde{u}(t, s) \equiv u^0(t, s)$, $\tilde{v}(t, s) \equiv v^0(t, s)$, $t \leq s \leq T^0$.

Proof. According to the condition, $T^1(0)$ is the first zero of the function $\Lambda(s, \tilde{v}(\cdot))$. Therefore $T^0 \geq T^1(0)$. But, by virtue of relation (14b) only the reverse inequality is possible. Therefore $T^1(0) = T^0$.

According to assumption (15), the functions $\tilde{u}(\cdot)$, $u^0(\cdot)$, $\tilde{v}(\cdot)$, $v^0(\cdot)$ are uniquely defined. Therefore, $\tilde{u}(t, s) \equiv u^0(t, s)$, $\tilde{v}(t, s) \equiv v^0(t, s)$, $s \in [t, T^0]$. Q. E. D.

Theorem 5. If $T^0 < \infty$ and

$$\Lambda(T^0) = \max_{\|g\|=1} \{(g, c_{T^0}) + \ell_2\|P_{T^0}^* g\| - \ell_1\|S_{T^0}^* g\|\} \leq 0,$$

then $T^0 = T^1(0)$ and $u^0(t, s) \equiv \tilde{u}(t, s)$, $v^0(t, s) \equiv \tilde{v}(t, s)$, $s \in [t, T^0]$.

Proof. By virtue of the condition of the theorem, $T^1(0) \leq T^o$. But it follows from (14b) that only the relation $T^1(0) = T^o$ is possible. Then, also, $u^o(t, s) \equiv \tilde{u}(t, s)$, $v^o(t, s) \equiv \tilde{v}(t, s)$.

The assertion has been proved.

4. The Construction of strategies for the point x. Until now, optimal programmed controls have been investigated. Ordinarily, one prefers optimal strategies, i.e., rules which enable the objects to make definite decisions based on current positions.

Let us give the definition of the optimal strategy for one of the problems.

Let $T(u(\cdot), v(\cdot))$ be the time required for the point x to capture the point y, using the control $v(\cdot)$.

The points x and y know each other's state, $x = x(t)$, $y = y(t)$ at the time t, and the possibilities (1), (2).

Find a rule for choosing the controls $u^* = u^*(x, y, t)$ and $v^* = v^*(x, y, t)$ for which

$$T(u^*(\cdot), v(\cdot)) \leq T(u^*(\cdot), v^*) \leq T(u(\cdot), v^*(\cdot))$$

for all admissible $u(\cdot), v(\cdot)$.

We shall call the functions $u^*(x, y, t)$, $v^*(x, y, t)$, the optimal strategies.

The most general results with respect to the existence of strategies were obtained by L. S. Pontryagin (2). A series of papers (see (10)) has been devoted to particular problems of determining optimal strategies.

Several Recommendations for choosing strategies for the point x.

(a) Let $\tilde{u}(t, \theta)$, $\tilde{v}(t, \theta)$, $t \leq \theta \leq s$, be solutions of the absorption problem.

We set $u(x, y, t) \equiv \tilde{u}(t, t)$, $t \geq t_o$.

If there exists a T such that $\Lambda(T) < 0$, then the proposed strategy guarantees that the point y can be captured in a time $\tau \leq T^1(0) - t_o$.

(b) Let the optimal strategies $u^* = u^*(x, y, t)$, $v^* = v^*(x, y, t)$ be defined by the inequalities

$$\| x(t, T, u^*(\cdot)) - y(t, T, v(\cdot)) \| \leq$$
$$\leq \| x(t, T, u^*(\cdot)) - y(t, T, v^*(\cdot)) \| \leq$$
$$\leq \| x(t, T, u(\cdot)) - y(t, T, v^*(\cdot)) \| .$$

If $u^1(t, s)$, $v^1(t, s)$ is the solution of the problem of determining the semi-distance $\beta(T)$, then, in place of the optimal strategy, one could have utilized the function $u = u^1(t, t)$.

It follows from the results of Section 3 that the previously proposed selection rules for the controls coincide with the optimal strategies if the conditions of Theorems 3 and 4 are satisfied.

(c) Suppose that the behaviors of the points x and y are given by the single equation

$$\frac{dz^i}{dt} = A(t)\, z^i + C(t)\, w^i(t), \quad i = 1, 2, \quad t \geq t_o.$$

Here, $A(t)$ and $C(t)$ are given matrices, $z^1 = x$, $z^2 = y$, $w^1(\cdot) = u(\cdot)$, $w^2(\cdot) = v(\cdot)$, $\|u(\cdot)\| \leq \ell_1$, $\|v(\cdot)\| \leq \ell_2$, $\ell_1 > \ell_2$.

The basic relation (13) for the absorption problem takes the form:

$$\Lambda(T) = \max_{\|g\| = 1} \{(g, y(t_o) - x(t_o)) - (\ell_1 - \ell_2) \| S_s^* g \| \} = 0$$

$$S_s w(\cdot) = \int_{t_o}^{s} F^{-1}(\tau)\, C(\tau)\, w(\tau)\, d\tau, \quad \frac{dF(\tau)}{d\tau} = A(\tau) F(\tau), \; F(t_o) = E,$$

where E is the identity matrix.

This relation coincides with the condition under which the time-optimal problem (5) has a solution for the case of one player. Therefore, all the results for the time-optimal problem (with respect to the existence of a solution, necessary and sufficient conditions for optimality, and uniqueness of the optimal controls) can be reformulated for this pursuit problem.

If, for some $\varepsilon > 0$,

$$\Lambda(T) > \Lambda(T^o), \quad T \in [T^o - \varepsilon, T^o],$$

then the optimal controls of the absorption problem coincide with the optimal pursuit strategies, since, in this case, the conditions of Theorem 4 are satisfied.

References

1. Isaacs R., "Differential Games", John Wiley and Sons, New York, 1965.

2. Pontryagin L. S., "On Some Differential Games", Dokl. Akad. Nauk SSSR, 1964, vol. 156, No. 4.

3. Krasovskii N. N., "On a Tracking Problem", J. Appl. Math Mech. (P. M. M.), 1963, vol. 27, No. 2, pp. 363-377.

4. Barbashin E. A., "On the General Theory of Dynamical Systems", Uchenye Zapiski Moskovskogo Universiteta, Matem., (Scientific Reports of Moscow University, Math.), 1949, vol. 2, No. 135.

5. Gabasov R., Kirillova F. M., "The Solution of Some Problems in the Theory of Optimal Control", Automation and Remote Control, 1964, vol. 25, No. 7, pp. 945-955.

6. Kirillova F. M., "Optimal Control in a Statistical Problem", Differencial'nye Uravnenija, 1966, vol. 11, No. 11.

7. Gnoenskii L. S., "On the Tracking Problem", J. Appl. Math. Mech. (P. M. M.), 1962, vol. 26, No. 5, pp. 1451-1460.

8. Kelendzheridze D. L., "On the Theory of Optimal Pursuit", Dokl. Akad. Nauk SSSR, 1961, vol. 138, No. 3, pp. 529-532 (English Translation in Soviet Math., 1961, vol. 2, pp. 654-656).

9. Kirillova F. M., Poletaeva I. A., "Some Problems of Pursuit", Annotation Reports of the International Congress of Mathematicians, Moscow, 1966, Nauka, 1966.

10. Simakova E. N., "Differential Games", Avtomatika i Telemekhanika, 1966, vol. 27, No. 11, pp. 161-178.

A Nonlinear System of Integrodifferential Equations

J. J. Levin and J. A. Nohel
Department of Mathematics
University of Wisconsin, Madison, Wisconsin

1. We study the qualitative behavior of solutions of the real system

$$u'(t) = -\int_0^{\pi} \alpha(x)T(x,t)\,dx, \quad T_t(x,t) = T_{xx}(x,t) + \eta(x)g(u(t)) \qquad (1)$$

on $0 < x < \pi$, $0 < t < \infty$ satisfying the initial conditions

$$u(0) = u_0, \qquad T(x,0) = f(x) \quad (0 \leq x \leq \pi) \qquad (2)$$

and the boundary conditions

$$T_x(0,t) = T_x(\pi,t) = 0 \quad (0 < t < \infty). \qquad (3)$$

We wish to obtain sufficient conditions to insure that the solution $u(t)$, $T(x,t)$ of (1) satisfying (2) and (3) exists on $0 < t < \infty$ and approaches zero as $t \to \infty$.

The special case $g(u) = -1 + \exp u$ describes the dynamic behavior of a continuous medium nuclear reactor modeled as a slab of length π with insulated faces; $u(t)$ is the logarithm of the reactor power and $T(x,t)$ is the deviation of the temperature from equilibrium (with $u(t) \equiv 0$ and $T(x,t) \equiv 0$ at equilibrium). In a recent paper (1) we studied the system (1) subject to the initial condition (2) on the infinite interval $-\infty < x < \infty$, where the integral in (1) is replaced by $\int_{-\infty}^{\infty} \alpha(x)\,T(x,t)\,dx$ and the boundary condition (3) is dropped. For actual reactors the present model may be more realistic. With some modifications homogeneous boundary conditions more general than (3) can be treated.

Supported by U. S. Army Research Office-Durham.

We assume throughout that

$$g(u) \in C(-\infty, \infty), \ ug(u) > 0 \ (u \neq 0), \int_0^u g(\sigma) d\sigma \to \infty \ (|u| \to \infty), \tag{4}$$

and

$$\alpha, \eta, \eta', f, f' \in L_2(0, \pi). \tag{5}$$

While these conditions guarantee the local existence of a solution of the problem, they are not sufficient even for existence on $0 < t < \infty$. For that some condition relating α and η must be assumed. In order to state the additional assumptions we need to introduce the Fourier coefficients

$$\alpha_0 = \frac{\sqrt{2}}{\pi} \int_0^\pi \alpha(\xi) d\xi, \quad \alpha_n = \frac{2}{\pi} \int_0^\pi \alpha(\xi) \cos n\xi \, d\xi \quad (n=1, 2, \ldots),$$

so that

$$\alpha(x) = \underset{N \to \infty}{\text{l. i. m.}} \left(\frac{\alpha_0}{\sqrt{2}} + \sum_{n=1}^{N} \alpha_n \cos nx \right),$$

and similarly for $\eta(x)$ and $f(x)$.

A special condition sometimes satisfied in reactor dynamics is $\alpha(x) = k\eta(x)$, where $k > 0$ is a constant and $\eta(x) \not\equiv$ a constant. The reason for the last part of this condition is that if $\alpha(x), \eta(x), f(x)$ are all constant and $\alpha/\eta > 0$, then (as may be easily shown) the solutions of (1) are periodic and so do not tend to zero as $t \to \infty$. From $\alpha(x) = k\eta(x)$ it follows that $\alpha_n = k\eta_n$ $(n = 0, 1, \ldots)$.

We shall establish our result under a hypothesis which includes the above as a very special case. Define

$$h_{1n} = \alpha_n \eta_n, \quad h_{2n} = \alpha_n f_n \quad (n = 0, 1, \ldots), \tag{6}$$

and assume there exists a sequence $\{h_{3n}\}_{n=0}^{\infty}$ such that

$$\begin{gathered} h_{2n}^2 \leq h_{1n} h_{3n}, \quad h_{1n} \geq 0, \quad h_{3n} \geq 0 \quad (n = 0, 1, \ldots) \\ 0 \leq \sum_{n=0}^{\infty} h_{3n} < \infty, \ \underline{\text{and there exists}} \ n_1 \geq 1 \ \underline{\text{such that}} \ h_{1n_1} > 0. \end{gathered} \tag{7}$$

The main result is the following.

Theorem. Let (4), (5), (7) *be satisfied. Then the system* (1) *has a solution* $u(t)$, $T(x, t)$ *on* $0 < x < \pi$, $0 < t < \infty$ *which satisfies* (2), (3) *and also*

$$\lim_{t\to\infty} u^{(k)}(t) = 0 \quad (k = 0, 1, 2). \tag{8}$$

If $\alpha_0 \neq 0$, *one also has*

$$\lim_{t\to\infty} \sup_{0\leq x\leq\pi} |T(x,t)| = 0; \tag{9}$$

while if $\alpha_0 = 0$ *and* $\eta_0 = 0$, *then*

$$\lim_{t\to\infty} T(x,t) = \frac{f_0}{\sqrt{2}} \qquad (\text{uniformly in } x). \tag{10}$$

The behavior of $T(x, t)$ as $t \to \infty$ seems difficult to analyze if $\alpha_0 = 0$ and $\eta_0 \neq 0$.

Because of certain changes which are possible in the proof for the finite interval, condition (7) is simpler than the corresponding one in (1) for the infinite interval--where an additional inequality is required.

The proof of the theorem involves the analysis of the behavior of solutions of the Volterra equation (13) below. That equation can also be written in the form

$$u(t) = p(t) + \int_0^t (q(t-\tau) - \rho)g(u(\tau))\, d\tau \tag{11}$$

where

$$q(t) = \frac{\pi}{2}\Big(\sum_{n=1}^{\infty} \frac{h_{1n}}{n^2} e^{-n^2 t} - h_{10}t\Big), \quad \rho = \frac{\pi}{2} \sum_{n=1}^{\infty} \frac{h_{1n}}{n^2} > 0$$

$$p(t) = u_0 + \frac{\pi}{2}\Big(\sum_{n=1}^{\infty} \frac{h_{2n}}{n^2} e^{-n^2 t} - h_{20}t - \sum_{n=1}^{\infty} \frac{h_{2n}}{n^2}\Big).$$

The Popov criterion of control theory (2) has recently been extended to Volterra equations by C. Corduneanu (3). His criterion can be applied to Eq. (11) only if $h_{10} = h_{20} = 0$. (The reason for this is that in (3) it is assumed that

$p'(t), q(t) \in L_1(0,\infty)$.) However, situations in which $h_{10} \neq 0$, $h_{20} \neq 0$ are also of interest.

Finally, we remark that $g \in C(-\infty,\infty)$ does not guarantee the uniqueness of solutions of Eq. (11). However, any assumption (such as $g(u) \in \text{Lip}$, $-\infty < u < \infty$) which does insure this, combined with any uniqueness theorem for solutions of the homogeneous heat equation satisfying $T(x,0) = f(x)$ and (3), yields a uniqueness theorem for solutions of (1) satisfying (2) and (3). (Theorem 2 of (1) is an example of such a result on the infinite interval.)

2. We now sketch the proof of the theorem. From (5), (6), (7) one has

$$\sum_{n=0}^{\infty} h_{1n} < \infty, \qquad \sum_{n=0}^{\infty} |h_{2n}| < \infty. \tag{12}$$

Thus the functions

$$a(t) = \frac{\pi}{2} \sum_{n=0}^{\infty} h_{1n} e^{-n^2 t}, \qquad b(t) = \frac{\pi}{2} \sum_{n=0}^{\infty} h_{2n} e^{-n^2 t}$$

are continuous on $0 \leq t < \infty$. Consider the Volterra equation

$$u'(t) = -\int_0^t a(t-\tau) g(u(\tau))\, d\tau - b(t) \tag{13}$$

subject to the initial condition $u(0) = u_0$. It is useful to write (13) in the equivalent form

$$u'(t) = -\frac{\pi}{2} \sum_{n=0}^{\infty} (h_{1n}\gamma_n(t) + h_{2n}) e^{-n^2 t} \tag{14}$$

with

$$\gamma_n(t) = \int_0^t e^{n^2 \tau} g(u(\tau))\, d\tau. \tag{15}$$

For as long as a solution $u(t)$ of (13) exists, define

$$E(t) = \int_0^{u(t)} g(\sigma)\, d\sigma + \frac{\pi}{4} \sum_{n=0}^{\infty} (h_{1n}\gamma_n^2(t) + 2h_{2n}\gamma_n(t) + h_{3n}) e^{-2n^2 t}. \tag{16}$$

Using (14) one obtains

$$E'(t) = -\frac{\pi}{2}\sum_{n=1}^{\infty} n^2(h_{1n}\gamma_n^2(t) + 2h_{2n}\gamma_n(t) + h_{3n})e^{-2n^2t}. \tag{17}$$

From (4), (7) $E(t) \geq 0$ and $E'(t) \leq 0$, and therefore

$$0 \leq E(t) \leq E(0) = \int_0^{u_0} g(\sigma)\, d\sigma + \frac{\pi}{4}\sum_{n=0}^{\infty} h_{3n}$$

for as long as $u(t)$ exists. Since the right hand side of this inequality is independent of t, a well-known argument shows that $u(t)$ can be continued to the interval $0 \leq t < \infty$ and that there exists a constant $K < \infty$ such that

$$|u(t)| \leq K \qquad (0 \leq t < \infty). \tag{18}$$

Hence one also has

$$n^2|\gamma_n(t)|\, e^{-n^2t} \leq K \qquad (0 \leq t < \infty), \tag{19}$$

where the constant K is not necessarily the same as in (18). From (17) one has

$$\begin{aligned} E''(t) = {} & \pi\sum_{n=1}^{\infty} n^4(h_{1n}\gamma_n^2(t) + 2h_{2n}\gamma_n(t) + h_{3n})e^{-2n^2t} \\ & - \pi g(u(t))\sum_{n=1}^{\infty} n^2(h_{1n}\gamma_n(t) + h_{2n})e^{-n^2t} \quad (0 < t < \infty), \end{aligned} \tag{20}$$

and therefore, using (18), (19) one has $|E''(t)| \leq K$ $(1 \leq t < \infty)$. This together with $E(t) \geq 0$, $E'(t) \leq 0$ and the mean value theorem gives

$$\lim_{t\to\infty} E'(t) = 0. \tag{21}$$

It now follows easily from (17), (19) and (21) that

$$\lim_{t\to\infty}\sum_{n=1}^{\infty} n^2 h_{1n}\gamma_n^2(t)e^{-2n^2t} = 0,$$

and therefore, using (7),

$$\lim_{t\to\infty} \gamma_{n_1}(t)e^{-n_1^2 t} = \lim_{t\to\infty} \int_0^t e^{-n_1^2(t-\tau)} g(u(\tau))\, d\tau = 0. \tag{22}$$

Differentiating (14) and using (18) one obtains $|u''(t)| \le K$ $(1 \le t < \infty)$ and thus also that $|u'(t)| \le \hat{K}$ $(0 \le t < \infty)$. It may now be shown, in several ways, that the conclusion (8) follows from (22) (one such argument is given in (1)).

Define

$$T(x, t) = \int_0^\pi G(x,\xi;t)f(\xi)d\xi + \int_0^t\int_0^\pi G(x,\xi;t-\tau)\eta(\xi)g(u(\tau))\, d\xi\, d\tau,$$

where $0 \le x \le \pi$, $0 < t < \infty$ and

$$G(x,\xi;t) = \frac{1}{\pi}\left(1 + 2\sum_{n=1}^{\infty} \cos nx \cos n\xi e^{-n^2 t}\right) \quad (0 \le x \le \pi, 0<t<\infty)$$

is the Green's function associated with the homogeneous heat equation and the boundary condition (3), and $u(t)$ is the function defined above. From $\eta, f \in L_2(0, \pi)$ it follows that $T(x, t)$ may also be written as

$$T(x, t) = \frac{T_0(t)}{\sqrt{2}} + \sum_{n=1}^{\infty} T_n(t) \cos nx \quad (0 \le x \le \pi, 0<t<\infty), \tag{23}$$

where

$$T_n(t) = (f_n + \eta_n\gamma_n(t))e^{-n^2 t} \quad (n=0, 1, \ldots). \tag{24}$$

It can also be shown that $T(x, t)$, $T_x(x, t)$, $T_{xx}(x, t)$, $T_t(x, t)$ are continuous in (x, t) for $0 \le x \le \pi$, $0 < t < \infty$ and that $T(x, t)$ satisfies the second equation in (1); moreover, $T(x, t)$ satisfies $T(x, 0) = f(x)$, $0 \le x \le \pi$ and (3). From the Parceval theorem and (23) one has

$$\int_0^\pi \alpha(x)T(x, t)dx = \frac{\pi}{2}\sum_{n=0}^{\infty} \alpha_n f_n e^{-n^2 t} + \frac{\pi}{2}\sum_{n=0}^{\infty} \alpha_n\eta_n\gamma_n(t)\, e^{-n^2 t},$$

which, together with (6) and (14), implies that $u(t)$, $T(x.t)$ satisfy the first equation in (1). This establishes the global existence of the solution $u(t), T(x,t)$ of (1), (2), (3) and with $u(t)$ satisfying (8).

To establish the asserted behavior of $T(x,t)$ as $t \to \infty$ one observes that

$$|T(x,t)| \leq \frac{|T_0(t)|}{\sqrt{2}} + \sum_{n=1}^{\infty} |T_n(t)| \quad (0 \leq x \leq \pi, 0 \leq t < \infty).$$

Hypothesis (5) implies that $\sum_{n=1}^{\infty} |f_n| < \infty$, $\sum_{n=1}^{\infty} |\eta_n| < \infty$.

Hence

$$\sum_{n=1}^{\infty} |T_n(t)| \leq e^{-t} \sum_{n=1}^{\infty} |f_n| + \int_0^t e^{-(t-\tau)} |g(u(\tau))| \, d\tau \sum_{n=1}^{\infty} |\eta_n| ,$$

and therefore from (8) one has

$$\lim_{t\to\infty} \sum_{n=1}^{\infty} |T_n(t)| = 0. \qquad (25)$$

Substituting (23) in the first equation in (1) one obtains

$$u'(t) = -\frac{\pi}{2} \sum_{n=0}^{\infty} \alpha_n T_n(t) \quad (0 < t < \infty),$$

which, together with $|\alpha_n| \leq K < \infty$ $(n = 0, 1, \ldots)$ and (25) yields

$$\lim_{t\to\infty} (u'(t) + \frac{\pi}{2}\alpha_0 T_0(t)) = 0.$$

If $\alpha_0 \neq 0$, $(8, k = 1)$ now implies that $\lim_{t\to\infty} T_0(t) = 0$, and using (23), (25) one obtains (9). If $\alpha_0 = 0$ and also $\eta_0 = 0$, one has $T_0(t) \equiv f_0$. This, together with (23), (25) establishes (10) and completes the proof.

References

1. Levin, J. J. and Nohel, J. A., A system of nonlinear integrodifferential equations, Mich. Math. J. 13 (1966), 257-270.

2. Popov, V. M., Absolute stability of nonlinear systems of automatic control. Automat. i Telemeh. 22 (1961), 961-979.

3. Corduneanu, C., Sur une équation intégrale de le théorie du réglage automatique, C. R. Acad. Sci. Paris 256 (1963), 3564-3567.

STABILITY PROPERTIES OF A SECOND ORDER SYSTEM SATISFYING THE HURWITZ CRITERION

RICHARD DATKO

Department of Mathematics,
McGill University, Montreal, Quebec, Canada

Introduction

For systems of ordinary differential equations given by the equation $\frac{dx}{dt} = Ax$ where A is a constant nxn matrix and x is an n-vector it is known that a necessary and sufficient condition that the origin be asymptotically stable is that A have all its eigenvalues with real parts less than zero. In the case where the constant matrix A is replaced by matrices A(t) or A(x) which have the above mentioned eigenvalue property the sufficiency condition has been extended somewhat (for example see [1],[2],[3]). In the first two papers cited the primary tool used in the investigation was Lyapunov's second method. In [3] a combination of the second method and examination of the phase portrait of solutions was used to obtain stability properties.

Our aim in this paper is to study the problem of global stability for a general case where A = A(x), n = 2 and A(x) has characteristic roots with real parts negative. The conclusion we arrive at is that the system under consideration is either globally stable or that there is a limit cycle bounding the region of asymptotic stability.

I. Consider the second order system of ordinary differential equations given by:

$$\dot{x} = ax + by \qquad (1)$$
$$\dot{y} = cx + dy$$

where it is assumed that:

H_1. a,b,c,d are continuously differentiable functions of (x,y) and are uniformly bounded by some constant K on all of E^2.

H_2. There exist positive constants S_1, S_2, V_1 and V_2 such that
$$-S_2 \leq a+d \leq -S_1 \text{ and } V_2 \leq ad-bc \leq V_1$$
for all (x,y) in E^2.

H_3. There exists a smooth curve C which does not intersect itself, is of infinite extent, whose rotation angle changes by less than 2π radians and which satisfies the following properties relative to system (1):

(i) C intersects the region of asymptotic stability α of system (1).

(ii) The vector field determined by (1) is never tangent to C.

In effect H_3 postulates the existence of an infinite transversal for trajectories which are solutions of (1).

Let (x(t), y(t)) be an arbitrary solution of (1) with initial conditions (x_o, y_o) at time t = 0. Then because of H_1 and the Gronwall inequality we see that
$$\|x(t)\| \leq \|x_o\| e^{K_1 t} \qquad (2)$$
where $\|\cdot\|$ denotes the Euclidean norm and K_1 is a positive constant. H_1 also guarantees the uniqueness of all solutions of (1).

Consider the polar representation $x = r \cos \phi$, $y = r \sin \phi$ of points (x,y) in E^2. The polar form for the system (1) is:
$$r^2\dot{\phi} = -\dot{x}y + \dot{y}x = -by^2 + (d-a)xy + cx^2$$
$$r\dot{r} = x\dot{x} + y\dot{y} = ax^2 + (b+c)xy + dy^2 . \qquad (3)$$
The following properties of the system (1) or its polar equivalent (3) will be developed which are necessary in the proof of our main result.

PROPERTY 1. If at any point $(x_o, y_o) \neq (0,0)$
$$\dot{\phi}(x_o, y_o) = 0 \quad \text{then} \quad \dot{r}(x_o, y_o) < 0.$$

Proof. Let $(x_o, y_o) \neq (0,0)$ be a point where $\dot{\phi} = 0$. By means of a rotation of the (x,y) coordinate system we can transform (x_o, y_o) into a point $(\bar{x}_o, 0)$ in some barred system $(\bar{x}, \bar{y})$.

Equations (1) transform into equations of the same form in the new coordinates:

$$\dot{\bar{x}} = \bar{a}\bar{x} + \bar{b}\bar{y}$$
$$\dot{\bar{y}} = \bar{c}\bar{x} + \bar{d}\bar{y} \qquad (4)$$

which satisfy hypotheses $H_1 - H_3$. Moreover

$$\bar{a}(\bar{x}_o,0) + \bar{d}(\bar{x}_o,0) = a(x_o,y_o) + d(x_o,y_o) < 0,$$

$$\bar{a}\bar{d}-\bar{b}\bar{c}\Big|_{(\bar{x}_o,0)} = ab-bc\Big|_{(x_o,y_o)} > 0,$$

$$\bar{r}\dot{\bar{r}}\Big|_{(\bar{x}_o,0)} = r\dot{r}\Big|_{(x_o,y_o)} \quad \text{and}$$

$$\bar{r}^2\dot{\bar{\phi}}\Big|_{(\bar{x}_o,0)} = r^2\dot{\phi}\Big|_{(x_o,y_o)} .$$

This implies that at $(\bar{x}_o,0)$

$$\bar{r}^2\dot{\bar{\phi}} = 0 = \bar{c}\bar{x}_o^2 \quad \text{i.e.} \quad \bar{c} = 0$$

and

$$\bar{r}\dot{\bar{r}} = \bar{a}\bar{x}_o^2 . \quad \text{But } \bar{a}+\bar{d} < 0 \text{ and } \bar{a}\bar{d} > 0.$$

Hence $\bar{a} < 0$ and $\dot{\bar{r}} < 0$ at $(\bar{x}_o,0)$ which proves the property.

PROPERTY 2. If $\dot{r} \geq 0$ then $|\dot{\phi}| \geq \frac{V_2}{K}$.

Proof. Let $\dot{r} \geq 0$ at some point p. As in the proof of property 1 we may assume that p has coordinates $(x_o,0)$, $x_o \neq 0$. From the second equation in (3) we deduce that $a(x_o,0) \geq 0$ and $|\dot{\phi}(x_o,0)| = |c(x_o,0)|$. By H_2 this implies the inequality $K|\dot{\phi}| = K|c| \geq |bc| = bc \geq V_2-ad \geq V_2$ which establishes property 2.

One consequence of properties one and two is that any connected region R in E^2 where $\dot{r}(x,y) \geq 0$ has $\dot{\phi}(x,y)$ of one sign and $|\dot{\phi}(x,y)| \geq \frac{V_2}{K}$. Hence any trajectory of (1) starting in R must either leave R in a finite time, which is to say it passes into a connected region where $\dot{r} < 0$ or the polar angle makes a circuit of 2π radians on the unit circle in time $T \leq \frac{2\pi K}{V_2}$.

Let P denote a positive semi-orbit determined by a given solution of Eq.(1) starting at (x_o, y_o) at time $t = 0$ and let $P(t)$ denote the points on the orbit for $t \geq 0$. Our next property essentially states that if $P(t)$ does not tend to the origin as $t \to \infty$ then the argument $\phi(t)$ of $P(t)$ tends to either $+\infty$ or $-\infty$ as $t \to \infty$.

PROPERTY 3. Suppose $P(t)$ does not tend to $(0,0)$ as $t \to \infty$. Then the argument $\phi(t)$ associated with $P(t)$ makes one revolution of the unit circle in either a clockwise or a counterclockwise direction in a finite interval of time.

Proof. If $P(t)$ does not tend to $(0,0)$ as $t \to \infty$ there exists a time $t_o \geq 0$ such that $\dot{r}(t_o) = r(\dot{x}(t_o), y(t_o)) \geq 0$. Since the system Eq. (1) is autonomous we may assume that $t_o = 0$ and that $\dot{\phi}(0) = \dot{\phi}(x(0), y(o)) > 0$. Hence by property two $\dot{\phi}(0) \geq \frac{V_2}{K}$. There are two possible cases to consider.

Case (i). If $\dot{r}(t) \geq 0$ for all $t \geq 0$ then $\dot{\phi}(t) \geq \frac{V_2}{K}$ for all $t \geq 0$ and $\phi(t)$ makes one counterclockwise revolution of the unit circle in time $T \leq \frac{2\pi K}{V_2}$.

Case (ii). $\dot{r}(t) < 0$ for some values of t. This case has two subcases.

Subcase (a). $\phi(t)$ satisfies the stated property.

Subcase (b). $\phi(t)$ does not satisfy the property.

We want to show that subcase (b) is impossible. If subcase (b) holds we may assume without loss of generality that at $t = 0$ $\dot{\phi}(0) \geq \frac{V_2}{K}$, $\dot{r}(0) = 0$ and $\dot{r}(t) < 0$ on some open interval $(0, t_o)$ where $t_o \neq 0$.

Let $r(0) = r_o$. We claim that if $r(t) \geq r_o$ for some $t > 0$ then $\phi(t) > \phi_o$. To see this consider the circle $r = r_o$ and assume there exists a first $t_1 > 0$ such that $r(t_1) = r_o$ and $\phi(t_1) < \phi_o$. By hypothesis $|\phi(t) - \phi_o| < 2\pi$ for all t in $I = [0, t_1]$. Let

$$\alpha_1 = \phi_o + \max_{t\in I} \; (\phi(t) - \phi_o)$$

$$\alpha_2 = \phi_o + \min_{t\in I} \; (\phi(t) - \phi_o)$$

$$J = \bigcup_{t\in I} P(t) \quad \text{and let}$$

J be directed with increasing t. J cannot intersect itself since all solutions of Eq. (1) are unique and self-intersection would imply P is periodic of period T with $T \leq t_1$. But this is impossible if $\phi(t)$ does not change by 2π radians, because the interior of J would not contain the origin, the only singular point of Eq. (1). Along the points of intersection of J and the rays $\phi = \alpha_1$ and $\phi = \alpha_2$, $\dot{\phi} = 0$. However, at least one of these points must have $\dot{r} \geq 0$ otherwise it would be impossible for $r(t_1) \geq r_o$ (see the figure below). But this situation is ruled out by property 1.

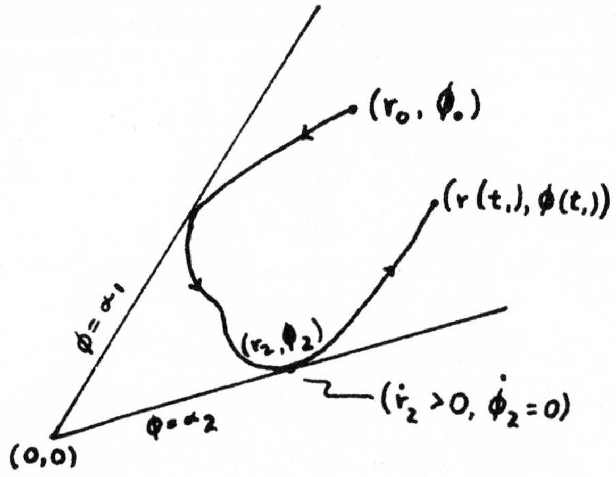

Let $\Delta(\phi(t)) = \int_o^t \dot{\phi}(s)ds$. As we have shown above if $\Delta(\phi(t)) \leq 0$ and $t > 0$, then $r(t) < r_o$. Suppose $\Delta(\phi(\bar{t})) = 0, \Delta(\phi(t)) > 0$ and $\dot{r} \geq 0$ on some interval $[\bar{t},\bar{\bar{t}}]$. Then $r(t) \leq r_o$ and $\phi(\bar{\bar{t}}) \geq \phi(\bar{t}) + \frac{V_2}{K}(\bar{\bar{t}}-\bar{t})$ (This last is a consequence of property 2.) This implies that $\bar{\bar{t}} - \bar{t} \leq \frac{\Delta(\phi(t))K}{V_2}$. Hence using the estimate in Eq. (2) we conclude that $r(\bar{\bar{t}}) \leq r(\bar{t})\exp\frac{K_1(\phi(t))K}{V_2} < r_o \exp\frac{K_1 2\pi K}{V_2}$.

if $\Delta(\phi(t)) \geq 0$ and $\dot{r} \geq 0$ on $[\bar{t}, \bar{\bar{t}}]$. This result shows that the half trajectory P must lie in a compact set which does not contain the origin as an ω-limit point. By the Poincaré Bendixson theorem (see e.g. [4]) this implies that the ω-limit set of P is a limit cycle. This however implies that $\phi(t)$ changes by 2π radians in a finite interval of time which contradicts the hypothesis of subcase (b). Hence property 3 is proved.

We are now in a position to establish the main result.

Theorem. All non-trivial solutions of Eq.(1) tend to the origin as $t \to \infty$ or there exists a limit cycle which contains the region of asymptotic stability in its interior.

Proof. Because of H_1 system Eq.(1) can be written

$$\dot{x} = a(0,0)x + b(0,0)y + f_1(x,y)$$

$$\dot{y} = c(0,0)x + d(0,0)y + f_2(x,y)$$

where $\dfrac{|f_i(x,y)|}{\sqrt{x^2 + y^2}} \to 0$ as $x^2 + y^2 \to 0,\ i = 1,2$.

Hence (see e.g. [4] or [5]) the origin is asymptotically stable. The region α of asymptotic stability is open. Suppose it is not all of E^2 . Then there exists at least one point (x_o, y_o) on the boundary of α. Let P denote the positive half trajectory through (x_o, y_o) which is a solution of Eq.(1). According to property 3 the polar angle $\phi(t)$ associated the P(t) makes a rotation on the unit circle an infinite number of times. Thus the trajectory P intersects the curve C of H_3 also an infinite number of times. Let p_1 and p_2 denote two successive intersections. If $p_1 = p_2$ then P is periodic and hence a limit cycle of Eq.(1).

Thus suppose $p_1 \neq p_2$. Then p_2 must not separate p_1 from the origin along C, otherwise successive intersections p_{n-1} and p_n would have the property that p_n separated p_{n-1} from the origin along C. This would imply that P(t) tended to a limit cycle J and that it was on the outside or unbounded region determined by J. This is impossible since P is on the boundary of the region of asymptotic stability.

It is equally impossible for p_1 to separate p_2 from

the origin along C, since by continuity of solutions of Eq.(1) with respect to initial conditions the same characteristic would be true for at least one positive half trajectory $\bar{P}$ lying in α.

Let $\bar{p}_1$ and $\bar{p}_2$ be two successive intersections of C by points on $\bar{P}$ and let $\bar{p}_1$ separate $\bar{p}_2$ from the origin along C. Construct the Jordan curve consisting of the arc of $\bar{P}$ joining $\bar{p}_1$ and $\bar{p}_2$ and the arc of C joining $\bar{p}_1$ and $\bar{p}_2$

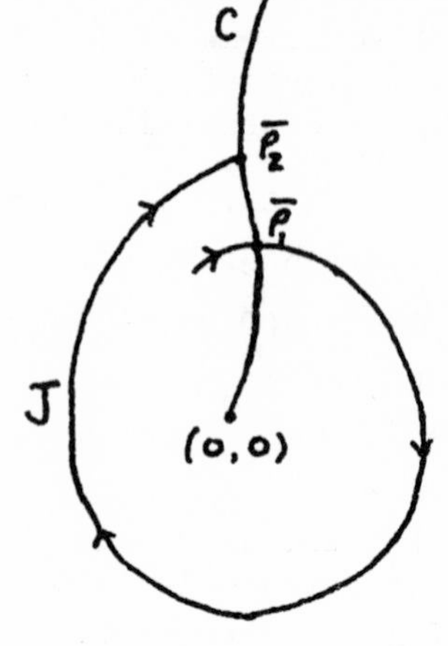

The inside of this curve contains the origin and $\bar{P}$ cannot reenter this region. Hence $\bar{P}$ would not be in α, which is impossible. Thus the assumption that p_1 separated p_2 along C led to a contradiction.

Consequently the only possibilities are that either the whole plane is the region of stability or the region of asymptotic stability is bounded by a limit cycle.

Remark 1. Any system of the form

$$\dot{x} = P(x,y)$$
$$\dot{y} = Q(x,y)$$

where the origin is asymptotically stable and which satisfies H_3 and property 3 is either globally stable or has a limit cycle bounding the region of asymptotic stability. The systems considered in Eq.[1],[2] and [3] all had these properties. The possibility of a limit cycle in these cases was eliminated by the construction of a Lyapunov function, examination of the phase portrait or noticing that

$$\frac{\partial P}{\partial x} + \frac{\partial Q}{\partial y} \leq 0 \quad \text{for all} \quad (x,y) \text{ in } E^2.$$

Remark 2. The boundedness assumption on the coefficients a, b, c and d in H_1 may seem a bit severe. However property 2 need not be true if this condition is relaxed. As an example consider the following system:

$$\frac{dx}{dt} = -x + 2x^2 y$$
$$\frac{dy}{dt} = -y. \qquad (5)$$

Using Zubov's method a stability determining function is $V(x,y) = \exp[-\frac{y^2}{2} - \frac{x^2}{2(1-xy)}] - 1$ and the boundary of the region of asymptotic stability is $xy = 1$ which is not a limit cycle.

It might be mentioned that in this case all other assumptions in $H_1 - H_3$ are satisfied. A transversal being the curve

$$x = -y, \ x > 0.$$

Notice also that for the system (5)

$$\dot{\phi}(x,y) = -2x^2 \sin^2\phi - \sin\phi \cos\phi$$

$$\frac{\dot{r}}{r} = -\cos^2\phi + 2x^2 \sin\phi \cos\phi - \sin^2\phi .$$

Along the curve $xy = 1$, $\sin\phi \cos\phi = \frac{1}{r^2}$. Hence along this curve

$$\dot{\phi} = -\frac{3}{r^2} \quad \text{and} \quad \frac{\dot{r}}{r} = 2\cos^2\phi \geq 0 \quad \text{for } \phi \leq \frac{\pi}{4} .$$

Thus $\dot{\phi} \to 0$ as $r \to \infty$ in a region where $\dot{r} > 0$. This violates property 2.

References

1. Malkin, I.G.; On a problem of the theory of stability of system of automatic regulation, PMM 16, 365-368(1952)
2. Krasovsii, N.N.; On stability of solutions of a system of two differential equations, PMM 17, 651-672 (1953).
3. Mufti, I.H.; Stability in the large of systems of two equations, Arch. Rat. Mech. Anal. 7,118-134 (1961).
4. Hartman, P.; Ordinary Differential Equations, Wiley, New York, (1964).
5. Coddington, E.A. and Levinson, N.; Theory of ordinary differential equations, McGraw-Hill, New York (1955).

ON THE STABILITY OF SYSTEMS WITH MONOTONE AND ODD MONOTONE NONLINEARITIES†

by G. Zames[1] and P.L. Falb[1,2]

1. INTRODUCTION

Consider the feedback system illustrated in Figure 1 where $\underset{\sim}{H}$ is a time invariant linear operator and $\underset{\sim}{N}$ is a memoryless monotone (or odd monotone) nonlinearity. Representing the

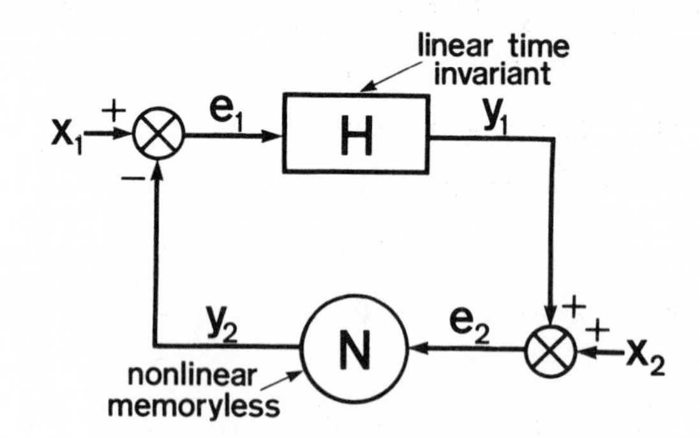

FIG.1 A FEEDBACK SYSTEM

---

[1]NASA, Electronics Research Center, Technology Square, Cambridge, Massachusetts 02139, and

[2]Brown University, Division of Applied Mathematics, Providence, Rhode Island, research supported by the Air Force Office of Scientific Research, Office of Aerospace Research, United States Air Force, under AFOSR Grant No. AF-AFOSR-693-66.

†This paper is extracted from a more complete report, which can be obtained from the authors.

system by an integral equation, we derive stability conditions in terms of the frequency response of $\underset{\sim}{H}$ and a suitable multiplier. Our derivation draws on the theory of positive operators on a Hilbert space and involves the factorization of a convolution operator into a product of two positive operators.

The problem of stability for feedback systems with a single nonlinearity was initially considered by Lur'e and a well known frequency response condition is Popov's Theorem. Lur'e and Popov assumed that the system was represented by a differential equation and that the nonlinearity was confined to the first and third quadrants. We pose our problem in the framework of operator equations and make quite different assumptions on $\underset{\sim}{N}$.

An operator approach to stability was used by Zames (1a,b), who showed that a feedback system was stable if its "open loop" operator could be factored into two positive definite parts. The class of "R.C." multipliers having the form $(1-Z(s))^{-1} = \sum_1^\infty h_i/s+a_i$, $h_i > 0$, $a_i > 0$ played a crucial role in (1a,b). Closely related results were obtained, in the framework of Lyapunov theory, by Brockett and Willems (2), Yakubovicz (3), and Narendra and Neuman (4), and, using operator methods, by Dewey and Jury (5) and Lee and Desoer (6). A more general class of multipliers was introduced by O'Shea (7a) and used to prove stability by Zames and Falb (8). (The original results of O'Shea were incorrectly proved.) In a subsequent report (7b), O'Shea used multipliers defined on $(-\infty,\infty)$ rather than on $[0,\infty)$; however, the results of O'Shea are valid for a very limited class of nonlinearities since his proof in effect involves the a priori assumption that the solutions are bounded. We require no such boundedness assumption here and our method of proof is novel. In point of fact, the main feature of this paper is a method for proving stability with multipliers defined on $(-\infty,\infty)$, which involves the factorization of a convolution operator on $L_2(-\infty,\infty)$ into a product of two operators, one having a kernel which vanishes on $(-\infty,0]$ and the other having a kernel which vanishes on $[0,\infty)$.

2. THE MAIN PROBLEM AND ITS SOLUTION

We consider the feedback equations (see Figure 1)

$$e_1 = x_1 - y_2 \quad (1) \qquad\qquad e_2 = x_2 + y_1 \quad (2)$$

$$y_1(t) = \underset{\sim}{H}e_1(t) = \sum_{i=1}^{\infty} h_i e_1(t-\tau_i) + \int_0^{\infty} h(\tau)e_1(t-\tau)d\tau \tag{3}$$

$$y_2(t) = \underset{\sim}{N}e_2(t) = N(e_2(t)) \tag{4}$$

under the following assumptions:

A1. $N(\cdot)$ _is a real valued function on_ $(-\infty,\infty)$ _with the following properties:_

(i) $N(0) = 0$;

(ii) N _is monotone nondecreasing_, _i.e._, $(r-s)[N(r)-N(s)] \geq 0$;

(iii) _there is a constant_ $C > 0$ _such that_ $|N(r)| \leq C|r|$ _for all_ r.

A2. $h(\cdot)$ _is a_ (_real valued_) _element of_ $L_1[0,\infty)$, _i.e._, $\int_0^{\infty}|h(\tau)|d\tau < \infty$.

A3. $\{\tau_i\}$ _is a sequence in_ $[0,\infty)$ _and_ $\{h_i\}$ _is a sequence in_ ℓ_1, _i.e._, $\sum_{i=1}^{\infty}|h_i| < \infty$.

A4. x_1, x_2, y_1, y_2, e_1, _and_ e_2 _are real valued functions on_ $(-\infty,\infty)$ _and_

(i) $\int_{-\infty}^{t} e_1(\tau)^2 d\tau < \infty$, $\int_{-\infty}^{t} e_2(\tau)^2 d\tau < \infty$ _for all_ (_finite_) t ;

(ii) $x_1(\cdot)$ _and_ $x_2(\cdot)$ _are elements of_ $L_2(-\infty,\infty)$, _i.e._,

$$\int_{-\infty}^{\infty} x_1^2(\tau)d\tau < \infty \quad \text{and} \quad \int_{-\infty}^{\infty} x_2^2(\tau)d\tau < \infty .$$

Let $H(j\omega)$ denote the frequency function of $\underset{\sim}{H}$, i.e., $H(j\omega) = \sum_{i=1}^{\infty} h_i \exp(-j\omega\tau_i) + \int_0^{\infty} h(t)\exp(-j\omega t)dt$. We shall seek a solution to the following problem:

MAIN PROBLEM _Find conditions on_ $H(j\omega)$ _which ensure that_ e_1 _and_ e_2 _are in_ $L_2(-\infty,\infty)$ _and that_ $\lim_{t\to\infty} y_1(t) = 0$. Our solution, which is given in Theorem 1, involves the following inequality

$$\mathrm{Re}(\{1-Z(j\omega)\}H(j\omega)) \geq \delta > , \quad \omega \in (-\infty,\infty) \tag{5}$$

where $Z(j\omega)$ is a suitable frequency function. We refer to $1-Z(j\omega)$ as the stability multiplier. More precisely, we have:

THEOREM 1 *If there is an element $z(\cdot)$ in $L_1(-\infty,\infty)$, if there are sequences $\{\sigma_i\}$ and $\{z_i\}$ in $(-\infty,\infty)$ such that*

$$\int_{-\infty}^{\infty} |z(\tau)|\,d\tau + \sum_{i=1}^{\infty} |z_i| < 1 \tag{6}$$

and (5) is satisfied for $Z(j\omega)$ given by

$$Z(j\omega) = \sum_{i=1}^{\infty} z_i \exp(-j\omega\sigma_i) + \int_{-\infty}^{\infty} z(t)\exp(-j\omega t)\,dt \tag{7}$$

and if either $z(\cdot) \geqq 0$ and $z_i \geqq 0$, $i = 1,2,\ldots,$ or $N(\cdot)$ is odd, then e_1 and e_2 are in $L_2(-\infty,\infty)$.

COROLLARY 1 *If, in addition to the hypotheses of the theorem, $h(\cdot)$ is in $L_2[0,\infty)$ and $h_i = 0$, $i = 1,2,\ldots,$ then $\lim_{t\to\infty} y_1(t) = 0$.*

COROLLARY 2 (*slope-restricted nonlinearities*) *If, in addition to assumptions A1-A4, the following conditions are satisfied:*

(a) *there are constants $a, b, \epsilon > 0$ such that $a \leqq N(x)-N(y)/x-y \leqq b-\epsilon$ for all $x \neq y$* (Note that this implies that $|bx-N(x)| \geqq \epsilon|x|$ for all x.);

(b) $h_i = 0$ *for* $i = 1,2,\ldots;$

(c) *there is an element $z(\cdot)$ in $L_1(-\infty,\infty)$ and there are sequences $\{\sigma_i\}$ and $\{z_i\}$ in $(-\infty,\infty)$ such that (6) holds and there is a constant $\delta > 0$ for which the inequality*

$$\mathrm{Re}\{(1-Z(j\omega))(H(j\omega)+b^{-1})(H^*(j\omega)+a^{-1})\} \geqq \delta > 0 \tag{5'}$$

is satisfied;

(d) *either $z(\cdot) \geqq 0$ and $z_i \geqq 0$, $i = 1,2,\ldots,$ or $N(\cdot)$ is odd;*

(e) *the Nyquist diagram of $H(j\omega)$ does not encircle the point $(-1/a,0)$.* [The Nyquist diagram of $H(\cdot)$ is the subset of the complex plane consisting of

(i) the image of the $j\omega$-axis under $H(\cdot)$, and (ii) the origin. In our case, $H(j\omega)$ is a continuous curve with $\lim_{\omega \to \infty} H(j\omega) = 0$.];

Then $e_1(\cdot)$ *and* $e_2(\cdot)$ *are in* $L_2(-\infty,\infty)$ *and* $\lim_{t \to \infty} y_1(t)=0$.

3. A METHOD FOR GENERATING STABILITY CONDITIONS

In this section we develop the basic ideas underlying our method for generating stability conditions. We let Ω be a real Hilbert space, R be the reals, and $L_2(R,\Omega) = \{x(\cdot): x(t) \in \Omega$ and $\int_{-\infty}^{\infty} \|x(t)\|^2 dt < \infty\}$. We view this space as a Hilbert space with inner product given by

$$\langle x(\cdot),y(\cdot)\rangle = \int_{-\infty}^{\infty} \langle x(t),y(t)\rangle_{\Omega} dt \qquad (8)$$

We now have:

DEFINITION 1 *Let* $x(\cdot)$ *be a mapping of* R *into* Ω *and let* t *be an element of* R. *Then the t-truncation of* $x(\cdot)$, *in symbols* $x_t(\cdot)$, *is the function defined by* $x_t(s) = x(s)$ *for* $s \leqq t$ *and* $x_t(s) = 0$ *for* $s > t$. *We let* $L_{2e}(R,\Omega)$ *denote the set of all mappings* $x(\cdot)$ *of* R *into* Ω *such that* $x_t(\cdot) \in L_2(R,\Omega)$ *for all* t, *i.e.*, $L_{2e}(R,\Omega) = \{x(\cdot): x_t(\cdot) \in L_2(R,\Omega)$ *for all* t *in* $R\}$. $L_{2e}(R,\Omega)$ *shall be called the extension of* $L_2(R,\Omega)$.

For economy of notation, we write "L_2" and "L_{2e}" in place of "$L_2(R,\Omega)$" and "$L_{2e}(R,\Omega)$", respectively.

If $x(\cdot)$ is an element of L_{2e}, then the *extended norm* of $x(\cdot)$, in symbols: $\|x(\cdot)\|_e$, is given by $\|x\|_e = \|x\|$ if $x(\cdot) \in L_2$, and $\|x\|_e = \infty$ if $x(\cdot) \notin L_2$, where $\|\cdot\|$ denotes the norm on L_2. Now let $\underset{\sim}{T}$ be a mapping of L_2 into L_2 (or of L_{2e} into L_{2e}); then we have:

DEFINITION 2 $\underset{\sim}{T}$ *is nonanticipative if* $(\underset{\sim}{T}x)_t = (\underset{\sim}{T}x_t)_t$ *for all* x *in* L_2 (*or* L_{2e}) *and all* t *in* R.

Nonanticipative mappings play an important role in the sequel. We now have:

DEFINITION 3 *Let* $\underset{\sim}{T}$ *be a nonanticipative mapping of* L_{2e} *into* L_{2e}. *Then the gain of* $\underset{\sim}{T}$, $\gamma_e(\underset{\sim}{T})$, *is given by*

$$\gamma_e(\underset{\sim}{T}) = \sup_{\substack{x \in L_{2e} \\ t \in (-\infty,\infty) \\ x_t \neq 0}} \{ \|(\underset{\sim}{T}x(\cdot))_t\|_e / \|x_t(\cdot)\|_e \} \tag{9}$$

$\underset{\sim}{T}$ <u>is said to be positive(e) if</u>

$$\langle x_t(\cdot), (\underset{\sim}{T}x(\cdot))_t \rangle \geq 0 \tag{10}$$

<u>for all</u> $x(\cdot)$ <u>in</u> L_{2e} <u>and all</u> t <u>in</u> R, <u>and to be strongly positive(e) if</u>

$$\langle x_t(\cdot), (\underset{\sim}{T}x(\cdot))_t \rangle \geq \delta \|x_t(\cdot)\|_e^2 \tag{11}$$

<u>for all</u> $x(\cdot)$ <u>in</u> L_{2e}, all t <u>in</u> R, <u>and some</u> $\delta > 0$. <u>A mapping</u> $\underset{\sim}{T}^*$ <u>of</u> L_{2e} <u>into</u> L_{2e} <u>is said to be a conjugate(e) (or adjoint(e)) of</u> $\underset{\sim}{T}$ <u>if</u>

$$\langle x_t(\cdot), (\underset{\sim}{T}y_t(\cdot)) \rangle = \langle (\underset{\sim}{T}^*x_t(\cdot)), y_t(\cdot) \rangle \tag{12}$$

<u>for all</u> $x(\cdot), y(\cdot)$ <u>in</u> L_{2e} <u>and all</u> t <u>in</u> R.

Definition 3 is a natural generalization of the corresponding properties for maps $\underset{\sim}{T}$ of L_2 into L_2, and for maps of L_2 into L_2, we shall say without further ado that $\underset{\sim}{T}$ has a gain $\gamma(\underset{\sim}{T})$, $\underset{\sim}{T}$ is positive, $\underset{\sim}{T}$ has a conjugate $\underset{\sim}{T}^*$, etc.

Now consider the feedback system

$$f_1(\cdot) = v_1(\cdot) - w_2(\cdot) \tag{13}$$
$$f_2(\cdot) = v_2(\cdot) + w_1(\cdot) \tag{14}$$
$$w_1(\cdot) = \underset{\sim}{G}_1 f_1(\cdot) \tag{15}$$
$$w_2(\cdot) = \underset{\sim}{G}_2 f_2(\cdot) \tag{16}$$

where (a) $\underset{\sim}{G}_1$ and $\underset{\sim}{G}_2$ are nonanticipative maps of L_{2e} into L_{2e}; (b) $f_1(\cdot), f_2(\cdot), v_1(\cdot), v_2(\cdot), w_1(\cdot)$, and $w_2(\cdot)$ are in L_{2e}; and, (c) $v_1(\cdot)$ and $v_2(\cdot)$ are in L_2 i.e. $\|v_1(\cdot)\|_e$ and $\|v_2(\cdot)\|_e$ are finite. We wish to determine conditions which ensure that $f_1(\cdot)$ and $f_2(\cdot)$ are in L_2. In particular, we want to prove a stability theorem for this system under the assumption that $\underset{\sim}{G}_1$ and $\underset{\sim}{G}_2$ are extensions of maps of L_2 into L_2 in the following sense:

DEFINITION 4 <u>Let</u> $\underset{\sim}{T}$ <u>be a nonanticipative map of</u> L_2 <u>into</u>

L_2. *A map* T_e *of* L_{2e} *is an extension of* T *if* $(T_e x(\cdot))_t = (T x_t(\cdot))_t$ *for all* $x(\cdot)$ *in* L_{2e} *and all* t *in* R.

Clearly T_e is nonanticipartive and uniquely defined. Moreover, it is easy to see that T_e has the following properties:

(i) $T_e x(\cdot) = T x(\cdot)$ for all $x(\cdot)$ in L_2;

(ii) if T is linear (positive, strongly positive), then T_e is linear (positive(e), strongly positive(e));

(iii) $\gamma_e(T_e) = \gamma(T)$;

(iv) if T^{-1} is defined and nonanticipative, then T_e^{-1} is defined and $T_e^{-1} = (T^{-1})_e$.

These properties will be used shortly.

LEMMA 1 *if* G_1 *and* G_2 *are positive(e) and if either* G_1 *is strongly positive(e) and* $\gamma_e(G_1)$ *is finite or* G_2 *is strongly positive(e) and* $\gamma_e(G_2)$ *is finite, then* $f_1(\cdot)$ *and* $f_2(\cdot)$ *are in* L_2.

The proof of Lemma 1, which will be omitted†, is based on Schwartz's inequality.

Now let us suppose that there are nonanticipative maps H' and N' of L_2 into L_2 such that $G_1 = H'_e$ and $G_2 = N'_e$. We then have:

THEOREM 2 *Suppose that there is a mapping* M *(the multiplier, which may be anticipative) of* L_2 *into* L_2 *such that*

(1) *there are linear maps* M_+ *and* M_- *of* L_2 *into* L_2 *with the following properties:*

(a) $M = M_- M_+$;

(b) M_- *and* M_+ *are invertible;*

(c) M_+, M_+^{-1}, M_-^*, *and* M_-^{*-1} *are nonanticipative and have finite gains* $\gamma(\cdot)$ *(i.e. are bounded);*

(2) MH' *and* M^*N' *are positive;*

(3) *either* MH' *is strongly positive and* $\gamma(H')$ *is finite or* M^*N' *is strongly positive and* $\gamma(N')$ *is finite.*

Then $f_1(\cdot)$ *and* $f_2(\cdot)$ *are in* L_2 *i.e.* $\|f_1(\cdot)\|_e$ *and* $\|f_2(\cdot)\|_e$ *are finite.*

PROOF: We shall transform the feedback equations (13)-(16)

and apply Lemma 1. So let

$$v_1' = (M^*_-)_e v_1 \qquad v_2' = (M_+)_e v_2$$
$$f_1' = (M^*_-)_e f_1 \qquad f_2' = (M_+)_e f_2 \qquad (18)$$
$$w_2' = (M^*_-)_e w_2 \qquad w_1' = (M_+)_e w_1$$

and

$$G_1' = (M^*)_e H_e'(M^{*-1}_-)_e\,, \quad G_2' = (M^*_-)_e N_e'(M^{-1}_+)_e. \qquad (19)$$

Then the feedback equations become

$$f_1' = v_1' - w_2',\ f_2' = v_2' + w_1',\ w_1' = G_1' f_1',\ w_2' = G_2' f_2'. \qquad (20)$$

We shall show that (20) satisfies the hypotheses of Lemma 1.

Since G_1' and G_2' are compositions of nonanticipative maps, G_1' and G_2' are nonanticipative. Clearly f_1', v_1', w_1', f_2', v_2', and w_2' are in L_{2e}. Moreover, v_1' and v_2' are in L_2 since $\|v_1'\|_e = \|(M^*_-)_e v_1\|_e = \|(M^*_-)v_1\| \leq \gamma(M^*_-)\|v_1\| < \infty$ as v_1 is in L_2 and $\|v_2'\|_e = \|(M_+)_e v_2\| = \|M_+ v_2\| \leq \gamma(M_+)\|v_2\| < \infty$ as v_2 is in L_2.

By virtue of Lemma 2 which follows the theorem, G_1' and G_2' are positive(e). Moreover, if (say) MH' is strongly positive and $\gamma(H')$ is finite, then it follows from Lemma 2 that G_1' is strongly positive(e). As $\gamma(H') = \gamma_e(H_e')$ we have $\gamma_e(G') \leq \gamma(M_+)\gamma(H')\gamma(M^{*-1}_-) < \infty$. Thus, in this case, all the hypotheses of Lemma 1 are satisfied and so $\|f_1'\|_e < \infty$ and $\|f_2'\|_e < \infty$. But $\|f_1\|_e = \|(M^{*-1}_-)_e f_1'\|_e \leq \gamma(M^{*-1}_-)\|f_1'\|_e < \infty$ and similarly, $\|f_2\|_e < \infty$. The case where M^*N' is strongly positive is treated in the same way and thus the theorem is established.

LEMMA 2 <u>Let P, Q and R be nonanticipative maps of L_2 into L_2. If $\gamma(Q) < \infty$, if Q^{-1} exists and is nonanticipative and if $Q^*P\,R$ is positive (strongly positive), then $P_e R_e Q_e^{-1}$ is positive(e) (strongly positive(e)).</u>

PROOF: We have

$$\langle x_t, (P_e R_e Q_e^{-1} x)_t\rangle = \langle x_t, (P_e R_e Q_e^{-1} x_t)_t\rangle = \langle x_t, (PRQ^{-1} x_t)\rangle = \langle y, Q^*PRy\rangle$$

where $y = Q^{-1}x_t$, since $P_e R_e Q_e^{-1}$ is nonanticipative. The lemma follows immediately as $\|x_t\| \leq \gamma(Q)\|y\|$.

4. FACTORIZATION OF OPERATORS

In view of Theorem 2, we can see the importance of determining conditions which insure that an operator has a suitable factorization. If $\mathfrak{B}$ is some Banach algebra, $\mathcal{L}(\mathfrak{B},\mathfrak{B})$ is the space of all continuous linear maps of $\mathfrak{B}$ into $\mathfrak{B}$, and P is an element of $\mathcal{L}(\mathfrak{B},\mathfrak{B})$, then we shall call P a _projection_ if (a) $P^2 = P$ and (b) xy is in the range of P if both x and y are in the range of P. The factorization that we shall ultimately use involves projections in a Banach algebra of convolution operators.

We now have:

LEMMA 3 _Let $\mathfrak{B}$ be a commutative Banach algebra with an identity E, and with norm $\rho(\cdot)$. Let P_+ be a projection on $\mathfrak{B}$ and let $P_- = E-P_+$. Denote the ranges of P_+ and P_- by $\mathfrak{B}_+$ and $\mathfrak{B}_-$ respectively and let Z be a nonzero element of $\mathfrak{B}$. If $\rho(Z) < 1$, then there are elements Z_+ of $\mathfrak{B}_+$ and Z_- of $\mathfrak{B}_-$ such that_

(i) $E + Z = Z_- Z_+$;

(ii) _Z_+ and Z_- are invertible and Z_+^{-1}, Z_-^{-1} are in $\mathfrak{B}_+$, $\mathfrak{B}_-$ respectively._

Moreover,

$$Z_+ = \exp[P_+(\log\{E+Z\})], \quad Z_- = \exp[P_-(\log\{E+Z\})] \tag{21}$$

and

$$Z_+^{-1} = \exp[-P_+(\log\{E+Z\})], \quad Z_-^{-1} = \exp[-P_-(\log\{E+Z\})] \tag{22}$$

5. THE BANACH ALGEBRA OF CONVOLUTION OPERATORS

Suppose that $g_c(\cdot)$ is an element of $L_1(-\infty,\infty)$ and that $g_d(\cdot)$ is a real valued function on $(-\infty,\infty)$ which has a countable support $S(g_d)$ [i.e., $g_d(\tau) = 0$ for all $\tau \notin S(g_d)$ and which is absolutely summable on $S(g_d)$ [i.e., $\sum_{\tau_i \in S(g_d)} |g_d(\tau_i)| < \infty$]. Then we shall consider convolutions of the form

$$y(t) = \sum_{\tau_i \in S(g_d)} g_d(\tau_i)x(t-\tau_i) + \int_{-\infty}^{\infty} g_c(\tau)x(t-\tau)d\tau \tag{23}$$

where $x(\cdot)$ is an element of $L_2(-\infty,\infty)$. We call the pair $\{g_d, g_c\}$ _the kernel of the convolution._ It can be shown that any convolution of the form (23) is a linear transformation of $L_2(-\infty,\infty)$ into itself.

Let $\mathcal{L}$ be the set of all operators $\underset{\sim}{G}$ in $\mathcal{L}(L_2(-\infty,\infty), L_2(-\infty,\infty))$ which are defined by convolutions of the form (23). Addition and scalar multiplication for operators in $\mathcal{L}$ are defined in the usual way, the product $\underset{\sim}{K}\underset{\sim}{H}$ is taken to be the composition of $\underset{\sim}{K}$ following $\underset{\sim}{H}$ in $\mathcal{L}$, and the identity $\underset{\sim}{I}$ is in $\mathcal{L}$. Moreover, a function $\rho(\cdot)$ is defined on $\mathcal{L}$ by the equation

$$\rho(\underset{\sim}{G}) = \sum_{\tau_i \in S(g_d)} |g_d(\tau_i)| + \int_{-\infty}^{\infty} |g_c(\tau)|\, d\tau \tag{24}$$

where $\underset{\sim}{G}$ is any operator in $\mathcal{L}$ with kernel $\{g_c, g_d\}$. It can be shown† that $\rho(\cdot)$ is a norm on $\mathcal{L}$, and that $\mathcal{L}$ can be viewed as a communitative Banach Algebra with identity $\underset{\sim}{I}$.

Furthermore, there is a natural projection $\underset{\sim}{P}_+$ on $\mathcal{L}$, defined as follows: If $\underset{\sim}{G}$ in $\mathcal{L}$ has kernel $\{g_d, g_c\}$, then $\underset{\sim}{P}_+\underset{\sim}{G}$ is the operator in $\mathcal{L}$ whose kernel is $\{g_d^+, g_c^+\}$, where: $g_d^+(\tau) = g_d(\tau)$ for $\tau \leqq 0$, $g_d^+(\tau) = 0$ for $\tau > 0$, $g_c^+(\tau) = g_c(\tau)$ for $\tau \geqq 0$, and $g_c^+(\tau) = 0$ for $\tau < 0$. It can be shown† that $\underset{\sim}{P}_+$ is a projection on $\mathcal{L}$. Letting $\underset{\sim}{P}_- = \underset{\sim}{I} - \underset{\sim}{P}_+$, we denote the ranges of $\underset{\sim}{P}_+$ and $\underset{\sim}{P}_-$ by $\mathcal{L}_+$ and $\mathcal{L}_-$, respectively. We observe that now the factorization Lemma 3 applies to the Banach algebra $\mathcal{L}$.

The operators in $\mathcal{L}_+$ are nonanticipative. Furthermore, if $\underset{\sim}{G}$ is any operator in $\mathcal{L}$ with kernel $\{g_d(\tau_i), g_c(\tau)\}$ then the adjoint $\underset{\sim}{G}^*$ of $\underset{\sim}{G}$ is an operator in $\mathcal{L}$ with kernel $\{g_d(-\tau_i), g_c(-\tau)\}$, and so we can see that the adjoint of any operator in $\mathcal{L}_-$ lies in $\mathcal{L}_+$ and is, therefore, nonanticipative. This fact is relevant to the proof of Theorem 1.

6. POSITIVITY CONDITIONS

We now develop conditions for the positivity of compositions of operators. Our derivations are based on an area inequality which is closely related to Young's inequality.

We let $N(\cdot)$ be a real valued function on $(-\infty,\infty)$ such that $N(0) = 0$ throughout this section.

LEMMA 7 (<u>an area inequality</u>) <u>If</u> $N(\cdot)$ <u>is monotone nondecreasing, then</u>

$$xN(x) - yN(x) \geqq P(x) - P(y) \tag{25}$$

for all x and y where $P(x) = \int_0^x N(s)ds$.

PROOF: Since $N(\cdot)$ is monotone nondecreasing, $[N(x+k\Delta x)-N(x)]k\Delta x \geqq 0$ for any integer k and hence $\sum_{k=1}^{m}[N(x+k\Delta x)-N(x)]\Delta x \geqq 0$ for any integer m. Setting $\Delta x = (y-x)/m$ and letting m approach infinity, we deduce that

$$\int_x^y N(s)ds - N(x)\int_x^y ds \geqq 0 \tag{26}$$

which is equivalent to (25).

LEMMA 8 If $N(\cdot)$ is monotone nondecreasing and if there is a constant $C > 0$ such that $|N(s)| \leqq C|s|$, then

$$\int_{-\infty}^{\infty} x(t+\tau)N(x(t))dt \leqq \int_{-\infty}^{\infty} x(t)N(x(t))dt \tag{27}$$

for all τ and any $x(\cdot)$ in $L_2(-\infty,\infty)$. If, in addition, $N(\cdot)$ is odd, then

$$\left|\int_{-\infty}^{\infty} x(t+\tau)N(x(t))dt\right| \leqq \int_{-\infty}^{\infty} x(t)N(x(t))dt \tag{28}$$

for all τ and any $x(\cdot)$ in $L_2(-\infty,\infty)$.

The proof is a straightforward application of Lemma 7.

Now suppose that $N(\cdot)$ satisfies the assumption A1 or section 2 and let $\underset{\sim}{N}$ be the mapping of $L_2(-\infty,\infty)$ into $L_2(-\infty,\infty)$ given by $\underset{\sim}{N}x(t) = N(x(t))$. We then have:

PROPOSITION 1 If $\underset{\sim}{Z}$ is an element of $\mathcal{L}$ with kernel $\{z_d, z_c\}$ and with $\rho(\underset{\sim}{Z}) < 1$, and if either $\{z_d, z_c\}$ is nonnegative or $N(\cdot)$ is odd, then $(\underset{\sim}{I}-\underset{\sim}{Z})\underset{\sim}{N}$ is positive.

PROOF: If $x(\cdot)$ is in $L_2(-\infty,\infty)$, then

$$\begin{aligned}\langle x(\cdot), \underset{\sim}{Z}\underset{\sim}{N}x(\cdot)\rangle &= \sum_{\tau_i \in S_{z_d}} z_d(\tau_i)\int_{-\infty}^{\infty} x(t)N(x(t-\tau_i))dt \\ &\quad + \int_{-\infty}^{\infty} z_c(\tau)\int_{-\infty}^{\infty} x(t)N(x(t-\tau))dtd\tau\end{aligned} \tag{29}$$

If $\{z_d, z_c\}$ is nonnegative, then (27) and (29) yield

$$\langle x(\cdot), \underset{\sim}{Z}\underset{\sim}{N}x(\cdot)\rangle \leqq \rho(\underset{\sim}{Z})\langle x(\cdot), \underset{\sim}{N}x(\cdot)\rangle \tag{30}$$

which implies that

$$\langle x(\cdot),(\underset{\sim}{I}-\underset{\sim}{Z})\underset{\sim}{N}x(\cdot)\rangle \geq \langle x(\cdot),\underset{\sim}{N}x(\cdot)\rangle\{1-\rho(\underset{\sim}{Z})\} \geq 0 \qquad (31)$$

If $N(\cdot)$ is odd then (28) and (29) yield (30).

Proposition 1 is a positivity condition for the composition of a linear operator $\underset{\sim}{I}-\underset{\sim}{Z}$ and a nonlinear operator $\underset{\sim}{N}$. In proposition 2 which follows, we give a positivity condition for the composition of two convolution operators.

PROPOSITION 2 <u>If $\underset{\sim}{G}$ and $\underset{\sim}{H}$ are elements of $\mathcal{L}$ with Fourier transforms $G(j\omega)$ and $H(j\omega)$ respectively, and if $\mathrm{Re}\{G(j\omega)H(j\omega)\} \geq \delta$ then $\underset{\sim}{G}\underset{\sim}{H}$ is positive (strongly positive) if $\delta = 0$ $(\delta > 0)$.</u>

The proof, which is based on Parseval's Theorem is omitted.

7. PROOF OF THE MAIN RESULT

Theorem 1 is now a simple consequence of Theorem 2. The hypotheses of Theorem 2 are satisfied by virtue of Propositions 1 and 2, the fact that $\mathcal{L}$ is a commutative Banach algebra with an identity and a projection P_+, and the fact that $\rho(\underset{\sim}{Z}) < \infty$ implies $\gamma(\underset{\sim}{Z}) < \infty$ for $\underset{\sim}{Z}$ in $\mathcal{L}$.

The proofs of Corollaries 1 and 2 are omitted†. Corollary 1 can be proved† using Schwartz's inequality. Corollary 2 can be proved† by transforming the feedback equations, and showing that the transformed equations satisfy the hypotheses of Theorem 1.

8. CONCLUDING REMARKS

We have derived stability conditions for a class of feedback systems in terms of the frequency response of the linear part $\underset{\sim}{H}$ and a suitable multiplier $\underset{\sim}{I}-\underset{\sim}{Z}$. The key point was that $\underset{\sim}{I}-\underset{\sim}{Z}$ was defined on $(-\infty,\infty)$. The proof involved the factorization of operators in the Banach algebra $\mathcal{L}$ of convolution operators and the development of positivity conditions for compositions of linear and nonlinear operators.

Although we have considered only the case of scalar valued functions here, we can easily generalize Theorem 1 to the case of vector valued e_i, x_i, and y_i, $i = 1,2,\ldots$. Another avenue of generalization is via the extension of the kernel space to an $L^1(G)$ where G is a locally compact group; this generalization will be studied in a later paper.

REFERENCES

[1](a) G. Zames, "On the Stability of Nonlinear, Time-Varying Feedback Systems", Proc. NEC, Vol. 20, pp. 725-730, October 1964.

(b) G. Zames, "On the Input-Output Stability of Time-Varying Nonlinear Feedback Systems, Parts I and II"; IEEE Trans. Automatic Control; Part I in Vol. AC-11, No. 2, April, 1966, pp. 228-238; Part II in Vol. AC-11, No.3, July, 1966, pp. 465-476.

[2] R.W. Brockett and J.W. Willems, "Frequency Domain Stability Criteria", Pts. I and II, 1965 Proc. Joint Automatic Control Conf., pp. 735-747.

[3] V.A. Yakubovich, "Frequency Conditions for the Absolute Stability and Dissipativity of Control Systems with a Single Differentiable Nonlinearity", Soviet Mathematics, Vol.6, No.1, Jan.-Feb. 1965a,pp.98-101.

[4] K.S. Narendra and C.P. Neuman, "Stability of a Class of Differential Equations with a Single Monotone Nonlinearity", J. SIAM Control, Vol.4, No.2, 1966.

[5] A.G. Dewey and E.I. Jury, "A Stability Inequality for a Class of Nonlinear Feedback Systems", IEEE Trans. Automatic Control, Vol. AC-11, No.1, Jan. 1966, pp. 54-62.

[6] C.T. Lee and C.A. Desoer, "Stability of Single-Loop Nonlinear Feedback Systems", Report No. ERL 66-13, ERL, Univ. of Calif., Berkeley, May 1966.

[7](a) R.P. O'Shea, "A Combined Frequency-Time Domain Stability Criterion for Automomous Continuous Systems", Proc. 1966 Joint Automatic Control Conference, pp. 832-840.

(b) R.P. O'Shea, "An Improved Frequency-Time Domain Stability Criterion for Continuous Autonomous Systems", unpublished report.

[8] G. Zames and P.L. Falb, "On the Stability of Systems with monotone and Odd Monotone Nonlinearities", IEEE Trans. Automatic Control, April, 1967.

[9] R.E.A.S. Paley and N. Wiener, Fourier Transforms in the Complex Domain, Am. Math. Soc. Publications, Providence, Rhode Island, 1934.

SOME ASYMPTOTICAL PROPERTIES OF DOMAINS OF CONTROLLABILITY FOR LINEAR CONTROL SYSTEMS

Zdenek Vorel, Rose Polytechnic Institue, Department of Mathematics, Terre Haute, Indiana and Mathematical Institute of Czechoslvak Academy of Science, Prague.

Consider the system

$$\frac{dx}{dt} = Ax + Bu \qquad (1)$$

where $x \in R^n$, A, B constant n x n and n x r matrices, respectively, A in real Jordan canonical form with eigenvalues with zero real parts, $A = \text{diag}\,(C_1, \ldots, C_m, D_1, \ldots, D_p)$, $C_i = \begin{vmatrix} 0 & & & & \\ 1 & 0 & & & \\ 0 & 1 & 0 & & \\ \vdots & & \ddots & \ddots & \\ 0 & \ldots & & 1 & 0 \end{vmatrix}$,

$$D_i = \begin{vmatrix} M_i & & & & \\ I_2 & M_i & & & \\ 0_2 & I_2 & M_i & & \\ \vdots & & \ddots & \ddots & \\ 0_2 & \ldots & & I_2 & M_i \end{vmatrix}, \qquad M_i = \begin{vmatrix} 0 & -\beta_i \\ \beta_i & 0 \end{vmatrix},$$

$u(t)$ is a real function of t, Lebesque measurable in $[0,\infty)$, $u = (u_1, u_2, \ldots, u_r)^T$, $\sup_{i,t} |u_i(t)| \le 1$. The class of all such functions $u(t)$ is denoted by W. Let I be the index set $\{1,2,\ldots,n\}$ and let I_1 be its subset corresponding to the indexes of the first rows of the submatrices C_i and of the first pairs of rows of the submatrices

D_i, i. e. $I_1 = \{1, k_1+1, \dots, k_1+k_2+\dots k_{m-1}+1,$ $\sum_{i=1}^{m} k_i+2, \dots,$ $\sum_{i=1}^{m} k_i+2l_1+1,$ $\sum_{i=1}^{m} k_i+2l_1+2, \dots,$ $\sum_{i=1}^{m} k_i+2l_1+2, \dots,$ $\sum_{i=1}^{m} k_i+2\sum_{i=1}^{p-1} l_i+1,$ $\sum_{i=1}^{m} k_i+2\sum_{i=1}^{p-1} l_i+2\}$.

Let $U_T = \{x \in R^n: x = e^{AT}\int_0^T e^{-A\tau} Bu(\tau)d\tau,\ u \in W\}$ for $T>0$. As $U_T = \{x \in R^n: x = Te^{at}\int_0^1 e^{-AT\tau} Bu(\tau)d\tau, u \in W\}$, define the matrix $Q(T,\tau)$ by the relation $e^{-AT\tau} =$ $= \operatorname{diag}(1,T,\dots,T^{k_1-1},1,T,\dots,T^{k_2-1}\dots, 1,T\dots, T^{k_m-1}, 1,1,T,T,\dots, T^{l_1-1},T^{l_1-1},\dots, 1,1,\dots, T^{l_p-1}, T^{l_p-1}) \cdot Q(T,\tau) = T^* \cdot Q(T,\tau)$. $Q(T,\tau)$ is obviously bounded for all T and its columns with indexes from the set $I-I_1$ tend to zero as $T \to \infty$. Consider the set $V_T = \{y \in R^n: y = (T \cdot T^*)^{-1} \cdot e^{-AT}x,$ $x \in U_T\}$. It is well known that U_T and V_T are compact convex sets and that they contain the origin in their interiors if the system (1) is proper, i.e. if the set of vectors $\{B_{\cdot 1}, B_{\cdot 2}, \dots, B_{\cdot r},$ $AB_{\cdot 2}, \dots, AB_{\cdot r}, \dots, A^{n-1}B_{\cdot 1}, \dots, A^{n-1}B_{\cdot r}\}$ span R^n (1). If E_1, E_2 are non-empty compact sets in R^n denote their Hausdorff distance $d_H(E_1,E_2) =$

$$= \max\Big[\sup_{x_1 \in E_1}\ \inf_{x_2 \in E_2} \|x_1 - x_2\|,\ \sup_{x_2 \in E_2}\ \inf_{x_1 \in E_1} \|x_1 - x_2\|\Big].$$

Theorem 1. Suppose that (1) is proper. Then there exists a compact, convex set $V \subseteq R^n$, which contains a neighbourhood of the origin, such that $d_H(V_T, V) \to 0$ as $T \to \infty$.

Theorem 1 will be proved by means of Lemma: Let $S_1 = \{x \in R^n: \|x\| = 1\}$ and let for each

$\eta \in S_1$, $\eta_T = \sup_{x\in V_T} (\eta, x)$, where (η,x) is the scalar product in R^n. There a) $\lim_{T\to\infty} \eta_T$ exists uniformly with respect to $\eta\in S_1$ and is independent from the rows $B_{i\cdot}$ of B for $i\in I-I_1$; b) η_T is uniformly continuous in S_1 for each $T>0$; c) if (1) is proper, then $L(\eta) = \lim_{T\to\infty} \eta_T > 0$.

Proof: As $V_T = \{x\in R^n: x = \int_0^1 Q(T,\tau)Bu(\tau)d\tau, u\in W\}$ and $(\eta,x) = \int_0^1 \eta^T Q(T,\tau)Bu(\tau)d\tau$, $\eta_T = \sup_{x\in V_T}(\eta,x)$ is reached with control $u(\tau) = \operatorname{sgn}(\eta^T Q(T,\tau)B)$. For sake of simplicity it will be assumed that the matrix A in (1) has three Jordan blocks C_1, D_1, D_2, $\frac{\beta_1}{\beta_2}$ irrational. Other cases can be treated in a similar or simpler manner.

Then $\eta_T = \int_0^1 \sum_{j=1}^{r} \Big| \sum_{i=1}^{k_1} \eta_i \tau^{i-1} \frac{(-1)^{i-1}}{(i-1)!} B_{1j} + \sum_{i=1}^{l_1} \eta_{k_1+2i-1} \cdot$

$\frac{(-\tau)^{i-1}}{(i-1)!} (B_{k_1+1,j} \cos \beta_1 T\tau + B_{k_1+2,j} \sin T\beta_1\tau) +$

$\eta_{k_1+2i} \frac{(-\tau)^{i-1}}{(i-1)!} (-B_{k_1+1,j} \sin T\beta_1\tau + B_{k_1+2,j} \cos T\beta_1\tau)]$

$+ \sum_{i=1}^{l_2} [\eta_{k_1+2l_1+2i-1} \frac{(-\tau)^{i-1}}{(i-1)!} (B_{k_1+2l_1+1,j} \cos T\beta_2\tau$

$+ B_{k_1+2l_1+2,j} \sin T\beta_2\tau) + \eta_{k_1+2l_1+2i} \frac{(-\tau)^{i-1}}{(i-1)!}$.

$$(-B_{k_1+2l_1+1,j} \sin T\beta_2\tau + B_{k_1+2l_1+2,j} \cos T\beta_2\tau)]| \cdot$$

$$d\tau + O(T^{-1}) = \int_0^1 \sum_{j=1}^{r} | B_{1j}P_1(\tau) + (B^2_{k_1+1,j} + B^2_{k_1+2,j})^{1/2} P_2(\tau) \cos(T\beta_1\tau+\phi_j^{(1)}) + (B^2_{k_1+2l_1+1,j}+ B^2_{k_1+2l_1+2,j})^{1/2} P_3(\tau) \cos(T\beta_2\tau+\phi_j^{(2)})|\tau + O(T^{-1}), \tag{2}$$

where $P_i(\tau)$ are polynomials and $\phi_j^{(i)}$ are constants. For a natural q divide $[0,1]$ into q equal subintervals of length $\Delta = \frac{1}{2}$, and in each $[(k-1)\Delta, k\Delta]$ choose a point τ_k. Then by (2)

$$|\eta_T - \sum_{j=1}^{r}\sum_{k=1}^{q}\int_{(k-1)\Delta}^{k\Delta} |B_{1j}P_1(\tau_k)+(B^2_{k_1+1,j}+B^2_{k_1+2,j})^{\frac{1}{2}} \cdot P_2(\tau_k)\cos(T\beta_1\tau+\phi_j^{(1)})+(B^2_{k_1+2l_1+1,j}+B^2_{k_1+2l_1+2,j})^{1/2} \cdot P_3(\tau_k)\cos(T\beta_2\tau+\phi_j^{(2)})|d\tau| \leq \sum_{j=1}^{r}\sum_{k=1}^{q}\int_{(k-1)\Delta}^{k\Delta} |B_{1j} \cdot [P_1(\tau)-P_1(\tau_k)]+(B^2_{k_1+1,j}+B^2_{k_1+2,j})^{1/2}[P_2(\tau)-P_2(\tau_k)] \cdot \cos(T\beta_1\tau+\phi_j^{(1)})+(B^2_{k_1+2l_1+1,j}+B^2_{k_1+2l_1+2,j})^{1/2}[P_3(\tau) - P_3(\tau_k)]\cos(T\beta_2\tau+\phi_j^{(2)}|d\tau + |O(T^{-1})|. \tag{3}$$

From the uniform continuity of $P_i(\tau)$ and from the known fact that for a continuous almost periodic function $f(\tau)$ $\lim_{T\to\infty} \frac{1}{T} \int_0^T f(\tau)d\tau$ exists one obtains in a standard way that $\lim_{T\to\infty} \eta_T$ exists. From the definition of η_T it follows for every $\eta^{(1)}, \eta^{(2)} \in S_1$, $T>0$, that $|\eta_T^{(1)} - \eta_T^{(2)}| \leq \theta \| \eta^{(1)} - \eta^{(2)} \|$, where θ is a constant independent from $\eta^{(1)}, \eta^{(2)}$. Thus η_T is an equicontinuous family of functions on S_1, and, by Ascoli's theorem, $\lim_{T\to\infty} \eta_T$ exists uniformly with respect to $\eta \in S_1$, which proves assertions a) and b). Assertion c) follows from the facts that at least one of $P_i(\tau)$ is not identically zero on $[0,1]$ and that $\lim_{T\to\infty} \int_{(k-1)\Delta}^{k\Delta} |\alpha+\beta \cos(T\beta_1\tau+\phi^{(1)}) + \gamma \cos(T\beta_2\tau+\phi^{(2)})| d\tau$ can be zero only if $\alpha = \beta = \gamma = 0$.

Proof of Theorem 1: Let $H(T,\eta) = \{x \in R^n : (x,\eta) \leq \eta_T\}$ for $\eta \in S_1, T>0$. As V_T is convex, $V_T = \bigcap_{\eta \in S_1} H(T,\eta)$, i.e. V_T is the intersection of all halfspaces defined by supporting hyperplanes of V_T. Define $H_\eta = \{x \in R^n : (x,\eta) \leq L(\eta)\}$ for $\eta \in S_1$, and $V = \bigcap_{\eta \in S_1} H_\eta$. V is closed and convex as the intersection of closed convex sets and is bounded in view of the boundedness of η_T. By the Lemma $L(\eta)$ is positive (as (1) is proper) and continuous on S_1. Thus $L(\eta)$ is bounded away from zero and the origin is an interior point of V. To prove that $d_H(V_T,V)$ 0 with T ∞, consider the sets $H_\epsilon^+(\eta) = \{x \in R^n : (x,\eta) \leq L(\eta)+\epsilon\}$, $H_\epsilon^- = \{x \in R^n : (x,\eta) \leq L(\eta) - \epsilon\}$ for

$\epsilon>0$ sufficiently small, $\eta \in S_1$, and the sets $V_\epsilon^+ = \bigcap_{\eta \in S_1} H_\epsilon^+(\eta)$, $V_\epsilon^- = \bigcap_{\eta \in S_1} H_\epsilon^-(\eta)$. From the uniform convergence of $\eta_T \quad L(\eta)$ it follows that for every $\epsilon>0$ there is a $T_0>0$ such that $T>T_0$ implies $V_T \subseteq V_\epsilon^+$, $V_T \supseteq V_\epsilon^-$. Further, $d_H(V_T,V) < d_H(V_\epsilon^+,V_\epsilon^-)$ and $d_H(V_\epsilon^+,V_\epsilon^-) \to 0$ with $\epsilon \to 0$, which is an easy consequence of the fact that V_ϵ^- can be separated from a point $x \notin V_\epsilon^-$ by a hyperplane.

Note: Theorem 1 was proved in (2) by an analogous method for case that the matrix A in (1) consisted of exactly one Jordan block. Theorem 1 suggests the following definition: Two system of type (1) with the same matrix A are called asymptotically equivalent, if the sets V are identical for both systems. The following sufficent condition for asymptotic equivalence is a direct consequence of Theorem 1 and the Lemma:

Theorem 2. Systems (1) and $\dot{x} = Ax+\tilde{B}u$ are asymptotically equivalent if the rows of B and $\tilde{B}$ corresponding to the index set I_1 are equal, i.e. if $B_{j\cdot} = \tilde{B}_{j\cdot}$ for $j \in I_1$.

Note: From Theorem 2 it follows that the rows $B_{j\cdot}$ for $j \in I-I_1$ have little steering effect on large time intervals, whereas the decisive role is played by $B_{j\cdot}$ for $j \in I_1$. From Theorem 1 and from the definition of V_T it follows that every point of R^n is attainable for proper systems, where A has eigenvalues with non-positive real parts.

References:

(1) LaSalle, J.P. The time optimal control problem, Contribvtions to the theory of non-linear oscillations, Vol. 5, Princeton, 1960.
(2) Imaz C., Vorel Z. On domains of controllability of proper and normal systems. Boletin de la Sociedad Mat. Mex., 1963.

STOCHASTIC LAGRANGE MULTIPLIERS

Wendell H. Fleming*

1. We are concerned with optimal control problems which are stochastic analogues of the problem of Lagrange in calculus of variations. Two methods will be outlined for getting formulas for the first variation and necessary conditions for a minimum. For the first method we assume that the response process to the control is a diffusion (Markov process with continuous sample paths), and that the controls admitted are based on possibly partial observations of the current states of the response. The problem can then be rephrased as one about linear second order parabolic equations. The necessary conditions involve boundary problems 3.3, 4.3 for the backward and forward operators of the response process, together with a minimum condition (§4) in terms of conditional expectations. A detailed exposition will appear in (2).

The second method proceeds as in ordinary (nonstochastic) control theory. The formula for the first variation involves multipliers which satisfy at least formally a linear system of stochastic differential equations 6.2 dual to the linearized state equations. This extends results of H. Kushner (3).

2. Consider stochastic processes on a fixed time interval $0 \leq t \leq T$ governed by a system of stochastic differential equations

$$d\xi(t) = f[t,\xi(t),u(t)]dt + \sigma[t,\xi(t),u(t)]dw(t), \tag{2.1}$$

* This work was supported by a grant from the National Science Foundation.

together with a given distribution for $\xi(0)$. The process $w = (w_1, \ldots, w_m)$ is an m-dimensional Brownian motion independent of $\xi(0)$, the control $u = (u_1, \ldots, u_k)$ is a k-dimensional process which does not anticipate the future of the Brownian motion, and the solution $\xi = (\xi_1, \ldots, \xi_n)$ of 2.1 an n-dimensional process with continuous sample paths called the response to the control process u. We require that $u(t) \in K$ for each t, where K is a given closed convex set. Moreover, $u(t)$ is to be chosen using only certain information available to the controller at time t. The problem is to minimize

$$J(u) = E\int_0^T L[t,\xi(t),u(t)]dt. \qquad (2.2)$$

We assume throughout that the functions f, σ, L are of class $C^{(1)}$.

Moreover, let there exist $\gamma > 0$ such that $f(t,x,u)$, $\sigma(t,x,u)$, and $(1 + |x|)^{-\gamma}L(t,x,u)$ are bounded together with their first order partial derivatives when u is restricted to any bounded subset of K.

3. (First method) Let us suppose that at time t the controller can observe the first ℓ components of the repsonse $\xi(t)$, and bases his control on this observation. More precisely, let $\hat{x} = (x_1, \ldots, x_\ell)$ and let $\mathcal{Y}_K$ denote the class of all functions $Y(t,\hat{x})$ which are bounded, Lipschitz, and have values in K. In 2.1 we now require that

$$u(t) = Y(t,\hat{\xi}(t)), \qquad (3.1)$$

where $Y \in \mathcal{Y}_K$. Let us also assume that

$$\sum_{i,j=1}^{n} a_{ij}(t,x,u)\beta_i\beta_j \geq m|\beta|^2, \; m > 0, \qquad (3.2)$$

for all β, where $a = \frac{1}{2}\sigma\sigma^*$. Let $\psi(t,x)$ solve the terminal value problem

$$\frac{\partial\psi}{\partial t} + A^Y\psi + L^Y(t,x) = 0, \quad 0 \leq t \leq T \tag{3.3}$$

$$\psi(T,x) = 0,$$

where if $g = L, f$, or a, then $g^Y(t,x) = g(t,x,Y(t,\hat{x}))$, and

$$A^Y = \sum a^Y_{ij} \frac{\partial^2}{\partial x_i \partial x_j} + \sum f^Y_i \frac{\partial}{\partial x_i} .$$

The backward operator of the Markov process ξ is $\frac{\partial}{\partial t} + A^Y$. If the distribution of the initial value $\xi(0)$ has density $q_0(x)$, then (writing $J(Y)$ for $\mathcal{J}(u)$ in 2.2)

$$J(Y) = \int \psi(0,x) q_0(x) dx. \tag{3.4}$$

4. Let us replace Y by $Y + \varepsilon Z$, and calculate the first variation

$$I(Y,Z) = \frac{d}{d\varepsilon} J(Y + \varepsilon Z)\Big|_{\varepsilon=0}.$$

Let

$$\Phi(t,x,u) = A\psi + L, \tag{4.1}$$

where the coefficients a_{ij}, f_i of A, and L, are evaluated at (t,x,u). It turns out that

$$I(Y,Z) = \tag{4.2}$$

$$E\int_0^T \Phi_u(t,\xi(t),u(t)) Z(t,\hat{\xi}(t)) dt,$$

where Φ_u denotes gradient in the third set of variables and $u(t)$ is as in 3.1. From 4.2 we can deduce the following necessary conditions that Y be minimizing in $\mathcal{Y}_K$:

1) If $K = R^k$ (no constraints), then $E\{\Phi_u(t,\xi(t),u(t)) | \hat{\xi}(t)\} = 0$.

2) If L is convex in u and f, a are linear in u, then $E\{\Phi(t,\xi(t),u)|\hat{\xi}(t)\}$ is minimum when $u = u(t)$.

The density $q(t,x)$ of $\xi(t)$ satisfies the forward equation

$$-\frac{\partial q}{\partial t} + (A^Y)^* q = 0,\ 0 \leq t \leq T \tag{4.3}$$
$$q(0,x) = q_0(x).$$

Our rather weak assumptions on the smoothness of Y do not guarantee that the initial value problem 4.3 has a solution in the usual sense. However, if q_0 is smooth enough (for example, $C^{(1)}$ with bounded first order derivatives), then q exists as a weak solution, which is continuous for $t > 0$ with first order derivatives locally square integrable (4). The necessary conditions 1), 2) can be written in terms of the conditional density $q(t, x_{\ell+1}, \ldots ,x_n|\hat{x})$, which can be calculated from q.

5. (Second method) Let us consider, more generally, controls which are bounded and nonanticipative (a precise definition appears in (1, §3)). If u and v are such controls we again seek a formula for the first variation

$$I(u,v) = \frac{d}{d\varepsilon} J(u + \varepsilon v)\Big|_{\varepsilon=0}.$$

Let η satisfy the linearized form of 2.1:

$$d\eta = (f_x\eta + f_u v)dt + \tag{5.1}$$
$$(\sigma_x\eta + \sigma_u v)dw,\ 0 \leq t \leq T,$$

with initial data $\eta(0) = 0$. Using some standard estimates for stochastic integrals one can prove:

<u>Lemma 1</u>. <u>There is a constant</u> C <u>such that</u>

$$E \max_{0\leq r\leq t} |\xi^\varepsilon(t) - \xi(t) - \varepsilon\eta(t)|^2$$
$$\leq C\varepsilon^4\, E\int_0^t v(r)^4 dr,$$

where ξ^{ε} is the response to $u + \varepsilon v$ and ξ the response to u.

Lemma 2. $I(u,v) = E\int_0^T (L_x\eta + L_u v)dt.$

6. Following the usual technique for the Lagrange problem we seek to replace the term $L_x\eta$ in Lemma 2 by $\lambda f_u v$, where λ is a suitable multiplier. If σ is a constant matrix, then Kushner (3) showed that one can find λ from the ordinary differential equations

$$d\lambda = -(\lambda f_x + L_x)dt,\ 0 \leq t \leq T \tag{6.1}$$

with $\lambda(T) = 0$, just as for the nonstochastic problem. When $\sigma = \sigma(t,x)$ does not explicitly involve u, then we can extend his result. Equation 6.1 must be replaced by

$$d\lambda = -(\lambda f_x + L_x)dt - \lambda\sigma_x \tilde{d}w,\ 0 \leq t \leq T, \tag{6.2}$$

where the differential $\tilde{d}w$ means essentially dw with time reversed. If time is reversed, then σ_x involves the Brownian future and the usual proof that the stochastic integral exists fails. One can replace 5.1 and 6.2 by their time-discrete analogues, obtaining if the difference between successive times is δ piecewise constant processes η^{δ}, λ^{δ}. Using the duality between η^{δ} and λ^{δ} and a standard estimate for $\max_{0\leq r\leq t} |\eta^{\delta}(r) - \eta(r)|$, one can define λ by

$$\| \lambda^{\delta} - \lambda \|_p = (E\int_0^T |\lambda^{\delta} - \lambda|^p)^{1/p} \to 0$$

as $\delta \to 0$, for $p = 4/3$.

However, there is a more direct way to define λ by duality. Consider the following Banach spaces: a) L_0^2, whose elements are all nonanticipative processes g with values in R^n and $\|g\|_2^2 = E\int_0^T |g(t)|^2 dt < \infty$; b) C_0, whose elements are all nonanticipative η with continuous sample paths and $\eta(0) = 0$, the norm in C_0 being $\|\eta\| = E \max_{0 \leq t \leq T} |\eta(t)|$. The stochastic differential equations

$$d\eta = f_x \eta dt + \sigma_x \eta dw + gdt, \quad 0 \leq t \leq T \tag{6.3}$$

with $\eta(0) = 0$ and f_x, σ_x evaluated as usual at $(t,\xi(t),u(t))$, determine $\eta = Bg$, where B is a bounded linear operator from L_0^2 into C_0. The adjoint B^* is given by

$$\langle h, Bg \rangle = \langle B^* h, g \rangle,$$

for $g \in L_0^2$ and h in the dual C_0^* of C_0. In particular, take $g = f_u v$, $h = L_x$ (regarded as an element of C_0^*), and recall that by assumption $\sigma_u = 0$. From Lemma 2 we get

$$I(u,v) = E\int_0^T (\lambda f_u + L_u) v dt, \tag{6.4}$$

where $\lambda = B^* L_x$.

7. We can define (random) fundamental matrices for the linear system 6.3, by the stochastic integral equations

$$W(s,t) = \int_s^t f_x(r) W(s,r) dr + \tag{7.1}$$

$$\sigma_x(r) W(s,r) dw(r) + I, \text{ if } s < t \leq T,$$

$$W(s,t) = 0 \text{ if } 0 \leq t < s,$$

where $f_x(r)$ means $f_x[r,\xi(r),u(r)]$ etc. and I is the identity matrix. For each s and $s' > s$,

$$E \max_{0\le t\le T} |W(s,t)|^4 \le C,$$

$$E \max_{s\le t\le t'} |W(s,t') - W(s,t)|^2 \le C(t' - t),$$

$$E \max_{s'\le t\le T} |W(s',t) - W(s,t)|^2 \le C(s' - s),$$

where C is some constant. If g, h are bounded processes and g is nonanticipative, then

$$Bg(t) = \int_0^t W(s,t)g(s)ds, \tag{7.2}$$

$$B^*h(s) = \int_s^T h(t)W(s,t)dt.$$

In particular, if we take $h(t) = L_x(t)$ as above, then we see that $E|\lambda(s)|^4$ is bounded uniformly in s. We do not know whether the process λ has continuous sample paths.

8. We have considered a fixed stopping time T for the response process ξ. The first method can be used when the stopping time is the hitting time for a "terminal set" Σ contained in the strip $0 \le t \le T$ of (t,x)-space. One then has to solve 3.3, 4.3 in the appropriate region, rather than in the whole strip. The second method seems unlikely to work well for non-constant stopping times.

From 6.4 one would like to derive necessary conditions for an extremum like those in §4. Let us suppose that the information available to the controller at time t is specified by a σ-field $\mathcal{O}_t$ of subsets of the probability space Ω on which the processes $w,u,\xi, \ldots$ are defined. We require that $u(t)$ be $\mathcal{O}_t$-measurable. If we assume that $\mathcal{O}_t$ is the same for all controls u admitted, then as a necessary condition for a minimum we get (as in (3))

$$E\{\lambda(t)f_u(t) + L_u(t) | \mathfrak{A}_t\}$$

$$= \min \quad \text{when} \quad u = u(t)$$

with probability 1 for almost all t. [Unless L is convex in u and f linear in u, in order to prove this we need to admit variations other than $u + \varepsilon v$ in §5.]

In many interesting problems, the data fields $\mathfrak{A}_t$ are different for different controls. For instance, if at time t the controller has observed $\hat{\xi}(r) = (\xi_1(r), \ldots, \xi_\ell(r))$ for $0 \leq r \leq t$, then we let $\mathfrak{A}_t$ be the least σ-algebra with respect to which these random variables $\hat{\xi}(r)$ are measurable. Generally $\mathfrak{A}_t$ changes when the control changes.

If we let the controller base his choice only on the current observation $\hat{\xi}(t)$, not on past observations for $0 \leq r \leq t$, then this difficulty can be avoided by the method outlined in §'s 3,4.

REFERENCES

1. W.H. Fleming, J. Math. Anal. Appl. 16 (1966), 254-279. 2. W.H. Fleming, Optimal control of partially observable diffusions (to appear).
3. H. Kushner, J. Math. Anal. Appl. 11 (1965), 78-92. 4. A.M. Il'in, A.S. Kalashnikov, and O.A. Oleinik, Uspekhi Mat. Nauk 17 No.3 (transl. in Russian Math. Surveys).

EXISTENCE AND UNIQUENESS OF MEASURE-VALUED SOLUTIONS TO A STOCHASTIC INTEGRAL EQUATION*

R. E. Mortensen
Department of Aerospace Engineering Sciences
University of Colorado
Boulder, Colorado

Introduction

The problem considered in this paper arose during an investigation (1) of optimal nonlinear filtering of continuous-time stochastic processes. The object of the investigation was to find a fully rigorous way of computing the conditional probability distribution of the present state of a dynamical system, given the past history of noisy observations of the state. The result of the investigation was a stochastic integral equation obeyed by a random time-varying measure. From this measure, the desired conditional probability measure can be directly computed. The purpose of the present paper is to study this stochastic integral equation. We begin by establishing some basic results.

The Ito Stochastic Integral for Hilbert Space Valued Integrands

Let [0,T] be a compact interval of the real line. For each $t \in [0,T]$, let H_t be a real separable Hilbert space with inner product $\langle \cdot , \cdot \rangle_t$ and norm $|| \cdot ||_t$. Let the family H_t be nested in the sense that $s < t$ implies $|| \cdot ||_s \geq || \cdot ||_t$, or equivalently, $H_s \subseteq H_t$. Let (Ω, A, μ) be a probability triple. Consider a function $f(\cdot,\cdot)$ defined on $[0,T] \times \Omega$, such that for each $t \in [0,T]$ and for almost every $\omega \in \Omega$, $f(t,\omega) \in H_t$.

---

*This research was partially supported by National Science Foundation Grant GK-806.

Let $v(\cdot,\cdot) : [0,T] \chi \Omega \to (-\infty,\infty)$ be a real valued Wiener process. Let A_t be the smallest sub-σ-algebra of A with respect to which $v(t,\cdot)$ is measurable. We now place the further restrictions on the function $f(\cdot,\cdot)$ that for each $t \varepsilon [0,T]$, $f(t,\cdot)$ be A_t-measurable, and that

$$\int_0^T \int_\Omega ||f(t,\omega)||_t^2 \ \mu(d\omega)\ dt < \infty \tag{1}$$

Our first task is to assign a precise meaning to the stochastic integral

$$I\ (t,\omega) = \int_0^t f\ (\tau,\omega) dv(\tau,\omega) \tag{2}$$

for each $t \varepsilon [0,T]$.

For each $n = 1, 2, \ldots,$ let $0 = t_o < t_1 \leq t_2 \leq \ldots$ $t_n = t$ be a partition of $[0,t]$. Let $\Delta_n = \max_{1 \leq i \leq n} |t_i - t_{i-1}|$. Let the sequence of partition be such that $\Delta_n > \Delta_{n+1}\ \forall n$, and $\Delta_n \to 0$ as $n \to \infty$.

Then there exists a sequence $\{f_n(\cdot,\cdot)\}$ of simple functions converging to f in the sense that

$$\lim_{n \to \infty} \int_0^t \int_\Omega ||f(\tau,\omega) - f_n(\tau,\omega)||_\tau^2 \ \mu(d\omega) d\tau = 0 \tag{3}$$

and further, for each n, for almost all ω,

$$f_n(\tau,\omega) = f(\tau_{i-1},\omega),\ t_{i-1} \leq \tau < t_i,\ i = 1,2,\ldots,n \tag{4}$$

For each n, define

$$I_n(t,\omega) = \sum_{i=1}^{n} f_n(t_{i-1},\omega)\ [v(t_i,\omega) - v(t_{i-1},\omega)] \tag{5}$$

For any μ-integrable function $g(\cdot)$, write

$$E\{g(\omega)\} = \int_\Omega g(\omega)\ \mu(d\omega) \tag{6}$$

for brevity.

Lemma 1.

$$E\ \{||\ I_n(t,\omega)\ ||_t^2\} = \int_0^t E\ \{||\ f_n(\tau,\omega)\ ||_t^2\}\ d\tau \tag{7}$$

Proof For brevity, write $f_{ni} = f_n(t_{i-1},\omega)$ and $\Delta v_i = v(t_i,\omega) - v(t_{i-1},\omega)$, and suppress the dependence of $I_n(t,\omega)$ on t and ω. Then

$$|| I_n ||_t^2 = \langle I_n, I_n \rangle_t = \left\langle \sum_{i=1}^{n} f_{ni}\Delta v_i, \sum_{j=1}^{n} f_{nj}\Delta v_j \right\rangle_t$$

$$= \sum_{i=1}^{n} ||f_{ni}||_t^2 \Delta v_i^2 + 2 \sum_{i=2}^{n} \sum_{j=1}^{i-1} \left\langle f_{ni}, f_{nj} \right\rangle_t \Delta v_i \Delta v_j \qquad (8)$$

For $j < i$, f_{nj} and Δv_j are A_{tj}-measurable, while Δv_i is independent of A_{tj}. Also, Δv_i is independent of f_{ni}. Hence for $j < i$

$$E \{ \left\langle f_{ni}, f_{nj} \right\rangle_t \Delta v_i \Delta v_j \} = E \{ \left\langle f_{ni}, f_{nj} \right\rangle \Delta v_j \} E\{\Delta v_i\} \qquad (9)$$

Now $E \{\Delta v_i\} = 0$, and $E \{\Delta v_i^2\} = t_i - t_{i-1}$, from the definition of the Wiener process. Thus

$$E \{|| I_n ||_t^2\} = \sum_{i=1}^{n} E\{|| f_{ni} ||_t^2\} [t_i - t_{i-1}]$$

$$= \int_0^t E \{|| f_n(\tau,\omega)||_t^2\} d\tau \qquad (10)$$

This proves lemma 1.

Observe that since $||f_n(\tau,\omega)||_t \leq ||f_n(\tau,\omega)||_\tau$, we have

$$\int_0^t E\{|| f_n(\tau,\omega) ||_t^2\} d\tau \leq \int_0^t E\{|| f_n(\tau,\omega) ||_\tau^2\} d\tau \qquad (11)$$

Lemma 2. For each fixed $t \varepsilon [0,T]$, the sequence of H_t-valued random variables $I_n(t,\cdot)$ is a Cauchy sequence in mean square.

Proof. For any two integers n and m, there always exists an integer r and a common refinement $0 = t_o \leq t_1 \leq \dots \leq t_r = t$ of the partitions corresponding to n and m. Then

$$I_n - I_m = \sum_{i=1}^{r} (f_{ni} - f_{mi}) \Delta v_i \qquad (12)$$

By lemma 1 and the observation (11),

$$E\{\|I_n - I_m\|_t^2\} = \int_0^t E\{\|f_n(\tau,\omega) - f_m(\tau,\omega)\|_t^2\}\,d\tau$$
$$\leq \int_0^t E\{\|f_n(\tau,\omega) - f_m(\tau,\omega)\|_\tau^2\}\,d\tau \tag{13}$$

Recollection of the convergence of the sequence $\{f_n(\cdot,\cdot)\}$, as given in (3), proves the lemma.

The mean square convergence of the sequence $\{I_n(t,o)\}$ establishes an equivalence class of H_t-valued random variables any two members of which differ only on an Ω set of μ measure zero. We accept any member of this equivalence class as the meaning of $I(t,\omega)$ in (2).

The Stochastic Integral Equation

Let X be Euclidean n-dimensional space, and let $\mathcal{B}$ be the Borel σ-algebra of subsets of X. In reference 1, there was defined a random time-varying measure $R(\cdot,\cdot,\cdot)$ which has the following properties:

(a) For each fixed $A \in \mathcal{B}$ and $t \in [0,T]$, $R(A,t,\cdot)$ is a real-valued random variable.

(b) For each fixed $t \in [0,T]$ and almost all $\omega\in\Omega$, $R(\cdot,t,\omega)$ is a measure on $\mathcal{B}$.

(c) For each fixed $A \in \mathcal{B}$ and almost all $\omega\in\Omega$, $R(A,\cdot,\omega)$ is a bounded, Lebesgue measurable function on [0,T].

In reference 1, it was shown that if one has the function $R(\cdot,\cdot,\cdot)$ at hand, then it will necessarily be found to satisfy a stochastic integral equation which may be written in the form

$$R(A,t,\omega) = Q(A,t) + \sum_{i=1}^{m} \int_0^t \int_X P(A,t|x,\tau)g_i(x,\tau,\omega)R(dx,\tau,\omega)d\tau$$
$$+ \sum_{i=1}^{m} \int_0^t \int_X P(A,t|x,\tau)h_i(x,\tau)R(dx,\tau,\omega)dv_i(\tau,\omega) \tag{14}$$

Here $g_i(\cdot,\cdot,\cdot)$, $i = 1, \ldots, m$, are jointly measurable on $X \times [0,T] \times \Omega$ and jointly continuous on $X \times [0,T]$ for almost all ω; $h_i(\cdot,\cdot)$, $i = 1, \ldots, m$, are jointly continuous on $X \times [0,T]$; $v_i(\cdot,\cdot)$, $i = 1, \ldots, m$, are independent Wiener processes; all the preceding functions are real valued. Further, the functions $g_i(\cdot,\cdot,\cdot)$ and $h_i(\cdot,\cdot,\cdot)$ are all bounded: $|g_i(x,t,\omega)| \le c^2 < \infty$, $i = 1,\ldots, m$, $\forall x\varepsilon X$, $\forall t\varepsilon [0,T]$, a.e.$\omega$ $|h_i(x,t)| \le c < \infty$, $i = 1,\ldots, m$, $\forall x\varepsilon X$, $\forall t\varepsilon [0,T]$.

In(14), the function $P(\cdot,\cdot|\cdot,\cdot)$ is a normal, complete transition function for a Markov process on the state space $(X,\mathcal{B})$(see ref. 2, p. 98). The function $Q(\cdot,\cdot)$ is given, for each $t \varepsilon [0,T]$, by

$$Q(A,t) = \int_X P(A,t \mid x,0)Q_0(dx),\ A \varepsilon \mathcal{B} \tag{15}$$

Here $Q_0(\cdot)$ is some given measure on $\mathcal{B}$.

It is known that for each fixed $t \varepsilon [0,T]$ and almost all ω, $R(\cdot,t,\omega)$ is absolutely continuous with respect to $Q(\cdot,t)$. Also for each fixed $t \varepsilon [0,T]$, for each $x \varepsilon X$, for each τ, $0 \le \tau < t$, $P(\cdot,t \mid x,\tau)$ is assumed absolutely continuous with respect to $Q(\cdot,t)$.

Define the Hilbert space H_t as the set of all real valued functions $\phi(\cdot)$ on X such that

$$\int_X \phi^2(x)\, Q\,(dx,t) < \infty .$$

The inner product is given by

$$\left\langle \phi(\cdot),\psi(\cdot)\right\rangle_t = \int_X \phi(x)\psi(x)\, Q\,(dx,t) \tag{16}$$

It is assumed that $s < t$ implies $||\phi(\cdot)||_s \ge ||\phi(\cdot)||_t$.

For simplicity in what follows, we will consider only the case m = 1 in (14), since the treatment of the general case runs exactly parallel and only complicates the exposition.

For each $\phi(\cdot) \varepsilon H_\tau$, define $\Psi_{1\phi}(A,t,\tau,\omega)$ and $\Psi_{2\phi}(A,t,\tau)$, for $A \varepsilon \mathcal{B}$, $0 \le \tau \le t \le T$, $\omega\varepsilon\Omega$, by respectively

$$\Psi_{1\phi}(A,t,\tau,\omega) = \int_X P(A,t|x,\tau)g(x,\tau,\omega)\phi(x)Q(dx,\tau) \tag{17}$$

$$\Psi_{2\phi}(A,t,\tau) = \int_X P(A,t|x,\tau)h(x,\tau)\phi(x)Q(dx,\tau) \tag{18}$$

From the assumptions made previously, it follows that $\Psi_{1\phi}(\cdot,t,\tau,\omega)$ and $\Psi_{1\phi}(\cdot,t,\tau,\omega)$ are both absolutely continuous with respect to $Q(\cdot,t)$. Define the Radon-Nikodym derivatives

$$\psi_{1\phi}(x,t,\tau,\omega) = \frac{\Psi_{1\phi}(dx,t,\tau,\omega)}{Q(dx,t)} \tag{19}$$

$$\psi_{2\phi}(x,t,\tau) = \frac{\Psi_{2\phi}(dx,t,\tau)}{Q(dx,t)} \tag{20}$$

Using certain results in reference 1, it is not difficult to show that $\psi_{1\phi}(\cdot,t,\tau,\omega)$ and $\psi_{2\phi}(\cdot,t,\tau)$ both belong to H_t.

Define the random linear operator $K_1(t,\tau,\omega)$: $H_\tau \to H_t$ and the linear operator $K_2(t,\tau) : H_\tau \to H_t$, by respectively

$$K_1(t,\tau,\omega)\phi(\cdot) = \psi_{1\phi}(\cdot,t,\tau,\omega) \tag{21}$$

$$K_2(t,\tau)\phi(\cdot) = \psi_{2\phi}(\cdot,t,\tau) \tag{22}$$

Both $K_1(t,\tau,\omega)$ and $K_2(t,\tau)$ are bounded for $0 \le \tau \le t \le T$:

$$|| K_1(t,\tau,\omega)\phi(\cdot) ||_t \le k_1 \; ||\phi(\cdot)||_\tau \tag{23}$$

$$|| K_2(t,\tau)\phi(\cdot) ||_t \le k_2 \; ||\phi(\cdot)||_\tau$$

Let $\phi(x,t,\omega)$ denote the Radon-Nikodym derivative

$$\phi(x,t,\omega) = \frac{R(dx,t,\omega)}{Q(dx,t)} \tag{24}$$

Again by certain results in reference 1, it is known that $\phi(\cdot,t,\omega) \in H_t \; \forall \; t \in [0,T]$, for almost all ω. Write $\phi(t,\omega)$ in place of $\phi(\cdot,t,\omega)$ for brevity. Also let $u \in H_t$ be the element of H_t corresponding to the function on X which is identically equal to unity.

Using equation (14) for m = 1 and the above definitions, one finds that $\phi(t,\omega)$ obeys the following stochastic integral equation:

$$\phi(t,\omega) = u + \int_0^t K_1(t,\tau,\omega)\phi(\tau,\omega)d\tau + \int_0^t K_2(t,\tau)\phi(\tau,\omega)dv(\tau,\omega) \tag{25}$$

In (25), the second integral is an Ito stochastic integral with a Hilbert space valued integrand, as defined in the preceding portion of the present paper. Equation (25) provides the rigorous interpretation of equation (14). Also, under the assumptions we have made, it is clear that a proof of existence and uniqueness of solutions to (25) is a corresponding proof for (14).

Theorem. Under the preceding assumptions, the solution to (25) exists and is unique, with probability 1.
Proof. The proof is by Picard iteration. Take $\phi_0(t,\omega) = 0$, the zero element of H_t, and let, for $n = 0,1,2,\ldots$

$$\phi_{n+1}(t,\omega) = u + \int_0^t K_1(t,\tau,\omega)\phi_n(\tau,\omega)d\tau + \int_0^t K_2(t,\tau)\phi_n(\tau,\omega)dv(\tau,\omega). \quad (26)$$

Let L denote the set of all measurable real-valued functions on $X \times [0,T] \times \Omega$ such that, for $\phi(\cdot,\cdot,\cdot) \in L$,

$$\int_0^T \int_\Omega \int_X \phi^2(x,t,\omega)Q(dx,t)\mu(d\omega)dt < \infty \quad (27)$$

If $(\cdot,\cdot,\cdot) \in L$, then for almost all t and ω, $\phi(\cdot,t,\omega) = \phi(t,\omega) \in H_t$. Thus, (27) could be written

$$\int_0^T E\{ \|\phi(t,\omega)\|_t^2 \}dt < \infty \quad (28)$$

Define a norm $|||\cdot|||$ on L as

$$|||\phi||| = \int_0^T E\{ \|\phi(t,\omega)\|_t^2 \} dt \quad (29)$$

Equation (26) defines a linear mapping $S : L \to L$. In terms of S, (26) may be written abstractly as

$$\phi_{n+1} = u + S\phi_n \quad (30)$$

We will show that for some integer N, the mapping S^N is a contraction mapping. Let ϕ, $\psi \in L$ be arbitrary. Let $\xi = \phi - \psi$. When evaluated at fixed t,ω, we denote the corresponding elements of H_t by $\phi(t,\omega)$, $\psi(t,\omega)$, $\xi(t,\omega)$. Then

$$S\phi - S\psi = S(\phi - \psi) = S\xi \quad (31)$$

$$(S\xi)(t,\omega) = \int_0^t K_1(t,\tau,\omega)\xi(\tau,\omega)d\tau + \int_0^t K_2(t,\tau)\xi(\tau,\omega)dv(\tau,\omega) \quad (32)$$

$$\|(S\xi)(t,\omega)\|_t^2 \le 2\left\| \int_0^t K_1(t,\tau,\omega)\xi(\tau,\omega)d\tau \right\|_t^2 + 2\left\| \int_0^t K_2(t,\tau)\xi(\tau,\omega)dv(\tau,\omega) \right\|_t^2 \quad (33)$$

Since it follows readily that the stochastic integral defined in lemma 2 obeys the equality in the assertion of lemma 1,

$$E\{||(S\xi)(t,\omega)||_t^2\} \leq 2T \int_0^t E\{||K_1(t,\tau,\omega)\xi(\tau,\omega)||_t^2\}\, d\tau + 2 \int_0^t E\{||K_2(t,\tau)\xi(\tau,\omega)||_t^2\}\, d\tau \tag{34}$$

Using (23),

$$E\{||(S\xi)(t,\omega)||_t^2\} \leq 2(k_1T + k_2) \int_0^t E\{||\xi(\tau,\omega)||_\tau^2\}\, d\tau \tag{35}$$

Let $a = 2(k_1T + k_2)$. Iterating the mapping S,

$$E\{||(S^n\xi)(t,\omega)||_t^2\} \leq a \int_0^t E\{||(S^{n-1}\xi)(\tau,\omega)||_\tau^2\}\, d\tau \leq a^2 \int_0^t \int_0^\tau E\{||(S^{n-2}\xi)(s,\omega)||_s^2\}\, ds\, d\tau \tag{36}$$

Hence

$$E\{||(S^n\xi)(t,\omega)||_t^2\} \leq a^n \int_0^t \frac{(t-\tau)^{n-1}}{(n-1)!} E\{||\xi\ \tau\ \omega\ ||_\tau^2\} d\tau \tag{37}$$

So

$$|||\ S^n\ \xi\ ||| = \int_0^T E\{||\ (S^n\xi)(t,\omega)\ ||_t^2\}\, dt \leq a^n \int_0^T \int_0^t \frac{(t-\tau)^{n-1}}{(n-1)!} E\{||\xi(\tau,\omega)||_\tau^2\}\, d\tau\, dt = a^n \int_0^T \frac{(T-t)^n}{n!} E\{||\xi(t,\omega)||_t^2\}\, dt \leq \frac{a^nT^n}{n!} \int_0^T E\{||\xi(t,\omega)||_t^2\}\, dt \tag{38}$$

Thus we have

$$|||\ S^n\ \xi\ ||| \leq \frac{a^nT^n}{n!}\ |||\ \xi\ ||| \tag{39}$$

Since $\frac{a^nT^n}{n!}$ is the nth term of a known convergent series, for some N,

$$\frac{a^NT^N}{N!} < 1 \tag{40}$$

Setting n = 1 in (40) shows that S is continuous. Therefore, by the generalized contraction mapping theorem (ref. 3, p. 43 and p. 50), the sequence $\{\phi_n\}$ generated by (30) converges to a unique element $\phi^* \in L^n$ such that

$$\phi^* = u + S\phi^*$$

The corresponding element $\phi(t,\omega) \in H_t$ is the desired solution of (25) for $t \in [0,T]$.

Conclusion. Under certain assumptions, an interpretation of eq. (14) has been given and the existence and uniqueness of its solution has been proven. The methods used are a straightforward generalization of the methods of ref. 4.

References

1. Mortensen, R. E., "Optimal Control of Continuous-time Stochastic Systems," Report No. ERL-66-1, Electronics Research Laboratory, College of Engineering, University of California, Berkeley, 19 August 1966.
2. Dynkin, E. B., Theory of Markov Processes, Prentice-Hall, 1961.
3. Kolmogorov, A.N., and Fomin, S.V., Functional Analysis, Vol. I, Gralock Press, 1957.
4. Skorokhod, A.V., Studies in the Theory of Random Processes, Addison-Wesley, 1965.

INVARIANT SOLUTIONS OF DIFFERENTIAL EQUATIONS WITH DISCONTINUOUS COEFFICIENTS. DESIGN PRINCIPLES OF VARIABLE STRUCTURE CONTROL SYSTEMS

S. V. Emelyanov and V. I. Utkin
Institute of Automation and Telemechanics
Moscow, U.S.S.R.

When synthesizing an automatic control system with a non-stationary plant, in many cases, there arises the problem of choosing a control function such that the dynamic properties of the system change negligibly even in the presence of wide variations in the plant's parameters. We shall show that, on the basis of the solution of this problem, it is possible to make use of families of differential equations with discontinuous coefficients. We shall examine these properties in detail. Let the dynamical system be described by the differential equation

$$\frac{d\bar{x}}{dt} = \bar{f}(\bar{x}, t, u), \qquad (1)$$

where $\bar{x} = (x_1, \ldots, x_n)$, $\bar{f} = (f_1, \ldots, f_n)$, $f_i = x_{i+1}$ $(i=1, \ldots, n-1)$, and f_n is a continuous scalar-valued function. The control u is a discontinuous function:

$$u = \begin{cases} u_1(\bar{x}) & \text{if } s(\bar{x}) > 0 \\ u_2(\bar{x}) & \text{if } s(\bar{x}) < 0, \end{cases} \qquad (2)$$

where $u_1(\bar{x})$, $u_2(\bar{x})$, and $s(\bar{x})$ are continuous scalar-valued functions that depend only on the state of the system, $s(\bar{x})$ is differentiable with respect to all of its arguments, and the equation $s(\bar{x}) = 0$ can be solved for x_n. In such systems, a sliding-regime type of motion can arise if, in a neighborhood of the hypersurface S defined by the equation $s(\bar{x}) = 0$, the following conditions are satisfied

$$\left(\frac{d\bar{x}}{dt}, \text{grad } s(\bar{x})\right) > 0 \quad \text{when } s < 0$$
$$\left(\frac{d\bar{x}}{dt}, \text{grad } s(\bar{x})\right) < 0 \quad \text{when } s > 0 \,. \tag{3}$$

According to (1), a sliding-regime motion can be defined in a generalized way such that

$$\left(\frac{d\bar{x}}{dt}, \text{grad } s(\bar{x})\right) \equiv 0 \,, \tag{4}$$

and such that the phase trajectory in the space $(x_1, \ldots, x_n)$ lies on the surface given by $s(\bar{x}) = 0$. In this generalized definition, the motion of the system must be described not by Eq. (1), but rather by the differential equation

$$\frac{d\bar{x}^o}{dt} = \bar{f}^o(\bar{x}^o) \,, \tag{5}$$

where $\bar{x}^o = (x_1, \ldots, x_{n-1})$, $\bar{f}^o = (f_1^o, \ldots, f_{n-1}^o)$, $f_i^o = f_i$ $(i=1, \ldots, n-2)$, and $f_{n-1}^o = s^o(\bar{x}^o)$, where $s^o(\bar{x}^o)$ is the solution of $s(\bar{x}) = 0$ with respect to x_n. It follows from Eq. (5) that the sliding-regime motion of the system does not depend on the form of the function f_n. Hence, a solution of Eq. (5) will be called an invariant solution. If the control u is chosen such that any solution of Eq. (1) always intersects the hypersurface S, and if, at any point of the hypersurface, the conditions for the existence of a sliding regime (4) are satisfied, then, in the dynamical system, beginning at some time there arises a non-terminating motion whose properties, according to Eq. (5), do not change with time. We shall make use of this approach to solve a problem of controlling a linear plant whose parameters may vary within a wide range, and in the case where external disturbances are applied to the plant. We shall try to find this solution within the class of automatic control systems with variable structure, i.e., systems in which the relationships between the various functional elements change in some fashion depending on the state of the system. Namely, as will be shown below, in this class of systems, it will be possible to realize the concept of making use of invariant solutions of differential equations with discontinuous coefficients.

It is assumed that the control of the plant, which is

subjected to external disturbances $g_1, \ldots, g_k$, is realized with the aid of a linear control apparatus (L.C.A.). The plant and the linear control apparatus are described, respectively, by (n-m)-th and m-th order equations:

$$\varphi^{(n-m)} + \sum_{i=0}^{n-m-1} b_i(t)\varphi^{(i)} = y - G_1(t), \tag{6}$$

$$y^{(m)} + \sum_{i=0}^{m-1} d_i y^{(i)} = u. \tag{7}$$

Here, φ is the coordinate being controlled, y is the output of (L.C.A.), $G_1(t)$ is a function of time which is a linear combination of $g_1, \ldots, g_k$ and their derivatives, u is the control generated at the output of the control apparatus (C.A.), the d_i are the constant parameters of (L.C.A.), $b_i(t)$ are the variable parameters of the plant satisfying the relations

$$b_{imin}^{(j)} \leq b_i^{(j)}(t) \leq b_{imax}^{(j)}, \tag{8}$$

$$i=0,1,\ldots,n-m-1;\ j=0,1,\ldots,m,$$

where $b_i^{(j)}(t)$ denotes the j-th derivative of $b_i(t)$ with respect to time, and $b_{imin}^{(j)}$, $b_{imax}^{(j)}$ are constants. The problem consists in the fact that, as a result of the control, the controlled variable φ is to follow, to within a decaying transient component, the reference action g_o. The control u must be constructed with the aid of the coordinates of $x = g_o - \varphi$, y, and their derivatives under the assumption that one cannot measure the values of the plant's varying parameters and the external disturbances.

We shall consider the motion of the system in the space of the coordinates of the error $x_1 = x$ and (n-1) of its derivatives.

From Eq. (6) and $x_1 = g_o - \varphi$, we obtain that

$$y^{(i)} = -\sum_{j=1}^{n-m+i+1} r_{ij}(t)x_j + G^{(i)},\ i=0,1,\ldots,m-1, \tag{9}$$

where

$$x_j = x^{(j-1)},\ j=1,\ldots,n;\ G=G_1 + g_o^{(n-m)} + \sum_{j=0}^{n-m-1} b_i(t)g_o^{(j)},$$

the $r_{ij}(t)$ are certain bounded functions depending on the $b_i^{(j)}(t)$, and $r_{i,n-m+i+1} = -1$.

We shall construct the control as a sum of terms that depend on the coordinates $x_1, \ldots, x_{n-1}, y, \dot{y}, \ldots, y^{(m-1)}$:

$$u = \sum_{i=1}^{n-1} \psi_i^x x_i - \sum_{i=0}^{m-1} \psi_i^y y^{(i)}. \tag{10}$$

Assuming that each of the coefficients ψ_i^x and ψ_i^y can take on one of two possible values: ω_i^x or λ_i^x, and ω_i^y or λ_i^y (ω_i^x, λ_i^x, ω_i^y, and λ_i^y are constants), we shall find a sequence of variations for ψ_i^x and ψ_i^y (and hence also the structure of the system), and values ω_i^x, λ_i^x, ω_i^y, λ_i^y, such that, as a result of the control process, the representative point, in the space of the error and its derivatives, asymtotically converges to the origin.

From Eqs. (7), (9), and (10) the motion of the dynamical system under consideration, relative to the coordinates $x_1, \ldots, x_n$, is described by a differential equation similar to Eq. (1):

$$\frac{d\bar{x}}{dt} = \bar{f}(x, t),$$

$$\bar{x} = (x_1, \ldots, x_n),\ \bar{f} = (f_1, \ldots, f_n),\ f_i = x_{i+1}\ (i = 1, \ldots, n-1),$$

$$f_n = -\sum_{i=1}^{n} a_i(t) x_i - \sum_{i=1}^{n-1} \psi_i^x x_i + \sum_{i=0}^{m-1} (d_i + \psi_i^y) G^{(i)} + G^{(m)}, \tag{11}$$

where the $a_i(t)$ are functions which are linear with respect to the $b_i^{(j)}(t)$, d_i, and ψ_i^y, and hence are bounded.

From the point of view of physically realizing hypersurface S, it is convenient to choose S as being given by the equation

$$s(\bar{x}) = (\bar{c}, \bar{x}) = 0,\ \bar{c} = (c_1, \ldots, c_n), c_i = \text{constant}, c_n = 1. \tag{12}$$

Then, the sliding regime conditions (3) will have the form

$$\bar{c}\,\frac{d\bar{x}}{dt} > 0 \quad \text{when } s < 0,$$

$$\bar{c}\,\frac{d\bar{x}}{dt} < 0 \quad \text{when } s > 0, \tag{13}$$

and the sliding-regime Eq. (5), which defines the invariant solutions, will be written in the following form:

$$\frac{d\bar{x}^o}{dt} = \bar{f}^o(\bar{x}),$$
$$\bar{x}^o = (x_1, \ldots, x_{n-1}),\ \bar{f}^o = (f_1^o, \ldots, f_{n-1}^o), \tag{14}$$
$$f_i^o = f_i\ (i=1,\ldots,n-2),\ f_{n-1}^o = -\sum_{i=1}^{n-1} c_i x_i .$$

It follows from Eq. (14) that the motion in the sliding regime depends neither on the parameters of the plant nor on the disturbances applied to it, and that, by an appropriate choice of the coefficients c_i, it is possible to assign to this motion the specified dynamical properties.

As was already noted previously, it is necessary to choose the control for which there exists, in the space of $(x_1, \ldots, x_n)$, a sliding hypersurface, i.e., a hypersurface at each point of which conditions (13) are satisfied. Then, after the representative point reaches the sliding hypersurface, the subsequent motion of the system will be invariant under changes in the plant's parameters and under external disturbances.

Let us now proceed directly to the synthesis of a variable structure system.

We shall try to find those logical rules for varying the coefficients ψ_i^x and ψ_i^y for which the hypersurface S (Eq. (12)) will be a sliding hypersurface. From Eq. (11), we determine $\bar{c}\,\frac{d\bar{x}}{dt}$, the scalar product of the normal vector to the hypersurface S and the phase velocity vector, keeping in mind that, for points belonging to S, $x_n = -\sum_{i=1}^{n-1} c_i x_i$.

$$\bar{c}\,\frac{d\bar{x}}{dt} = \sum_{i=1}^{n-1} N_i x_i + \sum_{i=0}^{m-1} (d_i + \psi_i^y)\, G^{(i)} + G^{(m)}, \tag{15}$$

where $N_i = c_{i-1} - a_i - \psi_i^x - c_{n-1} c_i + a_n c_i$, $c_o = 0$.

We shall assume that, for the external disturbances belonging to a sufficiently wide class of functions*,

---

* This class of functions, for example, for m=2 includes exponential and sinusoidal functions, polynomials beginning at some instant of time, products of these functions, etc.

$$\frac{|G^{(m)}|}{\sum_{i=0}^{m-1} |G^{(i)}|} \leq A, \; A = \text{constant}, \; A > 0, \tag{16}$$

and that the logical rules for the variation of ψ_i^x and ψ_i^y have the form

$$\psi_i^x = \begin{cases} \omega_i^x & \text{when } x_i s > 0, \\ \lambda_i^x & \text{when } x_i s < 0; \end{cases} \quad i=1, \ldots, n-1, \tag{17}$$

$$\psi_i^y = \begin{cases} \omega_i^y & \text{when } G^{(i)} s > 0, \\ \lambda_i^y & \text{when } G^{(i)} s < 0. \end{cases} \quad i=0, 1, \ldots, m-1, \tag{18}$$

Then, according to relations (15)-(18), S will be a sliding hypersurface if

$$\begin{aligned} \omega_i^x &\geq \max_{b, \psi^y} (c_{i-1} - a_i - c_{n-1} c_i + a_n c_i), \quad i=1, \ldots, n-1 \\ \lambda_i^x &\leq \min_{b, \psi^y} (c_{i-1} - a_i - c_{n-1} c_i + a_n c_i) \end{aligned} \tag{19}$$

$$\omega_i^y = -A - d_i, \quad \lambda_i^y = A - d_i, \quad i=0, 1, \ldots, m-1, \tag{20}$$

(in relations (19), the maximum and minimum values are defined over all $b_i^{(j)}$ and ψ_i^y). Indeed, if relations (19) and (20) hold, we have, by virtue of relations (16)-(18), that

$$\begin{aligned} N_i x_i &\geq 0 \quad \text{when} \quad s < 0, \\ N_i x_i &\leq 0 \quad \text{when} \quad s > 0 \end{aligned} \quad i=1, \ldots, n-1, \tag{21}$$

$$\begin{aligned} \sum_{i=0}^{m-1} (d_i + \psi_i^y) G^{(i)} + G^{(m)} &\geq 0 \quad \text{when} \quad s < 0, \\ \sum_{i=0}^{m-1} (d_i + \psi_i^y) G^{(i)} + G^{(m)} &\leq 0 \quad \text{when} \quad s > 0. \end{aligned} \tag{22}$$

Comparing Eqs. (13), (15), (21), and (22), we arrive at the conclusion that there exists a sliding regime at every point of S. However, it may turn out that the logical rules for varying the coefficients, with respect to the output variable of the linear control apparatus and its derivatives, may not be realizable in practice, since the required information about the external disturbances applied to the plant is not always available. We shall formally replace Eq. (18) by a logical rule which does not depend on the external disturbances:

$$\psi_i^y = \begin{cases} \omega_i^y \text{ for } y^{(i)}s > 0, \\ \lambda_i^y \text{ for } y^{(i)}s < 0. \end{cases} \quad i=0,1,\ldots,m-1 \qquad (23)$$

We shall formulate the problem as follows: for ω_i^y and λ_i^y chosen in accordance with Eq. (20), find the values of ω_i^x and λ_i^x for the system with a control of the form of Eqs. (10), (17), and (23), such that S will as before be a sliding hypersurface.

Suppose that the inequalities (19) are satisfied. Then, by virtue of (13), (15), and (21), at every point of S with free motion ($G \equiv 0$), there exists a sliding regime. In the case of forced motion, regardless of the values of ψ_i^y, according to (13), (15), (21), one can guarantee that the conditions under which a sliding regime can arise are satisfied only outside of some non-stationary region E_1, given on S by the inequality

$$\left|\sum_{i=1}^{n-1} N_i x_i\right| < \left|\sum_{i=0}^{m-1} (d_i + \psi_i^y) G^{(i)} + G^{(m)}\right|. \qquad (24)$$

From (16), (18), (20), (24) and the equation of the hypersurface (Eq. (12)), we obtain the coordinates of the (2n-2) vertices of E_1:

$$(0,\ldots,0,\pm x_i^1, 0,\ldots,0,-c_i x_i^1), i=1,\ldots,n-1,$$

$$|x_i^1| < \frac{2m\, A\, |G^{(k)}|}{\min\limits_{b,\psi^y} |N_i|}, \qquad (25)$$

where $|G^{(k)}| = \max |G^{(i)}|$, $i=0,1,\ldots,m-1$.

We shall require that, for i=k, the logical rules, Eqs. (18) and (23), coincide within E_1. It is obvious that this occurs if

$$\operatorname{sign} G^{(k)} = \operatorname{sign} y^{(k)}. \qquad (26)$$

Equation (9) permits us to obtain the condition under which $G^{(k)}$ and $y^{(k)}$ have the same sign:

$$\left|G^{(k)}\right| \geq \left|\sum_{j=1}^{n-m+k+1} r_{kj} x_j\right|. \qquad (27)$$

Inequality (27) defines a closed convex region D in the space $(x_1, \ldots, x_n)$. If $E_1 \subset D$, then Eq. (26) is valid for the entire region E_1. By virtue of the convexity of D, $E_1 \subset D$ if each vertex of E_1 belongs to D or, according to (25) and (27), that

$$\max_{b,\psi^y} \frac{2mA|r_{ki}|}{|N_i|} \le 1, \; k=0,1,\ldots,m-2, i=1,\ldots,n-1,$$
$$\max_{b,\psi^y} \frac{2mA|r_{m-1,i}-c_i|}{|N_i|} \le 1, \; i=1,\ldots,n-1. \tag{28}$$

Since the logical rules (18) and (23) coincide within E_1 when the inequalities (28) are satisfied, then, for this region,

$$(d_i+\psi_k^y)G^{(k)} \ge 0 \text{ when } s<0,$$
$$(d_i+\psi_k^y)G^{(k)} \le 0 \text{ when } s>0. \tag{29}$$

The remaining arguments are similar to those already made. Suppose that inequalities (28) are satisfied. Then, according to (13), (15), (21), and (29), regardless of the values of ψ_i^y $(i \ne k)$, one can guarantee that a sliding regime will arise on S outside of the bounded, non-stationary region E_2, contained in E_1, and given by the inequality

$$\left|\sum_{i=1}^{n-1} N_i x_i\right| + A|G^{(k)}| < \left|\sum_{i=0,\, i\ne k}^{m-1} (d_i+\psi_i^y)G^{(i)} + G^{(m)}\right|. \tag{30}$$

From (20), (23), (30) and (12), we obtain the coordinates of the (2n-2) vertices of the region* E_2:

$$(0,\ldots,0,\pm x_i^2, 0,\ldots,0,-c_i x_i^2), \; i=1,\ldots,n-1,$$

$$|x_i^2| < \frac{A\sum\limits_{i=0,\, i\ne k}^{m-1} |G^{(i)}| + |G^{(m)}| - A|G^{(k)}|}{\min\limits_{b,\psi^y} |N_i|}. \tag{31}$$

---

*In case $A\sum\limits_{i=0,\, i\ne k}^{m-1} |G^{(i)}| + |G^{(m)}| - A|G^{(k)}| < 0$, E_2 is empty, and S is a sliding hypersurface.

We note that, in accordance with the constraint (16),

$$\frac{|G^{(m)}| - A|G^{(k)}|}{\sum\limits_{i=0,\, i\neq k}^{m-n} |G^{(i)}|} \leq A.$$

Therefore, in place of (31), one can write

$$|x_i^2| < \frac{2(m-1)A|G^{(i)}|}{\min\limits_{b,\,\psi^y} |N_i|}, \tag{32}$$

where

$$|G^{(i)}| = \max_{i=0,\ldots,m-1,\, i\neq k} |G^{(i)}|.$$

Further, we shall require that the logical rules (18) and (23) coincide within E_2 for $i=\ell$. For this to take place, there must be satisfied conditions which are similar to (28), which can be obtained from (9), (27), and (32):

$$\max_{b,\,\psi^y} \frac{2(m-1)A|r_{\ell i}|}{|N_i|} \leq 1, \quad \ell=0,1,\ldots,m-2, \ell\neq k, \quad i=1,\ldots,n-1,$$
$$\max_{b,\,\psi^y} \frac{2(m-1)A|r_{m-1,i}-c_i|}{|N_i|} \leq 1, \quad i=1,\ldots,n-1. \tag{33}$$

We note that when (28) is satisfied, then inequalities (33) also hold. Repeating the described procedure, we consequently obtain a region E_m outside of which, so long as inequalities (28) are satisfied, a sliding regime always exists, and in the interior of which the logical rules (18) and (23) coincide for any i. But for a control of the form of (10), (17), (18), (19), and (20), a sliding regime takes place on the entire hypersurface S. Hence, when (19) and (28) are both satisfied, then the control given by (10), (16), and (23) ensures that there exists a sliding hypersurface. We note that these inequalities can always be satisfied with an appropriate choice of the coefficients ω_i^x and λ_i^x. In a system constructed in this manner, after the representative point has reached the sliding hypersurface, the subsequent motion is described by system (14) and is independent of the characteristics of the plant and the disturbances applied to it. It is an essential point that the described method of controlling the plant with variable parameters by a forced motion has been realized with the help of finite coefficients ψ_i^x, ψ_i^y, relative to the various coordinates of the system, and that this has been accomplished without having had to measure either the plant's parameters, which may vary over a wide range, or the external disturbances.

Reference

1. A. F. Filippov, "Differential Equations with Discontinuous Right-Hand Sides," Mat. Sb., Vol. 51, No. 1, 1960, pp. 99-128.

SOCIAL SCIENCE LIBRARY

Manor Road Building
Manor Road
Oxford OX1 3UQ

302546784$